Element	Symbol	Atomic Number	Atomic Weight
Neodymium	Nd	60	144.24
Neon	Ne	10	20.183
Neptunium	Np	93	(237)
Nickel	Ni	28	58.71
Niobium	Nb	41	92.906
Nitrogen	N	7	14.0067
Nobelium	No	102	(256)
Osmium	Os	76	190.2
Oxygen	O	8	15.9994 (±0.0001, nat.)
Palladium	Pd	46	106.4
Phosphorus	P	15	30.9738
Platinum	Pt	78	195.09
Plutonium	Pu	94	(242)
Polonium	Po	84	(210)
Potassium	K	19	39.102
Praseodymium	Pr	59	140.907
Promethium	Pm	61	(147)
Protactinium	Pa	91	(231)
Radium	Ra	88	(226)
Radon	Rn	86	(222)
Rhenium	Re	75	186.2
Rhodium	Rh	45	102.905
Rubidium	Rb	37	85.47
Ruthenium	Ru	44	101.07
Samarium	Sm	62	150.35
Scandium	Sc	21	44.956
Selenium	Se	34	78.96
Silicon	Si	14	28.086 (±0.001, nat.)
Silver	Ag	47	107.870 (±0.003, exp.)
Sodium	Na	11	22.9898
Strontium	Sr	38	87.62
Sulfur	S	16	32.064 (±0.003, nat.)
Tantalum	Ta	73	180.948
Technetium	Tc	43	(99)
Tellurium	Te	52	127.60
Terbium	Tb	65	158.924
Thallium	Tl	81	204.37
Thorium	Th	90	232.038
Thulium	Tm	69	168.934
Tin	Sn	50	118.69
Titanium	Ti	22	47.90
Tungsten	W	74	183.85
Uranium	U	92	238.03
Vanadium	V	23	50.942
Xenon	Xe	54	131.30
Ytterbium	Yb	70	173.04
Yttrium	Y	39	88.905
Zinc	Zn	30	65.37
Zirconium	Zr	40	91.22

nat. = Variation in atomic weight due to natural variation in the isotopic composition.

exp. = Experimental uncertainty of magnitude given.

Numbers in parentheses are mass numbers of most stable or most common isotope.

INSTRUMENTAL METHODS

OF ANALYSIS

INSTRUMENTAL METHODS

OF ANALYSIS

HOBART H. WILLARD
Professor Emeritus of Chemistry, University of Michigan

LYNNE L. MERRITT, JR.
Vice President for Research and Dean of Advanced Studies,
Professor of Chemistry, Indiana University

JOHN A. DEAN
Professor of Chemistry, University of Tennessee

4th edition

D. VAN NOSTRAND COMPANY, INC.

Princeton, New Jersey / Toronto / London

Van Nostrand Regional Offices: *New York, Chicago, San Francisco*

D. Van Nostrand Company, Ltd., *London*

D. Van Nostrand Company (Canada), Ltd., *Toronto*

First Published September 1948
Three Reprintings

Second Edition, March 1951
Four Reprintings

Third Edition, January 1958
Seven Reprintings

Fourth Edition, August 1965
Reprinted March 1966,
May 1967

PRINTED IN THE UNITED STATES OF AMERICA

Preface

This fourth edition continues to survey modern instrumental methods of chemical analysis. The revisions for this fourth edition, the authors believe, are both timely and extensive. All but four chapters have been completely rewritten.

Two new chapters devoted to electronics fulfill a long-felt need. Here electronic circuitry is considered in terms of individual components and as functional units. Because of its present importance, gas chromatography has been expanded to fill a separate chapter. Raman Spectroscopy and Electron Spin Resonance Spectroscopy also appear as short separate chapters. A discussion of spectrophosphorimetry has been grouped with an expanded treatment of fluorescence methods. Thermoanalytical methods are gathered together and considered separately. A final chapter on continuous (in-line) methods of analysis is a unique addition.

There have been changes in emphasis and style, along with additions of useful material, throughout the text. More emphasis has been placed on structural identification of compounds through infrared spectra, nuclear magnetic resonance spectroscopy (NMR), ultraviolet absorption spectra, and mass spectrometry. This trend is also continued in the chapters dealing with fluorescence, electron spin resonance spectroscopy (ESR), Raman spectroscopy, thermoanalytical methods, potentiometry, and polarography.

The material on absorption spectrophotometry in the visible and ultraviolet portions of the spectrum has been divided into two parts. First comes a treatment of instrument types and their components; then methodology is discussed. This arrangement seems more logical than the usual order of presentation. In the electroanalytical sections the recommendations of the International Union of Pure and Applied Chemistry (Stockholm Convention) are followed.

One style change is the inclusion of numerous examples, including those illustrating mathematical operations. These introduce the student to the units of measurement and reduce, or even eliminate, the dependence upon additional problem books. There are 371 numerical problems, many with

v

multiple parts, at the chapter ends, with over 35 percent answered. Many of these problems contain data that would be obtained in the laboratory experiments described and are thus of particular value for schools unable to furnish equipment for specific areas of instrumentation or for supplementing experiments when laboratory periods are limited in number. Line drawings and block diagrams of the instruments have replaced many relatively uninformative views of packaged equipment.

Individual chapters are designed, in general, to stand alone. Consequently, the order of presentation is not critical. Instructors will be able to select material for several levels of achievement. Literature and collateral reading references are included in each chapter. The book should also be suitable as a reference manual.

Experiments have been selected to illustrate the principles discussed in the theoretical portions of each chapter. Some experiments are described in considerable detail, and thus are suitable for use by less experienced undergraduate students. Others are merely sketched outlines or suggestions for work, included in the belief that instructors in advanced courses will desire flexibility and will wish to elicit from students a degree of independence and originality in the outline and execution of experimental work.

To conserve space and because of the futility of including all the diverse commercial units, directions for the operation of specific instruments have been largely eliminated. Exceptions are made for a few very popular instruments likely to be found in most laboratories.

Because confusion easily arises over the meaning of abbreviations and the use of symbols, particularly the overlapping use of certain symbols in the diverse techniques covered in this book, separate listings of abbreviations and symbols precede Chapter 1. In addition, a fairly comprehensive tabulation of standard electrode potentials in aqueous solution, polarographic half-wave potentials and diffusion-current constants, acid dissociation constants, and formation constants of some metal complexes has been provided in the Appendix. Inclusion of a four-place table of common logarithms, a table of atomic weights, and a periodic chart of the elements will facilitate computations and provide ready reference data.

The authors remain greatly indebted to the manufacturers who have so generously furnished schematic diagrams, photographs, and technical information of their instruments. Thanks are expressed also to many colleagues who have kindly helped with suggestions and have pointed out errors in the previous editions.

HOBART H. WILLARD
LYNNE L. MERRITT, JR.
JOHN A. DEAN

Contents

List of Experiments

EXPERIMENT

EXPERIMENT

Abbreviations

alternating current (adj.)	a-c
American Society for Testing Materials	A.S.T.M.
ampere	amp
ampere-hour	amp-hr
angstrom	Å
atomic weight	at. wt.
barn	barn
billion electron volts	BeV
boiling point	b.p.
centimeter-gram-second	cgs
coulomb	Q
cubic centimeter	cm^3
cycles per second	cps
curie	curie
decibel	db
degrees Celsius (centigrade)	°C
degrees Kelvin (absolute)	°K
direct current (adj.)	d-c
dyne	dyne
electromagnetic unit	emu
electromotive force	emf
electron paramagnetic resonance	EPR
electron spin resonance	ESR
electron volt	eV
electrostatic unit	esu
farad	f
gauss	gauss
henry	h
height equivalent to a theoretical plate	HETP
hour	hr
inch	in.
inside diameter	i.d.
joule	joule

kilocalorie	kcal
kilocycles per second	kc/sec
kiloelectron volt	keV
kilogram	kg
kilogram-meter	kg-m
kilohm	$k\Omega$
kilometer	km
kilovolt	kV
kilovolt-ampere	kVa
kilowatt	kW
kilowatt-hour	kW-hr
liter	liter
megacycles per second	Mc/sec
megohm	$M\Omega$
melting point	m.p.
meter	m
microampere	μa
microcoulomb	μQ
microfarad	μf
micron	μ
microgram	μg
microsecond	μsec
milliampere	ma
milliliter	ml
milligram	mg
million electron volts	MeV
millisecond	msec
normal hydrogen electrode	NHE
nuclear magnetic resonance	NMR
nuclear spin resonance	NSR
ohm	Ω
radio frequency	rf
roentgen	R
saturated calomel electrode	SCE
second	sec
standard temperature and pressure	STP
torr	torr
versus	vs
vacuum tube voltmeter	VTVM
volt	V
watt	W
weber	Wb
X unit (X rays)	XU

Symbols

A	absorbance; activity (radiochemistry); area; atomic weight
a	specific absorptivity (optical)
a_x	activity of species x
b	optical path length
C	concentration; capacitance (electrical)
C_L	concentration in liquid (stationary) phase
C_M	concentration in mobile phase
c	velocity of light in vacuum
D	dielectric constant; diffusion coefficient (electrochemistry)
D_{MO}	dissociation energy (of metal oxide)
d	distance or spacing; days (radioactive half-lives)
E	electrode potential; potential of a half-reaction; energy
E^0	standard electrode potential
$E_{1/2}$	polarographic half-wave potential
E_i	energy of ionization
E_j	energy of electronic transition; liquid junction potential
e	electron (symbol); electronic charge; Naperian base (logarithms)
F	faraday
F_c	volume flow rate of gas (chromatography)
$\Delta \mathfrak{F}$	free energy charge
f	fractional abundance; frequency of alternating voltage; oscillator strength (optical)
f_x	activity coefficient of species x
$f/16$	aperture ratio 16
G	high-frequency conductance
g	statistical weights of particular energy levels (optical)
H	magnetic field strength
ΔH	enthalpy change
ΔH_f	enthalpy of formation
h	Planck's constant

I	radiant intensity; spin number (NMR, ESR)
I_d	diffusion current constant (polarography)
I_v, I_h	vertical and horizontal component of electric vector in scattered beam
i	current
i_d	diffusion current (electrochemistry)
J	coupling constant (NMR)
j	correction factor for pressure drop across chromatographic column
K_a	acid dissociation constant
K_f	formation constant
K_{sp}	solubility product constant
K_w	ion product of water
k	Boltzmann constant; general constant
L	inductance
M	molar (concentration unit)
MeV	million electron volts
m	magnetic quantum number; mass; minutes (radiochemistry half-lives); molality; order of diffraction interference (optical); rate of mercury flow (polarography); (as superscript) metastable isotope (radiochemistry)
m_e	mass of electron (at rest)
N	number of something
N_A	Avogadro number
N_j	occupational number of an excited energy level
N_0	number of species in ground energy level
n	unshared p-electrons; index of refraction; number of moles
n^0	neutron (symbol)
n_D	refractive index (D sodium line)
P	pressure; radiant power (optical)
P_M	monoisotopic mass peak
P_0	incident radiant power
p	depolarization factor (Raman); type of electrons
p-	negative logarithm of (prefix)
Q	relative peak sharpness (chromatography)
R	resistance; gas constant; resolving power (optical)
r	counting rates (radiochemistry); radius of curvature
r_D	specific refraction
r_p	plate resistance (electronics)
S	saturation factor (radiochemistry); relative peak separation (chromatography); entropy
s	seconds (radiochemistry half-lives)
T	temperature; transmittance (optical)
t	time

$t_{1/2}$	half-life
t_R	retention time (chromatography)
V	voltage; volume
V_g	specific retention volume
V_N	net retention volume
V_R	retention volume (uncorrected)
V^0_R	corrected retention volume
V'_R	adjusted retention volume
W	weight
y	years (radiochemistry half-lives)
Z	atomic number
α	alpha particle (symbol); relative retention ratio; rotation of polarized light
$[\alpha]$	specific rotation
β	beta particle; Van Slyke buffer value
γ	gamma radiation; magnetogyric ratio (NMR); emulsion characteristic (photography)
Δ	symbol for finite change (prefix)
δ	chemical shift (NMR); thickness of diffusion layer (electrochemistry)
∂	partial derivative (symbol)
ϵ	molar absorptivity
ϵ_{max}	molar absorptivity at wave length of an absorption maximum
Θ	cell constant (conductance)
θ	angle of diffraction
κ	specific conductance
Λ	equivalent conductance
Λ_∞	equivalent conductance at infinite dilution
λ	wavelength of radiation; decay constant (radiochemistry)
λ_+, λ_-	ionic conductance
λ_{max}	wavelength of an absorption maximum
μ	micron; ionic strength; dipole moment; linear absorption coefficient (X rays); nuclear magnetic moment
μ_m	mass absorption coefficient
μ_N	nuclear magneton
μ/p	proton moment
μ/ρ	mass absorption coefficient
ν	frequency of radiation; designation of vibrational levels
$\tilde{\nu}$	wavenumber
π	pi; type of electrons or bond
ρ	density
σ	standard deviation; type of bond; capture cross section; shielding or screening constant
τ	chemical shift (NMR); resolving time; mean emission lifetime

v	velocity
Φ	neutron flux
ϕ	quantum efficiency
χ	Pauling electronegativity
μ_P	proton moment
ω	angular velocity; symbol for energy in units of cm^{-1}; overpotential
[ ]	molar concentration of

Electronics: Passive Elements and Basic Electrical Measurements

This chapter should be a review for those who have had a course in physics covering a-c and d-c circuits or a course in electrical measurements and may be omitted if these subjects are still well in mind. The material in this section is not intended to be a complete discussion but only a review. The following units of measurement and definitions should be kept in mind.

Units

Coulomb. The coulomb (Q) is the unit of electrical charge or quantity of electricity. Since one electron carries a charge of 1.602×10^{-19} coulomb, the coulomb represents 6.24×10^{18} electrons.

Faraday. The faraday (F) is the charge carried by an equivalent weight of an ion and is 96,487 Q per equivalent.

Ampere. The common unit of current (symbol i) is the ampere (abbreviated amp) which corresponds to a charge flow rate of one coulomb per second.

Ohm. The unit of resistance (symbol R) is the ohm (Ω). It is that resistance through which a difference of potential of one volt will produce a current of one ampere.*

---

* See *Nat. Bur. Standards Circ. 524*, August 1953, p. 103, for references to publications describing these measurements.

Conductance. The reciprocal of the resistance, $1/R$, is known as the conductance and is measured in reciprocal ohms, ohms^{-1}, often written as mho.

Volt. The volt (V), the unit of electrical potential or pressure, is the potential developed across a resistance of one ohm when carrying a current of one ampere. The abbreviation of potential is E; for potential measured in volts, V.

Watt. The unit of electrical power, the watt (W) is the time rate of work equal to one joule per second. It is equal to the product of current times potential; thus:

$$W = Ei, \tag{1-1}$$

Decibel. The decibel (db) is often used to express the ratio of two power levels and is defined as $10 \log P_1/P_2$.

d-c Circuits

Fundamental Laws and Principles, d-c Circuits

Perhaps the most important law in electrical measurements, Ohm's law, concerns the relationship between current, potential, and resistance in a circuit containing pure resistance only. The law can be simply stated thus:

$$E = iR \tag{1-2}$$

The following two laws, first expressed by Kirchhoff, are very useful in analyzing circuits: (a) The sum of the currents about any single point of an electrical circuit is zero, and (b) the sum of the voltages around a closed electrical circuit is zero.

Analysis of Simple d-c Circuits

With the above laws one may determine the currents and voltages in a simple or complex circuit consisting of batteries and resistances. As examples of such analyses, consider the circuits in Fig. 1-1.

For the circuit shown in Fig. 1-1(a), application of Kirchhoff's second law starting clockwise from point *a* gives

$$-i_1 R_1 - i_1 R_2 + E = 0 \tag{1-3}$$

or

$$i_1(R_1 + R_2) = E. \tag{1-4}$$

which leads to a value of 2/3 amp for the current i_1 after substitution of the values of R_1, R_2 and E in Eq. 1-4. Furthermore, Eq. 1-3 shows that resistances in series such as R_1 and R_2 simply are additive. Thus the rule for resistances in series can be stated by Eq. 1-5:

$$R = R_1 + R_2 + \cdots \tag{1-5}$$

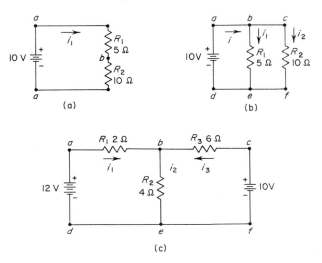

Fig. 1-1. Circuits containing only batteries and resistances.

By application of Kirchhoff's second law to the circuit of Fig. 1-1(b), one can arrive at three equations for the three possible closed paths, but of these only two, any two, are independent. Thus, for the two paths a-b-e-d-a and a-c-f-d-a, the equations are

$$-i_1R_1 + 10 = 0 \tag{1-6}$$

$$-i_2R_2 + 10 = 0 \tag{1-7}$$

To continue the analysis, one must apply Kirchhoff's first law. Selecting point b, one finds

$$i - i_1 - i_2 = 0 \tag{1-8}$$

or

$$i = i_1 + i_2 \tag{1-9}$$

Substituting Eqs. 1-6 and 1-7 in Eq. 1-9 yields

$$i = \frac{10}{R_1} + \frac{10}{R_2} = 10\left(\frac{1}{R_1} + \frac{1}{R_2}\right) \tag{1-10}$$

When the values of R_1 and R_2 are substituted in these equations, one finds that $i_1 = 2$ amp; $i_2 = 1$ amp, and $i = 3$ amp. Furthermore, Eq. 1-10 indicates that the rule for adding resistances in parallel is

$$\frac{1}{R} = \frac{1}{R_1} + \frac{1}{R_2} + \cdots \tag{1-11}$$

The analysis of a more complex circuit, such as that shown in Fig. 1-1(c), follows the same rules and leads to the following equations:

$$12 - 2i_1 - 4i_2 = 0 \qquad (1\text{-}12)$$

$$10 - 6i_3 - 4i_2 = 0 \qquad (1\text{-}13)$$

and

$$i_1 - i_2 + i_3 = 0 \qquad (1\text{-}14)$$

Solving these three equations for the three currents leads to the values $i_1 = 20/11$ amp, $i_2 = 23/11$ amp, $i_3 = 3/11$ amp. A negative answer for a current would mean that the actual current was flowing in the opposite direction to the direction arbitrarily chosen at the start of the analysis.

Designation of Values of Commercial Resistors

Most commercial resistors are marked with a color code which indicates their resistance value and the tolerance of this value. The code is indicated in Fig. 1-2 and Table 1-1. The value is given by the relationship

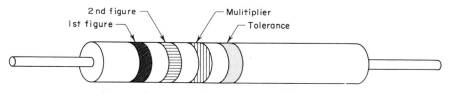

Fig. 1-2.   Color code of resistors.

$$R = (1\text{st figure} \times 10 + 2\text{nd figure}) \times 10^{\text{multiplier}} \pm \text{tolerance} \ \% \quad (1\text{-}15)$$

Table 1-1	Meaning of Colors in Resistor Color-Code		
black 0	yellow 4	violet 7
brown 1	green 5	gray 8
red 2	blue 6	white 9
orange 3		

For the tolerance band, silver represents 10% and gold 5%. Resistors more precise than 5% are known as *precision resistors* and the value is stamped on the resistor. A resistor with the colors yellow, violet, green, and silver would have a resistance of 4,700,000 Ω (or 4.7 megohms, MΩ), within 10%.

The Potentiometer

The potentiometer is widely used for the accurate measurement of electrical potentials. It employs the null-balance principle, by which the potential to be measured is balanced by an equal potential but in the opposing sense, so that no current is drawn from the circuit whose potential is to be measured. This potentiometric compensation technique forms the basis of many electrical and electronic measuring circuits and automatic recording devices. The simplified circuit is shown in Fig. 1-3.

A battery of constant emf, larger than any to be measured, is connected across a uniform wire $\overline{AB}$ of high resistance. The emf to be measured, such as a titration cell, is connected to A, with the polarity such that the negative pole of the battery corresponds to the negative pole of the unknown emf. The positive pole of the unknown is connected to the galvanometer G, thence through a key which can be closed momentarily by tapping, and finally to the sliding contactor C, which can be moved across $\overline{AB}$. By trial, the position of C is so adjusted that no current flows through the galvanometer G. Using

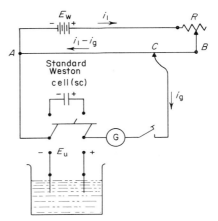

Fig. 1-3. The potentiometer.

Kirchhoff's laws, we can derive the condition for balance, i.e., zero current through the galvanometer.

Let the currents i_1 and i_g be as shown on Fig. 1-3, and let E_W and E_u be the potentials of the working cell and the unknown, respectively. Let R_g be the resistance of the galvanometer, R_{AC} the resistance of the $\overline{AC}$ section of the wire, R_{CB}, the resistance of the $\overline{BC}$ section of the wire, and R_R, the resistance of the variable, calibrating resistor R. Then

$$E_u - i_g R_g + (i_1 - i_g)R_{AC} = 0 \qquad (1\text{-}16)$$

Solving Eq. 1-16 for i_g and equating this to zero gives Eq. 1-17 and the condition for balance, Eq. 1-18.

$$i_g = \frac{E_u + i_1 R_{\overline{AC}}}{R_g + R_{\overline{AC}}} = 0 \qquad (1\text{-}17)$$

or

$$E_u = i_1 R_{\overline{AC}} \qquad (1\text{-}18)$$

Thus the potential of the unknown is exactly equal and opposite to the potential developed across the AC section of the slidewire.

If the double-throw double-pole switch is now thrown so that the Weston standard cell $\overline{SC}$, with an exactly known potential E_{SC}, replaces the unknown

E_u, and the contactor C is readjusted until a new point of balance is reached at C', an analysis of the circuit would give Eq. 19:

$$E_{SC} = -i_1 R_{AC'} \tag{1-19}$$

Elimination of i_1 from Eq. 1-18 and 1-19 yields Eq. 1-20:

$$E_u = \frac{R_{AC}}{R_{AC'}} E_{SC} \tag{1-20}$$

Since the slidewire has a uniform resistance along its length, the resistances are directly proportional to length, and Eq. 1-20 can be rewritten in terms of length, as in Eq. 1-21:

$$E_u = \frac{AC}{AC'} E_{SC} \tag{1-21}$$

By placing a variable resistance R between one of the ends of the slidewire and the battery, it is possible to vary i_1 so that $E_{SC}/R_{AC'}$ in Eq. 1-19 is some simple number, and thus the slidewire can be made direct-reading in millivolts per millimeter or some other simple function of voltage per unit of length.

As the balance-point detector for general purposes, a simple pointer galvanometer whose sensitivity is of the order of 0.2 μa/mm is satisfactory. For more accurate work a suitably damped mirror galvanometer (Fig. 1-4) should be used. In the latter type the optical lever arm is made very long, yet the entire instrument is kept to a reasonable size by using mirrors to give a folded optical path. When the potential to be measured has a very high resistance, greater than 1 MΩ, the ordinary type of galvanometer is not sensitive enough to serve as the null-balance detector; see Example 1, Chapter 21. Resort must be had to a vacuum tube voltmeter (VTVM).

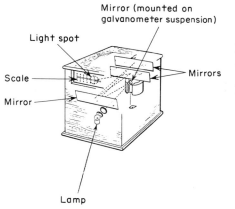

Fig. 1-4. Optical design principle of a high sensitivity, portable galvanometer based upon a folded optical lever arm of long total path length. (Courtesy of Rubicon Instrument Co.)

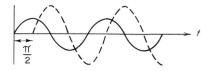

Fig. 1-5. Two sine waves with different amplitudes and 90° phase difference.

a-c CIRCUITS

Fundamental Laws and Principles

An alternating current is one in which the direction of the flow of electrons reverses periodically. The brief discussion which follows will be limited to pure sine waves which can be described by Eq. 1-22.

$$i = I_P \sin 2\pi f t \qquad (1\text{-}22)$$

where I_P represents the peak or maximum current, i is the instantaneous current at time t, and f is the frequency in cycles per second. A second sine wave might have the same frequency as the first but differ in the times at which the current starts from zero. Such waves are said to be out of phase, and the different waves can be expressed by similar equations, such as

$$i' = I'_P \sin (2\pi f t + \theta) \qquad (1\text{-}23)$$

where θ is the phase angle between the wave and the reference wave. Two sine waves with a phase difference of 90° are shown in Fig. 1-5.

If an a-c generator is connected to a pure resistance R, the voltage at any instant across the resistor is given by Ohm's law, $e = iR$, and thus the equation for the instantaneous voltage e will have the same form as that for the current i. For example, the voltage across a resistor of 10 Ω connected across an a-c generator with current output given by Eq. 1-22 would be

$$e = 10 I_P \sin 2\pi f t \qquad (1\text{-}24)$$

The current and voltage are said to be "in phase."

The average voltage or current in a sinusoidal wave is given by integrating current times the time over one-half cycle and dividing by the time for one-half cycle π, as in Eq. 25.

$$I_{av} = \frac{1}{\pi} \int_0^\pi I_P \sin 2\pi f t \, \partial t \qquad (1\text{-}25)$$

$$= \frac{2 I_P}{\pi} = 0.637 I_P \qquad (1\text{-}26)$$

Another value characteristic of sinusoidal waves needed in power calculations is the root-mean-square value, rms. This value is given by Eq. 1-27 and 1-28.

$$I_{rms} = \left(\frac{1}{\pi} \int_0^\pi I_P^2 \sin^2 2\pi f t \, \partial t \right)^{1/2} \qquad (1\text{-}27)$$

$$= \frac{I_P}{2} \sqrt{2} = 0.707 I_P \qquad (1\text{-}28)$$

Capacitors

A capacitor consists of two sheets of conducting metal separated by a thin film of a dielectric material. The dielectric material commonly consists of paper, mica, plastics of various kinds, oil, ceramics, or a thin film of the metallic oxide formed by electrolytic action on the metal sheet. Electrolytic capacitors must always be used in a circuit where the polarity remains in one direction. If the polarity is reversed, the oxide film will be reduced and the capacitor will be destroyed.

If a capacitor is connected across the terminals of a battery, electrons will start to flow from the negative terminal of the battery to one of the metal foils. Electrons on the other metal foil are repelled and flow to the positive terminal of the battery. This flow of current gradually slows down and eventually ceases when the potential across the capacitor terminals equals the potential of the battery. The capacitance C of the capacitor is given by Eq. 1-29.

$$C = \frac{Q}{e} \qquad (1\text{-}29)$$

where C is capacitance in farads, Q is the charge in coulombs, and e is the voltage across the capacitor.

Capacitors of various types are available in ranges from a few picofarads (pF) $(10^{-12}$ farad), to several thousand microfarads, $(\mu F)\,(10^{-6}$ farad). Electrolytic capacitors generally have the highest capacitances but, at the same time, the lowest breakdown voltages, the voltage at which the dielectric breaks down and the capacitor becomes ruined. The larger the area of the metal foil, the thinner the dielectric, and the higher the dielectric constant of the dielectric, the higher the capacitance.

Capacitors connected in parallel are additive, that is,

$$C = C_1 + C_2 + C_3 + \cdots \qquad (1\text{-}30)$$

and capacitors connected in series follow Eq. 1-31:

$$1/C = 1/C_1 + 1/C_2 + 1/C_3 + \cdots \qquad (1\text{-}31)$$

If one considers the occurrence of events as a capacitor is being charged as described above, one notices that the current will be at a maximum when the charging cycle begins and that the voltage is zero at this point. When the voltage reaches a maximum, the current has ceased. In other words, the potential across a capacitor lags behind the current by 90° or $\pi/2$. Thus, if the current is given by Eq. 1-22, the potential across a capacitor will be given by Eq. 1-32.

$$e = E_P \sin\left(2\pi ft - \pi/2\right) \qquad (1\text{-}32)$$

The relationship between I_P and E_P for a capacitor can be obtained if one remembers that the current is the time rate of flow of charge.

$$i = \partial Q/\partial t \qquad (1\text{-}33)$$

From Eqs. 1-29, 1-32, and 1-33,

$$i = \frac{\partial Q}{\partial t} = C\frac{\partial e}{\partial t} = C\frac{\partial}{\partial t}\left[E_P \sin\left(2\pi ft - \frac{\pi}{2}\right)\right] \qquad (1\text{-}34)$$

$$i = 2\pi fC\, E_P \cos\left(2\pi ft - \frac{\pi}{2}\right) \qquad (1\text{-}35)$$

The maximum value of i, I_P, is then clearly given by Eq. 1-36, since the maximum value of the cosine is 1.

$$I_P = 2\pi f C E_P \tag{1-36}$$

The equivalent of the resistance R, or E/i in a purely resistive circuit, is in a capacitive circuit given by the ratio of E_P/I_P, and is called the capacitive reactance, X_C.

$$X_C = \frac{E_P}{I_P} = \frac{1}{2\pi f C} \tag{1-37}$$

The capacitive reactance is a measure of the impedance to the flow of charge by the capacitor and is measured in ohms, as for resistors. The capacitive reactance, or impedance, decreases with increasing frequency, and it is also infinite when the frequency is zero. Thus capacitors offer infinite resistance to direct currents (except for negligible leakage resistances) and can be used to isolate direct from alternating currents.

Inductors

An inductor is a loop or coil of wire which may be wound around an iron core to increase the magnetic flux through the coil. An inductor resists a change in current passing through it, because a conductor which carries a current generates a magnetic field around the wire. A varying magnetic field, in turn, induces a potential in any conductor in that field in such a way as to oppose the change in the magnetic field. Thus when a current starts to pass through the wires of an inductor, a magnetic field is generated which induces a counter-potential in the wires. This counter-potential tends to impede, or hinder, the flow of current. When the current is steady, the magnetic field does not vary and no counter-potential is induced.

The inductance L of a coil is given by Eq. 1-38:

$$e = L\frac{\partial i}{\partial t} \tag{1-38}$$

where L represents the inductance in henrys, e is the counter-potential or emf in volts, and i is the current in amperes. Inductors are available in the range of several hundred henrys down to microhenrys. It should be pointed out that whereas capacitors can be made with almost negligible leakage—that is, with extremely high resistances—inductors cannot be made with zero resistances but always have appreciable resistances, and therefore they are not "pure" inductances.

Inductors connected in series are additive, that is,

$$L = L_1 + L_2 + L_3 + \cdots \tag{1-39}$$

while inductors connected in parallel act according to Eq. 1-40:

$$1/L = 1/L_1 + 1/L_2 + 1/L_2 + \cdots \tag{1-40}$$

From Eq. 1-38 and 1-22, the relationship in Eq. 1-42 can be derived:

$$e = L\frac{\partial i}{\partial t} = L\frac{\partial}{\partial t}(I_P \sin 2\pi ft) \qquad (1\text{-}41)$$

$$= 2\pi fLI_P \cos 2\pi ft = 2\pi fLI_P \sin\left(2\pi ft + \frac{\pi}{2}\right) \qquad (1\text{-}42)$$

This shows that the potential leads the current by 90° or $\pi/2$ in an inductor. The value of the peak potential, E_P, is also obtained as

$$E_P = 2\pi fLI_P \qquad (1\text{-}43)$$

In a manner analogous to that used for capacitors and resistors, the ratio of E_P/I_P is called the *inductive reactance* and is given by Eq. 1-44.

$$\frac{E_P}{I_P} = 2\pi fL = X_L \qquad (1\text{-}44)$$

Inductive reactance X_L is frequency-dependent and is greater with higher frequencies.

Analysis of Simple a-c Series Circuits

Simple a-c circuits containing resistors, capacitors, and inductors can often be understood by the use of vector diagrams. As an example, consider the circuit shown in Fig. 1-6(a). If the current is represented by a horizontal vector

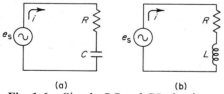

(a)   (b)

Fig. 1-6.   Simple *RC* and *RL* circuits.

$\vec{i}$, the potential across the resistor will be a parallel vector of length $\vec{i}R$ and the potential across the capacitor will be a vector at right angles (90° behind) the current vector and of length $\vec{i}X_C$. The potential vectors then form a diagram as shown in Fig. 1-7. The vector $\vec{i}Z$ represents the potential of the source given by the product of the current i and the total impedance Z of the circuit. Since i can be eliminated from each quantity represented in

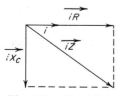

Fig. 1-7.   Potential vectors for a series *RC* circuit.

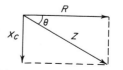

Fig. 1-8.   Impedance vectors for a series *RC* circuit.

Fig. 1-6, an exactly similar diagram for impedances can be drawn as in Fig. 1-8. It is apparent from the diagram that

$$Z = \sqrt{R^2 + X_C^2} \tag{1-45}$$

and that

$$\tan \theta = \frac{X_C}{R} \tag{1-46}$$

A similar set of diagrams can be constructed for the series RL circuit shown in Fig. 1-6(b), except that the potential in the inductor leads the current by 90°. The diagrams are shown in Figs. 1-9 and 1-10.

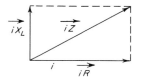

Fig. 1-9. Potential vectors for a series RL circuit.

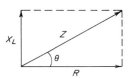

Fig. 1-10. Impedance vectors for a series RL circuit.

For a series RL circuit, the impedance Z is given by Eq. 1-47, and the phase angle θ is given by Eq. 1-48:

$$Z = \sqrt{R^2 + X_L^2} \tag{1-47}$$

$$\tan \theta = \frac{X_L}{R} \tag{1-48}$$

A series circuit containing resistance, inductance, and capacitance is represented in Fig. 1-11, and the corresponding vector diagram for the impedances is shown in Fig. 1-12.

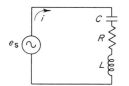

Fig. 1-11. A simple series RLC circuit.

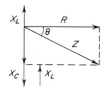

Fig. 1-12. Impedance vectors for a series RLC circuit.

It is apparent that the impedance and the phase angle for a series RLC circuit is given by the Eqs. 1-49 and 1-50, respectively.

$$Z = \sqrt{R^2 + (X_L - X_C)^2} \tag{1-49}$$

$$\tan \theta = \frac{X_L - X_C}{R} \tag{1-50}$$

Note that when $X_L = X_C$ the impedance becomes merely R. For this to be true, the frequency must be given by Eq. 1-52.

$$X_L = 2\pi f L = \frac{1}{2\pi f C} = X_C \qquad (1\text{-}51)$$

$$f = \frac{1}{2\pi \sqrt{LC}} \qquad (1\text{-}52)$$

Such a circuit is known as a *series resonant circuit*. It can be used as a selective filter for the resonant frequency given by Eq. 1-52.

Analysis of Simple a-c Parallel Circuits

Simple parallel RC and RL circuits and an RLC resonant circuit are shown in Fig. 1-13. In parallel circuits, the potential across each unit must be the same.

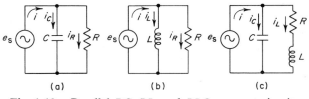

Fig. 1-13.   Parallel RC, RL, and RLC resonant circuits.

This leads to the following relationships between the currents, potentials, and impedances for the circuit shown in Fig. 1-13(a).

$$e_S = e_C = e_R \qquad (1\text{-}53)$$

$$i_C = \frac{e_S}{X_C} \quad \text{and} \quad i_R = \frac{e_S}{R} \qquad (1\text{-}54)$$

$$i = \sqrt{\left(\frac{e_S}{X_C}\right)^2 + \left(\frac{e_S}{R}\right)^2} = e_S\sqrt{\left(\frac{1}{X_C}\right)^2 + \left(\frac{1}{R}\right)^2} \qquad (1\text{-}55)$$

The vector relationships between the currents for the circuits diagramed in Fig. 1-13 are shown in Fig. 1-14. The circuit shown in Fig. 1-13(c) is more complex, and the current diagram is an approximation to the actual situation. This circuit is, however, very interesting. It can be seen from the current diagram that when the vertical component of i_L is equal (but of opposite sense)

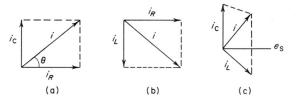

Fig. 1-14.   Current vector diagrams for parallel RC, RL, and RLC circuits.

to i_C, then i will be in phase with e_S. Furthermore, it is the effect of the resistance R which makes i_L not exactly parallel with i_C. If this resistance is small, then the resultant i is small and the circuit will possess a high impedance. Ideally, the maximum impedance occurs when i_C is equal to i_L, or in other words, when X_L is equal to X_C, since e_S is the same for both branches. This condition of resonance results when the frequency is given by Eq. 1-52. Note that the parallel resonant circuit shows a high impedance to the resonant frequency, whereas the series resonant circuit shows a low impedance.

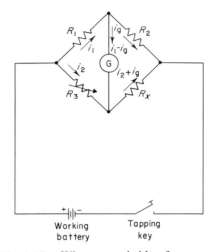

The Wheatstone Bridge

The value of an unknown resistance R_x can be accurately determined by comparison with known resistors R_1, R_2, and R_3 by the Wheatstone bridge method, which employs the arrangement shown in Fig. 1-15. The resistor R_3 is variable and is varied until a balance is obtained as shown by the fact that the galvanometer reads zero. When the galvanometer indicates that no current is flowing through it, that is, when i_g is zero, the following relationships can be derived with the use of Kirchhoff's laws.

Fig. 1-15. Wheatstone bridge for measuring resistances.

$$i_1 R_1 = i_2 R_3 \quad \text{and} \quad i_1 R_2 = i_2 R_x \qquad (1\text{-}56)$$

$$R_x = R_3 \cdot \frac{R_2}{R_1} \qquad (1\text{-}57)$$

By a very similar procedure, unknown capacitances or inductances can be measured. The setups are shown in Fig. 1-16. An a-c source (frequently

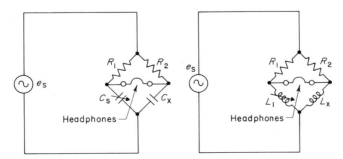

Fig. 1-16. Bridge method for measuring capacitance or inductance.

1000 cps) replaces the d-c source in Fig. 1-14, and an a-c detector, such as a set of headphones, replaces the galvanometer. When balance is obtained in the bridges,

$$C_x = C_S\left(\frac{R_1}{R_2}\right) \quad \text{or} \quad L_x = L_1\left(\frac{R_2}{R_1}\right) \tag{1-58}$$

Bibliography

Malmstadt, H. V., C. G. Enke, and E. C. Toren, Jr., *Electronics for Scientists*, W. A. Benjamin, New York, 1962.

Smith, A. W., *Electrical Measurements in Theory and Application*, McGraw-Hill, New York, 1934.

Electronics: Vacuum Tubes, Semiconductors, and Associated Circuits

In this chapter the treatment of circuits will be limited to those that are simplest and most widely used in analytical instrumentation. Operational amplifiers are introduced to give the student some ability in reading block diagrams and to indicate the many uses to which these commercially available units can be put.

Electronic Tubes

Diodes

A diode consists of a plate, or anode, and a cathode enclosed in a high vacuum. A diagram of a typical diode is shown in Fig. 2-1.

The cathodes are generally of two types, those heated directly and those heated indirectly. For the directly heated cathode a tungsten or thoriated tungsten wire is heated to 2200° or 1300°C, respectively, by the passage of a (usually direct) current. For the indirectly heated cathode, a nickel foil covered with a film of alkaline earth oxides is heated to 700°–900°C by a filament close to but not touching it. The filament is made of resistance

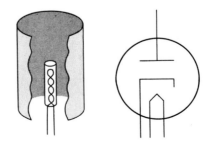

Fig. 2-1. Diode, indirectly heated. Envelope of glass or metal not shown.

wire and is heated by the passage through it of either alternating or direct current. The amount of electron emission by a cathode depends on the material of which it is made and its temperature.

The current density J_0, in amperes per centimeter squared, emitted by a cathode is closely represented by Eq. 2-1, where A is a constant

$$J_0 = AT^2e^{-w/kT} \qquad\qquad (2\text{-}1)$$

depending on the material (1×10^2 for oxide coated tungsten; 6×10^5 for tungsten); T is the temperature, k the Boltzmann coefficient, and w the work function in ergs (about 1 for oxide coatings and 4.5 for tungsten).

The anode is usually a cylinder which surrounds the cathode. When electrons strike the anode or plate, heat is generated and, if the temperature becomes too high, gases may be evolved which ionize and bombard the cathode, thus destroying it. Anodes are therefore usually blackened, increased in size, and in high-power tubes, made of some special material like platinum or tantalum. The *plate characteristic* of a typical diode is shown in Fig. 2-2.

When the plate of a diode is at zero potential or is negative with respect to the cathode, only electrons with appreciable kinetic energy can reach the plate. Over region A the number of electrons reaching the plate is nearly proportional to the applied voltage; at the end of region B, all electrons emitted by the cathode are being collected by the plate. Further increase of voltage, as in region C, succeeds in collecting only a few extra electrons which are emitted from the cathode due to the Schottky effect, a decrease in work function caused by the strong field.

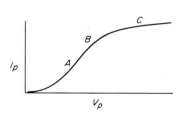

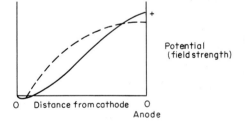

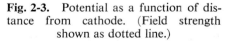

Fig. 2-2.   Plate characteristic of a diode.   **Fig. 2-3.**   Potential as a function of distance from cathode. (Field strength shown as dotted line.)

Unless the potential between the plate and cathode is high (regions B and C), the electrons emitted by the cathode are not all attracted to the plate and the excess form a cloud around the cathode. This "space charge" repels electrons emitted by the cathode, and some electrons return to the cathode. A plot of potential as a function of distance between the cathode and plate as well as the field strength is shown in Fig. 2-3. Note the minimum in the potential curve.

Rectifier Circuits

Since a diode conducts only when the plate is positive, it acts as a rectifier in a-c circuits. A half-wave rectifier circuit and the corresponding voltages and currents in it are shown in Fig. 2-4. The flow of electrons, which is opposite in direction to the conventional "current flow," is shown by an arrow.

A full-wave rectifier can be made by using two diodes or a double diode, that is, two diodes in one vacuum envelope. Such a circuit with the associated currents and voltages is shown in Fig. 2-5.

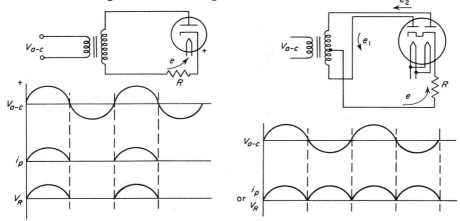

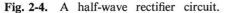

Fig. 2-4. A half-wave rectifier circuit. **Fig. 2-5.** Full-wave rectifier circuit.

Triodes

A triode has a cathode and plate similar to those in a diode. In addition, it has a control grid, an open mesh of wires or a screen, which is placed between the cathode and plate but closer to the cathode. In normal operation very little current flows to the control grid when it is kept negative with respect to the cathode. Grid current will be drawn, however, if the grid becomes positive, and in such a case a grid of larger wires will be needed to prevent damage.

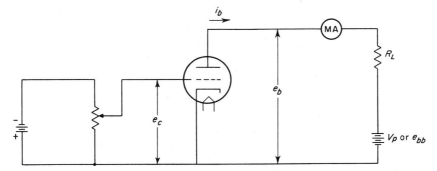

Fig. 2-6. Circuit for measuring characteristics of a triode with voltages and currents designated.

The circuit of Fig. 2-6 may be used for measurement of the characteristics of a triode. A typical set of curves for a triode is shown in Fig. 2-7.

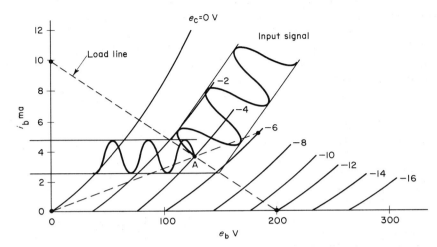

Fig. 2-7. Typical characteristic curves for a triode, with load line for $R_L = 20,000\ \Omega$ and operating point A for $R_K = 1000\ \Omega$ is shown. An input signal of 4 V is shown along with the corresponding output current.

The constants associated with any given triode are generally three in number and are defined in Eqs. 2-2, 2-3, and 2-4.

$$\text{plate resistance} = r_p = \left|\frac{\partial e_b}{\partial i_b}\right|_{e_c} \tag{2-2}$$

$$\text{amplification factor} = \mu = \left|\frac{\partial e_b}{\partial e_c}\right|_{i_b} \tag{2-3}$$

$$\text{transconductance} = g_m = \left|\frac{\partial i_b}{\partial e_c}\right|_{e_b} \tag{2-4}$$

A simple triode amplifier and the designations commonly used for the voltages in the circuit are illustrated in Fig. 2-8.

The actual operation of a tube can be understood by drawing a load line and establishing the operating point on the tube characteristic curves. The load line is given by Eq. 2-5, which can be derived by

$$E_{bb} = i_b R_L + E_B + i_b R_K \tag{2-5}$$

considering the plate current flowing in the output circuit. The two points on the extremities of the load line are given by the conditions of Eq. 2-6 and 2-7.

$$\text{If } E_B = 0, \qquad i_b(R_L + R_K) = E_{bb} \tag{2-6}$$

$$\text{If } i_b = 0, \qquad E_B = E_{bb} \tag{2-7}$$

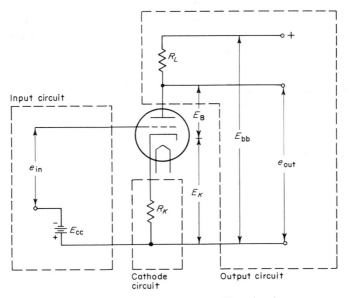

Fig. 2-8. Typical triode amplifier circuit.

Such a line—where R_L = 20,000 Ω, and R_K = 1000 Ω, and E_{bb} = 200 V—is shown in Fig. 2-7. The normal operating point—that is, the condition of the tube with no input signal—depends on the value of e_c and will be zero if no cathode resistor and no grid bias E_{cc} is used. If a cathode resistor is used, one can determine the operating point by noting the intersection of the load line with the cathode bias line drawn according to Eq. 2-8.

$$-e_c = i_b R_K \qquad (2\text{-}8)$$

The amplification properties of the tube can be understood by assuming that the input signal of magnitude 4 V shown in Fig. 2-7 is caused by a current flowing through an input resistor of 10,000 Ω. The signal current would then have been

$$i_{\text{signal}} = \frac{4}{10,000} = 0.4 \text{ milliamps (ma)} \qquad (2\text{-}9)$$

The output signal is of the order of 2 ma and the output signal would have a total magnitude of

$$e = (0.002)(20,000) = 40 \text{ V} \qquad (2\text{-}10)$$

The actual output signal, given by

$$e_{\text{out}} = E_{bb} - i_b R_L \qquad (2\text{-}11)$$

would vary by plus and minus 20 V around the value given by considering the normal operating point of the tube in this circuit, or, approximately,

$$e_{out} = 200 - (0.004)(20,000) = 120 \text{ V} \qquad (2\text{-}12)$$

Pentodes

A pentode contains two grids in addition to the control grid of a triode. These grids are (1) the screen grid, a mesh of wires closer to the plate than the control grid, and (2) a suppressor grid, a mesh of wires very close to the plate, that is, between the plate and the screen grid. The screen grid is maintained at a positive potential and serves to screen the plate from the effect of the control grid. The suppressor grid is usually connected to the cathode and is, therefore, negative with respect to the plate and serves to return to the plate any secondary electrons knocked out of it by the electrons from the cathode as they impinge on the plate. A pentode has quite different characteristic curves (Fig. 2-9) and

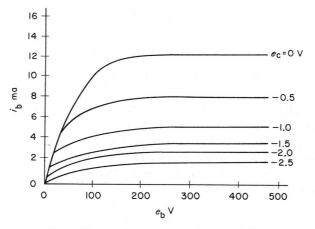

Fig. 2-9. Typical pentode characteristics.

shows high amplification factors, up to 2000, and plate resistances which may exceed 1 megohm (MΩ). The corresponding values for a triode are usually about two orders of magnitude less.

An exact treatment of the amplifying action of a vacuum tube can be made by noting that an input signal of value $e_{in} = e_c$ would cause the tube to produce a voltage e_b equal to $-\mu e_c$. This voltage would, in effect, be that produced by the plate current i_b flowing through the plate resistance r_p and the load resistor R_L connected in series. Thus,

$$i_b(R_L + r_p) = -\mu e_c \qquad (2\text{-}13)$$

The output signal, however, is

$$e_{out} = i_b R_L = \frac{-\mu e_c R_L}{R_L + r_p} \qquad (2\text{-}14)$$

and the gain A of the amplifier is given by

$$A = \frac{e_{out}}{e_{in}} = \frac{-\mu e_c R_L}{e_c(R_L + r_p)} = \frac{-\mu R_L}{R_L + r_p} \qquad (2\text{-}15)$$

The negative sign indicates that the output signal is 180° out of phase with the input signal. Since $\mu = g_m r_p$, Eq. 2-15 can also be written as

$$A = \frac{-g_m r_p R_L}{r_p + R_L} \qquad (2\text{-}16)$$

When r_p is very large compared with R_L, as it usually is in pentode amplifiers, the gain is approximately that given by Eq. 2-17.

$$A \approx -g_m R_L \qquad (2\text{-}17)$$

Inverse Feedback Principle

Equations 2-13 through 2-16 are developed for an amplifier circuit similar to that shown in Fig. 2-8 but without a cathode resistor R_K. If such a cathode resistor is added, the following equations indicate the behavior of the amplifier. Either a pentode or triode can be used as the tube.

Let a signal ∂e_s be impressed on the grid of the tube. The corresponding change in plate current is called ∂i_b. This current, flowing through the cathode resistor, would cause the cathode to become more positive by $R_K \partial i_b$ volts, and the signal would therefore be decreased by this amount. This is known as *inverse feedback*. The actual change in the grid voltage with respect to ground would be

$$\partial e_c = \partial e_s - R_K \partial i_b \qquad (2\text{-}18)$$

Substitution of Eq. 2-18 into Eq. 2-4 gives

$$\partial i_b = g_m \partial e_c = g_m \partial e_s - g_m R_K \partial i_b \qquad (2\text{-}19)$$

thus

$$\partial i_b = \frac{g_m \partial e_s}{1 + g_m R_K} \qquad (2\text{-}20)$$

Let us call g' the effective transconductance of this circuit with inverse feedback.

$$g' = \frac{\partial i_b}{\partial e_s} = g_m \left(\frac{1}{1 + g_m R_K} \right) \qquad (2\text{-}21)$$

We see from Eq. 2-21 that the introduction of the cathode resistor R_K reduces the effect of the tube constant g_m on the circuit by the factor $\frac{1}{1 + g_m R_K}$. If $R_K \gg 1$, then

$$g' \approx \frac{g_m}{g_m R_K} \approx \frac{1}{R_K} \qquad (2\text{-}22)$$

In this case the circuit would be independent of the tube constants. This is the advantage of inverse feedback; it makes circuits more stable, i.e., less dependent on the characteristics and vagaries of tubes, at the expense, however, of some loss in amplification.

Cathode Ray Tubes

A cathode ray tube, shown in schematic diagram in Fig. 2-10, forms the display unit in many modern electrical devices and especially in the oscilloscope.

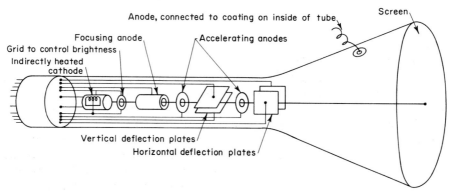

Fig. 2-10. Schematic diagram of cathode ray tube.

The oscilloscope is widely used as a major test instrument to display electrical signals, that is, voltage as a function of time.

The grid is normally negative with respect to the cathode—the more negative the grid the less intense the beam. The focusing anode is positive and is adjusted to give a sharp spot when the electrons strike the phosphorescent screen. The accelerating anodes are still more positive and serve, as the name indicates, to further accelerate the electron beam, the direction of which is determined by the sign and magnitude of the voltages on the horizontal and vertical deflecting plates. The electrons are further accelerated by application of a high positive charge to the inside of the tube near the screen. The screen is covered with a phosphor, and tubes may be obtained with different types of phosphors, those with long or short persistence and with various colors. Besides the cathode ray tube with electrostatic focusing and deflection illustrated here, tubes are also available with magnetic focusing or magnetic deflection, or both. In most uses, a voltage varying in a sawtooth fashion with respect to time is applied to the horizontal plates so that a "sweep" linear with time and recurring at regular intervals is obtained. The horizontal plates are connected to the signal to be displayed.

Semiconductors

Diodes

When a crystal of a semiconductor such as germanium or silicon is grown from a melt which contains a small amount of an impurity element of a higher group in the periodic table, an *n*-type crystal is obtained. Such crystals have an excess of electrons over those in a pure crystal. On the other hand, if the impurity element is of a periodic group lower than the main element, the semiconducting crystal which results is said to be a *p*-type. Such crystals contain a deficiency of electrons or, equivalently, an excess of holes. A semiconductor diode is prepared by arranging to have an *n*-type and *p*-type junction in a crystal. There are various ways of producing such a junction; for example, a bit of one type of impurity and then a bit of the other type may be added to a crystal as it is being drawn from a melt of the pure material.

The characteristics of a semiconductor diode are shown in Fig. 2-11.

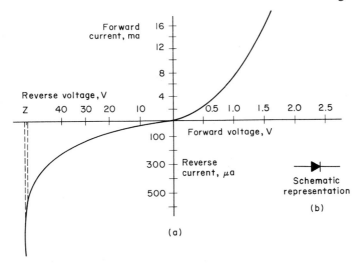

Fig. 2-11.   Characteristics of a semiconductor diode.

Note that there is a change in scale on both axes on either side of zero. When the diode is biased in the forward direction—that is, when the *n*-type part is connected to the negative terminal and the *p*-type part is connected to the positive terminal of a voltage source—a current flows easily. When the reverse is true—that is, when the diode is reverse-biased—only a very small current flows until the zener limit is reached, where breakdown occurs and a large current flows.

A semiconductor diode, then, operates in much the same fashion as a tube diode and can be used as a rectifier in much the same way as a tube. Semiconductors normally operate at considerably lower voltages than vacuum tubes and are usually used in low-voltage rectifier circuits.

Transistors

A transistor is a three-layer unit in which an emitter and collector of one type of semiconducting material are separated from each other by a thin slice (0.02 mm or less) of the other type of semiconducting material. Thus transistors are either *n-p-n* or *p-n-p* types.

An *n-p-n* type transistor is shown in Fig. 2-12. When the emitter is biased in

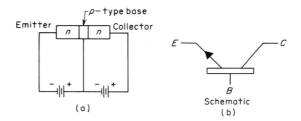

Fig. 2-12.   Transistor, *n-p-n* type.

the forward direction, i.e., the emitter is negative with respect to the base, electrons pass from emitter to base, and since the base is so thin, most of these electrons (95–99 percent) pass on into the collector region. From 1 to 5 percent of the electrons combine with holes in the *p* region, the base, and form the base current. The collector is biased in the reverse direction, i.e., positive with respect to the base.

Although the current is nearly the same in the emitter and collector circuits, reference to Fig. 2-11 will show that a small change of the voltage in the *forward* region causes a great change in the current which would require a large voltage change in the *reverse*-biased region. In other words, the emitter current flows in a circuit with a low resistance, and the collector current flows in a high-resistance circuit. If a signal is present in the emitter circuit and a load resistance of, say, 10,000 Ω is added to the collector circuit, a high-voltage signal will appear across the load resistance. Since the currents in the two circuits are approximately equal but the output voltage is much higher, *power* or *voltage* amplification has been achieved.

A *p-n-p* transistor is shown in Fig. 2-13. When this type of transistor is biased in the sense shown in the figure, similar considerations to those just discussed apply.

Typical Electronic Circuits

Some simple electronic circuits that are often met as component parts of more complicated circuits will be discussed below.

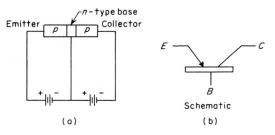

Fig. 2-13. Transistor, *p-n-p* type.

Filters Associated with Rectification

Rectifiers have already been discussed under diodes. When a rectifier is used to produce a d-c or voltage source from an a-c source, a filter circuit is usually necessary to smooth out the pulsating direct current which would be obtained directly from the rectifier (see Figs. 2-4 and 2-5). Filter circuits are generally classified as either capacitor or inductor (choke) input filters, depending upon the first element used after the rectifier. An example of a capacitor-input filter is shown in Fig. 2-14 and a choke-input filter in Fig. 2-15. The action of a

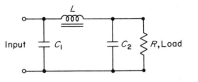

Fig. 2-14. Capacitor-input filter.

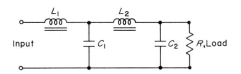

Fig. 2-15. Choke-input filter.

filter circuit can be understood by consideration of Fig. 2-16, which shows the effect of placing a capacitor such as C_1 of Fig. 2-14 across the terminals of a full-wave rectifier. The dotted line indicates the voltage across C_1, which is seen to be more constant than the voltage across a rectifier used alone, as indicated by the solid line. An inductance further smooths out the voltage, since inductances show high resistances to the ripple frequency (twice the line frequency), which still exists in the

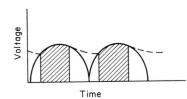

Fig. 2-16. Effect of a capacitor, such as C_1 of Fig. 2-14, on output voltage of a full-wave rectifier. Dotted line is voltage across capacitor. Solid line is rectifier output voltage. Shaded area is charging interval.

output of the rectifier-capacitor circuit, although the inductance presents only a very low resistance to the d-c component of the output.

The two types of filter circuits have somewhat different characteristics and therefore different uses. The rectifier current flows continuously in the choke-input filter and only intermittently in the capacitor-input variety. For the same load current, the peak anode current is higher in the capacitor-input circuit. The voltage regulation (the variation of voltage output with the current drawn from the circuit) is better with a choke-input filter. At very small current drains, however, the choke loses its effectiveness. The average rectified voltage is higher with a capacitor-input filter.

Regulated Power Supplies

For many uses, the d-c voltage output of a rectifier and filter circuit must be more closely controlled or regulated. Two methods of control are shown in Figs. 2-17 and 2-18.

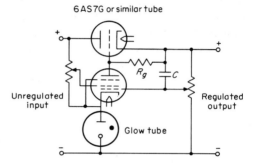

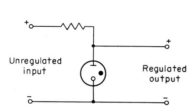

Fig. 2-17. Glow-tube regulated   **Fig. 2-18.**   Series-tube regulated circuit.
circuit.

The glow discharge tube contains a gas under reduced pressure and an anode and cathode. The cathode has a large area. When the glow discharge is started by application of a sufficiently high voltage to ionize the gas, the voltage across the tube remains fairly constant regardless of the current passing through the tube (up to a certain limit). It can thus serve as a voltage regulator.

The operation of the more elaborate regulator circuit shown in Fig. 2-18 can be understood by considering what would happen should the voltage across the output terminals suddenly increase. If this were to occur, the control grid of the pentode would suddenly become more positive than before with respect to the cathode. (Note that the cathode potential is regulated by the glow discharge tube.) More current would flow in the plate circuit of the pentode, creating a greater voltage drop across resistance, R_g. This, in turn, would make the grid of the series-regulator tube more negative with respect to its cathode than before and would decrease the current flow through the series tube, thus reducing or correcting the initial sudden increase of voltage which inaugurated this train of events.

Difference Amplifiers

A special type of amplifier circuit frequently used in instruments for analytical purposes is the difference amplifier, an example of which is shown in Fig. 2-19. Analysis of this circuit could be carried out in the following manner. A

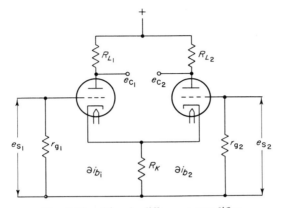

Fig. 2-19. Simple difference amplifier.

change of input signal by ∂e_{c_1} would cause the tube to produce an output voltage change of $\mu \partial e_{c_1}$. Similar results would occur if the other input grid signal, e_{c_2}, were varied. The input signal to the grid is not the same as the overall input signal, however, because of the effect of the cathode resistor R_K. Consideration of the circuit in a manner analogous to that described under inverse feedback shows that

$$\partial e_{c_1} = \partial e_{s_1} - (\partial i_{b_1} + \partial i_{b_2})R_K \qquad (2\text{-}23)$$

and

$$\partial e_{c_2} = \partial e_{s_2} - (\partial i_{b_1} + \partial i_{b_2})R_K \qquad (2\text{-}25)$$

Therefore,

$$\mu \partial e_{c_1} = \mu(\partial e_{s_1} - (\partial i_{b_1} + \partial i_{b_2})R_K) \qquad (2\text{-}25)$$

and

$$\mu \partial e_{c_2} = \mu(\partial e_{s_2} - (\partial i_{b_1} + \partial i_{b_2})R_K) \qquad (2\text{-}26)$$

This voltage change is, for each circuit, equal to the sums of the changes in current times the various resistances in series in the circuit. Thus

$$\mu \partial e_{c_1} = (\partial i_{b_1} + \partial i_{b_2})R_K + \partial i_{b_1} r_p + \partial i_{b_1} R_{L_1} \qquad (2\text{-}27)$$

and

$$\mu \partial e_{c_2} = (\partial i_{b_1} + \partial i_{b_2})R_K + \partial i_{b_2} r_p + \partial i_{b_2} R_{L_2} \qquad (2\text{-}28)$$

Combining Eq. 2-27 with 2-25 and Eq. 2-28 with 2-26 yields Eqs. 2-29 and 2-30.

$$\mu \partial e_{s_1} - \mu \partial i_{b_1} R_K - \mu \partial i_{b_2} R_K = \partial i_{b_1} R_K + \partial i_{b_2} R_K + \partial i_{b_1} r_p + \partial i_{b_1} R_{L_1} \quad (2\text{-}29)$$

$$\mu \partial e_{s_2} - \mu \partial i_{b_1} R_K - \mu \partial i_{b_2} R_K = \partial i_{b_1} R_K + \partial i_{b_2} R_K + \partial i_{b_2} r_p + \partial i_{b_2} R_{L_2} \quad (2\text{-}30)$$

These equations may be rewritten as

$$\partial i_{b_1}(R_{L_1} + r_p + (1 + \mu)R_K) + \partial i_{b_2}(1 + \mu)R_K = \mu \partial e_{s_1} \quad (2\text{-}31)$$

and

$$\partial i_{b_1}(1 + \mu)R_K + \partial i_{b_2}(R_{L_2} + r_p + (1 + \mu)R_K) = \mu \partial e_{s_2} \quad (2\text{-}32)$$

Solving these two equations simultaneously for ∂i_{b_1} and ∂i_{b_2} gives Eqs. 2-33 and 2-34:

$$\partial i_{b_1} = \frac{+\mu \left[\left(\dfrac{R_{L_2} + r_p}{\mu + 1} + R_K \right) \partial e_{s_1} - R_K \partial e_{s_2} \right]}{\dfrac{(R_{L_1} + r_p)(R_{L_2} + r_p)}{\mu + 1} + R_K(R_{L_1} + R_{L_2} + 2r_p)} \quad (2\text{-}33)$$

$$\partial i_{b_2} = \frac{-\mu \left[R_K \partial e_{s_1} - \left(\dfrac{R_{L_1} + r_p}{\mu + 1} + R_K \right) \partial e_{s_2} \right]}{\dfrac{(R_{L_1} + r_p)(R_{L_2} + r_p)}{\mu + 1} + R_K(R_{L_1} + R_{L_2} + 2r_p)} \quad (2\text{-}34)$$

The output signals e_{0_1} and e_{0_2} are, respectively, $-\partial i_{b_1} R_{L_1}$ and $-\partial i_{b_2} R_{L_2}$. A simplification can be achieved by noting that, under normal operating conditions of tubes, $\dfrac{R_L + r_p}{\mu + 1} \ll R_K$.

This leads to Eqs. 2-35 and 2-36.

$$e_{0_1} = -\partial i_{b_1} R_{L_1} = \frac{-\mu R_{L_1}}{R_{L_1} + R_{L_2} + 2r_p}(\partial e_{s_1} - \partial e_{s_2}) \quad (2\text{-}35)$$

$$e_{0_2} = -\partial i_{b_2} R_{L_2} = \frac{+\mu R_{L_2}}{R_{L_1} + R_{L_2} + 2r_p}(\partial e_{s_1} - \partial e_{s_2}) \quad (2\text{-}36)$$

The above equations show that the output signals are amplified differences of the two input signals. In many cases the two load resistors are equal, i.e., $R_{L_1} = R_{L_2} = R_L$. In such a case, Eqs. 2-35 and 2-36 become

$$e_{0_1} = \frac{-\mu R_L}{2(R_L + r_p)}(\partial e_{s_1} - \partial e_{s_2}) \quad (2\text{-}37)$$

$$e_{0_2} = \frac{+\mu R_L}{2(R_L + r_p)}(\partial e_{s_1} - \partial e_{s_2}) \quad (2\text{-}38)$$

It is also interesting to note that the difference between the two outputs as given by Eq. 2-39 is also directly proportional to the difference in the input signals.

$$e_{0_1} - e_{0_2} = \frac{-\mu R_L}{R_L + r_p}(\partial e_{s_1} - \partial e_{s_2}) \qquad (2\text{-}39)$$

Operational Amplifiers

High-gain d-c amplifiers with inverse feedback for stabilization and with high input impedances and low output impedances and with good high-frequency responses are now commercially available. Such amplifiers find many uses in instrumental design and are known as operational amplifiers. An operational amplifier has two input and two output terminals and is often indicated in schematic circuit drawings as a triangle, as shown in Fig. 2-20(a) and, in simplified form, in Fig. 2-20(b).

Fig. 2-20. Schematic representations of operational amplifiers.

The operational amplifier is really a high-gain difference amplifier. Very frequently the common input-output terminal of Fig. 2-20(a) is connected to ground, and an input impedance Z_1 and a feedback impedance Z_2 are added, as in Fig. 2-21.

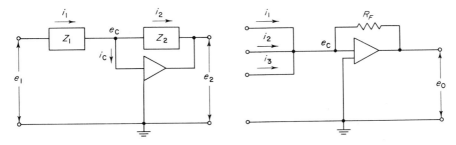

Fig. 2-21. Operational amplifier with impedances.

Fig. 2-22. Operational amplifier circuit to measure the sum of three currents.

Since the input impedance of the operational amplifier is so high, i_c is practically zero and can be neglected. Thus $i_1 = i_2$. Furthermore, the high gain of the operational amplifier ensures that the potential e_c must be very nearly equal to that of the other input terminal—in this case, ground potential. The point e_c, is said to be a *virtual ground*. Under these conditions,

$$i_1 = \frac{1}{Z_1}(e_1 - e_c) = \frac{e_1}{Z_1} = i_2 = \frac{1}{Z_2}(e_c - e_2) = \frac{-e_2}{Z_2} \qquad (2\text{-}40)$$

Therefore,

$$-e_2 = \frac{Z_2}{Z_1} e_1 \qquad (2\text{-}41)$$

The operational amplifier can be used in a large number of ways. One method is to furnish an output voltage which is proportional to the sum of several currents. Such a circuit is shown in Fig. 2-22. Since e_c must be zero and since the total current flows through R_F, there being practically no current through the amplifier,

$$e_0 = -(i_1 + i_2 + i_3)R_F \qquad (2\text{-}42)$$

Voltages can be added by the circuit shown in Fig. 2-23. Each voltage can be multiplied by a different factor if desired. In this case,

$$e_0 = -R_F\left(\frac{e_1}{R_1} + \frac{e_2}{R_2} + \frac{e_3}{R_3}\right) \qquad (2\text{-}43)$$

If the feedback impedance is a capacitance instead of a resistance, as in Fig. 2-24, a current integrator results.

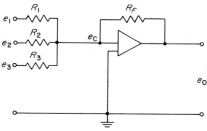

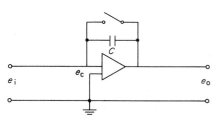

Fig. 2-23. Operational amplifier circuit to measure the sum of three voltages.

Fig. 2-24. Operational amplifier integrating circuit.

The point e_c must remain at ground potential and all of the current must pass through the capacitor. Thus the output potential e_0 always equals the potential of the capacitor. Since capacitance $C = Q/E$, where Q is charge and E is potential, and since the charge is the time integral of the current, or $Q = \int_0^t i\, \partial t$, it follows that

$$E = \frac{1}{C}\int_0^t i\, \partial t = -e_0 \qquad (2\text{-}44)$$

By placing a resistance in the input circuit, we can integrate potentials rather than currents. The discharge switch is necessary to reset the circuit.

A differentiating circuit for potentials can be obtained by using the circuit of Fig. 2-25. In this case, the output e_0 is given by Eq. 2-45.

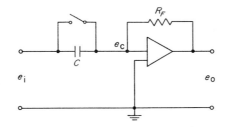

Fig. 2-25. Operational amplifier differentiating circuit.

$$e_0 = -R_F C \frac{\partial e_i}{\partial t} \qquad (2\text{-}45)$$

Many other examples of circuits which use operational amplifiers could be given, but these may serve to indicate the wide applicability of these amplifiers. It should be understood that several circuits can be combined, and complicated equations can therefore be solved by these devices.

Bibliography

Bair, E. J., *Introduction to Chemical Instrumentation*, McGraw-Hill, New York, 1962.

Elmore, N. C., and M. Sands, *Electronics*, McGraw-Hill, New York, 1949.

Hill, R. W., *Electronics in Engineering*, McGraw-Hill, New York, 1949.

Malmstadt, H. V., C. G. Enke, and E. C. Toren, Jr., *Electronics for Scientists*, Benjamin, New York, 1962.

Müller, R. H., R. L. Garman, and M. E. Droz, *Experimental Electronics*, Prentice-Hall, Englewood Cliffs, N.J., 1945.

Reilley, C. N., and D. T. Sawyer, *Experiments for Instrumental Methods*, Part V, McGraw-Hill, New York, 1961.

Seely, S., *Electron-Tube Circuits*, 2nd ed., McGraw-Hill, New York, 1958.

Ultraviolet and
Visible Absorption Instrumentation

Terminology and Basic Components

Instruments designed for measuring absorption of substances for radiant energy in the ultraviolet and visible portions of the spectrum have received various names: photometers, spectrometers, colorimeters, absorptometers, and spectrophotometers. In an attempt to reduce the confusion over nomenclature which has arisen through the years, the advisory board members of *Analytical Chemistry*[1] and ASTM Committee E-13 have made suggestions. From these two sources, the following definitions will be employed in this text:

Photometer. An instrument for measuring relative radiant power or some function of this quantity (as measured by receptors such as photocells, etc.)

Spectrometer, Optical. An instrument with an entrance slit, a dispersing device, and one or more exit slits, with which measurements are made at selected wavelengths within the spectral range, or by scanning over the range. The quantity detected is a function of radiant power.

Spectrophotometer. A spectrometer with associated equipment, so that it furnishes the ratio, or a function of the ratio, of the radiant power of two beams as a function of spectral wavelength. These two beams may be separated in time, space, or both.

The essential components of a filter photometer are (1) a source of radiant energy, (2) some type of filter for isolation of a band of radiant energy, (3) an optical system for producing a parallel beam of filtered light for passage through an absorption cell (cuvette), (4) a detector for unabsorbed radiant energy, and (5) associated readout meters. The more sophisticated spectrophotometer will substitute a prism or grating as dispersing device in place of filters for the isolation of the desired spectral band of radiant energy. A schematic diagram of the relationship of these components is shown in Fig. 3-1.

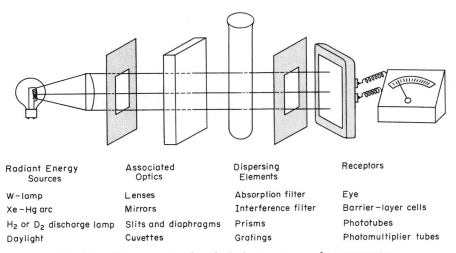

Radiant Energy Sources	Associated Optics	Dispersing Elements	Receptors
W–lamp	Lenses	Absorption filter	Eye
Xe –Hg arc	Mirrors	Interference filter	Barrier–layer cells
H_2 or D_2 discharge lamp	Slits and diaphragms	Prisms	Phototubes
Daylight	Cuvettes	Gratings	Photomultiplier tubes

Fig. 3-1. Components of optical photometers and spectrometers.

The components selected must be appropriate to their intended use. Sources are important from the viewpoint of their range and the relative spectral distribution within this range, their stability with respect to normal operating periods, their operating temperature, and any associated equipment required for operation and time stability. In design of equipment the general aim is to provide a wide range of wavelengths and some means for the isolation of a restricted band of wavelengths for a particular task at hand. When the incident radiant energy is instrumentally restricted to a range of frequencies absorbed by the ion or molecule in question, the percentage change in response for a given concentration change becomes greater. Such means vary from simple filters passing relatively wide spectral bands of energy to the finest slit assembly in a spectrometer. However, the decision at this point profoundly influences the choice and sensitivity demanded of the receptor. Fortunately, instrumental receptors are not limited to the visible range of light, as is the human eye, and permit work in the ultraviolet and near infrared portions of the spectrum.

Radiant Energy Sources

The function of the light source is to provide incident light of sufficient intensity for measurement. For work in the visible, near infrared, and near ultraviolet regions, the most common source is the glass-enclosed, tungsten-filament, incandescent lamp. In size and shape the tungsten lamp varies from a 100-watt projection lamp to a 6- or 12-volt automobile headlamp with coiled filament or a small flashlight bulb. Lamps with prefocus bases are useful with respect to easy replacement in an optical system. Unfortunately, the tungsten lamp emits the major portion of its energy in the near infrared region of the spectrum (Fig. 3-2). Only about 15 percent of the radiant energy falls within the visible region of the spectral distribution curve at an operating temperature of 2600°–3000°K. An increase in the operating temperature of the lamp increases the total energy output and decreases the wavelength of the energy maximum, but at the expense of drastically shortened lamp life. A heat-absorbing filter is often inserted between the lamp and sample holder to absorb most of the infrared radiation without seriously diminishing energy at other wavelengths. A high-intensity source can cause enough extraneous radiation to enter a monochromator so that scattered light reaching the detector can impair the validity of measurements, particularly if the sample compartment is positioned between the monochromator and the detector.

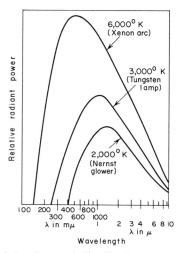

Fig. 3-2. Spectral distribution curves of radiant energy sources.

According to Planck's law the relationship between intensity of radiation I at a given wavelength λ and the operating temperature T is given by

$$I = \frac{A(8\pi hc)\lambda^{-5}}{e^{-hc/\lambda kT} - 1} \tag{3-1}$$

where A is the area of the radiator, h is Planck's constant (6.6256×10^{-27} erg sec), c is the velocity of light in vacuum (2.9979×10^{10} cm sec^{-1}), and k is the Boltzmann constant (1.3805×10^{-16} erg °K^{-1} mole^{-1}).

For work in the ultraviolet region, the continuous emission spectrum of the high-pressure hydrogen (or deuterium) discharge lamp is adequate down to the limit of transmission of the envelope material: quartz (200 mμ) or fused silica (185 mμ). The lamp's upper limit of usefulness is about 375 mμ, for at longer wavelengths the spectrum is no longer continuous. When deuterium replaces hydrogen, the wavelength range is the same, but the intensity is nearly tripled.

When very high levels of illumination are desired, a xenon arc or a mercury vapor lamp provides a large amount of continuous radiation plus additional intense radiation in the wavelengths characteristic of the xenon or mercury emission spectrum. These lamps become very hot in operation and must be well insulated thermally from other instrument components and may even require auxiliary cooling.

High short-term stability of these sources is required for single-beam, manual photometers. When a receptor is illuminated with any of these lamps, the photocurrent i can be expressed as a function of voltage V applied across the lamp terminals by the equation

$$i = KV^x \qquad (3\text{-}2)$$

where the exponent x has a value between 3 and 4 for tungsten lamps. This implies that to reproduce the photocurrent to within 0.2 percent, which is attainable spectrophotometric precision, the lamp voltage must not vary by more than a few thousandths of a volt. To attain such close voltage regulation, the lamp is frequently operated from a storage battery or from a well-regulated power supply. The effects of voltage fluctuations from an ordinary alternating current main can be cancelled by properly designed double-beam photometers.

Dispersing Devices

By restricting the band of wavelengths passing through the sample to those absorbed by the substance of interest, the sensitivity of instrumental measurements to concentration changes in the specimen is greatly enhanced. The important characteristics of a dispersing device are its band pass width (also called spectral bandwidth and effective bandwidth), the (nominal) wavelength of the band center, and its transmittance at the band peak (peak transmittance). These terms are illustrated in Fig. 3-3. The band pass width is the range of wavelengths between the two points at which the transmittance is one-half the peak transmittance.

Filters

Selection of a filter is usually a compromise between peak transmittance and band pass width; the former should be as high as possible, the latter as narrow as possible. Gelatin filters, liquid filters, and tinted glass filters function by selective absorption of unwanted wavelengths, whereas interference filters depend upon constructive interference of light rays for their transmission characteristics.

The gelatin (Wratten) filter consists of a layer of gelatin impregnated with suitable organic dyes and sandwiched between two sheets of glass. Liquid filters are solutions of appropriately absorbing components. The tinted glass filter consists of a solid sheet of glass that has been colored by a pigment which is either dissolved or dispersed in the glass. Often composite filters are constructed from sets of unit filters. One series consists of long wavelength, sharp cutoff filters (blue and green series), and the other comprises short wavelength cutoff filters (red and yellow series). The transmittance of the individual filter components and their combined transmittance for a glass absorption filter with a nominal wavelength at 590 mμ are shown in Fig. 3-3. Other standard com-

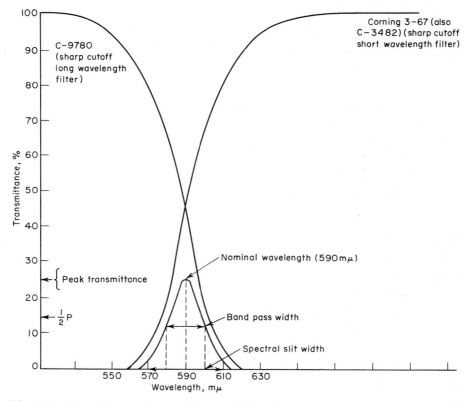

Fig. 3-3.   Spectral transmittance characteristics of a composite glass absorption filter and its components.

binations are available from about 360 to 720 mμ (Fig. 3-4). The usual glass filters have relatively wide band pass widths—35 to 50 mμ, and their peak transmittance is only 5–20 percent, decreasing with improved spectral isolation. Since the action of the filter is one of absorption of unwanted energy, the dissipation of heat must be considered, as must the resistance to change in spectral characteristics over long periods of usage. For these reasons, the gelatin filter is now seldom used because it tends to deteriorate with time due to alterations in the gelatin and to bleaching of the dyes.

Narrower bandwidths are obtained with interference filters. This type con-

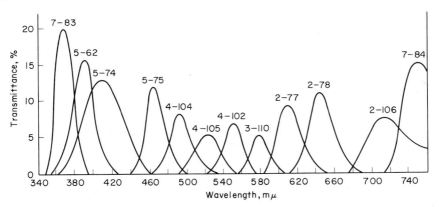

Fig. 3-4. Spectral transmittance curves of some glass absorption filters. Code numbers are from Corning Glass Works catalog.

sists of an evaporated coating of a transparent dielectric spacer of low refractive index sandwiched between semitransparent silver films (Fig. 3-5). Because of its hardness, magnesium fluoride (n_D = 1.38) is commonly used as dielectric. Light incident upon the face of the filter (usually at 90°) is reflected back and forth between the metal films. Constructive interference between different pairs of superposed light rays occurs only when the path difference is exactly one wavelength or some multiple thereof. The equation expressing a maximum for the transmission of a spectral band when light is normally incident (sin 90° = 1) is

$$m\lambda = 2d(n) \sin \theta = 2d(n) \qquad (3\text{-}3)$$

where d is the thickness of the dielectric spacer whose refractive index is n. The multiple of frequencies harmonically related to the wavelength of the first-order rays is the order (m) of the interference. These filters have a bandwidth of 10–17 mμ and peak transmittance of 40 to 60 percent.

Multilayer interference filters are prepared by successive evaporations of 5–25 layers of high- and low-refractive index dielectric in alternating layers. Each coating is a fraction of a wavelength thick. When the coating thickness is controlled, subtle interference arises among the light waves reflected and transmitted at the many interfaces. Unless the difference in path lengths travelled by the successive pairs of rays is an integral number of wavelengths, the emergent light will not be in phase. Frequencies harmonically related to the fundamental frequency of the filter are also transmitted. Thus, a second-order filter for 590 mμ also transmits energy of a nominal wavelength corresponding to its first, third, and fourth order—approximately 1180, 393, and 295 mμ, respectively. To absorb these other orders, a suitable glass blocking filter, shown by the dashed lines in Fig. 3-6, must be incorporated in the final filter assembly. Multilayer filters are characterized by a band pass width of 8 mμ or

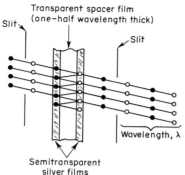

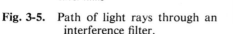

Fig. 3-5. Path of light rays through an interference filter.

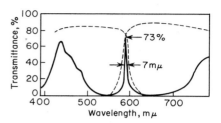

Fig. 3-6. Wavelength vs transmittance curve for a multilayer interference filter peaked at 591.7 mμ. The dashed lines are transmittance curves of glass (blocking) filters to cut out the side bands.

less, and a peak transmittance of 60–95 percent. In convergent or divergent light, the half width is increased. These are the most efficient transmittance filters available. They can be used with high-intensity light sources since they remove unwanted radiation by transmission and reflection and not by absorption.

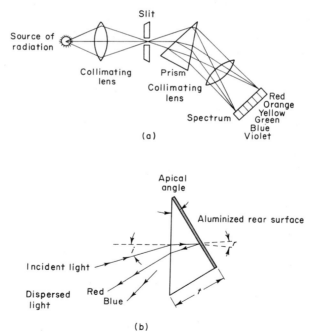

Fig. 3-7. Action of a prism as a dispersing medium. (a) Cornu-type mounting. (b) Littrow-type mounting: i is angle of incidence, r is angle of refraction, t is base width of prism, and apical angle is 30°.

Prisms

The action of a prism in dispersing a polychromatic beam of radiation into a spectrum depends on the variation of the index of refraction with wavelength; that is, the dispersive power is $\partial n/\partial\lambda$. As used in spectrometers, the light from the source is directed through a convergent lens onto an entrance slit at the focal point of the lens, thence through the prism and a second convergent lens. At an air-prism interface, an entering light ray at an angle of incidence i will be bent toward the vertical to the surface and, at the prism-air interface, it is bent away from the vertical. The image of the entrance slit is projected onto the exit slit as a series of colored images ranged next to each other, caused by violet light being more strongly diverted than the red, as shown in Fig. 3-7.

The actual separation in space between two wavelengths depends on the dispersive power of the prism material and the apical angle of the prism. The latter is usually 60°. A nonlinear wavelength scale results, accompanied by a crowding of the wavelength scale at longer wavelengths. When quartz is the prism material, the crowding becomes serious at wavelengths longer than about 600 mμ. The dispersion of glass is about three times that of quartz and is the material of choice for the visible portion of the spectrum. Quartz or fused silica prisms are mandatory for inclusion of the ultraviolet spectrum below 350 mμ. Figure 3-8 shows approximate range and dispersion of prism materials.

Resolving power is a measure of the ability of the dispersing device to separate distinctly two closely spaced wavelengths of about equal intensity, i.e., $R = \lambda/\partial\lambda$. For a prism,

$$R = t(\partial n/\partial\lambda) \qquad (3\text{-}4)$$

where t is the thickness of the base of the prism and the other term is the dispersive power of the prism material. Since the latter remains nearly constant for prism materials, except near the transmission cutoff, the thicker the base of the prism, the greater will be the resolving power.

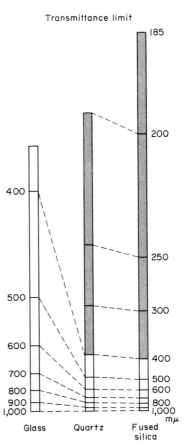

Fig. 3-8. Approximate range and dispersion of prism materials.

Quartz exhibits the property of double refraction. Consequently, two pieces of quartz, one right-handed and one left-handed, cemented back-to-back, must be used in the construction of a 60° prism (Cornu mounting) or the energy must be reflected and returned through a single 30° prism so that it passes through the prism in both directions (Littrow mounting). Failure to circumvent this difficulty with quartz would give rise to false transmittance readings when handling polarizing systems. With either type of mounting, two surfaces of the prism must be very carefully polished and optically flat. This requirement, coupled with the scarcity of quartz of suitable dimensions, increases the price of a prism spectrometer. On the other hand, the spectrum has only one order, and it is possible to predict the directions in which stray energy will be reflected and to place absorbing baffles in appropriate locations in the spectrometer.

Gratings

Dispersal of light may also be obtained by means of a diffraction grating. A grating consists of a large number of parallel lines (actually grooves) ruled at extremely close intervals, perhaps 15,000 or 30,000 lines per inch, on a highly polished surface, e.g., aluminum. The master grating is used as a mold in the production of replica gratings. A film of parting compound is applied to the master, the film is aluminized, the crevices are filled with epoxy resin, and an optical flat is bonded by the epoxy to the aluminum replica of the master ruling pattern. When the epoxy has hardened, the replica grating, completely aluminized, is separated from the master (Fig. 3-9).

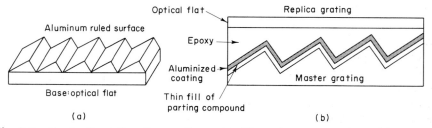

Fig. 3-9.   Production of replica gratings. (a) View of master grating; (b) cutaway view of steps in making a replica grating.

Each ruled groove functions as a scattering center for the light rays impinging on it (Fig. 3-10). Visualize two incoming rays, R_1 and R_2, which form a wave front. As the wave reaches the grating, R_2 must travel farther than R_1 by the distance $d \sin i$, where d is the distance between adjacent grooves and i is the angle of incidence. In leaving the grating, R_1 must go farther than R_2 by $d \sin \theta$, where θ is the angle of reflectance. When the net path difference for the two rays, $(d \sin i) - (d \sin \theta)$, is equal to an integral multiple of a wavelength, $m\lambda$,

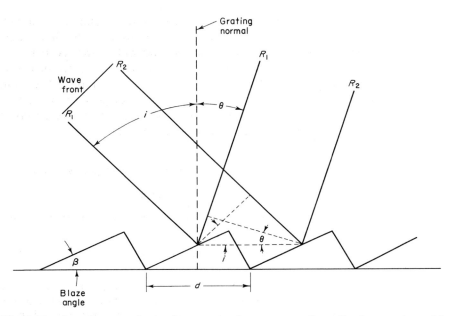

Fig. 3-10. Interference of rays from successive grooves of a reflection grating: i is angle of incidence, r is angle of reflectance, d is grating constant.

the rays will be in phase and will combine constructively. The conditions of constructive interference give the formula

$$m\lambda = d(\sin i \pm \sin \theta) \qquad (3\text{-}5)$$

where m is the order of interference. The positive sign applies where incoming and emergent beams are on the same side of the grating normal. When the angle of incidence is equal, but of opposite sign, to the angle of reflection, i.e.,

$$m\lambda = d(\sin i - \sin \theta) = 0 \qquad (3\text{-}6)$$

the grating acts as a plane mirror (zero order). In many gratings used in the visible and ultraviolet portions of the spectrum there are about 600 lines per millimeter.

An individual grating is restricted in range but can be blazed for a desired wavelength; that is, the bulk of the diffracted intensity can be concentrated in one of the orders of the spectrum by a special angle (echelette) of the groove (see Fig. 3-10). Viewing a grating on the normal results in a simple linear scale for wavelengths equal to m/d.* A fixed pair of entrance and exit slits provides

---

*An expression for dispersion is obtained by differentiating Eq. 3-5 with respect to λ, remembering that i is a constant independent of wavelength. This gives

$$\frac{\partial \theta}{\partial \lambda} = \frac{m}{d \cos \theta}$$

If θ does not become large, $\cos \theta$ will not differ much from unity.

a constant band pass through the dispersed spectrum. It should be noted, however, that the second-order spectrum is twice as wide as the first order; also, the smaller the d-value, the more widely spread will be the spectrum.

The resolving power of a grating, $R = \lambda/\partial\lambda$, is given by the product mN, where N is the total number of rulings and m is the order number. The main advantage of a finer ruling is that it permits a higher dispersion in the first order. Compared with prisms, much higher resolving powers are practical with gratings, and they can be used in all spectral regions.

Example 3-1

A grating ruled 600 lines/mm and 15 cm in width has a resolving power in the first order of

$$R = mN = (15)(6000) = 90,000$$

In the green region ($\lambda = 5400\text{Å}$), this means the smallest wavelength interval resolved will be

$$R = \lambda/\partial\lambda = 90,000$$
$$\partial\lambda = (5400)/(90,000) = 0.06 \text{ Å}$$

A smaller size grating will provide less resolution.

A glass prism with a resolving power comparable to this would be impractically large, since, according to Eq. 3-4, the length of base t would need to be $90,000/(\partial n/\partial\lambda)$. For flint glass the dispersive power is about 1200, so that the base would be 75 cm.

Stray light due to scattering and interference from other spectral orders is a drawback. Light at any point in the emergent spectrum is contaminated with light from other orders of another nominal wavelength. With continuous incident radiation the long wavelength portion of any order will generally overlap the short wavelength part of the next higher order. Double monochromators offer a solution. Blocking filters remove unwanted orders of the nominal wavelength as they do with interference filters (q.v.).

Slit Width

The relative distribution of energy to wavelength passing through the exit slit of a monochromator can be represented by an isosceles triangle if the entrance and exit slits are of equal width (Fig. 3-11). The middle wavelength (peak transmittance) is called the nominal wavelength and is the value read on the wavelength scale of the instrument. The band pass is taken as the bandwidth at one half the peak transmittance and is essentially the width of the exit slit. The total base line width (spectral slit width) is twice the band pass. Three-quarters of the transmitted radiant energy is contained within the band pass width. The relationship between slit width and band pass width depends on the design and focal length of the monochromator, and the nature of the dispersing unit. In a grating spectrometer the band pass for a given slit is constant throughout the spectrum and depends on the ruling of the grating. In a prism instrument, however, the dispersion of the prism varies with wavelength, as shown by the dispersion curve for the Beckman model DU quartz spectrometer in Fig. 3-11.

The spectral isolation of a monochromatic mercury line at 546 mμ with three different slit widths, using the Beckman model DU, is shown in Fig. 3-12. As the prism is turned from the long to the short wavelengths at a slit opening of 0.1 mm (3.4 mμ band pass), light of 546 mμ will just begin to enter the exit slit when the prism setting is 3.4 mμ longer than the true setting of the line, and will just leave the other side of the exit slit at a setting 3.4 mμ shorter than the true setting. When dealing with discrete line emissions, rather than continuous radiation, two emission lines of equal intensity will just be resolved by the instrument when their wavelengths are separated 6.8 mμ at a slit opening of 0.1 mm (cf. Chapter 11, Flame Photometry).

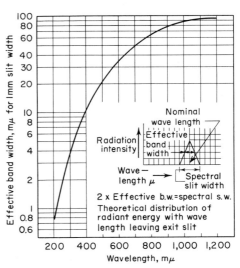

Fig. 3-11. Dispersion data for Beckman model DU quartz spectrophotometer. (Courtesy, Beckman Instruments, Inc.).

The more sensitive the measuring device for the emergent radiation, the narrower can be the slit opening and the purer the emergent beam of radiation, up to a point. At very narrow slit openings the reduction in slit width does not cause a proportional reduction in the spectral region isolated; compare the band pass for slit openings 0.02 and 0.01 mm in Fig. 3-12. This is caused by

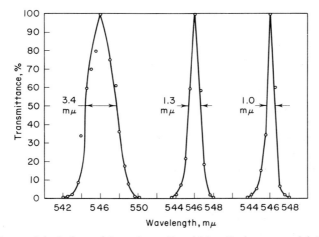

Fig. 3-12. Spectral isolation with various slit widths, Beckman model DU spectrophotometer. (After H. H. Cary and A. O. Beckman, *J. Opt. Soc, Am.*, **31**, 682 (1941), by permission.)

optical aberrations in the collimating mirror and diffraction effects at the slit edges which have the effect of widening the slits so far as spectral purity is concerned. For the Beckman model DU, the slit width required for a band pass W_E is given as $(W_E - 0.03 W_D)/W_D$, where W_D is the band pass per 1-mm slit opening (ordinate on Fig. 3-11); the factor $0.03\ W_D$ arises from the effects of aberration and diffraction and may differ slightly among instruments of the same model. An interesting treatment of the relationship between slit width and spectral purity is given by Hogness, Zscheile, and Sidwell.[4]

Below 220 mμ the slit widths have to be increased rapidly. The steep fall in available energy in this region is common to most instruments, and it is often accentuated by solvent absorbance. This can be reduced by using photomultiplier detectors, flushing the light path with nitrogen or argon, and using solution containers of shorter path length.

Associated Optics

The range of transmittance of materials suitable for windows, lenses, and sample containers is a critical factor. The absorbance (equal to negative log transmittance) of any material should be less than 0.2 at the wavelength of use. Ordinary silicate glasses transmit satisfactorily only from 350 to 3,000 mμ. Special Corex glass extends the ultraviolet range to about 300 mμ. Quartz or fused silica must be used for work below 300 mμ; the limit for quartz is about 210 mμ. If the monochromator is flushed with nitrogen or argon to eliminate absorption by atmospheric oxygen, useful work can be done in the range from 185 to 210 mμ with fused silica. See also Table 5-1.

Beam reduction is accomplished by condensers that function as simple microscopes. With these, it is possible to reduce the beam size by a factor of at least 25 with a loss in energy of less than two. It then is possible to achieve reliable spectra on microgram or submicrogram samples.

To minimize light losses, front-surfaced mirrors are used in place of lenses to focus or collimate (render parallel) light beams in spectrometers. Mirrors are aluminized on their front surfaces; other metallic surfaces show selective absorption at certain wavelengths. Chromatic aberrations and other imperfections of lenses are thereby also minimized.

Beam splitters and beam combiners are needed on double-beam instruments. A suitable multilayer coating on an optical flat produces a lossless light beam splitter; each beam retains the spectral properties of the incident beam. Half-silvered mirrors have long been used for this purpose, but they invariably absorb some of the light in the thin metallic coating. A prismatic mirror or a stack of thin horizontal glass plates, silvered on their edges and alternatively oriented to the incident beam, are other arrangements. Beam combination is the reverse process.

Reflections from glass surfaces are reduced by a coating of magnesium fluoride which is one-quarter wavelength in optical thickness. This reduces scattering errors in fine optical equipment.

Sample Holder

Provision is made for inserting the sample solution somewhere in the interval between the light source and the detector. Usually the sample holder is located immediately in front of the detector and after the dispersing device. If the holder is located in front of the dispersing device, all the light from the source passes through the sample. Scattering of light by the sample at this point does not produce serious errors with monochromators, since most of the scattered light will be rejected in passing through the monochromator. However, fluorescence and photosensitivity are more serious problems and, consequently, when measurements are made in the ultraviolet or visible wavelengths the sample holder is placed after the dispersing device.

The form of the absorption cell depends largely on the particular instrument. It will vary from a set of test tubes, matched and tested for uniform wall thickness and optical path length, to high-quality rectangular cuvettes, constructed of glass or quartz with uniformly clear and polished plane parallel faces.

The sample holder should be protected from the heat of the exciting lamp in filter photometers. Often the collimating lens is constructed from infrared absorbing glass, or filters of this type of glass are inserted between the lamp and sample holder. Special thermostated cell holders are available for some spectrophotometers. The cell location within the holder is not particularly critical so long as the light beam has a small cross section relative to the sensitive area of the detector and the surfaces of the cuvette do not distort the light path from the sensitive area. This factor is easily tested by moving the cuvette to and fro, up and down, and rotating it, if cylindrical. Standard conditions imply a rectangular cell with an inner optical path length of exactly 1.000 cm.

Photosensitive Detectors

Any photosensitive device may be used as a detector of the radiant energy, provided that it has a linear response in the part of the spectrum to be used and has a sensitivity high enough for the particular task at hand. A barrier-layer cell is the simplest and requires little additional equipment, but its response is difficult to amplify. Its use is restricted generally to instruments with an optical system that permits a wide band of radiant energy to strike the detector. Instruments that restrict the bandwidth of the radiant energy reaching the detectors employ phototubes and amplifier units to boost the output signal. In this respect, the electron multiplier phototube provides the maximum signal and permits use of extremely narrow slits.

Human Eye

The human eye is limited in response to visible light, and in this region, its response is most acute for green light. It suffers from numerous human frailties, including fatigue, slowness of response, and a tendency to respond more readily to dominant colors, but perhaps its more serious limitation is its inability to determine the radiant power level except by matching with a reference. To a human being color is a subjective, psychological reaction.

Barrier-Layer Cells

A barrier-layer cell (also called a photovoltaic cell) consists of a plate of metal upon which has been deposited a thin layer of a semiconductor. Very frequently selenium is deposited upon an iron base. A very thin transparent layer of silver is sputtered over the semiconductor to act as the collector electrode. The metal base acts as the second electrode. The construction is shown in Fig. 3-13.

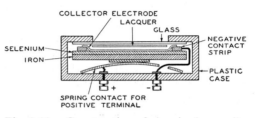

Fig. 3-13. Construction of a barrier-layer cell.
(Courtesy of General Electric Co.)

Radiant energy falling upon the semiconductor surface excites electrons at the silver-selenium interface which are released and pass to the collector electrode. A hypothetical barrier region appears to exist near the interface across which electrons pass easily from the semiconductor to the collector electrode, whereas a moderate resistance opposes the electron flow in the reverse direction. Consequently, this cell generates its own electromotive force and no external power supply need be applied to observe a photocurrent. If the cell is connected to a galvanometer, a current will flow if the resistance in the external circuit, including the resistance of the coil of the meter, is relatively small. This cell yields photocurrents as high as 0.08 μa per μW. When the external resistance is about 400 Ω or less, the photocurrent is very nearly proportional to the radiant power of the incident light beam at low levels of illumination, as shown in Fig. 3-14.

The spectral response of a selenium cell with a glass protective cover (Fig. 3-15) adequately covers the visible region, with its sensitivity greatest for the green through yellow wavelengths. Because of the low impedance of the cell, the output current cannot be amplified by conventional electronic circuits unless a cathode follower is employed. Consequently, this type of detector

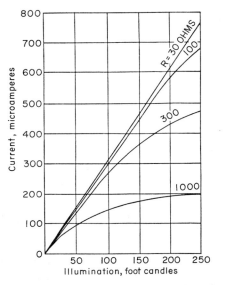

Fig. 3-14. Relationship between illumination and output for a typical barrier-layer cell.

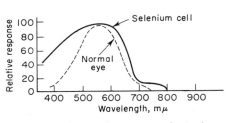

Fig. 3-15. Spectral response of selenium barrier-layer cell with protective glass cover. Response of human eye shown for comparison.

finds use mainly in filter photometers where fairly high levels of illumination exist and where there is no need to amplify the signal.

Barrier-layer cells show fatigue effects. Upon illumination, the photocurrent rises to a value several percent above the apparent equilibrium value and then falls off gradually with time. This difficulty can be overcome by the use of a gravity-controlled light shutter which permits light to strike the cell only while readings are being taken and a cuvette is inserted in the sample holder. The effect is more pronounced at high levels of illumination and with improper circuit resistances. The selenium cell also has a high temperature coefficient, and if readings are taken before the body of the instrument has attained ambient temperature after turning on the light source (or flame in Chapter 11, Flame Photometry), erroneous results are likely to occur. Its modulation ability is also poor; that is, the barrier-layer cell fails to respond immediately to changes in levels of illumination such as would occur if the light beam were to be interrupted 15–60 times per second by a mechanical chopper.

Photoemissive Tubes

The vacuum phototube comprises a negative electrode, often hemihedral in shape and coated with a light-sensitive layer, and an anode which is either an axially centered wire or a rectangular wire that frames the cathode. These electrodes are sealed within an evacuated glass envelope (Fig. 3-16). The anode is maintained at a positive potential by means of an auxiliary battery.

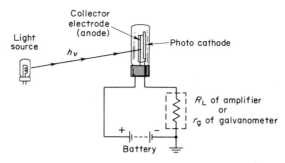

Fig. 3-16. Construction of photoemissive tube and typical detector circuit which gives a positive output signal.

When radiant energy falls on the photosensitive cathode surface, photo-electrons are emitted which pass over to the anode, where they are collected and return via the external circuit.

The spectral sensitivity of a tube depends on the nature of the substance coating the cathode and can be varied by using different alkali metals or by variation in the method of preparation of the cathode surface. For example, the Ag-O-Cs type cathode surface (S-1 response) is made in the following manner: A silver-plated nickel cathode of proper dimensions is carefully oxidized by means of a glow discharge to form a layer of silver oxide; then a layer of cesium metal is distilled onto the silver oxide surface; and finally the tube is subjected to a baking process which results in the formation of some cesium oxide on the surface through interaction of cesium metal with the silver oxide layer, and some formation of metallic silver throughout the silver oxide layer. The composite coating consists of cesium metal admixed with cesium oxide, silver oxide, and silver metal.

To achieve a sensitive surface, these conditions seem necessary: (1) An adequate absorption of radiant energy must occur; that is, the surface must not be transparent nor highly reflective. (2) An element must be used that has low atomic binding forces, such as one of the alkali metals, which, because of their low ionization energy, will easily part with their outer electron. (3) The surface layers through which the electrons must travel before escaping must possess small forces of attraction (low work function) for the photoelectrons. (4) The specific resistance of the cathode must approximate that of a semiconductor, since metallic conductors are too reflective and insulators prevent the replacement of electrons released by the radiant energy. The responses of some commercial cell surfaces are shown in Fig. 3-17. All the curves in the diagram are adjusted so that at the wavelength of maximum sensitivity the relative spectral sensitivity is 100. Phototubes with S-4 or S-5 surfaces are often used from 350 to 650 mμ, and those with S-1 surfaces from 600 to 950 mμ. The response of the former types are about 0.03 to 0.04 μa/μW, and the latter, 0.002 μa/μW.

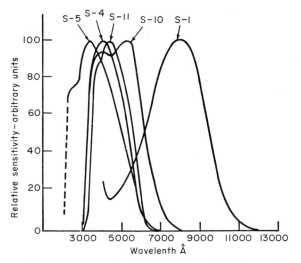

Fig. 3-17. Spectral response curves of some commercial photoemissive surfaces. All curves adjusted so that the wavelength of maximum sensitivity is 100 ordinate units.

Window inserts of quartz or fused silica extend the range of these tubes into the far ultraviolet.

Photoemissive tubes require an external power supply to maintain a fairly high voltage between the cathode and anode. As the voltage is increased, the point is reached where all the photoelectrons are swept to the anode as soon as they are released and a saturation photocurrent is obtained. The potential necessary to achieve saturation increases with an increase in the intensity of the radiant energy, as shown in Fig. 3-18. An excessively high voltage is

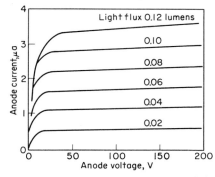

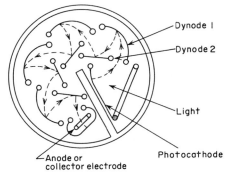

Fig. 3-18. Current-voltage characteristics of vacuum photoemissive tube with light flux the parameter.

Fig. 3-19. Schematic diagram of a photomultiplier tube. Dashed lines are the paths traveled by the secondary electrons as they are focused by each succeeding dynode's field in turn.

undesirable because it contributes to leakage (dark) currents without any gain in response. A high vacuum within the tube avoids scattering of the photoelectrons by collisions with gas molecules.

A typical circuit for use with a vacuum phototube is shown in Fig. 3-16. The resistor may be the coil of a very sensitive light-spot galvanometer, or it may be the grid load resistor for the amplifier input. In the latter case, care must be exercised so that the resulting iR drop across the resistor will not lower the voltage across the phototube to a value below the minimal anode potential for saturation photocurrents. Strict proportionality between saturation photocurrent and light intensity is a fundamental law of photoelectricity, but its realization in practice demands a carefully designed photocell and attendant circuits.

Photomultiplier Tubes

The electron multiplier phototube, or photomultiplier tube, as it is commonly called, is extremely sensitive, as well as extremely fast in response. The tube combines photocathode emission with multiple cascade stages of electron amplification to achieve a great amplification of primary photocurrent within the envelope of the phototube itself with retention of linear response. As shown in Fig. 3-19, the tube is constructed so that the primary photoelectrons from the cathode are attracted and accelerated to the first dynode with considerable energy. Each dynode consists of a plate of material coated with a substance having a small force of attraction for the escaping electrons. The impinging high-energy electrons strike with sufficient energy to dislodge and eject 2–5 secondary electrons. These secondary electrons are accelerated to the second dynode by an additional positive potential, and so on. This process is repeated at the successive dynodes of which there may be 9–16 stages. Successive stages are operated at voltages increasing in equal steps of 30–100 V, which require a very stable, high-voltage, low-current, power supply, since the overall sensitivity is very dependent upon the accelerating voltage per stage. A typical circuit is shown in Fig. 3-20.

The output of the photomultiplier tube is limited to an anode current of a few milliamperes. Consequently, only low-intensity radiant energy can be measured without serious deterioration of electrode surfaces due to local heating effects. Moreover, the region of linear response limits tube currents to a few microamperes. Amplification can be pushed to the limits set by the shot-effect noise; that is, the inherent dark current due to thermionic emission, and other random noise signals, which is approximately 6×10^{-12} amp. The dark current may be reduced by lowering the temperature at which the tube is operated, but this is not usually feasible. With respect to random noise, the superiority of a photomultiplier tube over an ordinary phototube increases as the level of illumination decreases. The photomultiplier tube can measure intensities about 200 times weaker than those measurable with an ordinary

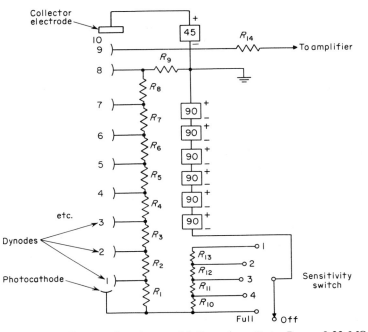

Fig. 3-20. Wiring diagram for photomultiplier tube. R_1 to R_9 are 0.33 MΩ; R_{10} is 0.51 MΩ; R_{11} is 0.68 MΩ; R_{12} is 0.68 MΩ; R_{13} is 0.75 MΩ; and R_{14} is 22 MΩ. Power supply is 45- and 90-V B batteries. (Courtesy of Beckman Instruments, Inc.)

phototube and amplifier. Because of their extreme sensitivity to light, photomultiplier tubes must be very carefully shielded from stray light. The tube will respond to light pulses as brief as 10^{-9} sec in duration (cf. use in scintillation counters).

Tube fatigue, leading to signal drift, can be a limitation unless overcome by proper circuit design and experimental conditions. The anode current drawn should be kept below 1 milliamp and the voltage between the last dynode and the anode restricted to 45 V.

A number of manufacturers offer photomultiplier search units, consisting of essentially a photomultiplier tube in a probe unit and connected to a power supply, amplifier, and readout meter.

Commercial Instruments

Instruments for absorption photometry may be classified as visual comparators, filter photometers, and spectrophotometers. In terms of construction, one also recognizes the differences between single-beam and double-beam light paths, and whether the photoelectric instrument is direct-reading or employs a balanced circuit. Special features include double monochromation and dual wavelength monochromators, plus automatic recording. In the final selection of an instrument, one should consider the initial cost, maintenance, flexibility of operation, and adaptation to special situations.

Visual Comparators

The simplest types of color comparators use side-by-side viewing of light from a common source, such as diffused daylight, through a pair of tubes containing the unknown and the standard, respectively. A series of standard solutions are prepared in tubes of constant depth and diameter, for example, Nessler tubes of 50- or 100-ml capacity. The sample solution is transferred to a duplicate tube and diluted to volume. When the color is matched, the test solution has the same concentration as the standard. When not matched exactly, the color can be adjudged to lie between two standard solutions and, perhaps, the position in the interval estimated. This method is especially valuable for faint colors or slight turbidities since the column of liquid can be quite long (10 or 20 cm). Nessler tubes are relatively inexpensive, but have the disadvantage that color standards must be freshly prepared which closely match the unknown in spectral distribution as well as absorbance.

In the slide type comparator the solutions for comparison are sealed in small glass vials. The operation of this type of comparator is described in Chapter 22. Semipermanent artificial color standards are available in the form of tinted glasses for a limited number of color reactions. A comparative color wheel contains a series of color standards which duplicate a range of concentrations for a given color reaction. The entire unit is held up to a light source, and the operator views the sample and color standard through either a split field eyepiece (Hellige, Fig. 22-8) or two round holes with an opal screen as background. The wheel is rotated until the color of one of the standards matches the test solution. Units of these types are compact, portable, and easily operated by nontechnical personnel. Often a second tube is mounted in line with the color disk and filled with the same medium as the test liquid, but no color-generating agent is added, so as to provide compensation for a turbidity or extraneous color in the original specimen. A duplicate tube filled with distilled water is placed behind the sample.

A match of the color between the unknown and the standard may also be obtained by varying the depth of two solutions whose concentrations are different, until the eye adjudges the light transmitted (P) through one solution equal to that transmitted through the other. It follows then, from Beer's law (page 77), where P_0 is the incident radiant energy, that when

$$\log (P_0/P)_{\text{unknown}} = \log (P_0/P)_{\text{standard}} \tag{3-7}$$

$$C_u b_u = C_s b_s \tag{3-8}$$

$$C_u = C_s(b_s/b_u) \tag{3-9}$$

where C_u and C_s denote the concentration of unknown and standard, and b_u and b_s denote the respective light path lengths. This is the fundamental relationship used in plunger type color comparators.

A very simple procedure uses two graduated tubes known as Hehner tubes (Fig. 3-21), each with a stopcock on the side at the base. Liquid is drawn from the more concentrated solution until the colors are adjudged to match when viewed axially.

The Duboscq colorimeter (Fig. 3-22) was probably the most widely used

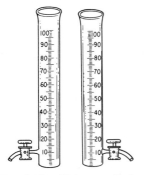

Fig. 3-21. Hehner cylinders.

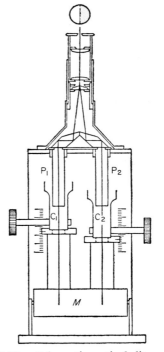

Fig. 3-22. Schematic optical diagram of Duboscq colorimeter: P1 and P2 are plungers; C1 and C2 are cups to hold the solutions; M is a white, matt-surface mirror. The two halves of the field are viewed through the ocular.

color comparator before the advent of photoelectric instruments. Light from a uniform source of illumination (and reflected from a matt white glass mirror) passes up through the bottom of a pair of matched cups, through the solution, and on up through a set of fixed glass plungers. The two beams of light from the plungers are then brought to a common axis by a prism system. On looking through the eyepiece, one sees a circular field, light from each cup illuminating one half of the field. The depth of solution traversed by one light beam is adjusted by rotating the milled heads, which raises or lowers one cup, until the two halves of the field are identical in intensity. Equation 3-9 then applies. The engraved scales for each cup are 50–60 mm in length, and a vernier scale enables readings to be estimated within 0.1 mm. Cups usually hold 15–25 ml of liquid.

The ability of the eye to discriminate between the intensities of two light beams is a function both of the wavelength of the light and of the intensity itself. Spectral sensitivity of the eye is best for wavelengths centered around 500 mμ. Under good illumination conditions, visual color comparison does not have a sensitivity of more than 1–2 percent, and under poor brightness-matching conditions the sensitivity may be much poorer than this.

Filter Photometers

A single-beam, direct-reading filter photometer is illustrated in Fig. 3-23. The optical path is simply from the light source, through the filter and sample holder, and to the detector. Light from the tungsten-filament lamp in the reflector is defined in area by fixed apertures in the sample holder and restricted to a desired band of wavelengths by an absorption or interference filter. After passing through the container for the solution, the light strikes the surface of

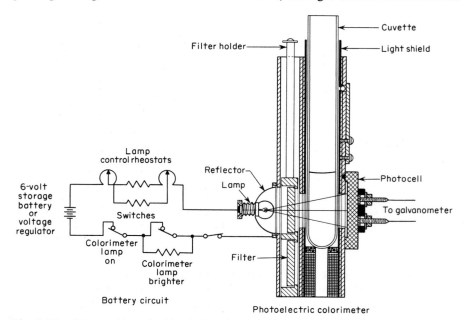

Fig. 3-23. Schematic optical and electrical diagram of a single-beam photometer. Evelyn photoelectric colorimeter. (Courtesy of Rubicon Company.)

the barrier-layer cell, the output of which is measured by the deflection of a microammeter or a light-spot galvanometer. The lamp is energized by a 6- or 12-V storage battery or by the output of a constant voltage transformer, to minimize the effect of voltage fluctuations. The location of the apertures in the sample container determines the minimum volume of solution on which a measurement can be made.

To operate instruments of this type, the blank (a pure solvent or a reference solution) is inserted into the light beam and the incident light intensity is regulated either by a diaphragm in the light beam (Instrumentation Associates model 76 Absorptiometer and EEL colorimeters), by rheostats in series with the lamp (Unicam SP .300, Hilger Biochem, and Evelyn photoelectric colorimeter), or by rotating the photocell about an axis perpendicular to the light beam (Leitz photometer), since the more oblique the angle of incidence, the greater the fraction of light reflected from its surface. These adjustments bring the readout meter to 100 linear scale divisions. Prior to this, and with the photocell darkened, the meter is adjusted mechanically to read zero. Subsequently, solutions of both standards and unknowns are inserted in place of the blank and the reading of the specimen relative to the blank is recorded. In this way correction is obtained for solvent absorption and cell reflectance losses. The meter scale is engraved in linear transmittance units (0–100 percent) and, perhaps, in logarithmic units.

During any series of measurements, the sensitivity of the detecting system must remain unchanged, as must also the radiant power of the source over the selected band of wavelengths being used. The method employed to bring the galvanometer reading to 100 units automatically compensates in part for the tendency of the spectral distribution of the lamp to change with age. Cost is minimal and operation is simple with this type of instrument.

A simple instrument which combines the features of a direct-reading filter photometer with the long path length of Nessler tubes is the Lumetron Colorimeter model 450. Essentially, a barrier-layer cell and galvanometer substitute for the human eye.

Double-beam photometers employing barrier-layer cells fall into two categories. In a bridge-potentiometer arrangement, Fig. 3-24, the null-balance galvanometer may be considered as receiving the photocurrent from each photocell through a universal shunt. Each shunt is a low-resistance (about 400 ohms), linearly wound potentiometer. The beam of filtered light is divided, part passing through the solution in the cuvette before falling on the measuring photocell, and the other part passing directly onto the reference photocell. The opposing currents through the galvanometer may be written

$$i_{g_m} = kTP\frac{a}{R_1 + r_g} \quad \text{and} \quad i_{g_r} = kP\frac{x}{R_2 + r_g}$$

where T is the transmittance of the cuvette and solution, P is the radiant power

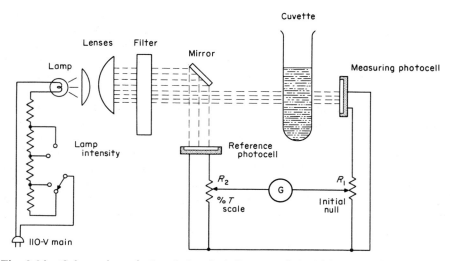

Fig. 3-24. Schematic optical and electrical diagram of the Fisher electrophotometer, a typical bridge-potentiometer circuit. (Courtesy of Fisher Scientific Co.)

of filtered light, and a and x are the contactor positions on R_1 and R_2, respectively. At balance these currents are equal; hence, since $R_1 = R_2$,

$$x = Ta \qquad (3\text{-}10)$$

In other words the potentiometer setting on R_2, namely, x, is directly proportional to the transmittance. The slidewire scale is calibrated usually in 100 linear scale divisions, or in logarithmic (absorbance) units, or both.

To operate this type of double-beam photometer, the null-balance galvanometer is adjusted mechanically to position the needle or light-spot at mid-scale with the lamp off. Then, with the lamp on, the blank solution in the light beam before the measuring photocell, and the measuring slidewire set at 100, balance is restored either by adjusting the contactor on the slidewire R_1 (Fisher electrophotometer, Fig. 3-24), adjusting the intensity of the reference light beam by means of a diaphragm (Klett-Summerson photoelectric colorimeter, Fig. 3-25), insertion of a neutral density wedge, or rotation of the reference photocell about an axis perpendicular to the light beam through an angle of 90°, plus a series of fixed apertures—reduction plates (Lumetron photoelectric colorimeter model 402, Fig. 3-26). Subsequently, these adjustments remain unchanged while standards and unknowns are introduced and the contactor on the slidewire R_2, in series with the reference photocell, is adjusted to obtain the scale reading.

The Hilger-Spekker photometer illustrates a purely optical arrangement. As shown in Fig. 3-27, a cam-shaped diaphragm, with an associated logarithmic scale, in the measuring circuit is adjusted to allow more light to reach the

Fig. 3-25. *Upper,* view of Klett-Summerson photoelectric colorimeter; *lower,* schematic representation of optics and electrical circuit. (Courtesy of Klett Manufacturing Co.)

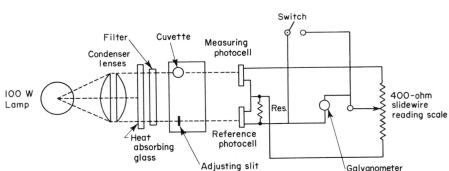

detector to compensate for the absorbance of the specimen. Adjustment to zero absorbance with a blank is accomplished by an iris diaphragm before the reference photocell.

All the double-beam circuits selected for illustration compensate for normal variations in the lamp supply voltage, enabling the lamp to be operated from ordinary alternating mains. However, not all double-beam circuits compensate for variations in the intensity of the source. Conformance can be demonstrated by employing Kirchhoff's laws to calculate the current flowing through the galvanometer just as balance is being attained, and then differentiating the current with respect to radiant power. This derivative, when set equal to zero, will show the conditions wherein the fluctuations in intensity of

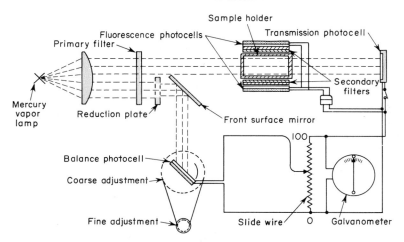

Fig. 3-26. Schematic electrical and optical diagram of Lumetron model 402 photoelectric colorimeter (and fluorescence meter). (Courtesy of Photovolt Corporation.)

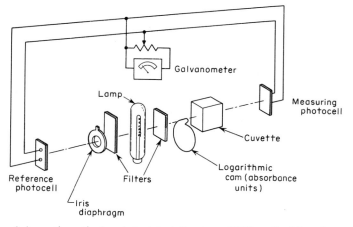

Fig. 3-27. Schematic optical and electrical diagram of Hilger-Spekker absorptiometer. (Courtesy of Hilger & Watts, Ltd.)

illumination do not affect the galvanometer reading or balance point. The analysis of the circuits illustrated will be left as a student exercise.[2, 6]

Single-Beam, Null-Balance Spectrophotometers

The path traveled by the beam of light in the Beckman model DU spectrophotometer[3] is shown in Fig. 3-28. The Unicam SP .500, the Hilger UVspek, and the Russian SF-4 differ only slightly in optical features and electrical circuit. A tungsten lamp or a hydrogen (or deuterium) discharge tube il-

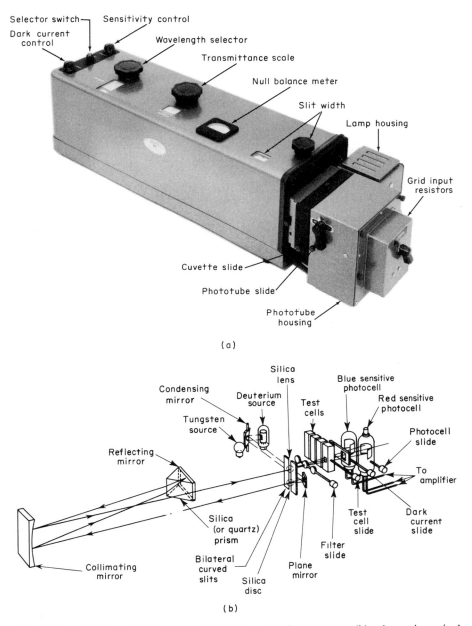

Fig. 3-28. (a) View of Beckman model DU spectrophotometer; (b) schematic optical arrangement of Littrow-mounted prism spectrophotometer. (Courtesy of Beckman Instruments, Inc.)

luminates a condensing mirror which brings the reflected beam to a focus on the plane of the entrance slit of the spectrometer. The magnified image of the filament fills the opening fairly uniformly with light. The resulting narrow beam of light is collimated (rendered parallel) by a spherical mirror and directed onto the quartz or fused silica prism in the form of a 30-60-90° triangle with an apical angle of 30°. The prism is backed by an aluminized mirror which reflects the refracted rays through the Littrow-mounted prism and back to the same collimating mirror at a different height. The collimated beam is then projected and focused onto the exit slit, which selects a portion of the dispersed spectrum for transmission through the sample holder and on to the detector.

A precise wavelength scroll and scale is calibrated relative to the refractive index of the prism material so that any segment of the spectrum may be selected by rotation of the prism mount. As the table on which the prism is mounted is slowly rotated by the wavelength drum, the prism produces a series of images of the entrance slit at the exit slit as the spectrum is swept past. A Littrow type mounting is generally used because of its superior dispersion and compact design. The polarizing effect of quartz is eliminated while economy of prism material is achieved. In the Unicam SP .600 instrument, a 60° glass prism and separate Littrow mirror are turned through a small angle to obtain different wavelengths at the exit slit. The upper and lower parts of the same slit assembly are used as entrance and exit slits, providing perfect correspondence of slit widths.

Useful photometric sensitivity over a wide spectral range is achieved by the use of two interchangeable phototubes on a sliding carriage. A cesium oxide coated photocathode (S-1 response) is used for the region 625–1000 mμ. The range 210–625 mμ is covered by a cesium-antimony photosensitive surface (S-5 response) and an insert of fused silica in the envelope. Photomultiplier attachments can replace the UV/blue sensitive tube for increased sensitivity or for operation at smaller slit widths. The Unicam and Hilger monochromators contain a fused silica prism to extend the useful range down to 185 mμ.

The slit system is continuously adjustable. This provides flexibility and enables the width to be varied in accordance with the response of the detector and the spectral distribution of the light source. The slit jaws are operated by direct pressure on a steel spring. A visual slit-width indicator fitted to the control knob and the slit opening marked in millimeters serve as a performance check and allow resetting a previous slit opening.

A simplified diagram of the electrical circuit employed in the Beckman model DU spectrophotometer is shown in Fig. 3-29. Light striking the photocathode causes a current to flow through the 2000-MΩ resistor, generating an ohmic drop across it. This voltage is applied between the control grid and cathode of the input electrometer tube. It is opposed by an adjustable voltage taken from a linear slidewire (the 0–100 percent transmittance scale) and 0 to

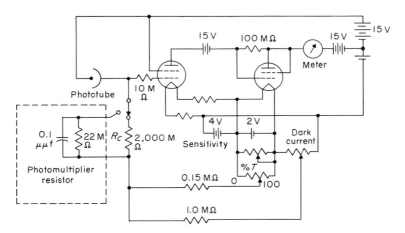

Fig. 3-29. Circuit of the Beckman model DU spectrophotometer., A 6-V storage battery supplies the 4 V and 2 V. Other voltages supplied by C batteries. (Courtesy of Beckman Instruments, Inc.)

−2 V battery in series with it. A signal of any difference alters the grid potential and thus ultimately controls the deflection produced on the readout meter. To operate, the circuit is brought initially to some arbitrary reference point. With no light striking the phototube and the contactor on the %T-slidewire set at zero, the voltage from an auxiliary potentiometer (the *dark-current* control) is applied between the grid and cathode of the input tube to whatever value is required to bring the meter deflection to midscale reading. The dark current control is left at this value, and with light now falling on the phototube after passage through the blank or reference solution and with the %T-slidewire placed at a setting of 100, the output meter is returned to the same deflection (midscale) by adjusting the slit width (subject to the band pass requirements for the spectrum being determined) or by varying the voltage actually placed across the %T-slidewire from the "sensitivity control," a rheostat in parallel with the %T-slidewire and battery. Finally, samples or standards are inserted and the contactor on the %T-slidewire is adjusted to restore the circuit to its null position. For each null point, the contactor position represents the transmittance of the solution in the light beam. This particular circuit is sensitive to photocurrents as small as 10^{-13} amp with an ordinary phototube and 2000-MΩ input load resistor. The latter can be increased to 10,000-MΩ for some applications. All bias and plate voltages are supplied by battery packs or special d-c power supply.

The transmittance slidewire is graduated from 0–110 percent, a useful feature if the transmittance of the sample cell is slightly greater than that of the control cell when cuvette corrections are being determined. A "functions" switch expands the 0–100 percent transmittance scale until it covers the range 0–10 percent, by reducing the total voltage across the slidewire by a factor of exactly 10. The corresponding absorbance readings are increased by unity.

Direct-Reading, Single-Channel Spectrophotometers

Instruments in this category are characterized by greater speed in operation and convenience, but lower accuracy and precision than the null-balance type. Both d-c and a-c operated circuits have been employed. These instruments tend to be restricted to the visual range of the spectrum.

The Beckman model B spectrophotometer uses a Féry glass prism as dispersive device (Fig. 3-30).[5] This type of prism has curved rather than con-

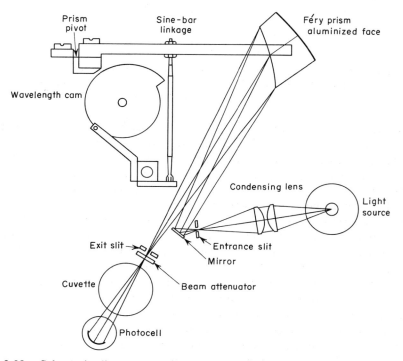

Fig. 3-30. Schematic diagram of the optical system of a monochromator equipped with Féry glass prism. (After the Unicam SP.1400 and Beckman model B.)

ventional flat faces (with an aluminized rear surface), which are endowed with the dual function of imaging and dispersion. Although the need for a collimating mirror is eliminated, the focal length varies with wavelength (a condition denoted as astigmatism). This fault is circumvented by mounting the prism on a carriage which moves on a sine-bar mechanism designed for rotation and simultaneous translation. The Unicam model SP .600 differs only in employing a focusing and collimating system that is separate from the dispersing element. In each instrument the ohmic drop generated by the photocurrent is amplified and read out by means of a high-gain, negative-feedback-stabilized, d-c amplifier.

An inexpensive, direct-reading grating spectrophotometer is illustrated in Fig. 3-31. A small replica grating provides the dispersion and, in conjunction

(a)

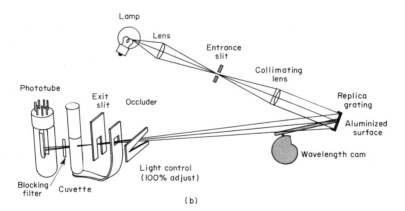

(b)

Fig. 3-31. Bausch & Lomb Spectronic 20 colorimeter: (a) view of instrument with controls labeled, (b) schematic optical diagram. (Courtesy of Bausch & Lomb Optical Co.)

with fixed slits, provides a band pass of 20 mμ. A difference amplifier is used (Fig. 3-32). Ejection of photoelectrons from the photocathode causes a corresponding number to be drawn from the grid of tube T_1, making it more positive and increasing the output voltage of the tube. The meter in the bridge circuit, which is graduated in linear scale divisions from 0 to 100 percent trans-

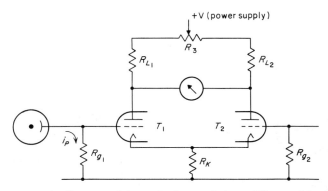

Fig. 3-32. Schematic diagram of the cathode-coupled amplifier used in the Bausch & Lomb Spectronic 20 colorimeter. $R_{g_1} = R_{g_2} = 10$ MΩ; $R_{L_1} = R_{L_2} = 0.1$ MΩ; $R_3 = 50,000$ Ω. (Courtesy of Bausch & Lomb Optical Co.)

mittance, indicates the intensity of the signal on grid 1 and thus the light incident on the phototube. Whenever the sample container is removed from the instrument, an occluder falls into the light beam so that, with the phototube dark, the amplifier control (left knob) is adjusted to bring the meter needle to zero on the transmittance scale. This is accomplished by varying the position of the tap on resistor R_3, which alters the relative value of the plate voltage furnished to each tube from the power supply. The instrument is balanced at 100 percent transmittance by means of a variable V-shaped slit (light control, lower right knob) in the dispersed light beam. The range of the spectrophotometer is from 340 to 650 mμ with a blue-sensitive phototube, and can be extended to 950 mμ by the addition of a red blocking filter and exchange of plug-in phototubes.

Several models of transmission grating spectrophotometers are available from Coleman Instruments, Inc. On the Universal and Junior models 6A and 6C, the band pass is 35 mμ; on the model 6D it is 20 mμ. The operation of the direct-reading instruments is similar to the description given for this class of filter photometer. The Universal model can also be operated as a null-balance circuit, wherein the current from the photocell produces across a resistor a voltage drop which is opposed by a signal from a dry-cell potentiometer circuit ($\%T$-scale). The Coleman Autoset is a semiautomatic instrument in which all dials and meters are replaced with digital readout systems. After the wavelength is selected on a four-digit counter, the reference solution is inserted and the spectrophotometer adjusts itself to the absorbance of the solution. Then the sample solution is inserted and another counter gives the percent transmittance or the absorbance. Bandwidth is normally fixed at 2 mμ.

Other commercial direct-reading instruments include the Zeiss PMQ.II, which employs a quartz prism in a Littrow mounting as dispersing system but uses a chopped beam a-c amplifier. The Jobin-Yvon monochromator incorporates a 180° constant deviation quartz prism. The Optica CF-4 and Perkin-Elmer Hitachi model 139 ultraviolet-visible spectrophotometers are grating instruments with band pass of 0.1–0.2 mμ. The Beckman model DB employs the quartz optical system of the model DU, but after leaving the exit slit, the light is directed alternately through the sample and reference paths by a vibrating mirror. The difference in intensities of the two light paths appears on a deflection type meter.

Double-Beam, Ratio-Recording Spectrophotometers

A recording spectrophotometer carries out the measuring sequence automatically and provides recorded data on the analyses. This eliminates many time-consuming adjustments and provides a rapid and accurate reproduction of spectrograms. These instruments are well suited for qualitative analysis where complex curves must be obtained over a large spectral range. In these instruments sample-beam energy is compared automatically with reference-beam energy, and the ratio is the transmittance of the sample. This procedure is followed over a sequence of wavelengths to plot a graph with transmittance (or absorbance) as ordinate and wavelength as abscissa, giving the absorption spectrum of the sample. Instruments using dual monochromation or involving a dual wavelength monochromator are discussed in later sections.

In the arrangement denoted *double beam in time*, a single beam of energy leaving the prism or grating monochromator is alternately switched between reference and sample paths to provide a double-beam system within the sample compartment. The two beams are then recombined, although separated in time, to fall on a single detector. The output of the detector is an alternating signal whose amplitude is proportional to the difference in intensities in the two channels.

For a prism monochromator a slit servo continuously adjusts the slit openings to keep the energy through the reference cell constant at a 100 percent setting when the reference solution is in the light beam. A control voltage, which varies with wavelength according to the prism dispersion curve, actuates the slit servo amplifier to keep the monochromator at a constant preselected bandwidth. The switching between reference and sample paths is done by a rotating half-sector mirror system (Beckman model DK-A, shown in Fig. 3-33), by a vibrating mirror assembly (Beckman model DB), or by a stack of thin horizontal glass plates, silvered along their edges and alternately oriented (Unicam SP.700 and Zeiss RPQ 20A). A chopper is placed either before the entrance slit or after the exit slit of the monochromator. The latter is often the same unit supplied by the manufacturers with their manual spectrophotometers.

Grating instruments are exemplified by the Bausch and Lomb Spectronic 505, Unicam SP.700 (prism or grating of 291 lines/mm), and the recording version of the Optica CF-4. A variable cam in the reference beam adjusts the 100 percent line. The wavelength scale is linear—a sine-bar linkage is used to

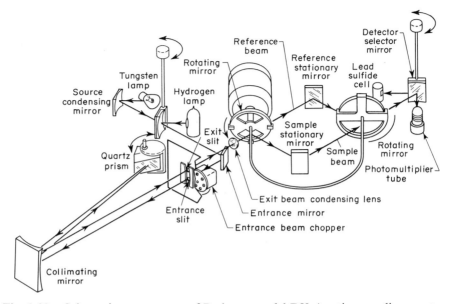

Fig. 3-33. Schematic arrangement of Beckman model DK-A ratio-recording spectrophotometer. (Courtesy of Beckman Instruments, Inc.)

solve the grating equation. A desirable feature is the automatic adjustment of the scanning speed to be inversely proportional to the rate of change of transmittance with wavelength. This permits faithful recording when a complex portion of the spectrum is encountered or when the level of energy reaching the detector is reduced as in differential analysis.

Variants in the general operating pattern involve different methods for keeping the signal strength at a predetermined level without exceeding the maximum permissible spectral bandwidth. Critical points occur either when the radiation level becomes very low and the slits are opened to the full extent, or when the source and detector are very efficient and the slits are driven almost totally closed. In a grating instrument with a constant, fixed band pass, an appropriate feedback circuit can control the voltage across the photomultiplier in proportion to the inverse of the light intensity. The voltage is increased as the light intensity falls to keep the output photocurrent constant.

Ratio recording eliminates inaccuracies due to such effects as source fluctuations, changes in amplifier gain, sensitivity or spectral response of the detector, and the presence of interfering absorption bands. Unwanted absorption is cancelled by placing equivalent quantities of the offending substance in the reference beam. This technique, often called "differential analysis," is highly effective in determining low concentrations of a component in the presence of large quantities of absorbing substances, in detecting minor variations in composition, and in improving analyses made with poor solvents (from a transmittance viewpoint). Greater care in double-beam systems is required, however, because the process of cancelling absorption bands also reduces the level of energy reaching the detector. When a strong reference band (due to an interference) is eliminated, the energy through both sample and reference paths is low and so is the corresponding detector signal. As a consequence, the recording system becomes sluggish and the data inaccurate. This difficulty can be overcome in some degree by reducing recording speed, albeit at a great sacrifice in time.

Double Monochromation

Stray light is a problem in precise measurements. The most general solution is the use of a double monochromator in which two dispersing systems are used in series with an intervening slit. The Cary model 15 and the Perkin-Elmer model 350 are dual prism spectrophotometers which utilize the *double beam in space* arrangement (Fig. 3-34). Two separate light paths are created by

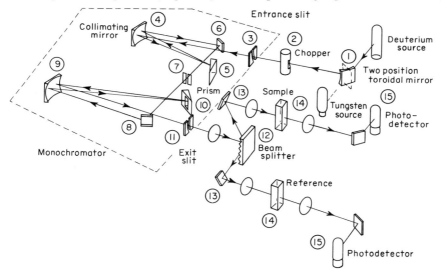

Fig. 3-34. Schematic optical diagram of dual prism, double beam-in-space spectro-photometer.

a beam splitter and mirrors; separate detectors measure the radiant power of each beam.

Radiation originating at the deuterium or tungsten source is focused on the entrance slit by a toroidal mirror. From the entrance slit radiation falls on a collimating mirror and thence to a Littrow-mounted, reflecting silica prism. Emergent dispersed radiation returns to the collimating mirror and is reflected to a plane mirror and then through an intermediate slit into a second monochromator where the light beam traverses a similar set of optical elements in reverse order so that the principal aberrations of the collimating mirrors are cancelled. However, the dispersion of the two prisms is additive. The dispersed radiation leaves the second monochromator by way of the exit slit and falls on a beam splitter which consists of an array of narrow plane mirrors arranged in a symmetrical sawtooth cross section (a compound prismatic mirror). The radiation divides into two beams, disposed one over the other. Each beam is reflected by appropriate mirrors through the sample and reference compartments. Unabsorbed radiation falls on individual, end-on photomultiplier tubes (or lead sulfide detectors for near infrared analyses, 780 mμ to 2.7 μ). The radiation is chopped by a cylindrical shutter either before entering or upon leaving the monochromator. The readout is based on measurement of the ratio of intensities in the two channels. Any unbalance is amplified by the sample amplifier and the pen amplifier and causes the pen motor to drive the slidewire contact toward the balance point.

The Cary model 14 instrument utilizes a 30° fused silica, Littrow-mounted prism in series with a 600-line/mm grating. The schematic optical diagram is shown in Fig. 3-35, from which the path traveled by the light can be traced. It is another example of a double beam-in-time arrangement. The entrance, intermediate, and exit slits are simultaneously adjustable in width. Radiation leaving the dual monochromator is chopped by a sectored disk and sent alternately through the sample and reference compartments by means of a rotating semicircular mirror driven by a synchronous motor.

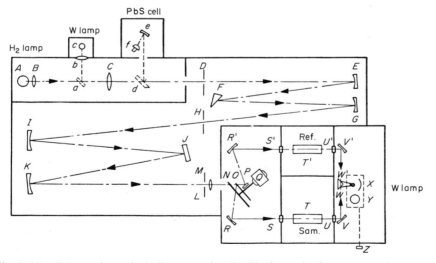

Fig. 3-35. Schematic optical diagram of a double beam-in-time spectrophotometer with double monochromation (prism and grating in series) — Cary model 14. (Courtesy of Applied Physics Corp.)

Dual Wavelength Spectrometer.

This type of instrument rapidly alternates two independent (and variable) wavelengths of light through a single sample holder. Each monochromator has a separate wavelength-drive system. In the Britton Chance spectrometer, shown in Fig. 3-36, the light beam falls upon a concave mirror (collimated for

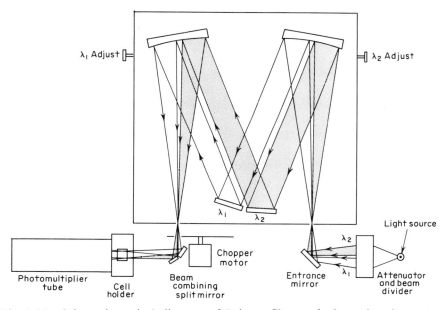

Fig. 3-36. Schematic optical diagram of Britton Chance dual-wavelength spectrophotometer. (Courtesy of American Instrument Co.)

all wavelengths), which reflects the beam onto two individually adjustable gratings. A concave telescope mirror intercepts the dispersed light beams from the two gratings and reflects them to the exit slit. A chopper alternately selects light from each emergent beam and flashes it upon the sample holder. Thus, radiant energy of two selected wavelengths passes alternately through the sample, where it is absorbed by, or transmitted through, the material under study. When a difference of transmittance along the two optical paths occurs, there is an alternating error signal which is amplified, demodulated, and read out as the difference between the absorbance readings at the two wavelengths.

The Beckman model DK-universal spectrophotometer utilizes a model DK-A prism monochromator and a grating monochromator—with the sample system between them. Similar arrangements can be devised with available modular units from other manufacturers.

Data Acquisition Systems

Fully automated and semiautomated systems are designed to improve the accuracy and reproducibility of repetitive spectrophotometric determinations. A special cuvette is inserted into the sample compartment. With the use of a vacuum probe pump or positive displacement plunger, a sample is withdrawn by means of a stainless steel or plastic probe into the microcell cuvette. One, two, or three optional rinses precede the final filling, each followed by emptying the solution from the sample cell into a waste jar. In the manual sample presentation, the operator places the cuvette sampling probe into a sample and presses the fill button on the spectrophotometer to initiate a programmed cycle—the rinsing, reading, and draining sequence. The reading signal is recorded on a strip-chart recorder to resemble a bar graph, presented in digital form, or presented on a visual readout meter for manual recording. A light indicates the proper time for the operator to place the probe into the next sample. The rigidity of the cuvette minimizes misalignment of cell holders and variations from cuvette to cuvette.

Accessories for completely programmed operation enable a series of samples inserted on a turntable to be measured automatically and the readings presented in digital form on tape. This is an excellent time-saver for repetitive analyses and eliminates operator mistakes in obtaining and recording readings (see also Chapter 28).

LABORATORY WORK

Instrument Calibration

The calibration of the wavelength scale should be checked occasionally. In the visible region the simplest method is to plot the absorption spectrum of a didymium glass which has been calibrated by the National Bureau of Standards (U.S.). The emission lines from a mercury lamp are useful. A hydrogen discharge tube gives a fairly intense line at 6563 Å. Atomic emission lines from the flame are well suited for calibration purposes (see Table 11-9).

For checking the transmittance scale, filters are available from the National Bureau of Standards (U.S.). A solution of potassium chromate, 0.004 gram per liter in 0.05 M aqueous potassium hydroxide, has been carefully studied. Haupt, G. W., Jr., *J. Res.*, Nat. Bur. Std. (U.S.), **48**, 364, 414 (1952).

E X P E R I M E N T 3 - 1   DETERMINATION   OF   SPECTRAL   RESPONSE   OF
PHOTOSENSITIVE DETECTORS

A direct-reading spectrometer will provide everything required. The following directions apply specifically to a Bausch & Lomb Spectronic 20 spectrometer.

Adjust the instrument, photocell dark, with the zero control in the normal manner. Insert into the sample holder a test tube filled with water. Rotate the 100 percent control until the meter needle reads near midscale. Now rotate the wavelength control until a maximum transmittance reading is achieved (readjusting the 100 percent control, if necessary, to keep the meter needle on scale).

At the wavelength of maximum transmittance, carefully balance the instrument at 100 percent transmittance. Without changing any controls, henceforth, change the wavelength in intervals of 20 mμ and record the corresponding transmittance reading (actually the relative response reading).

Repeat the series of operation with other phototubes. Plot the results on graph paper, plotting wavelength as abscissa. These results represent the overall response of the spectrometer — phototube, emissivity of light source, and intensity diffracted by the grating; each of which is a function of wavelength. Since the main difference lies for the most part with the tungsten source, it would be possible to estimate the relative response of the phototube to light of constant intensity by correcting each observed transmittance reading for the relative radiant power of the tungsten lamp.

E X P E R I M E N T   3 - 2   DETERMINATION OF EFFECTIVE SLIT WIDTH OF
SPECTROMETERS

An atomic line source—a mercury lamp or a flame emission attachment, and a spectrometer, either grating or prism, is required.

Insert the atomic line source in place of the usual continuous light source. Adjust the wavelength scale to the vicinity of one known emission line.

Adjust the slit aperture to a given width, if using a prism instrument; this term will be fixed for a grating instrument. Slowly rotate the wavelength drum until a signal is detected. Carefully adjust the dark current control, then rotate the wavelength drum until a signal is detected. Change the wavelength setting by a small increment, and measure the signal again. Repeat until the signal has risen to a maximum and diminished to zero.

Repeat the operation for additional slit apertures and for different nominal wavelengths.

Prepare your results as a series of graphs, each normalized to the same maximum reading at the nominal wavelength. From the known dispersion of the instrument, or from a graph of dispersion versus wavelength for prism instruments, compute the effective slit width at each nominal wavelength and compare with the experimental results.

Problems

1. In general a monochromator passes, in addition to an intensity P_0 of radiation of the nominal wavelength, an intensity S of stray radiation of other wavelengths. If a specimen whose absorbance is being measured transmits this stray radiation without an absorption, the apparent or measured value will be: $A = \log (P_0 + S)/(P + S)$. If the stray radiation is 1 percent of P_0, the apparent absorbance will approach what maximum value? Repeat the calculations when $S = 0.004P_0$. *Ans*. 2.0 when $S = 0.01P_0$.

2. A perfectly parallel beam of radiation must come from a point source and can carry only an infinitesimal amount of energy. For a beam of finite angular size passing through a specimen at an angle θ to the axis, the path length and hence

the absorbance will be increased by a factor: $1/\cos\theta$. What is the increase in absorbance when the value of θ is 3°? 5°? 9°? *Ans.* 1.2 percent when $\theta = 9°$.

3. If the instrument employed were the Beckman model DU quartz spectrometer, what would be the corresponding slit openings that correspond to band passes of 0.8 mμ and 5.3 mμ at 545 mμ? To 0.9 and 3.1 mμ at 575 mμ? *Ans.* 0.03 and 0.2 mm for 545 mμ.

4. For a spacing of 0.5 μ of MgF$_2$, at what wavelengths will the transmission peaks be observed when the angle of incident light is 90°? *Ans.* Second order peak is at 690 mμ.

5. If only the first and second order wavelengths produced significant intensity, would a blocking filter be necessary for a second order peak if the primary transmission peak is located at 600 mμ? *Ans.* No, an ordinary glass cover would remove the second order wavelength.

6. A certain grating has 1200 grooves/mm and a blaze angle of 37°. Calculate (a) the wavelengths and (b) the wave numbers that will be observed at the blaze angle in the first five orders. Assume that the angle of incidence is equal to the angle of diffraction. *Ans.* Second order at 501 mμ.

7. Calculate the primary angle at which (a) light of 3000 Å will be diffracted by a grating with 1000 grooves/mm and (b) light of 5000 Å will be diffracted by a grating with 600 grooves/mm. *Ans.* (a) Angle is 17.5°.

8. How many lines/mm will be necessary for a 64-mm grating to have a resolution of 10,000 for a second order line? *Ans.* 78 lines/mm (typical for an infrared grating).

9. In the Beckman model DU spectrometer, the read-out meter has a sensitivity of 1 ma full scale. What is the probable amplification factor for the two-tube d-c amplifier if the minimum detectable current is 10^{-13} amp?

10. Calculate the resolution at 600 mμ for a grating ruled 1200 lines/mm and 2 cm in width.

Bibliography

Bauman, R. P., *Absorption Spectroscopy*, Wiley, New York, 1962.

Clark, G. L. (Ed.), *The Encyclopedia of Spectroscopy*, Reinhold, New York, 1960.

Jenkins, F. A., and H. E. White, *Fundamentals of Optics*, 3rd ed., McGraw-Hill, New York, 1957.

Lothian, G. F., *Absorption Spectrophotometry*, 2nd ed., Hilger and Watts, London, 1958.

Mellon, M. G., (Ed.), *Analytical Absorption Spectroscopy*, Wiley, New York, 1950.

Strobel, H. A., *Chemical Instrumentation*, Addison-Wesley, Reading, Mass., 1960.

West, W., *Physical Methods of Organic Chemistry*, A. Weissberger (Ed.), 3rd ed., Vol. 1, Part III, Interscience, New York, 1960.

Literature Cited

1. Advisory Board, *Anal. Chem.*, **34**, 1852 (1962).
2. Brice, B. A., *Rev. Sci. Instruments*, **8**, 279 (1937).
3. Cary, H. H., and A. O. Beckman, *J. Opt. Soc. Am.*, **31**, 682 (1941).
4. Hogness, T. R., F. P. Zscheile, and A. E. Sidwell, *J. Phys. Chem.*, **41**, 379 (1937).
5. Miller, W. C., G. Hare, D. C. Strain, K. P. George, M. E. Stickney, and A. O. Beckman, *J. Opt. Soc. Am.*, **39**, 377 (1949).
6. Müller, R. H., *Ind. Eng. Chem.*, *Anal. Ed.*, **11**, 1 (1939).

C H A P T E R | 4

Ultraviolet and
Visible Absorption Methods

The Electromagnetic Spectrum

The absorption and the emission of energy in the electromagnetic spectrum occurs in discrete packets or photons. The relation between the energy of a photon and the frequency appropriate for the description of its propagation is

$$E = h\nu \qquad (4\text{-}1)$$

where E represents energy in ergs, ν represents frequency in cycles per second, and h is a universal constant known as Planck's constant (6.6256×10^{-27} erg-sec). For some purposes it is more convenient to think of radiant energy as a continuous wave motion in which λ represents the interval between nodes in the wave pattern. The relationship between wavelength and frequency is*

$$\nu = c/\lambda \qquad (4\text{-}2)$$

where λ is the wavelength in centimeters and c is the velocity of propagation of radiant energy in a vacuum (essentially the speed of light in a vacuum, 2.9979×10^{10} cm-sec^{-1}).

The intensity of a beam of radiation is characterized by its radiant power, which is proportional to the number of photons per second that are propagated in the beam. A beam carrying radiation of only one discrete wavelength is said to be monochromatic, and a beam containing radiation of several wavelengths is said to be polychromatic or heterochromatic.

The various regions in the electromagnetic spectrum are displayed in Fig. 4-1, along with the nature of the changes brought about by the radiation.

*In any material medium the speed of propagation is smaller than this and is given by $nc = 2.9979 \times 10^{10}$, where n is the refractive index of the medium.

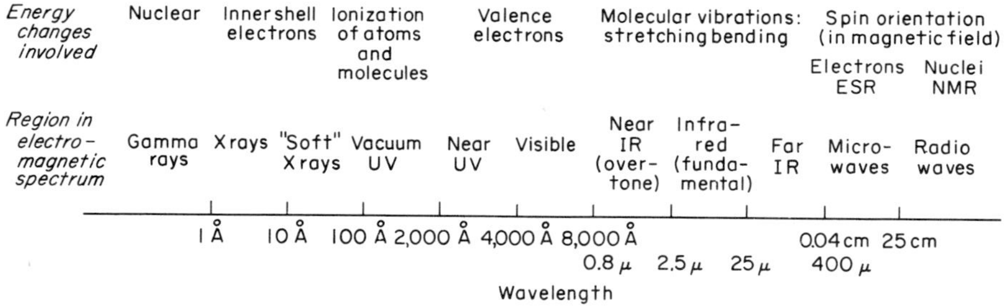

Energy changes involved	Nuclear	Inner shell electrons	Ionization of atoms and molecules	Valence electrons		Molecular vibrations: stretching bending	Spin orientation (in magnetic field)	
							Electrons ESR	Nuclei NMR
Region in electro- magnetic spectrum	Gamma rays	X rays	"Soft" X rays	Vacuum UV	Near UV Visible	Near IR (over- tone) Infra- red (funda- mental)	Far IR Micro- waves	Radio waves

$$\text{1 Å} \quad \text{10 Å} \quad \text{100 Å} \quad \text{2,000 Å} \quad \text{4,000 Å} \quad \text{8,000 Å} \qquad \qquad \text{0.04 cm} \quad \text{25 cm}$$
$$0.8\,\mu \quad 2.5\,\mu \quad 25\,\mu \quad 400\,\mu$$

Wavelength

Fig. 4-1. Schematic diagram of electromagnetic spectrum. Note that wavelength scale is nonlinear.

Table 4-1 contains some energy unit conversions. Individual areas of spectroscopy were developed rather independently of each other, which explains the lack of a consistent set of units.

Table 4-1 | *Energy Unit Conversions*

WAVELENGTH	ENERGY
10^{-4} cm	10,000 cm^{-1} (symbol, ω)
$1\,\mu$	2.998×10^{14} cps
1000 mμ	2.998×10^{8} Mc/sec
10,000 Å	1.2398 eV
	28,590 cal mole^{-1}

1 eV $\equiv$ 23,063 cal mole^{-1} $\equiv$ 8,066 cm^{-1} (1 Kaysner)

Visible light represents only a very small part of the electromagnetic spectrum and is generally considered to extend from 380 to 780 mμ. Table 4-2 shows an

Table 4-2 | *Relation Between Absorption of Light and Color*

WAVELENGTH REGION, mμ	TRANSMITTED COLOR	COMPLEMENTARY HUE
<380	Ultraviolet	
380–435	Violet	Yellowish green
435–480	Blue	Yellow
480–490	Greenish blue	Orange
490–500	Bluish green	Red
500–560	Green	Purple
560–580	Yellowish green	Violet
580–595	Yellow	Blue
595–650	Orange	Greenish blue
650–780	Red	Bluish green
>780	Near infrared	

enlargement of the visible region, with the transmitted colors that correspond to various wavelengths. The ultraviolet region extends from 185 mμ to the visible; shorter wavelengths are considered to be the far (or vacuum) ultraviolet region. The extreme ultraviolet overlaps the soft X-ray portion of the spectrum.

When a beam of radiant energy impinges upon a substance, several things may happen to it (Fig. 4-2): (1) It may pass through the matter with little absorption taking place and, therefore, little energy loss. (2) The direction of propagation of the beam may be altered by reflection, refraction, or diffraction. Scattering by particulate suspended matter must also be included. (3) The radiant energy may be absorbed entirely or in part. The absorption involves a transfer of energy to the medium, and the absorption process is a specific phenomenon related to characteristic molecular structures.

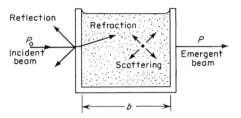

Fig. 4-2. Incident radiation impinging on a system whose optical path length is b.

The rate at which energy is transported in a beam of radiant energy will be denoted by the symbol P_0 for the incident beam and by P for the quantity remaining unabsorbed after passage through a sample or container. Radiant power is the quantity measured by detectors such as photocells and phototubes. The ratio of the radiant power transmitted by a sample to the radiant power incident on the sample is the transmittance T (not transmittancy or transmission).

$$T = P/P_0 \qquad (4\text{-}3)$$

The logarithm to the base 10 of the reciprocal of the transmittance is the absorbance (not optical density, absorbancy, or extinction).

$$A = \log_{10}(1/T) = \log_{10}(P_0/P) \qquad (4\text{-}4)$$

These terms, their definitions and abbreviations, have been endorsed by the advisory board members of *Analytical Chemistry*[1] in an attempt to obtain some consistency in a field where much discrepancy in terminology exits.

Fundamental Laws of Photometry

Two fundamental laws underlie the practice of photometry. The Bouguer (1729) or Lambert (1760) law states that when a beam of monochromatic light, previously rendered plane-parallel, enters an absorbing medium at right angles to the plane, parallel surfaces of the medium (or container for a solution), the rate of decrease in radiant power with the length of light path through the absorbing medium b is proportional to the radiant power of the beam; that is, the light will be diminished in geometric (not arithmetic), or exponential, progression. In other words, if a certain thickness absorbs half the light, then the thickness which follows the first and is equal to it will not absorb the entire second half, but only the half of this half and will consequently reduce it to one-quarter. Thus,

$$\frac{-\partial P}{P} = k \, \partial b \tag{4-5}$$

On integration and changing to logarithms of base 10, and putting $P = P_0$ when $b = 0$, one obtains

$$2.303 \log (P_0/P) = kb \tag{4-6}$$

This is equivalent to stating that the radiant power of the unabsorbed light decreases exponentially as the thickness of the absorbing medium increases arithmetically; that is,

$$P = P_0 e^{-kb} = P_0 10^{-0.434kb} \tag{4-7}$$

Bernard's (1852) or Beer's (1852) law states that the radiant power of a beam of parallel monochromatic radiation decreases in a similar manner as the concentration of the light-absorbing constituent increases. Thus,

$$2.303 \log (P_0/P) = k'C \tag{4-8}$$

The two laws may be combined and written with a single constant:

$$\log (P_0/P) = abC \tag{4-9}$$

or

$$P = P_0 10^{-abC} \tag{4-10}$$

where a is the absorptivity (not absorbancy index, specific extinction, or extinction coefficient), a constant dependent upon the wavelength of the radiation and the nature of the absorbing material, whose concentration C is expressed in grams per liter. The product of the absorptivity and the molecular weight of the substance is called "molar absorptivity" and is given the symbol ϵ. The combined law is generally referred to as Beer's law, even though it is recognized that others contributed to its formulation.

Absorbance is the product of absorptivity, the optical path length, and the analyte concentration, namely,

$$A = abC \quad \text{or} \quad A = \epsilon bC \tag{4-11}$$

The term $A_{1\,cm}^{1\%}$ represents the absorbance of a 1-cm layer of solution which contains 1 percent by weight of absorbing solute.

The relationship between percent transmittance, absorbance, and concentration is illustrated in Fig. 4-3.

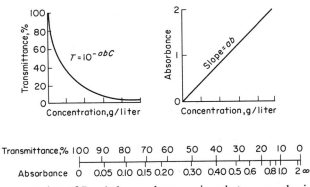

Fig. 4-3. Representation of Beer's law and comparison between scales in absorbance and transmittance.

Example 4-1

Later it will be shown that the relative concentration error is minimal over the transmittance range from 0.200 to 0.650. (a) Over what concentration range could analyses be performed for an iron chelate which possesses a molar absorptivity of 12,000? (b) To be able to determine 0.200 μg/ml of an element (at. wt. = 65) with maximum precision, i.e., $T = 0.368$, what must be the minimum value of the molar absorptivity?

Ans. (a) From Eq. 4-11, and an optical path length of 1.00 cm assumed, the concentration could range from $C_1 = A_1/\epsilon b$ to $C_2 = A_2/\epsilon b$. Conversion of the transmittance readings to corresponding absorbance units gives

$$A = \log(1/T)$$
$$A_1 = \log(1/0.200) = 0.699$$
$$A_2 = \log(1/0.600) = 0.222$$

from which

$$C_1 = 0.699/[(12,000)(1.00)] = 5.83 \times 10^{-5} \text{ moles/liter}$$
$$C_2 = 0.222/[(12,000)(1.00)] = 1.85 \times 10^{-5} \text{ moles/liter}$$

For iron, the limits would extend from 1.03 to 3.25 mg/liter.

(b) The absorbance of 0.434 corresponds to a transmittance of 0.368, and 0.200 μg/ml is equivalent to 3.08×10^{-6} moles/liter. Thus,

$$\epsilon = 0.434/[(3.08 \times 10^{-6})(1.00)] = 141,000$$

if an optical path length of 1.00 cm were used, but proportionally less if longer optical path lengths were used.

Deviations from Beer's Law

The behavior of a substance should always be tested by constructing a plot of absorbance vs concentration (Fig. 4-3). A straight line passing through the origin indicates conformity to Beer's law. Lack of conformity may be ascribed either to failure of a chemical system to remain invariant or to defects of a physical nature.

Discrepancies are usually found when the absorbing solute dissociates or associates in solution, since the nature of the species in solution will vary with the concentration. Absorbance readings taken at an isosbestic point usually circumvent difficulties when the absorbing species is part of an equilibrium system. Indicator systems of weak acids or weak bases are discussed in Chapter 22. Potassium dichromate solutions involve the chromate ion-dichromate ion equilibrium:

$$2CrO_4^{-2} + 2H^+ \rightleftharpoons Cr_2O_7^{-2} + H_2O \qquad (4\text{-}12)$$

$$(\lambda_{max}\ 375m\mu) \qquad (\lambda_{max}\ 350,\ 450m\mu)$$

At relatively small hydrogen ion concentrations, the equilibrium is shifted by increasing the pH, upon dilution, or with changing total chromium concentration. In solutions of high hydrogen ion concentration, Beer's law is obeyed. Similarly, in 4 M HCl the equilibrium

$$4Cl^- + Co(H_2O)_4^{+2} \rightleftharpoons CoCl_4^{-2} + 4H_2O \qquad (4\text{-}13)$$

shifts from left to right as the concentration of cobalt increases. Beer's law is obeyed in each example cited if the actual absorbance of individual species is considered.

Temperature often shifts ionic equilibria and, in addition, an increase in temperature exerts a bathochromic effect on ions in solution; i.e., the absorption bands are shifted to longer wavelengths.

In the derivation of Beer's law the use of a beam of monochromatic radiation is implied. However, most spectrophotometers and all filter photometers employ a finite group of frequencies. The wider the bandwidth of radiation passed by the filter or other dispersing device, the greater will be the apparent deviation of a system from adherence to Beer's law. Often the deviation becomes evident at higher concentrations on an absorbance vs concentration plot when the curve bends towards the concentration axis. Fundamentally this departure is due to the fact that with all photometers it is the radiant power of the component wavelengths which are additive (or nearly so), whereas Beer's law requires the logarithms be additive. Only when the absorption curve is essentially flat over the spectral bandwidths employed can Beer's law be expected to apply. Lack of adherence to Beer's law in the negative direction is always undesirable because of the rather large increase in relative error of reported concentrations. By contrast, in trace analysis and in ultimate precision methods, it may be advantageous to devise a differential absorption system which exhibits a positive deviation from Beer's law.

Stray light which enters the detector housing is potentially a source of error. Although corrections for it may be made, estimation of stray radiation is always subject to some uncertainty. Elimination by a double monochromator or double-pass (infrared) design, or by suitable filters, is the only way to minimize this error. Scattered light from suspensions, or fluorescence, may also cause deviations from Beer's law.

Kortum and Seiler[15] point out that Beer's law is only a limiting law and should be expected to apply only at low concentrations. It is not a or ϵ which is constant, independent of concentration, but $an/(n^2 + 2)^2$, where n is the refractive index of the solution. At low concentrations n is practically constant, but at higher concentrations the refractive index may vary appreciably. This effect may be encountered in high absorbance differential spectrophotometry.

Presentation of Spectra

Absorption spectra are displayed in a number of ways, as shown in Fig. 4-4. Increasing values of molar absorptivity, absorbance, or transmittance as ordinate are plotted on a linear or logarithmic scale against increasing values of wavelength (in millimicrons) or decreasing values of frequency (usually in the

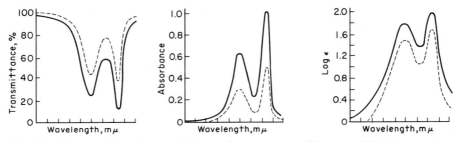

Fig. 4-4. Presentation of spectral absorption curves: solid curve, 0.01 M concentration; dashed curve, 0.005 M concentration.

form of wave numbers, $\bar{\nu}$ cm^{-1}). The wave number scale possesses the theoretical advantage of being a linear energy scale, and from a graph an integrated absorption value f (the oscillator strength) can be calculated from the area under the absorption band. The smallest significant energy change in the study of electronic spectra in solution is about 2 kcal mole^{-1}, a frequency difference of ± 700 cm^{-1} anywhere in the spectral range. The transmittance scale has nothing to recommend it except, perhaps, for characterization of filters and solvents.

To facilitate comparison of spectra in qualitative identification, spectral absorption data may be plotted as log A (or log ϵ) vs wavelength. The curve shape will be independent of cell length or sample concentration.

$$\log A = \log \epsilon + \log b + \log C \qquad (4\text{-}14)$$

Simple translation of comparison and sample spectra up or down the ordinate scale quickly establishes identity or nonconformity. The comparison of spectra taken in different cuvettes or at different concentrations is thereby simplified. Unfortunately, some absorption features may be indistinguishable. A plot with a precision consistent with the experimental reproducibility is achieved only when the ordinate in absorbance values is plotted on graph paper with 1 mm $\equiv$ 0.005 in absorbance. Tables of absorption maxima are no substitute for full absorption curves.

Spectrophotometric data should be accompanied by a statement that conveys the concentrations employed, the solvent used, the band pass, the make and model of spectrophotometer, and any other pertinent information which might affect the shape of an absorption curve. Water is a common solvent for many inorganic substances. The ultraviolet transmittance characteristics and cutoff wavelengths of a number of "spectroquality solvents" for organic substances are shown in Fig. 4-5. Cyclohexane is a desirable solvent for aromatic

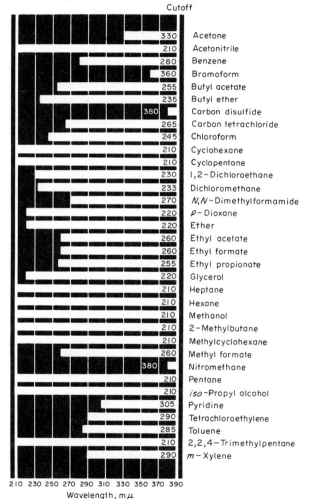

Fig. 4-5. Transmittance of selected solvents in the ultraviolet region. The cutoff point in the ultraviolet region is the wavelength at which the absorbance approaches unity using a 1-cm cell path with water as the reference. (Courtesy of Matheson, Coleman & Bell.)

compounds. When a more polar solvent is required, 95 percent ethanol is a good choice.

Correlation of Electronic Absorption Spectra with Molecular Structure

When molecules interact with radiant energy in the visible and ultraviolet region, the absorption consists in displacing an outer electron in the molecule, although sometimes the energy of the far ultraviolet is sufficient to exceed the energy of dissociation of certain bonds. Lesser amounts of energy are involved in excitation of molecular vibrations and still smaller amounts for molecular rotation. Consequently, rotational and vibrational modes will be found combined with electronic transitions. Broadly, the spectrum is a function of the whole structure of a substance rather than of specific bonds. No unique electronic spectrum will be found. On the other hand, electronic absorption is often a very intensive property. Molar absorptivity values frequently exceed 10,000, whereas in the infrared they rarely exceed 1000. Thus, dilute solutions are adequate in electronic spectrophotometry, and only undiluted samples or rather strong solutions are usable in the infrared. Ordinarily the interpretation of ultraviolet absorption spectra is aided by information available from previous history of a compound—its synthesis, auxiliary chemical tests, and comparison with reference spectra.

Electronic Spectra

When a molecule is placed in the alternating electromagnetic field of a beam of radiant energy, there is an induced oscillation of electrons throughout the molecule, in which the displacement is proportional to the polarizability of the molecule. If radiation of a frequency corresponding to one of the natural frequencies of a molecule strikes it, the radiant energy may be absorbed to increase momentarily its energy content by an amount equal to that of the quanta absorbed (Eq. 4-1), namely,

$$\Delta E = 286,000/\lambda \tag{4-15}$$

in kcal mole^{-1}. If the electronic energy of the molecule is thereby increased sufficiently, an electronic transition to an upper electronic state will take place.

A schematic energy-level diagram for a simple diatomic molecule is shown in Fig. 4-6. The lower curve represents the potential energy of the molecule in its ground or unexcited state as a function of the internuclear separation between the two atoms. The permissible energies associated with the ground state are represented by a set of vibrational levels ($v = 0, 1, 2, 3$, etc.). An electronic excited state of the same molecule is represented by the upper curve, with a different value of internuclear distance at the point of minimum potential energy and different slopes on either side of the minimum. The spacings between the vibrational energy levels are relatively small, 0.01–10 kcal mole^{-1}.

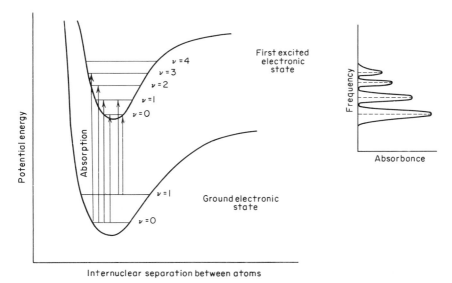

Fig. 4-6. Energy-level diagram of a diatomic molecule and partial absorption spectrum.

Thermal motion at room temperature is usually sufficient to populate a number of vibrational levels in the ground state. On the other hand, the energy difference between electronic levels is relatively large, involving 35–71 kcal mole^{-1} in the visible wavelengths, and continuing up to several hundred in the far ultraviolet. Only the lower electronic levels are occupied under normal conditions.

The lowest vibrational level ($\nu = 0$), corresponding to the equilibrium distance between the two nuclei, will be the most populated in the ground electronic state. Consequently, the absorption transition starting from this level will be the most probable and will produce the most intense peak. Absorption transitions originating from other vibrational levels in the ground state will occur, their intensity depending on the relative population levels. The electronic transition takes the form of a group of essentially vertical lines to the vibrational sublevels reached in the excited state. This is determined by the fact that electronic motion is so much faster than nuclear motion that no appreciable change in internuclear distance can take place during an electronic transition (Franck-Condon principle). Energy absorption is accomplished in about 10^{-15} sec, or within the period of the frequency of the radiation.

The absorption is a highly specific property of the molecular structure, and the frequency range within which energy can be absorbed is specifically dependent upon the molecular structure of the absorbing material. The more mobile or loosely bound are the electrons, the smaller the energy difference between the ground state and the excited electronic state and the lower the frequency of absorption (i.e., the longer the wavelength). Unfortunately for structure analysis, in molecules containing more than a few atoms, the number of vibrational sublevels becomes so large and their spacing so close that the discrete peaks tend to coalesce into broad absorption bands or merely a general band envelope. This tendency is enhanced in the liquid state and in solution when the vibrations are further damped by physical interaction between neighboring molecules and by chemical solvation. When photodissociation occurs, the vibrational energy of the excited states is no longer quantized, and this is reflected in the light absorption properties by the complete disappearance of vibrational structure in the electronic band concerned.

Molar Absorptivity

The molar absorptivity is governed largely by the probability of the electronic transition and the polarity of the excited state. In order that interaction may take place, a photon must obviously strike a molecule approximately within the space of the molecular dimensions, and the transition probability g will be the proportion of target hits which lead to absorption. Thus,

$$\frac{-\partial P}{P} = \frac{1}{3}gCN_{A}A(\partial b/1000) \tag{4-16}$$

where N_A is the Avogadro number, A is the cross-sectional target area (obtainable from X-ray diffraction data), and $1/3$ is a statistical factor to allow for random orientation. On integration and insertion of numerical constants,

$$\log (P_0/P)/bC = \epsilon = (0.87 \times 10^{20})gA \tag{4-17}$$

For many organic molecules the cross-sectional area is about 10 Å, so that for a transition of unit probability, $\epsilon \simeq 10^5$. The highest molar absorptivities observed are of this order. Absorption with $\epsilon > 10^4$ is considered high-intensity absorption.

Structural Features

Consideration will be limited to those molecules capable of absorption within the wavelength region from 185 to 800 mμ. Compounds with only single bonds involving σ-valency electrons exhibit absorption spectra only below 150 mμ and will be met only in interaction with other kinds. In covalently saturated compounds containing heteroatoms—e.g., nitrogen, oxygen, sulfur, and halogen—unshared p-electrons are present in addition to σ-electrons. Excitation promotes a p-orbital electron into an antibonding σ orbit, i.e., an $n \rightarrow \sigma^{\star}$ transition, such as occurs in ethers, amines, sulfides, and alkyl halides. In unsaturated compounds absorption results in the displacement of π-electrons. Molecules containing single absorbing groups, called chromophores, undergo transitions at approximately the wavelengths indicated in Table 4-3.

Molecules with two or more insulated chromophores will absorb light of nearly the same wavelength as a molecule containing only a single chromophore of a particular type, but the intensity of the absorption will be proportional to

Table 4-3 | *Electronic Absorption Bands for Representative Chromophores*

CHROMOPHORE	SYSTEM	λ_{max}	ϵ_{max}	λ_{max}	ϵ_{max}	λ_{max}	ϵ_{max}
Ether	—O—	185	1000				
Thioether	—S—	194	4600	215	1600		
Amine	—NH$_2$	195	2800				
Thiol	—SH	195	1400				
Disulfide	—S—S—	194	5500	255	400		
Bromide	—Br	208	300				
Iodide	—I	260	400				
Nitrile	—C≡N	160	—				
Acetylide	—C≡C—	175–180	6000				
Sulfone	—SO$_2$—	180	—				
Oxime	—NOH	190	5000				
Azido	>C=N—	190	5000				
Ethylene	—C=C—	190	8000				
Ketone	>C=O	195	1000	270–285	18–30		
Thioketone	>C=S	205	strong				
Esters	—COOR	205	50				
Aldehyde	—CHO	210	strong	280–300	11–18		
Carboxyl	—COOH	200–210	50–70				
Sulfoxide	>S→O	210	1500				
Nitro	—NO$_2$	210	strong				
Nitrite	—ONO	220–230	1000–2000	300–400	10		
Azo	—N=N—	285–400	3–25				
Nitroso	—N=O	302	100				
Nitrate	—ONO$_2$	270 (shoulder)	12				
	—(C=C)$_2$— (acyclic)	210–230	21,000				
	—(C=C)$_3$—	260	35,000				
	—(C=C)$_4$—	300	52,000				
	—(C=C)$_5$—	330	118,000				
	—(C=C)$_2$— (alicyclic)	230–260	3000–8000				
	C=C—C≡C	219	6,500				
	C=C—C≡N	220	23,000				
	C=C—C=O	210–250	10,000–20,000			300–350	weak
	C=C—NO$_2$	229	9,500				
Benzene		184	46,700	202	6,900	255	170
Diphenyl				246	20,000		
Naphthalene		220	112,000	275	5,600	312	175
Anthracene		252	199,000	375	7,900		
Pyridine		174	80,000	195	6,000	251	1,700
Quinoline		227	37,000	270	3,600	314	2,750
Isoquinoline		218	80,000	266	4,000	317	3,500

the number of that type of chromophore present in the molecule. Appreciable interaction between chromophores does not occur unless they are linked to each other directly; interposition of a single methylene group, or meta-orientation about an aromatic ring, is sufficient to insulate chromophores almost completely from each other.

Electronic interaction between chromophores can lead to π-π conjugation, involving two adjacent groups with π-electrons, and n-π conjugation, involving an atom containing p-electrons adjacent to a group containing π-electrons. Slight interaction is also noticed when alkyl radicals are attached to chromophores. This is called hyperconjugation.

Four types of absorption bands are recognized in the spectra of organic compounds. K-bands arise from π-π structures. They result from $\pi \rightarrow \pi^{\star}$ transitions and are characterized by high molar absorptivity. For a diene the K-band is ascribed to the resonance transition: $C{=}C{-}C{=}C$ to $C^{+}{-}C{=}C{-}C^{-}$; it also arises in aromatic compounds possessing chromophoric substitution, such as vinyl benzene or acetophenone. In extended open-chain conjugated systems, mutual repulsion of electrons in the individual double bonds displaces the absorption progressively toward longer wavelengths (bathochromic shift), accompanied by increases in molar absorptivity. The dependence of molar absorptivity on the number of conjugated chromophores n is approximately given by

$$\epsilon_{\text{max}} = (0.87 \times 10^{20})(2 \times 10^{-16})ng = 17,400n \qquad (4\text{-}18)$$

where the area of the chromophore is 2 Å and g is assumed to be unity.

R-bands arise from $n \rightarrow \pi^{\star}$ transitions. They rarely produce conspicuous results in nonaromatic compounds, but marked bathochromic shifts occur when —OH, —NH$_2$, and —SH replace hydrogen in unsaturated groups. Frequently R-bands remain in the absorption spectra when modifications in the electronic structure introduce additional bands and thus serve for confirmation of particular structures.

Also present are two other weak types of absorption bands. B-bands are characteristic of aromatic or heteroaromatic molecules and may contain fine vibrational sub-bands. E-bands arise from oscillations of electrons in aromatic ring systems.

Cumulated systems may not show the expected conjugated bands because orbitals of adjacent multiple bonds are at right angles instead of parallel and, consequently, resonating dipolar structures cannot be envisioned. The spectrum will revert to that which is a mere superposition of the spectra of the individual chromophoric groups. Examples are allene and ketene systems, and m-terphenyl among the polyphenyls. Steric hindrance may prevent coplanarity of two resonating structures, partially or completely. Partial hindrance leads to bands characteristic of those parts of conjugated systems which remain coplanar; bands of these partial structures will superimpose on the main absorption bands.

A great deal of "negative" information may be deduced concerning molecular structures. If a compound is highly transparent throughout the region from 220 to 800 mμ, it contains no conjugated unsaturated or benzenoid system, no aldehyde or keto group, no nitro group, and no bromine or iodine. If the screening for high selective absorption indicates the presence of chromophores, the wavelength(s) of maximum absorbance are ascertained and tables, similar to the abbreviated version give in Table 4-3, are searched for known chromophores. Once the material is classified according to chromophore, further information may be deduced from the shape, intensity, and detailed location of the bands. Finally, the absorption spectrum is compared with the spectra in standard compilations of ultraviolet spectra.[6,7,10,18,19] Oftentimes structural details can be inferred from the close resemblance of a compound's spectrum with that of a compound of known and related structure—e.g., in petroleum ether, the spectra of toluene and chlorobenzene are similar.

Inorganic Ions

Among inorganic compounds, the chromophoric groupings may involve several atoms, such as the permanganate and dichromate groups, or it may involve only single atoms with incomplete outer d-electron shells where closely spaced, unoccupied energy levels are available, such as with the rare earths and many transition elements in coordination compounds. Absorption spectra for these are thought to result from a charge transfer process whereby an electron is transferred from one part of the ion to another. The spectra are considerably altered by changes in the complexing groups. Addition of easily polarizable atoms exerts an effect similar to lengthening a conjugated chain. For example, $FeCl_3$ is yellow and $FeBr_3$ is orange and, in addition, the molar absorptivity increases from chloride to bromide. The isolation of the manganese atom in permanganate by the surrounding oxygen atoms protects it from solvent interaction and its spectrum resembles the sharply defined spectra of the rare earths which originate with their isolated f-electron shells.

Effect of Temperature

At low temperatures the absorption bands of most substances are sharper than at room temperature. The vibrational resolutions are better defined because fewer vibrational levels are occupied and the extent of solute-solvent interaction is decreased. Examination of samples in highly viscous or rigid media (i.e., glasses) is done routinely in phosphorescence methods and in certain fluorescence methods (q.v.).

Solvent Effects

The absorption bands of many substances are sharper and may show fine structure when measured in solvents of low dipole moment. Solvent-solute interactions are much stronger when strong dipole forces are involved. The magnitude of solvent effects is shown in Fig. 4-7 for benzene. In aqueous solution there is no fine structure, whereas in isooctane there are a number of bands with evidence of unresolved inflections. A wealth of fine structure appears in the spectrum of the vapor state.

Solvent effects aid in recognizing electronic transitions of the type $n \rightarrow \pi^{\star}$ which involve the nonbonding electrons of oxygen and nitrogen, among others. These interact strongly with polar solvents, giving rise to a characteristic shift to shorter wavelengths. For example, the spectrum of iodine is markedly different, even to the unaided eye, in a solvent such as $CHCl_3$ where it appears to be purple, as compared with its spectrum in an alcohol (Fig. 4-8), where it is

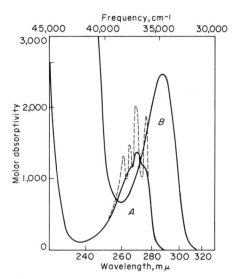

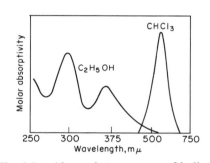

Fig. 4-7. *A*. Benzene absorption spectrum in water and (*dashed line*) in petroleum ether. *B*. Phenol in 0.01 *N* NaOH (phenolate anion.)

Fig. 4-8. Absorption spectrum of iodine in a polar and a nonpolar solvent.

a brownish color. A spectrum exhibits large alterations with changing *p*H when an ionizable group is present in the molecule and forms part of the chromophore structure. Specific applications to acid-base indicators is discussed in Chapter 22, but the methodology is equally applicable to compounds whose spectra lie in the ultraviolet region. The information can be used often to evaluate the acidic dissociation constant of the ionizing group. The reader is also referred to the discussion of structural factors as they affect fluorescence (page 373).

Synthetic Alterations

Chemical treatment enlarges the scope of absorption methods. Formation of metal-organic complexes is well known. A few moments of reflection will bring to mind a number of possibilities among organic compounds. For example, although alcohols possess no absorption spectra between 200 and 1000 mμ, treatment of an alcohol with phenyl isocyanate yields the corresponding phenyl alkyl carbamate which absorbs at about 280 mμ. Conversely, the strong absorption of anthracene can be eliminated by a Diels-Alder reaction with 1,2-dicyanoethylene. Prior separation by solvent extraction or gas chromatography improves selectivity and aids in final identification.

Quantitative Methods

The basic principle of most quantitative absorption methods consists in comparing the extent of absorption (or transmittance) of radiant energy at a particular wavelength by a solution of the test material and a series of standard solutions. Work with visual comparators, although requiring simple equipment, is subject to the vagaries of the human eye, in particular fatigue and unavoidable low sensitivity under 450 and above 675 mμ. Precision is always less than that attainable with photoelectric instruments except, perhaps, when dealing with very weak colors. Filter photometers are suitable for many routine methods that do not involve complex spectra. Precise work is done with a spectrophotometer which is able to employ narrow bandwidths of radiant energy and which can handle absorption spectra in the ultraviolet region if equipped with quartz or fused silica optics.

The limitations of many colorimetric procedures lie in the chemical reactions upon which these procedures are based rather than upon the instruments available. Many instances arise when a specimen does not possess suitable chromogenic properties; sometimes it may be converted to an absorbing species or be made to react with an absorbing reagent. Points that should be considered in selection of any colorimetric procedure include (1) specificity of the color-forming reaction, (2) time-stability of the system and color developer (i.e., reagent blank), (3) effect of excess reagent, diverse ions, pH, ionic strength, and temperature, (4) conformity to Beer's law (desirable but not essential), and (5) the molar absorptivity.

Although very few reactions are specific for a particular substance, many reactions are quite selective, or can be rendered selective through the introduction of masking agents, control of pH, use of solvent extraction techniques, adjustment of oxidation state, or by prior removal of interferents. Both the color-developing reagent and the absorbing product must be stable for a reasonable period of time. It is often necessary to specify that the color comparisons be made within a definite period of time, and it is always advisable to prepare standards and unknowns on a definite time schedule. When extraneous color bodies are present, the standards should match the composition of the sample solution. Adherence to Beer's law is desirable for then the absorbance is directly proportional to concentration and only a few points are required to establish the calibration curve. In any event the standard curve should be checked at frequent intervals. High ionic strength of the medium, appreciable temperature variations, and use of polychromatic radiation can cause departure of the calibration curve from linearity.

Relative Concentration Error

For an instrument which produces a response directly proportional to the light falling on the receiver, as do most photometers, the reasonable assumption of a constant uncertainty (ΔT) in the measurement of transmittance, which is the basic operation in photometric methods (i.e., meter or slidewire reading is in linear units), results in a corresponding uncertainty, ΔC, in concentration or absorptivity. The uncertainty arises from unavoidable electrical and mechanical imperfections in the instrument—nonuniformity in the slidewire of the measuring potentiometer, nonlinearity of the meter scale in direct-reading instruments, nonlinearity of the detector, variations in stray light—all random errors which depend not only on the particular instrument, but also upon the working procedures by which the instrument is used. Hence an analysis should be conducted at that value of transmittance for which a given error in transmittance (or scale reading) will cause least error in concentration. Rewriting Beer's law,

$$C = -(\log T)/ab \qquad (4\text{-}19)$$

and differentiating,

$$\frac{\partial C}{\partial T} = \frac{-0.4343}{T(ab)} \qquad (4\text{-}20)$$

Replacing the term ab by its equivalent gives

$$\frac{\partial C}{\partial T} = \frac{0.4343C}{T(\log T)} \qquad (4\text{-}21)$$

which on rearrangement gives the relative concentration error

$$\frac{\Delta C/C}{\Delta T} = \frac{0.4343}{T(\log T)} \qquad (4\text{-}22)$$

Thus the relative concentration error depends inversely on the product of transmittance and absorbance which vary in opposite manner. Differentiating Eq. 4-22 with respect to T and setting the function equal to zero gives the point of minimum error, i.e., when $T = 1/e = 0.368$ (or $A = 0.4343$). Thus, such variables as the cell path, sample size, and volume of the final solution should be so adjusted as to yield solutions whose transmittance is 0.368.[20,21]

A plot of the relative concentration error appears as the uppermost curve in Fig. 4-14. Evaluation of the relative concentration error for values of transmittance (Table 4-4) shows that the sample transmittance can lie in the range 0.200 to 0.650 (which is 0.7 to 0.2 absorbance unit) for a minimum and nearly constant error. The relative error increases rapidly at the extremes of the transmittance scale. Uncertainty of the transmittance setting of most com-

Table 4-4	Relative Concentration Error (in Percent)

	Evaluation of $\Delta C/C = 0.4343(\Delta T)/(T \log T)$ for ΔT at various values of T.	
TRANSMITTANCE, %	$\Delta T = 0.01(1.0\%)$	$\Delta T = 0.004(0.4\%)$
100	∞	∞
95	-20.5	-8.2
90	-10.6	-4.2
85	-7.2	-2.88
80	-5.6	-2.24
70	-4.0	-1.60
60	-3.26	-1.30
50	-2.88	-1.16
40	-2.72	-1.10
30	-2.77	-1.12
20	-3.11	-1.24
15	-3.51	-1.40
10	-4.34	-1.74
5	-6.7	-2.68
1	-21.7	-8.7

mercial instruments will be of the order of 0.01 to 0.002 of the total scale. The latter value is considered a practical limit in ordinary work. The uncertainty may be evaluated experimentally by taking a standard solution and measuring its transmittance repeatedly. Each measurement should include the operations of emptying, refilling, and repositioning the cuvette. Usually ΔT is taken as twice the average deviation of the replicate readings in order to include the uncertainty involved in setting the reading scale to zero and 100 scale units. Accordingly, this would result in a minimum concentration error of about 1.0 percent when working within the optimal concentration interval.

For double-beam spectrophotometers with a servo-balancing potentiometric recorder, the optimum transmittance interval is less easy to deduce, but appears to be over the range from 0.4 to 1.4 absorbance units. The minimum appears to be about $T = 2/\epsilon = 0.736$ ($A = 0.87$). Noise generated by the photomultiplier tube may be regarded as the principal source of error.[14]

The positive slope of a Ringbom-Ayres plot[2,17] of log C vs T gives an empirical relative error coefficient,

$$\frac{\Delta C/C}{\Delta T} = \frac{2.303}{\Delta T/(\Delta \log C)} = \frac{2.303}{\text{slope of Ringbom plot}} \qquad (4\text{-}23)$$

This expression is valid whether or not the system obeys Beer's law. However, the Ringbom plot provides no information concerning the concentration range of good precision unless it is combined with a ΔT vs T relation.[5]

Slit Width and Resolution

The purity of the radiant energy used in absorption measurements may profoundly affect the results, especially the absorption curves with abrupt changes in the extent of absorption or narrow absorption bands. Beer's law is valid only for light which is strictly monochromatic; however, a spectrophotometer must work with a finite band pass width. As long as the actual width of absorption bands is considerably greater than the wavelength interval included by the image of the exit slit, molar absorptivity will not be affected. On the other hand, if a measurement is made at a sharp maximum using a slit width which accepts wavelengths on either side of the maximum, the measured absorbance will be smaller than the true value, and the converse effect will be found at a minimum or in the vicinity of a shoulder. For example, the molar absorptivity for potassium permanganate at 545 mμ decreases by 2.4 percent when the band width increases from 0.8 to 5.3 mμ, whereas the shoulder at 575 mμ exhibits an apparent increase of 3.9 percent. The importance of good resolution is shown by the tracings of a portion of the absorption curve of a didymium glass filter (Fig. 4-9). Large dispersion and high resolving power in monochromators will more faithfully record spectra with fine structure.

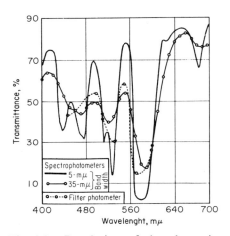

Fig. 4-9. Resolution of the absorption spectrum of a didymium glass at different band widths.

The true mean absorbance on an absorbance curve with sharp upward curvature will be greater than the measured value. If possible, these regions are shunned in quantitative work. The error due to the finite band width of radiation is given approximately by

$$\sigma = -0.093(\Delta A)^2 \tag{4-24}$$

which is always negative and independent of the absolute absorbance value.

Choice of Wavelength

The selection of a suitable region in the spectrum for quantitative analysis of a sample constituent can be handled in several ways. If the material has a characteristic visual color, its complementary color (see Table 4-2) may indicate the proper wavelength region. Unfortunately, the eye is not always a very good judge, and color properties often change with concentration or optical path length. When filter photometers are to be employed, the proper filter can be selected during the course of preparing the calibration curve for the unknown material. A series of standard solutions is prepared, including a blank. Using one filter at a time, a series of calibration curves is plotted in terms of absorbance vs concentration. The filter which permits closest adherence to linearity over the widest absorbance interval and which yields the largest slope (but with a zero intercept) will constitute the best choice for an analysis, as shown by a typical series of plots in Fig. 4-10. Of course, if a spectrophotometer is available, the wavelength of maximum absorbance is quickly ascertained from the absorbance-wavelength curve for the material. As pointed out in the preceding section, the wavelength chosen should fall in a region of absorbance where the absorbance is not changing rapidly with change in wavelength.

Dilemmas arise in practice. Consider the absorption curves shown in Fig. 4-11. The unreacted reagent and the metal complex absorb strongly in the blue

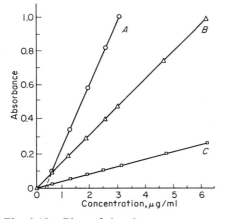 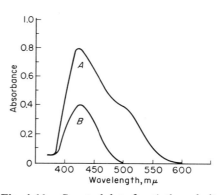

Fig. 4-10. Plots of absorbance vs concentration obtained with filters of various nominal wavelengths: *A*, 420 mμ; *B*, 500 mμ; *C*, 550 mμ. Spectral data for system is shown in Fig. 4-11.

Fig. 4-11. Spectral data for *A*, the cobalt complex, and *B*, 1-nitroso-2-naphthol-3, 6-sulfonic acid—reagent blank.

region of the spectrum and, although this region would yield the steepest calibration curve (and greatest sensitivity in analysis), the choice of wavelength must be on the shoulder of the metal-complex absorption curve where the unreacted reagent no longer absorbs. The unreacted reagent might somehow be removed from the system, thus permitting use of a wavelength in the vicinity of 420 mμ. Similar considerations apply to partially overlapping spectra of any two chromophores.

With photometers generally, and filter photometers in particular, the spectral response of the detector and the spectral distribution curve of the light source, as well as the absorption curve of the sample and any filter employed, must be considered. For example, the silica-molybdenum blue complex exhibits an absorption maximum at 820 mμ and an absorption plateau around 630 mμ, whose absorbance is about one-half the value observed at the absorption maximum. With instruments equipped with a red-sensitive photoemissive tube, the choice is obviously the maximum at 820 mμ. But with filter photometers equipped with a barrier-layer cell, the measurements should be made with a filter whose nominal wavelength lies close to the absorption plateau, around 630 mμ.

For systems sensitive to pH, and for which an isosbestic point can be found, measurements at the wavelength of the latter are advised when the pH is not, or cannot, be controlled.

Simultaneous Spectrophotometric Determinations

When no region can be found in which just one component absorbs, it is still possible to determine two substances by making measurements at two wavelengths. Two dissimilar chromophores must necessarily have different powers of light absorption at some point or points in the spectrum. If, therefore, measurements are made on each solution at two such points, a pair of simultaneous equations may be obtained from which the two unknown concentrations may be determined. First, it is necessary to select two points on the wavelength scale where the ratio of the molar absorptivities are maxima; that is, $(\epsilon_1/\epsilon_2)_{\lambda_1}$ and $(\epsilon_2/\epsilon_1)_{\lambda_2}$ are maxima for the system illustrated in Fig. 4-12.

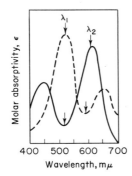

Neither of these wavelengths need necessarily coincide with an absorption maximum for either component; on the other hand, neither should fall on a sharply curving portion of the absorption curve. Next, it is necessary to calculate the molar absorptivity for each component using a particular set of sample containers and spectrophotometer to be employed in the analyses. Since absorbance is directly proportional to the product of molar absorptivity and concentration, if the light path remains constant, it is possible to set up two simultaneous equations:

Fig. 4-12. Simultaneous spectrophotometric analysis of a two-component system. Selection of analytical wavelengths indicated by arrows.

$$C_1(\epsilon_1)_{\lambda_1} + C_2(\epsilon_2)_{\lambda_1} = A_{\lambda_1} \qquad (4\text{-}25)$$

$$C_1(\epsilon_1)_{\lambda_2} + C_2(\epsilon_2)_{\lambda_2} = A_{\lambda_2} \qquad (4\text{-}26)$$

and solve for the concentration of each component

$$C_1 = \frac{(\epsilon_2)_{\lambda_2}A_{\lambda_1} - (\epsilon_2)_{\lambda_1}A_{\lambda_2}}{(\epsilon_1)_{\lambda_1}(\epsilon_2)_{\lambda_2} - (\epsilon_2)_{\lambda_1}(\epsilon_1)_{\lambda_2}} \qquad (4\text{-}27)$$

$$C_2 = \frac{(\epsilon_1)_{\lambda_1}A_{\lambda_2} - (\epsilon_1)_{\lambda_2}A_{\lambda_1}}{(\epsilon_1)_{\lambda_1}(\epsilon_2)_{\lambda_2} - (\epsilon_2)_{\lambda_1}(\epsilon_1)_{\lambda_2}} \qquad (4\text{-}28)$$

The same procedure may be applied, in principle, to multicomponent systems. However, the accuracy is poor unless the spectra are quite discrete, which is seldom true of electronic spectra. Simultaneous determinations rest on the assumption that the substances concerned contribute additively to the total absorbance at an analytical wavelength. This assumption should be tested with known mixtures of the test materials.

Calculations are simplified considerably if a wavelength is available at which only one of the two components absorbs. If this situation obtains (Fig. 4-11), the concentration of the single absorber is ascertained in the usual manner from a calibration curve. Then, from the ratio of its molar absorptivities at the two wavelengths, its contribution to the overall absorbance at the second wavelength is readily computed and subtracted from the total observed to give the net absorbance at the second wavelength that is due to the second component.

Relative Absorbance (Differential) Spectrophotometry

Special problems arise in the analysis of very concentrated or very dilute solutions; that is, solutions whose transmittances lie outside the range 0.200 to 0.650. Furthermore, even in the "ordinary" method, wherein the transmittance scale is set at zero with the receiver dark (to represent infinite concentration) and at 100 scale units with the pure solvent (to represent zero concentration), precision is less than that attainable with volumetric or gravimetric techniques (Fig. 4-13). These two limitations in absorbance methods may sometimes be circumvented by a differential approach.

In handling solutions of high absorbance, for which dilution is not feasible, the instrument scale reading is set to 100 scale units with a standard solution of finite, but lesser, concentration than that of the least concentrated sample solution. To compensate for the lesser amount of transmitted energy reaching the detector, the spectrophotometer is brought to a balance with the reading scale set at 100 scale units by increasing the slit width, by increasing the source intensity, or by increasing the amplifier-phototube sensitivity (without, however, increasing noise). Not all instruments possess these provisions for reserve sensitivity. Under these new conditions, the actual reading scale is effectively lengthened, although there is no change in its physical dimensions. Thus, if a sample series lies in the 0–20 percent transmittance range, with the high-absorbance procedure, the 0–20 percent transmittance range is made to cover 0–100 scale units by using the standard with 20 percent transmittance to make the 100 percent setting.

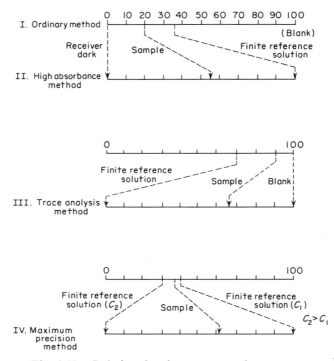

Fig. 4-13.   Relative absorbance spectrophotometry.

The shape of the relative error curve is altered and, at 100 percent trans-mittance, becomes finite. The relative error coefficient becomes dependent in a pronounced manner on the value of the transmittance of the comparison standard, and is equal to $0.4343 [T (\log T + \log T_r)]^{-1}$ where T_r is the actual transmittance of the reference solution used for setting the scale to 100 scale units.[11] Figure 4-14 is a plot of the relative error coefficient as a function of the relative transmittance (expressed, however, as absorbance) of the solution used for setting the reading scale at 100 scale units ($\Delta T = 0.010$). The param-eters are multiple values of 0.4343, namely, 0.0, 0.25, 0.50, 1.0, and 4.0. Cor-responding transmittance values of reference solution are 1.00, 0.779, 0.606, 0.368, and 0.018, respectively. The position of the minimum error gradually shifts from a transmittance value of 0.368 to 1.000 as the concentration of the reference standard is progressively increased. When the comparison standard has a transmittance of 0.690, the relative error becomes identical with the minimum error achieved in the ordinary method. For lower transmittance values of the comparison standard, the error is even less and remains so until the transmittance of the comparison solution decreases to 0.200, at which point it becomes equal again to the minimum of the ordinary method. There is always a gain in precision (product of slope and concentration) until the deviation from Beer's law in a negative direction gives a slope which is falling off more rapidly than the concentration term of the comparison standard is increasing. If standard and unknown solutions are compared at the same scale reading, the relative accuracies depend on the actual scale reading of the differential zero solution.[4] With an assumed constant error of 0.2 percent in determining transmittance, the values of A corresponding to given absorbance readings are listed in the second column of Table 4-5. In the next column the errors in concentration resulting from various scale readings in the normal procedure are given, expressed in parts per thousand. In the succeeding columns the assumption is made that the same readings

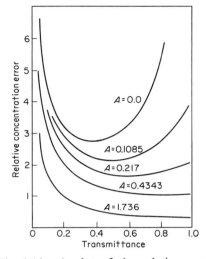

Fig. 4-14. A plot of the relative error coefficient. From C. F. Hiskey, *Anal. Chem.*, **21**, 1440 (1949). (Courtesy of *Analytical Chemistry*.)

| Table 4-5 | Optimum Scale Reading for Differential Zero Method |

ABSORBANCE READING	ΔA FOR 0.2% ERROR IN TRANSMITTANCE	$(\Delta A/A) \times 1000$ SCALE ZERO SET WITH REAGENT BLANK	$(\Delta A/A) \times 1000$† SCALE ZERO SET WITH SOLUTIONS HAVING A VALUES OF:			
			0.434	1.0	2.0	4.0
0.00	0.00087	∞	2.00	0.87	0.44	0.22
0.10	0.00109	10.9	2.04	0.99	0.53	0.27
0.20	0.00138	6.9	2.2	1.15	0.63	0.33
0.30	0.00173	5.8	2.4	1.33	0.75	0.40
0.434	0.00236	5.4	2.7	1.6	0.97	0.53
0.50	0.00275	5.5	2.9	1.8	1.1	0.61
0.60	0.00346	5.8	3.3	2.2	1.3	0.75
0.70	0.00435	6.2	3.8	2.6	1.6	0.93
0.80	0.0055	6.9	4.5	3.0	2.0	1.1
0.90	0.0069	7.7	5.2	3.6	2.4	1.4
1.00	0.0087	9.7	6.1	4.3	2.9	1.7
2.00	0.087	44	36	36	22	15

[From R. Bastian, R. Weberling and F. Palilla, *Anal. Chem.*, **22**, 160 (1950).]
†$\Delta A/A \equiv \Delta C/C$.

were made against differential zero solutions having absorbance values of 0.434, 1.0, 2.0, and 4.0, respectively. In these cases, the absorbance for the solutions read equals the actual absorbance of the zero solution plus the observed absorbance reading. For example, for a solution with a scale reading (absorbance) of 0.434:

$$\frac{\text{Accuracy of differential method at } 0.434}{\text{Maximum accuracy of normal method}} =$$

$$\frac{\text{Absorbance for differential zero solution} + 0.434}{0.434} \quad (4\text{-}29)$$

As can be seen from Table 4-5, ΔA increases steadily with the scale reading, and is about 2.7 times as great at 0.434 as at 0.000. Thus, upon comparing a standard and unknown solution, each having absorbance values of 0.434 at zero on the scale, one would obtain 2.7 times as much accuracy as by reading the same unknown solution against a reagent blank. The concentration error in normal spectrophotometry reaches a minimum at 0.434 absorbance not because the scale can be read best at 0.434, but because up to this point on the scale the absorbance increases more rapidly than ΔA. As one goes beyond 0.434, ΔA increases more rapidly than A.

It is impossible to balance the instrument at 100 scale units indefinitely for progressively more concentrated comparison standards without adverse effects. Noise in the phototube and amplifier circuit places a lower limit on the photocurrent that can be amplified.[13] Increasing the width of the slit aperture invites interference from other absorbing materials and deviations from Beer's law because of the increasing amounts of polychromatic radiation passing through the solution.[13] At higher concentrations the refractive index change may become significant. If a choice is permissible, the analytical wavelength should give major consideration to a wavelength consistent with high instrumental response rather than merely maximum absorbance.

For interesting analyses of the high-absorbance method and a rigorous mathematical treatment of the complete error function, the reader is referred to papers by Bastian,[3, 4] Hiskey,[6, 12] and Reilley and Crawford.[16]

In the trace analysis procedure,[16] the reading scale is set to 100 with the solvent in the usual manner, but the reading is set to zero with a standard whose concentration is somewhat larger (but not infinite) than that of the most concentrated unknown solution that is anticipated. The effective length of the transmittance scale is again increased, this time favoring low absorbance systems. For example, if a sample series falls in the 70–100 percent transmittance range, this range can be made to cover 0–100 scale units by using the standard with 70 percent transmittance to make the zero setting. The error at this end of the scale now becomes finite. The relative error coefficient is

$0.4343(1 - T_0)/(T \log T)$ where T_0 is the actual transmittance of the reference solution used for setting the zero reading. There is a limitation to the trace analysis method which is related to the balancing voltage attainable from the "zero" or "dark current" control. The range can be expanded with the introduction of additional voltage from an auxiliary zero-suppressor circuit. In using this method, one is forced to construct a calibration curve, since the increase in sensitivity was achieved at the expense of a positive deviation from Beer's law.

Both the high and low absorbance methods permit determinations at the 1 percent error level, or less, in concentration intervals where the ordinary method is inapplicable. However, the optical path length of the sample containers must be known with a precision equal to the best precision expected for the determination, or else one cuvette must be used for all absorbance measurements. Directions for calibrating cuvettes are given in the literature.[5,11] To minimize volumetric errors, aliquots are taken by weight, and to minimize errors due to calibration of volumetric ware, the same volumetric flask is used for diluting all standards and unknowns.

These ideas can be carried one step further by using a finite standard solution to define both ends of the reading scale. Setting errors and slidewire nonlinearities are minimized by making the relative error coefficient small by using reference solutions closely spaced around a transmittance of 0.370. The relative error coefficient is given by $0.4343(T_r - T_0)/(T \log T)$. For a component present at a level of $C \pm x$ g/liter, reference solutions for the ends of the reading scale should contain the desired component in the concentration of $C + 2x$ and $C - 2x$ for setting the zero and 100 percent readings, respectively. In addition, three more solutions having intermediate concentrations should be prepared such that the range is divided into four equal concentration intervals. With the solution of lowest concentration in the light beam and the reading scale at 100, the circuit is balanced by using the slit width control or the gain control in the amplifier. Next, the solution of highest concentration is introduced into the light beam and, with the reading scale at zero, the circuit is balanced by using the dark current control. These two operations are repeated successively until balance is maintained both with the least concentrated solution in the light beam and 100 percent reading and with the most concentrated solution in the beam and zero reading. The readings of the remaining standards are then obtained and the calibration curve constructed. This is the "maximum precision" method of differential spectrophotometry. One important feature of this method is that it can provide the kind of advantage (decrease in numerator of the error coefficient) gained in the high absorbance method and low absorbance methods, while still using the optimum denominator value, namely 36.8 percent transmittance. Both the high and low absorbance methods must accept a penalty in the denominator to obtain a profit in the numerator. For trace analysis the penalty is unavoidable, but this is not true of the high absorbance method.

Photometric Titrations[8,9]

The change in absorbance of a solution may be used to follow the change in concentration of a light-absorbing constituent during a titration. The absorbance is proportional to the concentration of absorbing constituent linearly, rather than logarithmically as in potentiometric methods. This means that in a titration in which the titrant, the reactant, or a reaction product absorbs, the plot of absorbance vs titrant will consist, if the reaction be complete, of two straight lines intersecting at the end point—similar to amperometric and conductometric titrations. For reactions that are appreciably incomplete, extrapolation of the two linear segments of the titration curve establishes the intersection and end-point volume.

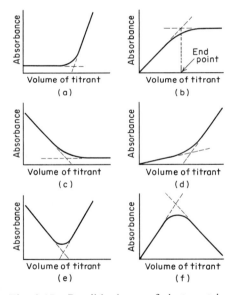

Possible shapes of photometric titration curves are shown in Fig. 4-15. Curve (a), for example, is typical of the titration where the titrant alone absorbs, as in the titration of arsenic (III) with bromate-bromide, where the absorbance readings are taken at the wavelength where the bromine absorbs. Curve (b) is characteristic of systems where the product of the reaction absorbs, as in the titration of copper(II) with EDTA. When the analyte is converted to a nonabsorbing product—e.g., titration of p-toluidine in butanol with perchloric acid at 290 mμ—curve (c) results. When a colored analyte is converted to a colorless product by a colored titrant —e.g., bromination of a red dyestuff —curves similar to (e) are obtained. Curves (d) and (f) might represent

Fig. 4-15. Possible shapes of photometric titration curves.

the successive addition of ligands to form two successive complexes of different absorptivity.

Photometric titrations have several distinct advantages over a direct photometric determination. The presence of other absorbing species at the analytical wavelength, as in curve (a) of Fig. 4-15, does not necessarily cause interference, since only the change in absorbance is significant. However, the absorbance of nontitratable components (color or turbidity) must not be intense because, if so, the absorbance readings will be limited to the undesirable upper end of the scale unless the slit width or amplifier gain can be increased. Only a single absorber needs to be present from among the reactant, the titrant, or the reaction products. This extends photometric methods to a large number of nonabsorbing constituents. Precision of 0.5 percent or better is attainable because a number of pieces of information are pooled in constructing the segments of the titration curve.

The analytical wavelength is selected on the basis of two considerations: (1) avoidance of interference by other absorbing substances and (2) need for a molar absorptivity which will cause the change in absorbance during the titration to fall within a convenient range. Often the chosen wavelength lies well apart from an absorption maximum.

Volume change is seldom negligible, and straight lines are obtained only if correction is made. This is done simply by multiplying the measured absorbance by the factor $(V + v)/V$ where V is the volume initially and v is the volume of titrant added up to any point. If the correction is not made, the lines are curved down towards the volume axis and erroneous intersections are obtained. Use of a micro-syringe and relatively concentrated titrant is desirable. Stray-light error also affects the linearity of the titration curve. The upper limit of concentration permissible is found by delivering from the buret into a beaker of transparent liquid measured portions of a colored substance known to obey Beer's law. After correcting for dilution, the plot of absorbance vs concentration will be a straight line up to the absorbance value, where the stray light error becomes detectable.

Areas of particular applicability are for solutions so dilute that the indicator blank is excessive by other methods, or when the color change is not sharp due perhaps to titration reactions which are incomplete in the vicinity of the equivalence point, or when extraneous colored materials are present in the sample. Ordinarily there is no difficulty in working in solutions of either high or low ionic strength or in nonaqueous solvents. One of the attractive features of photometric titrations is the ease with which the sensitivity of measurements can be changed, simply by changing the wavelength or the length of the light path. When self-indicating systems are lacking, an indicator can be deliberately added, but in relatively large amount to provide a sufficient linear segment on the titration curve beyond the equivalence point.

All one needs to carry out photometric titrations in the visible region is a light source, a series of narrow-band pass filters, a titration vessel (which can be an ordinary beaker), a receptor, and a buret or other titrant-delivery unit. The entire assembly is housed in a light-tight compartment. Photometers or spectrophotometers with provision for inclusion of a suitable titration vessel from 5- to 100-ml capacity are suitable. It is imperative that the titration vessel remain stationary throughout the titration. By the use of Vycor beakers and an appropriate spectrophotometer, titrations may be conducted in the ultraviolet region. Provision for magnetic stirring from underneath or some type of overhead stirrer is desirable; otherwise, manual agitation after the addition of

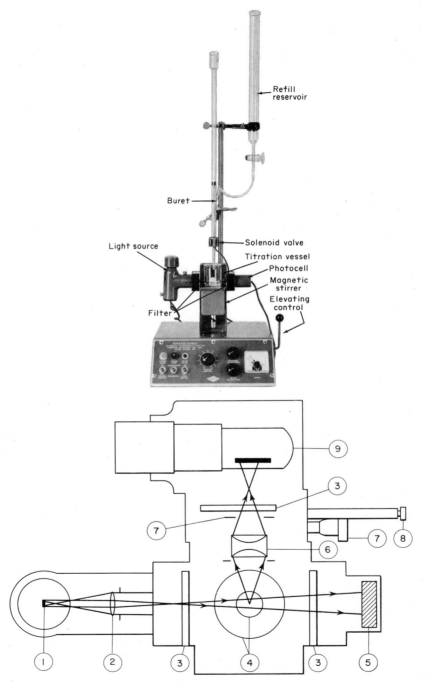

Fig. 4-16. *Above:* photometric titrator, without automatic titrator and recorder. (Courtesy of American Instrument Co.) *Below:* optical diagram.

each increment of titrant is necessary. Automatic titrators are commercially available with or without recorders (American Instrument Co., E. H. Sargent & Co.), as shown in Fig. 4-16. Changes in the absorbance of the solution are used to operate a magnetic valve which controls the delivery of titrant.

Reflection Measurements

Attachments for making reflectance measurements are available for many standard spectrophotometers. The narrow band of dispersed light from a monochromator passing through the slit enters the reflectance attachment (see Fig. 4-17) and is directed onto the opaque, colored sample. The sample

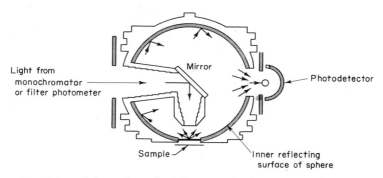

Fig. 4-17. Schematic optical diagram of reflectance attachment.

absorbs some of the light, the rest is reflected. An integrating sphere directs the reflected light through the phototube aperture where it is measured by a photo-multiplier tube and is registered on the meter. The reflectance curve (Fig. 4-18) is the result of a series of such measurements made at different wavelengths. It is the only true picture of a color when dealing with paints, textiles, plastics, inks, dyes, glass, tile, and wide variety of other products. If desired, these readings can be converted to world standard C.I.E. trichromatic values.

In the simplest case, that of white light or daylight in which the monochromatic colors of all wavelengths are present in nearly equal intensities, the spectral reflectance curve would approximate a horizontal line with a position on the vertical axis (percent reflectance) depending upon the relative brightness of the sample (relative to the light reflected by pure magne-

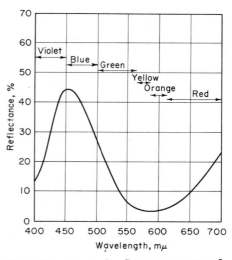

Fig. 4-18. Spectral reflectances curve of a typical blue color.

sium oxide which is chosen as the standard of comparison). A horizontal line at any point between 100 percent and zero percent reflectance would indicate the equal absorption of all wavelengths of radiation in the visible spectrum to produce a resulting gray appearance to the eye.

If the intensities of certain wavelengths of radiation are increased or decreased with respect to the others, this pattern of reflected energy produces upon the eye the sensation of color, as shown by the spectral reflectance curve of a typical blue color in Fig. 4-18.

LABORATORY WORK

Operation of Photometers

For an instrument which produces a response R, directly proportional to the radiant power P falling on the detector, as do most photometers, the response is given by

$$R = k_\lambda k_a P + k'$$

where k_λ is a proportionality constant which depends on the slit width and response of the detector, k_a is a second constant which reflects the gain in the amplifier control (or sensitivity setting), and k' is the term which reflects the current that flows in the receiver and amplifier circuit when the receiver is dark. In the ordinary method of operation, with the receiver dark to represent infinite concentration of sample, a dark current or zero suppressor control is adjusted to balance the circuit with the reading scale at zero. For instruments with barrier-layer cells, this involves merely the mechanical alignment of the galvanometer index at the zero mark for direct-reading instruments or at midscale for null-balance photometers. Next, with the solvent or a reference solution in the light beam and the reading scale set at 100 percent transmittance (zero absorbance) to represent zero concentration, the slit width control or amplifier control, or both, are adjusted to balance the circuit once again. Finally, the series of standards are inserted successively into the light beam and the scale reading is noted. From these readings a calibration curve can be constructed.

Selected Colorimetric Methods

EXPERIMENT 4-1   DETERMINATION OF IRON WITH 1,10-PHENAN-THROLINE

Standard iron solution. Dissolve 0.7022 g of reagent grade ferrous ammonium sulfate in 100 ml of distilled water, add 3 ml of 18 M H_2SO_4, and dilute to 1 liter. One milliliter contains 0.100 mg of iron(II).

For a standard iron(III) solution, dissolve 0.864 g of ferric ammonium sulfate in water, add 3 ml of H_2SO_4, and dilute to 1 liter. Alternatively, the ferrous ammonium sulfate solution can be carefully oxidized with $KMnO_4$ added dropwise until a slight pink coloration remains after stirring well, before diluting to 1 liter. One milliliter contains 0.100 mg of iron.

1,10-Phenanthroline. Dissolve 0.25 g of the monohydrate in 100 ml of water, warming if necessary.

Hydroxylamine hydrochloride, 10 percent (w/v). Dissolve 10 g in 100 ml of water.

Sodium acetate, 2 M. Dissolve 17 g of sodium acetate in 100 ml of water.

PROCEDURE

Take an aliquot portion of the unknown solution containing 0.1 to 0.5 mg of iron and transfer it to a 100-ml volumetric flask. Determine by the use of a similar aliquot portion containing a few drops of bromphenol blue, the volume of sodium acetate solution required to bring the pH to 3.5 ± 1.0 (or use a pH meter). Add the same volume of acetate solution to the original aliquot and then 5 ml each of the hydroxylamine hydrochloride and 1,10-phenanthroline solutions. Dilute to the mark, mix well, and measure the absorbance after 10 min in the region 460–520 mμ.

Both ferrous and ferric iron can be determined simultaneously. Only the ferrous complex absorbs at 515 mμ, and both complexes have identical absorption at 396 mμ, the amount being additive. The solution should be buffered at pH 3.9.

EXPERIMENT 4-2 DETERMINATION OF MANGANESE AS PERMANGANATE

Standard manganese solution. Reduce 200 ml of 0.0100 M KMnO$_4$ solution with a little sodium sulfite after the addition of 1 ml of 18 M H$_2$SO$_4$. Remove the SO$_2$ by boiling and dilute to 1 liter. One mililiter contains 0.110 mg of Mn.

PROCEDURE

Weigh out accurately a suitable quantity of a steel sample (0.1–0.2 g for average steels) into a conical flask, dissolve it in about 40 ml of water and 10 ml of 15 M HNO$_3$, and boil for 2–3 min after any violent bubbling subsides to expel oxides of nitrogen. Cool the solution, and add slowly about 1 g of ammonium peroxydisulfate [(NH$_4$)$_2$S$_2$O$_8$]. Boil gently for 10 min to oxidize carbon compounds and to destroy the excess peroxydisulfate. Dilute to about 100 ml with water, add 10 ml of 85% H$_3$PO$_4$, and then add 0.5 g of potassium periodate. Boil gently for 3 min and keep hot for 10 min. Cool to room temperature and transfer to a 250-ml volumetric flask; dilute to the mark with distilled water. Measure the absorbance at either 525 or 545 mμ (Fig. 4-19).

When ready for measurement, the solution should not contain more than 2 mg of Mn per 100 ml. Ferric ammonium sulfate solution can be added to aqueous standard

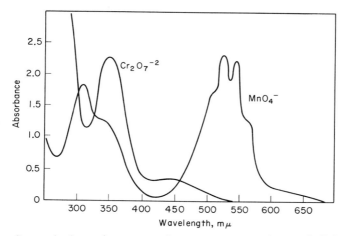

Fig. 4-19. Spectral absorption curves for permanganate ion and dichromate ion (each 0.001 M) in 1 M sulfuric acid.

solutions of manganese to match the iron content in steel samples. The interference of chromium(VI) may be removed by decolorizing one portion by the dropwise addition of potassium nitrite solution until the permanganate color just disappears. The decolorized solution is then used as the reference solution.

EXPERIMENT 4-3   DETERMINATION OF TITANIUM AS ITS PEROXIDE

Standard titanium solution. Fuse 0.2500 g of TiO_2 with 3–4 g of potassium pyrosulfate in a platinum or a porcelain crucible. Dissolve the melt in 50 ml of hot 4 N H_2SO_4 and dilute to 250 ml with the same acid. One milliliter contains 1.00 mg of TiO_2.

PROCEDURE

Take an aliquot of the standard or unknown solution such that the final concentration is 1–8 mg of TiO_2 in 100 ml. Add sufficient H_2SO_4 to adjust the final acidity to 1.5–3.5 N. Add 10 ml of 3 percent hydrogen peroxide solution and dilute the solution to 100 ml in a volumetric flask. Measure the absorbance at 400–420 mμ (see Fig. 4-20).

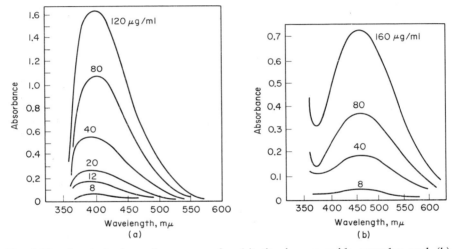

Fig. 4-20. Spectral absorption curves for (a) titanium-peroxide complex and (b) vanadium-peroxide complex, each in 1 M perchloric acid solution.

EXPERIMENT 4-4   COMPARISON OF DICHROMATE SOLUTIONS

Standard chromium(VI) solution. Dissolve 2.823 g of $K_2Cr_2O_7$ in water and dilute to 1 liter. One milliliter contains 1.00 mg of Cr.

PROCEDURE

Take an aliquot of the standard or unknown solution such that the final concentration of chromium is 2–10 mg per 100 ml. Add 1.5 ml of 18 M H_2SO_4 and dilute to 100 ml in a volumetric flask. Measure the absorbance at 440 mμ.

EXPERIMENT 4-5   DETERMINATION OF COBALT WITH NITROSO-R-SALT

Standard cobalt solution. Dissolve 0.404 g of $CoCl_2 \cdot 6H_2O$ in water and dilute to 1 liter. One milliliter contains 0.100 mg of Co.

Nitroso-R-salt, 1 percent (w/v). Dissolve 1 g of reagent in 100 ml of water.

PROCEDURE

Take an aliquot that contains 0.1–0.4 mg of cobalt. Evaporate almost to dryness, add 1 ml of 15 M HNO$_3$, and continue the evaporation just to dryness. Dissolve the residue in 20 ml of water containing 1 ml each of 6 M HCl and 1 M HNO$_3$. Boil for a few minutes. Cool to room temperature, add 2 ml of 1 percent nitroso-R-salt solution, and 2 g of hydrated sodium acetate. The pH of the solution should be close to 5.5 (check with a pH meter or test with bromcresol green indicator on a drop of the solution). Boil for 1 min, add 1 ml of 12 M HCl, and boil again for 1 min. Cool, and dilute to 100 ml in a volumetric flask. Measure the absorbance at 500 mμ (see Fig. 4-11).

EXPERIMENT 4-6   SCANNING A SPECTRAL ABSORPTION CURVE

Each student will be assigned an organic compound or an inorganic colorimetric system. The range of wavelengths to be scanned and the particular spectrophotometer to be used will be designated. No general rule can be stated concerning the strength of solution to be prepared if definite instructions are unavailable. Usually a 0.01–0.001 M solution is sufficiently concentrated for the lowest absorption range, and other concentrations are prepared by dilution. The absorbance should lie between 0.1 and 0.7. Suitable solvents are suggested in Fig. 4-5.

PROCEDURE

Scan the wavelength range at intervals of 10 mμ, then rescan regions at smaller intervals where structural features are evident if the bandwidth of the particular instrument can be made sufficiently narrow. Consult the dispersion curve supplied with prism monochromators to ascertain the proper slit width at each nominal wavelength. It is desirable to measure the assigned system at several levels of concentration — ratios of concentrations of 1, 2, and 4 are suitable.

Plot the results three ways: (1) absorbance vs wavelength in millimicrons, (2) logarithm of molar absorptivity (or log absorbance) vs wavelength, and (3) absorbance vs frequency in cm^{-1}. Verify the ratio of concentrations used.

EXPERIMENT 4-7   PREPARATION OF A CALIBRATION CURVE

Each student will be assigned a colorimetric system. Measure the absorbances of 4–5 concentrations of the compound at the analytical wavelength. Plot absorbance vs concentration. Measure the absorbance of the unknown solution and obtain its concentration from the calibration curve. A blank solution should be prepared and used for the 100 percent transmittance setting.

Compute the molar absorptivity from each measured absorbance value. From the average value of molar absorptivity, compute the standard deviation at the 95 percent confidence level.

EXPERIMENT 4-8   SELECTION OF FILTER FOR USE WITH A FILTER PHOTOMETER

Prepare a set of 4–5 standard solutions of the assigned colorimetric system. The concentration range should span at least a 10-fold interval.

Insert the selected filter into the photometer. Measure the absorbance of each standard solution. Repeat the sequence with each filter in turn until all the filters available have been used.

On a single graph, plot the absorbance readings against the corresponding concentration of each solution. The optimum filter is ascertained from the absorbance-concentration curve which possesses the steepest slope and passes also through the origin.

E X P E R I M E N T   4 - 9   RELATIVE   CONCENTRATION   ERROR   FROM   A
                                 RINGBOM PLOT

Each student will be assigned a colorimetric system. Prepare a set of ten standards whose absorbance readings lie between 0.050 and 1.00; that is, a series of concentrations which extend from well below to well above the usual recommended range of concentrations.

Measure the transmittance of each solution at the specified wavelength. Prepare a graph of the transmittance as ordinate vs the logarithm of the concentration as abscissa. If the resulting curve does not possess a decided curvature at each extremity, prepare additional standard solutions as needed.

Draw a series of 3–5 tangents to the curve, including one at the inflection point of the curve. Compute the slope of each tangent. From Eq. 4-23, calculate the relative concentration error for twice the estimated uncertainty in reading the transmittance scale on the particular instrument employed.

E X P E R I M E N T   4 - 1 0   DETERMINATION   OF   THE   DISSOCIATION   CON-
                                   STANT OF INDICATORS

Indicator solution, 0.04 *percent* (w/v). Dissolve 0.1 g of the indicator (sulfonphthalein dyes) in water, adding 1–3 ml of 0.1 M NaOH, if necessary (see Table 22-7). Dilute to 250 ml.

Buffer solutions. Any standard buffer series, such as the Clark and Lubs buffers (Table 22-6), may be used. It is desirable to maintain the ionic strength constant. In the following directions, 0.1 M sodium acetate solution is employed. Dissolve 2.30 g of sodium acetate in water and dilute to 250 ml.

PROCEDURE

Transfer exactly 10.0 ml of 0.1 M sodium acetate solution to a 100-ml volumetric flask. Add exactly 5.00 ml of 0.04 percent bromcresol green solution and dilute to the mark with distilled water. Mix thoroughly. Determine the absorption spectrum of the sodium acetate solution of bromcresol green (the "alkaline" color).

Pour the contents of the cuvette and the volumetric flask into a 250-ml beaker. Add precisely 2.00 ml of an acetic acid solution (0.25 M in acetic acid and 0.1 M in KCl). Mix well with a stirring rod, and measure the pH with a pH meter. Measure the absorbance at the wavelength of maximum absorbance of the "alkaline" form of the indicator. Repeat this procedure for additional 2.00-ml increments of acetic acid solution. Determine the absorption spectrum for the buffer solution which is equimolar in acetate and acetic acid. After five such measurements have been made, add 1.0 ml of 3 M HCl and again determine the entire spectrum of the "acid" form of the indicator.

Correct all absorbance readings for the effect of dilution by multiplying each observed value by the factor $(100 + V)/100$, where V is the volume of acetic acid (and HCl) added. Plot the three absorption spectra on a single sheet of graph paper.

Another curve is plotted from the absorbance readings at the wavelength of maximum absorbance vs the pH value for each buffer solution. Draw a smooth line through the points. The "acid" and "alkaline" solutions are assumed to represent the limiting values of absorbance. Determine the value of pK_a in these ways: (1) from the inflection point of the absorbance-pH curve, and (2) by insertion of appropriate absorption readings into Eq. 22-4 and averaging the values obtained. Alternatively, the pH values may be calculated from the dissociation quotient of acetic acid in the particular electrolyte solution.

Other indicators in the sulfonphthalein series may be studied in the Clark and Lubs buffer solutions. These include bromphenol blue, bromcresol purple, bromthymol blue, phenol red, and cresol red. Select five buffer solutions whose values lie within the range $pK_{ind} \pm 1$. Also prepare the two "extreme" solutions.

A study of ionic strength effects merely involves assigning a fixed ionic strength to each of several individuals working with the same indicator. See R. W. Ramette, *J. Chem. Education*, **40**, 252 (1963).

EXPERIMENT 4-11   SIMULTANEOUS DETERMINATION OF BINARY MIXTURES

Each student will be assigned a pair of solutes and the type of sample to be analyzed. Suggested systems include the following:

1. Manganese, as permanganate, 0.0004–0.00008 M, plus chromium as dichromate, 0.0004–0.0017 M, in 0.5 M H_2SO_4. Analytical wavelengths are 440 and 525 mμ. See Fig. 4–17.

2. Titanium, 0.8–8.0 mg of TiO_2 per 100 ml, plus vanadium, 1.0–20 mg as V per 100 ml, as their peroxide complexes. Analytical wavelengths are 400 and 460 mμ. See Fig. 4–18.

3. Iron(II) and iron(III) as their 1,10-phenanthroline complexes at pH 3.9. Analytical wavelengths are 396 and 515 mμ.

PROCEDURE

Measure the absorbance of 3–5 standard solutions of each solute, whose concentrations span the interval suggested, at both analytical wavelengths. Compute the molar absorptivities from each individual measurement and determine the average value of the molar absorptivity and its associated deviation at the 95 percent confidence level.

Test the assumption that each solute contributes additively to the total absorbance at each analytical wavelength. Combine known aliquots of the individual solutions prepared for the preceding step, and measure the absorbance at each analytical wavelength. Calculate the amount of each solute present by means of Eqs. 4-27 and 4-28.

Determine the concentration of each solute in an unknown sample and report the results.

EXPERIMENT 4-12   HIGH-ABSORBANCE DIFFERENTIAL SPECTROPHOTOMETRY

Each student will be assigned a single solute or colorimetric system. The range of concentrations to be studied and the particular spectrophotometer to be used will be designated.

Prepare a series of solutions whose absorbance readings extend from 0.2 to 2.0 (or approximately three times the maximum strength usually recommended) and separated from each other by about 0.2 absorbance unit.

Proceed in the ordinary way to set the instrument scale reading to zero transmittance when the photocell is darkened, and to 100 scale divisions (zero absorbance) with pure solvent in the sample container. Measure the absorbance and transmittance of each solution. Prepare a graph of absorbance vs concentration.

Remove the solvent from its cuvette and substitute in it some of the solution which had the 0.2-absorbance value. Measure the transmittance to ascertain the ratio T_2/T_1. If not unity, this preliminary value can be used to correct subsequent readings for difference in path length of the two cuvettes: $-\log (T_2/T_1) = ab_1C[\beta - 1]$, where $\beta = b_2/b_1$. Place the comparison standard (i.e., solution with 0.2-absorbance value originally) in the light beam, with the reading scale set at 100 scale units, and balance the instrument by increasing the slit opening or by increasing the gain control. Measure the absorbance for the more concentrated solutions. Plot the results on the same graph.

Repeat the procedure with progressively more concentrated solutions being used as the comparison standard for setting the reading scale at 100 until it becomes impossible to establish the balance of the instrument.

For each series of readings, calculate the relative concentration error (assuming $\Delta T = 0.004$). Plot the relative concentration error vs transmittance for each series as a family of curves on a single graph (see Fig. 4-14).

From the series of graphs of absorbance vs concentration, determine when the average value $(S \times C)/\Delta A$ is a maximum, where S is the slope, C is the concentration at a given point, and ΔA is the minimum difference in absorbance that can be detected at that point (corresponding to $\Delta T = 0.004$). Report your calculations in tabular form. Suggested headings are (see also Table 4-5):

Concentration, M

To Set Scale Zero	To Obtain Reading	Slit Aperture	Absorbance Reading	Slope	$S \times C$ for $A = 0$	$(S \times C)/\Delta A$

EXPERIMENT 4-13   LOW-ABSORBANCE DIFFERENTIAL SPECTROPHO-TOMETRY

Each student will be assigned a specific system and instrument.

Prepare a series of solutions whose transmittance values range from 0.368 to 0.950 and are separated from each other by about 0.100 transmittance.

Proceed in the ordinary way to set the instrument scale reading to zero transmittance when the photocell is darkened, and to 100 scale units with pure solvent in the sample container. Measure the absorbance and transmittance of each solution. Prepare a graph of absorbance vs concentration; also of transmittance vs concentration.

Insert the most concentrated solution into the light beam and, with the reading scale set at zero transmittance, adjust the dark current or zero control. Then adjust the 100 setting with the solvent in the light beam. Recheck the zero setting and readjust if necessary. It may be necessary to repeat each setting, in sequence, several times until neither the zero nor the 100 setting change when going from one to the other. Measure the transmittance of the other solutions. Plot the results on the same graph of transmittance vs concentration. Calculate the relative concentration error for each measurement. Plot these results as relative concentration error vs transmittance. Assume $\Delta T = 0.004$.

If sufficient zero-suppression is available, repeat the cycle of balancing operations with a less concentrated reference solution.

EXPERIMENT 4-14   MAXIMUM PRECISION SPECTROPHOTOMETRY

Each student will be assigned a specific system and instrument.

Prepare a set of five solutions whose transmittance readings are approximately 0.200, 0.300, 0.350, 0.400, and 0.500. Measure the transmittance in the ordinary manner, using pure solvent for the setting at 100 percent transmittance.

Insert the least concentrated standard (ca. 50% T) and set the reading scale to 100; the most concentrated standard (ca. 20% T) is used to set the reading scale to zero transmittance. Readjust the 100 reading, if necessary. Recheck the zero reading and readjust if necessary. It may be necessary to repeat the cycle a few times until neither the zero nor the 100 setting change when going from one to the other. Measure the transmittance of the other solutions. Plot the results as transmittance vs concentration.

Calculate the relative concentration error for each reading. Plot these results as relative concentration error vs transmittance. Assume $\Delta T = 0.004$.

If sufficient zero-suppression and gain control are available, the balancing operation can be repeated with the solutions of 30 percent and 40 percent transmittance serving as comparison standards.

EXPERIMENT 4-15   PHOTOMETRIC TITRATIONS

Operating technique. Set the spectrophotometer to the analytical wavelength or insert the proper filter into the photometer. Adjust the dark current to zero. Place the sample to be titrated into the light beam and set the instrument to read zero absorbance (if the reactant is colorless) or to some other starting value (if the reactant is colored) that lies within the range of linearity of the instrument. If the initial absorbance reading is too large, readjust the concentration of reactant.

Place the buret so that the tip extends into the solution. Turn on the stirrer and adjust the stirring rate so that the vortex does not obstruct the light path. Commence the titration by adding an increment from the buret, waiting until the absorbance reading is constant, and recording that value. More increments are then added and the absorbance noted. For exploratory work, 0.2- to 0.5-ml increments are desirable when using a 10-ml buret. Once the shape of the titration curve is known, it is usually necessary to take only three to four points on each side of the end point.

A plot of absorbance vs milliliters of titrant is then made and the best straight lines are drawn between points taken well before and after the equivalence point. The intersection of the linear segments is taken as the end point. Correct all absorbance readings for the change in volume at each point on the titration curve.

Suggested Systems

Acid-base titrations. Mixture of acetic acid with *p*-nitrophenol, each 10^{-3} *M*, titrated with 0.1 *M* NaOH at 400–420 mμ.

A solution of any strong acid, 10^{-3} to 10^{-4} *M*, titrated with 0.01 *M* NaOH in the presence of thymol blue (pK$_a$ = 9.0) at 615 mμ.

Urea, 0.05 *M*, in glacial acetic acid titrated with 0.1 *M* HClO$_4$, using malachite green (10 ml of 0.01 percent (w/v) per 20 ml of solution volume) at 622 mμ.

Oxidation-reduction titrations. A solution of arsenic(III), 10^{-3} *M*, with ceric sulfate, 0.01 *M*, at 320 mμ, with a trace (10^{-5} *M*) of osmium tetroxide as catalyst.

Complexometric titrations. Copper(II), 0.04 *M*, with 0.1 *M* EDTA at *p*H 4.0 and a wavelength of 745 mμ or 585 mμ.

Calcium plus copper(II), each 0.02–0.06 *M*, with 0.1 *M* EDTA in a 1 *M* ammonia-ammonium chloride buffer adjusted to *p*H 9.0 ± 0.2 and at a wavelength of 745 mμ.

EDTA, 0.002 *M*, titrated with 0.02 *M* zinc solution in an approximately 1 *M* ammonia-ammonium chloride buffer adjusted to *p*H 9 and with 0.002 g of Superchrome Black TS indicator present. Wavelength is 550 mμ.

Iron(III), 0.05 *M*, titrated with 0.1 *M* EDTA in an acetic acid solution (1.0 *M*) adjusted to *p*H 1.7–2.3 with HCl. Salicylic acid (4 ml of a 1 percent solution is added per 100 ml total volume) serves as indicator; the analytical wavelength of the iron-salicylic acid complex is at 525 mμ.

Problems

1. Convert each of the following wavelengths into their corresponding frequency and wave number: 250 mμ, 700 mμ, 400 mμ. Calculate the energy associated with each of these wavelengths in terms of kcal mole^{-1} of photons and in terms of electron volts per mole of photons.

2. A Duboscq colorimeter has a 50.0-mm scale for measuring the depth of each solution. The colors for a known and an unknown solution macthed when the known solution was set at 40.0 mm and that for the unknown at 33.0 mm. Calculate how much iron must be in 50 ml of unknown solution if the known solution contained 2.00 mg of iron per 100 ml of solution.

3. The molar absorptivity of a particular solute is 2.1×10^4. Calculate the transmittance through a cuvette with a 5.00-cm light path for a 2.00×10^{-5} M solution.

4. With a certain photoelectric photometer using a 510-mμ filter and 2-cm cells, the reading on a linear scale for P_0 was 85.4. With a 1.00×10^{-4} M solution of a colored substance, the value of P was 20.3. Calculate the molar absorptivity of the colored substance. *Ans.* $\epsilon = 3120$.

5. A substance is known to have a molar absorptivity of 14,000 at its wavelength of maximum absorption. With 1-cm cells, calculate what molarity of this substance could be measured in a spectrophotometer if the absorbance reading is to be 0.850. *Ans.* 6.07×10^{-5} M/liter.

6. From the data contained in Fig. 4-10, evaluate the relative concentration error by means of a Ringbom-Ayres plot for each of the filters employed.

7. When placed in two nominally identical cuvettes, a solution of potassium permanganate, 1.0×10^{-4} M, gave these absorbance readings: $A_r = 0.220$ $A_s = 0.222$. Calculate the correction factor for all samples measured in the second cuvette. *Ans.* $\beta = b_r/b_s = 0.991$.

8. Consider a solution whose absorbance increases from 0.4 to 0.8 over a wavelength interval of 1 mμ. The true mean absorbance is 0.6, but what will the measured value be? When this solution is diluted four-fold, the measured value becomes 0.149. What is the discrepancy between the two measured values considered in terms of the absorption of the solute? *Ans.* (a) 0.585; (b) nearly 2 percent.

9. The simultaneous determination of titanium and vanadium, each as their peroxide complex, can be done in steel. When 1.000-g samples of steel were dissolved, colors developed, and diluted to 50 ml exactly, the presence of 1.00 mg of Ti gave an absorbance of 0.269 at 400 mμ and 0.134 at 460 mμ. Under similar conditions, 1.00 mg of V gave an absorbance of 0.057 at 400 mμ and 0.091 at 460 mμ (see Fig. 4-18). For each of the following samples, 1.000 g in weight and ultimately diluted to 50 ml, calculate the percent titanium and vanadium from these absorbance readings:

SAMPLE	A_{400}	A_{460}	SAMPLE	A_{400}	A_{460}
1	0.172	0.116	5	0.902	0.570
2	0.366	0.430	6	0.600	0.660
3	0.370	0.298	7	0.393	0.215
4	0.640	0.436	8	0.206	0.130
4 (duplicate)	0.649	0.440	9	0.323	0.177

Ans. Sample 1, 0.054% Ti and 0.050% V; sample 6, 0.101% Ti and 0.581% V.

10. Determine the increase in precision that is achieved when a solution that contains 42.4054 g of 0.01667 M potassium dichromate solution per liter is read against a solution containing 34.1830 g per liter. A weight buret is employed. The former reads 0.438 absorbance unit when the latter is used to set the absorbance scale to zero. The absorbance of the comparison standard, against pure solvent, is 1.82. Assume the calibration curve is linear. *Ans.* An increase of 5.2-fold.

11. Estimate the minimum concentration of a chromophore that can be measured photometrically in a 10-cm light path under ideal conditions.

12. Mesityl oxide exists in two isomeric forms: $CH_3—C(CH_3)=CH—CO—CH_3$ and $CH_2=C(CH_3)—CH_2—CO—CH_3$. One exhibits an absorption maximum at 235 mμ with a molar absorptivity of 12,000; the other shows no high-intensity absorption beyond 220 mμ. Identify the isomers. *Ans.* Structure I contains the conjugated arrangement of unsaturated groups.

13. Pyrethrolone contains a five-membered carbon ring, three ethylenic bonds, and one keto group; $\lambda_{max} = 227$ mμ and $\epsilon_{max} = 28,000$. Upon catalytic hydrogenation of the ethylenic groups, $\lambda_{max} = 230$ mμ and $\epsilon_{max} = 12,000$. Write the structural formula for pyrethrolone.

Ans.

 $CH_2CH=CH—CH=CH_2$ is pyrethrolone (OH group could not be placed from the information supplied).

14. Assign the structures shown to the respective isomer on the basis of this information: the α-isomer shows a peak at 228 mμ ($\epsilon = 14,000$) while the β-isomer has a band at 296 mμ ($\epsilon = 11,000$). *Ans.* Structure II is the α-isomer.

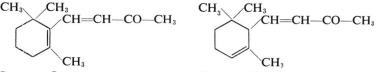

Structure I   Structure II

15. Determine the acid dissociation constant for each indicator from the absorbance, at the wavelength of maximum absorbance, measured as a function of pH. Ionic strength was 0.05.

BROMPHENOL BLUE $\lambda_{max} = 592$mμ		METHYL RED $\lambda_{max} = 530$ mμ		BROMCRESOL PURPLE $\lambda_{max} = 591$ mμ	
ABSORBANCE	pH	ABSORBANCE	pH	ABSORBANCE	pH
0.00	2.00	2.00	3.20	0.00	4.00
0.18	3.00	1.78	4.00	0.24	5.40
0.58	3.60	1.40	4.60	0.66	6.00
0.98	4.00	0.92	5.00	0.87	6.20
1.43	4.40	0.48	5.40	1.13	6.40
1.75	5.00	0.16	6.00	1.37	6.60
2.10	7.00	0.00	7.00	1.72	7.00
				2.00	8.00

16. From the data contained in Fig. 4-19, estimate the molar absorptivity for permanganate ion and for dichromate ion at each of the prominent absorption maxima. Assume a cell path of 1.00 cm.

17. From infrared spectral information, it is known that a compound whose empirical formula is $C_9H_{10}O$ possesses a benzene ring, a carbonyl group, a methylene group, and a methyl group. The placement of the carbonyl group is uncertain; however, the ultraviolet absorption spectrum shows these bands: (with log ϵ_{max} values): 245 mμ(4.1); 280 mμ(3.1); and 320 mμ(1.9). Write the structure of the compound. *Ans.* A high-intensity three-conjugated system is indicated which would require the carbonyl to be adjacent to the ring.

18. A series of chromium(III) nitrate solutions were prepared and the transmittance (and absorbance) of each solution was measured according to the ordinary method with 0% T set with the phototube darkened and 100% T set with the pure solvent. These results were obtained at 550 mμ:

CONCENTRATION, M	TRANSMITTANCE	CONCENTRATION, M	TRANSMITTANCE
Blank	1.000	0.0600	0.199
0.0100	0.760	0.0700	0.147
0.0200	0.570	0.0800	0.112
0.0300	0.438	0.0900	0.091
0.0400	0.322	0.100	0.066
0.0500	0.258	0.110	0.055

(a) Calculate the relative concentration error for each measurement, assuming $\Delta T = 0.004$. (b) Plot the results as relative concentration error vs transmittance. *Ans.* $\Delta C/C = -2.5$ percent for 0.11 M solution.

19. From the series of solutions used in Problem 18, the 0.0500 M solution was used to set the 100% T reading. These results were obtained:

CONCENTRATION, M	TRANSMITTANCE	CONCENTRATION, M	TRANSMITTANCE
0.0500	1.000	0.110	0:230
0.0600	0.775	0.120	0.162
0.0700	0.584	0.130	0.120
0.0800	0.453	0.140	0.097
0.0900	0.380	0.150	0.074
0.1000	0.295		

(a) Calculate the relative concentration error for each measurement, assuming $\Delta T = 0.004$. (b) Plot the results as relative concentration error vs transmittance. *Ans.* $\Delta C/C = -0.45$ percent for 0.0900 M solution.

20. In using the low absorbance method a 0.100 M solution of chromium(III) nitrate was used as the standard with which the scale was set at 0% T by means of the zero-suppressor (dark-current) control. Pure solvent was used for setting the 100% T point. These results were obtained:

CONCENTRATION, M	TRANSMITTANCE	CONCENTRATION, M	TRANSMITTANCE
Blank	1.000	0.0500	0.197
0.0100	0.745	0.0600	0.130
0.0200	0.546	0.0700	0.077
0.0300	0.420	0.0800	0.037
0.0400	0.286	0.0900	0.012

(a) Graph the results as absorbance vs concentration. (b) Calculate the relative concentration error for each measurement, assuming $\Delta T = 0.004$. (c) Plot the results as relative concentration error vs transmittance. *Ans.* $\Delta C/C = 1.14$ percent for 0.0200 M solution.

21. With the maximum precision method, a 0.0500 M chromium(III) nitrate solution was used to set the 100% T point, and a 0.100 M solution was used to set the 0% T point. These results were obtained:

CONCENTRATION, M	TRANSMITTANCE	CONCENTRATION, M	TRANSMITTANCE
0.0500	1.000	0.0800	0.247
0.0600	0.695	0.0900	0.128
0.0700	0.437	0.100	0.000

(a) Graph these results as absorbance vs concentration. (b) Calculate the relative concentration error for each measurement, assuming $\Delta T = 0.004$. (c) Plot the results as relative concentration error vs transmittance. *Ans.* $\Delta C/C = 0.212$ percent for 0.0700 M solution.

22. A mixture of sodium acetate and *o*-chloroaniline solution, 10 ml each, were titrated in glacial acetic acid at 312 mμ with a 0.1010 N HClO$_4$ solution. Sodium acetate does not absorb in the ultraviolet portion of the spectrum, but it is a stronger base than *o*-chloroaniline. These results were obtained (corrected for dilution):

VOLUME OF TITRANT, ml	ABSORBANCE	VOLUME OF TITRANT, ml	ABSORBANCE
0.00	0.68	8.25	0.37
1.00	0.68	8.50	0.32
2.00	0.68	8.75	0.26
3.00	0.68	9.00	0.20
4.00	0.67	9.25	0.14
5.00	0.66	9.50	0.09
6.00	0.63	10.50	0.02
7.00	0.56	11.00	0.02
8.00	0.42	11.50	0.02

Plot the results and calculate the concentration of the original aliquots of sodium acetate and of *o*-chloroaniline. *Ans.* 0.068 N in sodium acetate and 0.030 N in *o*-chloroaniline.

23. Mixtures of two amines can be determined if their rates of acetylation are sufficiently different and possess separate absorption bands. The following titration of aniline and 2-naphthylamine was carried out at the wavelength of maximum absorption of 2-naphthylamine, the amine with the slower rate of acetylation. Ascertain the volume of acetic anhydride consumed in reaching each end point (all volumes corrected for dilution).

VOLUME OF TITRANT, ml	ABSORBANCE	VOLUME OF TITRANT, ml	ABSORBANCE
0.150	0.460	1.500	0.233
0.300	0.460	3.000	0.040
0.450	0.460	3.250	0.034
1.300	0.318	3.500	0.034
1.400	0.275	4.000	0.034

24. In the determination of acetone in biological fluids, the following calibration curve between absorbance and concentration was obtained.

ACETONE STANDARDS (mg PER 100 ml)	ABSORBANCE
Reagent blank	0.045
0.5	0.057
1.0	0.069
2.0	0.092
4.0	0.137
6.0	0.182
8.0	0.229

(a) Calculate the molar absorptivity and the specific absorptivity. (b) Estimate the relative concentration error, and the increase in precision that would be obtained for each measurement if the solution containing 8.0 mg/100 ml were used for setting the zero transmittance reading. (c) Samples of blood and urine from a normal subject and from a ketotic patient were analyzed with these results: normal blood, $A = 0.068$; ketotic blood, $A = 0.189$; normal urine, 0.097; ketotic urine, $A = 0.198$ (1/25 dilution). Calculate the acetone concentration in each sample.

25. The absorbance of a series of phosphate solutions, using the phosphovanadomolybdate complex at 420 mμ, are as follows: when referred to a 5.0-mg phosphate solution as reference standard (actual $A = 1.075$):

mg P_2O_5 PER 100 ml	ABSORBANCE
5.0	0.000
5.2	0.064
5.4	0.104
5.6	0.149
5.8	0.194
6.0	0.233
6.2	0.278

(a) Determine the increase in precision for the measurement of the 5.2-mg phosphate solution as compared with the normal method (Beer's law is obeyed). (h) Estimate the relative concentration error for the 5.6-mg phosphate solution when the 6.0-mg phosphate solution is used to set the zero transmittance reading in addition to the 5.0-mg phosphate solution being used for the 100 percent transmittance reading. Assume Beer's law is obeyed when recalculating the expanded transmittances.

26. Develop equations for the spectrophotometric determination of the concentration of three substances present in a solution if the substances have the following specific absorptivity a at the following wavelengths. Express concentration in milligrams per milliliter. Let the cell thickness b be 1 cm.

SUBSTANCE	WAVELENGTH 400 mμ	500 mμ	600 mμ
A	0	0	1.00
B	2.00	0.05	0
C	0.60	1.80	0

27. In a photometric titration of magnesium with 0.00130 M EDTA at 222 mμ, the following procedure was employed. All reagents except the magnesium-con-

taining solution were placed in the titration cell, and the slit width was adjusted to give zero absorbance. The following readings were observed after additions of the standard EDTA:

ABSORBANCE	EDTA ADDED, ml
0.000	0.00
0.014	0.10
0.200	0.40
0.429	0.60
0.657	0.80
0.906	1.00

At this point, the magnesium solution was added and the absorbance fell to zero. The titration was continued with the following results

ABSORBANCE	EDTA ADDED, ml
0.000	1.00
0.060	1.50
0.126	2.00
0.196	2.50
0.251	2.80
0.360	3.00
0.580	3.20
0.803	3.40
1.000	3.60
1.220	3.80

Plot the results, explain the curves obtained, and calculate the number of micrograms of magnesium present, assuming that the reagent has exactly the concentration stated above.

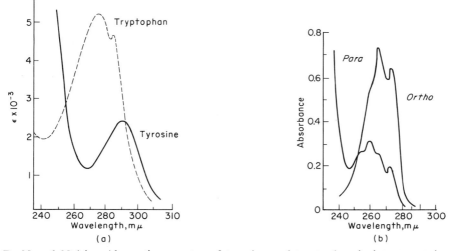

Problem 4-30 (a). Absorption spectra of tyrosine and tryptophan in intact proteins in 0.1 N NaOH. (**b**) Absorption spectra of para- and ortho-toluene sulfonamides (0.100 g/liter) in 0.1 N HCl.

28. The absorption spectra for tyrosine and tryptophan in 0.1 N NaOH is shown in Problem 4-30 (a). Select appropriate wavelengths for the simultaneous determination of each component in mixtures.

29. Toluene sulfonamides in 0.1 N HCl have the absorption spectra shown in Problem 4-30 (b). Select appropriate wavelengths for the determination of the *ortho* and the *para* fraction. *Ans.* 276 mμ and the isoabsorptive point at 256 mμ.

30. From the data contained in the figure, parts (a) and (b), derive expressions for the computation of the respective components in terms of simultaneous absorbance values at the selected wavelengths. *Ans.* (b) See *Anal. Chem.*, **31**, 1806 (1959).

Bibliography

Bauman, R. P., *Absorption Spectroscopy*, Wiley, New York, 1962.

Brand, J. C. D., and A. I. Scott, "Elucidation of Structures by Physical and Chemical Methods," Part 1, Vol. XI *Technique of Organic Chemistry*, Interscience, New York, 1963.

Braude, A. E., *Determination of Organic Structures by Physical Methods*, Vol. 1, Academic Press, New York, 1955.

Brode, W. R., *Chemical Spectroscopy*, Wiley, New York, 1943.

Flett, M. St. C., *Physical Aids to the Organic Chemist*, Elsevier, Amsterdam, 1962.

Gillam, A. E., and E. S. Stern, *An Introduction to Electronic Absorption Spectroscopy in Organic Chemistry*, Edward Arnold, London, 1957.

Hershenson, H. M., *Ultraviolet and Visible Absorption Spectra Index for 1930–1954*, Academic Press, New York, 1956; ibid., *1954–1957*, 1959.

Mellon, M. G., *Analytical Absorption Spectroscopy*, Wiley, New York, 1950.

Silverstein, R. M., and G. C. Bassler, *Spectrometric Identification of Organic Compounds*, Wiley, New York, 1963.

Literature Cited

1. Advisory Board, *Anal. Chem.*, **34**, 1852 (1962).
2. Ayres, G. H., *Anal. Chem.*, **21**, 652 (1949).
3. Bastian, R., ibid., **21**, 972 (1949).
4. Bastian, R., R. Weberling, and F. Palilla, ibid., **22**, 160 (1950).
5. Crawford, C. M., ibid., **31**, 343 (1959).
6. Friedel, R. A., and M. Orchin, *Ultraviolet Spectra of Aromatic Compounds*, Wiley, New York, 1951.

7. Gillam, A. E., and E. S. Stern, *An Introduction to Electronic Absorption Spectroscopy in Organic Chemistry*, Edward Arnold, London, 1957.
8. Goddu, R. F., and D. N. Hume, *Anal. Chem.* **26**, 1679, 1740 (1954).
9. Headridge, J. B., *Photometric Titrations*, Pergamon, New York, 1961.
10. Hershenson, H. M., *Ultraviolet and Visible Absorption Spectra Index for 1930–1954*, Academic Press, New York, 1956; ibid., *1954–1957*, 1959.
11. Hiskey, C. F., *Anal. Chem.*, **21**, 1440 (1949).
12. Hiskey, C. F., J. Rabinowitz, and J. G. Young, ibid., **22**, 1464 (1950).
13. Hiskey, C. F., and D. Firestone, ibid., **24**, 342 (1952).
14. Hughes, H. K., *Applied Optics*, **2**, 937 (1963).
15. Kortum, G., and M. Seiler, *Angew. Chem.*, **52**, 687 (1939).
16. Reilley, C. N., and C. M. Crawford, *Anal. Chem.*, **27**, 716 (1955).
17. Ringbom, A., *Z. anal. Chem.*, **115**, 332 (1939).
18. Sadtler Research Laboratories, 1517 Vine Ave., Philadelphia, Pa.
19. Silverstein, R. M., and G. C. Bassler, *Spectrometric Identification of Organic Compounds*, Wiley, New York, 1963.
20. Twyman, F., and C. B. Allsopp, *Practice of Absorption Spectrophotometry*, A. Hilger, London, 1934.
21. von Halban, H., and J. Eisenbrand, *Proc. Roy. Soc. (London)*, **A116**, 153 (1927).

The Absorption of Infrared Radiation

The range in the electromagnetic spectrum extending from 0.8 to 200 μ is referred to as the infrared. However, discussion in this chapter will be restricted to those regions from 0.8 to about 50 μ which can be explored with commercial infrared instruments, and wherein spectra originate primarily from the vibrational stretching and bending modes within molecules. Most organic and inorganic materials show absorption and, in all but a few cases, this absorption includes several characteristic wavelengths. In fact, the infrared spectrum is one of the most characteristic properties of a compound. It provides a fingerprint for identification and a powerful tool for the study of molecular structure. Empirical correlations of vibrating groups with specific, observed absorption bands offer the possibility of chemical identification and, coupled with intensity measurements, of quantitative determinations.

Basic Principles

Vibrational Modes

The vibrational possibilities of the atoms in a polyatomic molecule can be visualized from a mechanical model of the system. Atomic masses are represented by balls, their weight being proportional to the corresponding atomic weight, and arranged in accordance with actual space geometry of the molecule. Mechanical springs, whose forces are proportional to the bonding forces of the chemical links, connect and keep the balls in positions of balance (Fig. 5-1). If the model is suspended in space and struck a blow, the balls will appear to undergo random chaotic motions. However, if the vibrating model is observed

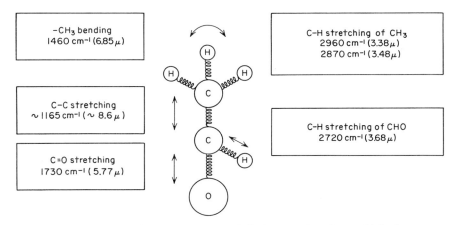

Fig. 5-1. Vibrations and characteristic frequencies of acetaldehyde.

with a stroboscopic light of variable frequency, certain light frequencies will be found at which the balls appear to remain stationary. These represent the normal modes of vibration and their corresponding frequencies.

To describe the normal modes of vibration in an orderly fashion, three co-ordinates in space must be specified for each nucleus (n). The system as a whole therefore has $3n$ degrees of freedom of motion. Of these, three degrees must be deducted from the whole system for translation of a molecule as a rigid unit, and three for rotations of the molecule about each principal axis (or two if the molecule is linear). This leaves a remainder of $3n - 6$ degrees of freedom for the description of independent modes of vibration of a molecule (or $3n - 5$ degrees of freedom for linear molecules). This number of fundamental absorption bands will not necessarily exist in the infrared spectrum. Apart from inactive vibrations, the symmetry of the molecule may be such that certain pairs (or triads) of the fundamental frequencies are exactly equal. These are called doubly (or triply) degenerate bands. They are observed only as one band but must be counted the appropriate number of times in the enumeration of normal frequencies.

The vibrations of two similar bonds joined by a common atom, such as H—C—H, usually produce two absorption bands because of the symmetrical and the asymmetrical movements of the same vibration type. The bands are relatively close together. In stretching vibrations the atoms move along the bond that joins them. In symmetrical stretching the two hydrogen atoms move towards and away from the central atom of carbon in unison, altering the interatomic distance without change in valence angle. In asymmetrical stretching one hydrogen atom approaches the carbon while the other moves away from the carbon. These fundamental stretching vibrations are illustrated in Fig. 5-2.

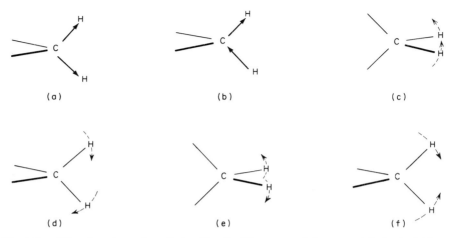

Fig. 5-2. Vibrational modes of the H—C—H group: (a) symmetrical stretching; (b) asymmetrical stretching; (c) wagging—out-of-plane bending; (d) rocking —asymmetrical in-plane bending; (e) twisting—out-of-plane deformation; (f) scissoring—symmetrical in-plane deformation.

When a three-atom system is part of a larger molecule, it is possible to have bending or deformation vibrations. Four types can be distinguished:

1. Rocking—the structural unit swings back and forth in the symmetry plane of the molecule; in-plane bending;

2. Wagging—the structural unit swings back and forth in a plane perpendicular to the molecule's symmetry plane; out-of-plane bending;

3. Twisting—the structural unit rotates back and forth around the bond which joins it to the rest of the molecule;

4. Scissoring—the two atoms connected to a central atom move toward and away from each other with deformation of the valence angle.

Splitting of bending vibrations due to in-phase and out-of-phase vibrations is found with larger groups joined by a central atom; for example, the doublet produced by the isopropyl group (*gem*-dimethyl groups).

The number of infrared absorption bands is increased by harmonic and combination vibrations. The harmonic (overtone) vibrations possess a frequency which represents approximately integral multiples of the fundamental frequency. The intensities are usually about one-hundredth those of fundamental bands. A combination band is the sum, or the difference between, the frequencies of two or more fundamental or harmonic vibrations. The uniqueness of an infrared spectrum arises largely from these bands.

Absorption of Infrared Radiation

A natural vibration mode within a molecule will absorb radiant energy provided two requirements are met: (1) If the natural frequency of vibration of the molecule is the same as the frequency of the radiation, and (2) if the vibration which is to be stimulated produces a change in the dipole moment of the molecule. The positions of the centers of gravity of the positive and negative electrical charges in a vibration mode determine the dipole moment. As the atoms undergo their characteristic vibrations the positions of the charges vary, and so also may the dipole moment. When the values of the dipole moment in the extreme positions differ, a periodically changing electric field will be produced around the molecule. As a result, absorption of radiant energy at the vibrating frequencies will occur — a resonance condition prevails. If a change in dipole moment of a molecule is made impossible by symmetry of the molecule, such as in homopolar molecules (O_2, H_2, etc.) or the $C{=}C$ mode in ethylene, no radiation corresponding to this oscillation is absorbed. The vibrational mode is said to be infrared inactive, although a vibration of this type is usually strongly active in Raman spectra. No dipole moment exists or is created in the symmetrical stretching vibration of a carbon dioxide molecule because the centers of gravity of the charges coincide in every vibrational position. However, in the case of the unsymmetrical stretching vibration, the centers of gravity of the charges do not coincide. A dipole moment is produced and absorption characteristic of this mode is observed in the infrared spectrum.

The intensity of an infrared absorption band is proportional to the square of the rate of change of dipole moment with respect to the displacement of the atoms. In some cases, the magnitude of the change in dipole moment may be quite small, producing only weak absorption bands, as in the relatively non-polar $C{=}N$ group. By contrast, the $C{=}O$ group, being partially ionic, causes strong absorption bands.

Position of Absorption Bands

Infrared spectroscopists use both wavelength and wave numbers as units to describe a position in the absorption spectrum. The wavelength, λ, is usually measured in microns, μ. The wave number, $\bar{\nu}$, is the "true" frequency divided by the speed of light; that is, it is the reciprocal of the wavelength. It indicates the number of wavelengths for 1 cm of distance traversed (cm^{-1}). A simple reciprocal relationship exists between these units, namely,

$$\bar{\nu} \text{ (in } cm^{-1}) = \frac{10^4}{\lambda(\text{in } \mu)} \tag{5-1}$$

Both units will be employed in the text.

The position of absorption bands can be predicted from the mechanical theory of harmonic oscillators; that is, a simple spring obeying Hooke's law.

The classical model of a vibrating diatomic molecule represents the simplest case. When two adjacent atoms, considered as approximating to point masses m_1 and m_2, and connected by a spring representing the strength of the bond, execute a simple harmonic motion about an equilibrium point, while linkages with the remaining atoms are ignored, the frequency will be given by

$$\bar{\nu} \text{ (in cm}^{-1}) = \frac{1}{2\pi c}\sqrt{\frac{k(m_1 + m_2)}{m_1 m_2}} \tag{5-2}$$

where k is the restoring force per unit displacement (dynes cm^{-1}) from the equilibrium point and the values of m_1, m_2 are in grams. The frequency is the greater the smaller the mass of the vibrating nuclei and the greater the force restoring the nuclei to the equilibrium position.

Example 5-1

Calculate the fundamental frequency expected in the infrared absorption spectrum for the C—O stretching frequency. The value of the force constant is 5.0×10^5 dynes cm^{-1}.

From Eq. 5-2,

$$\bar{\nu} \text{ (in cm}^{-1}) = \frac{1}{(2)(3.1416)(3 \times 10^{10})}\sqrt{\frac{(5 \times 10^5)(12 + 16)(6.023 \times 10^{23})}{(12)(16)}}$$

$$= 1307\sqrt{\frac{(5.0)(12 + 16)}{(12)(16)}}$$

$$= 1110 \text{ cm}^{-1}$$

To estimate the spectral region in which absorption might occur from application of Eq. 5-2, it is necessary to obtain some idea of the value of the force constant between the atom pair. A useful empirical relation, due to Gordy,[1] provides an estimate of k in units of 10^5 dynes cm^{-1}:

$$k = aN\left(\frac{\chi_A \chi_B}{d^2}\right)^{3/4} + b \tag{5-3}$$

where N is the bond order (i.e., the effective number of covalent or ionic bonds acting between the two atoms, χ_A and χ_B are the Pauling electronegativities of atoms A and B, d is the internuclear distance in angstroms, and the constants a and b are 1.67 and 0.30, respectively, for stable molecules exhibiting their normal covalencies.

Example 5-2

For the C—Cl stretching frequency, $\chi_C = 2.5$, $\chi_{Cl} = 3.0$, $d = 1.76$ Å, and $N = 1$. Estimate the value of the force constant from Gordy's rule.

$$k = (1.67)(1)\left(\frac{(2.5)(3.0)}{(1.76)^2}\right)^{3/4} + 0.30$$

$$= 3.54 \times 10^5 \text{ dynes cm}^{-1}$$

Except for the masses of the atoms, all other factors influencing characteristic group frequencies are included in the expression for the force constant. Any electronic displacement in the molecule which tends to increase the number of electrons residing in the bond, increases the frequency. Thus triple bonds are observed at higher frequencies than are double bonds which, in turn, occur at frequencies greater than those for corresponding single bonds. The force constant usually falls within the range $4\text{–}6 \times 10^5$ dynes cm^{-1} for single bonds, $8\text{–}12 \times 10^5$ dynes cm^{-1} for double bonds, and $12\text{–}18 \times 10^5$ dynes cm^{-1} for triple bonds. Bond length can also be a good guide to the direction of a shift of a stretching frequency resulting from a change in a chemical group — the greater the bond length, the lower the frequency.

Evaluation of Eq. 5-2 for various possible combinations of atoms shows that the frequencies of the normal vibrations of a molecule fall into the frequency range extending from 0.6×10^{13} to 12×10^{13} cps; that is, 4000–200 cm^{-1} (2.5–50 μ). Motions involving hydrogen atoms are found at much higher frequencies than are motions involving heavier atoms. A hydrogen atom bound to an oxygen atom, the O—H stretching frequency, vibrates back and forth 10^{14} times per second in the direction of the bond. Increasing the masses of the atoms decreases the frequency of the absorption band. Thus, the vibrations of a single carbon-carbon linkage range from 3.3×10^{13} to 3.9×10^{13} times per second, an understandable shift in resonance frequency since the mass of the carbon atom is 12 times greater than that of the hydrogen atom. In the case of multiple bond linkage, the force constants of double and triple bonds are roughly two and three times those of the single bonds, and the absorption position becomes, for carbon-carbon bonds, approximately $\sqrt{2}$ and $\sqrt{3}$ times higher in frequency. Interaction with neighbors may alter these values, as will resonating structures, hydrogen bonding, and ring strain. Also, when the mass of the involved atoms is large as compared to the force constants, the position of the absorption band may not be as characteristic as with lighter atoms. Consequently, it is wise to look for stretching frequencies in regions centering around the calculated values.

Bending motions produce lower frequency absorption than fundamental stretching modes, extending even beyond the range of most instruments.

Instrumentation

Spectrometers for the infrared region are composed of the same basic components as instruments in the ultraviolet and visible range, although the sources, the detectors, and the materials used in the construction of the optical components (except in the near-infrared) are different. Radiation from a source emitting in the infrared region passes alternately through the sample and the reference before entering the monochromator. This arrangement minimizes the effect of stray radiation, a serious problem in most of the infrared region. The transmitted beam is dispersed by passage through a prism or reflection from a grating. The dispersed light is focused to a spectrum in the plane of the vertical exit slit. The latter selects a narrow wavelength range, which is focused upon a detector. Rotation of the dispersing device causes the spectrum to move across the face of the exit slit and, ultimately, the detector. Mirror optics are universally used, the front surface usually being coated with aluminum. The inherent complexity of infrared spectra makes a recording instrument mandatory, since point-by-point plotting is extremely time-consuming.

Temperature and humidity in the room housing the instrument must be controlled. Humidity over 50 percent relative is deleterious to prism faces and windows of the alkali halides. Temperature changes over a few degrees seriously affect the accuracy of the wavelength calibration. The presence of carbon dioxide and water vapor in the optical path, both strong absorbers, tends to mask a sample spectrum unless a double-beam instrument is used.

Infrared equipment is obtainable from several manufacturers. The degree of sophistication depends largely on the use intended. Inexpensive utilitarian instruments possess minimal operating controls and are lower in cost but have some elements of flexibility curtailed. Single-beam instruments are reasonably satisfactory for a qualitative scan of a spectrum when the information is to be used internally. Since the intensity of the source may show considerable variation between runs, and since it is difficult to reproduce exactly the large number of different slit openings employed during a single run, single-beam instruments have never been popular. A double-beam instrument offers many advantages with only a slight increase in cost.

Several instrumental accessories aid in operation. An automatic slit control maintains the radiant energy in the reference beam at a level commensurate with the 100 percent transmittance desired. The wavelength scale is programmed by means of specially cut cams so that the chart record is linear in wavelength or in wave numbers, as desired by the user. An automatic gain control provides a constant gain over a transmittance range of 10 to 100 percent, and thus ensures a "live" pen under minimum energy conditions. Ordinate scale expansion permits up to a 20-fold expansion of any portion of the ordinate with, however, some loss in resolution. Often a 10-fold expansion may be achieved with minimal loss in resolution. Automatic scan rate permits transparent regions to be scanned rapidly at a preset scanning speed. However, when an absorption band is sensed, the scanning speed is automatically reduced in proportion to the intensity of the absorption. After the band is scanned, the speed selected is resumed.

Radiation Sources

The best source of infrared radiant energy approximates that from a black body (see Fig. 3-2 on page 34). However, the emission maximum lies in the near infrared. An increase in temperature only serves to increase the short wavelength radiation much more than the long wavelength radiation that is generally used. A certain fraction of the short wavelength radiation will find its way through the monochromator as stray light since it is relatively more intense. Because of this, the light beams are chopped at a low frequency (10 to 26 times per second) and, in more sophisticated instruments, double monochromation is employed. A separate compartment houses the source unit. Light from the source falls upon a concave spherical mirror which condenses the radiation into an image of the source which fills the entrance slit of the monochromator.

The Nernst glower is a mixture of zirconium and yttrium oxides which is formed into a small hollow rod about 2 mm in diameter and 30 mm in length. The ends are cemented to short ceramic tubes to facilitate mounting the glower; short electrical leads provide power connections. The glower is heated to surface temperatures between 1500° and 2000°C. It furnishes maximum radiation at about 7100 cm^{-1} (1.4 μ). The glower has a negative temperature coefficient of resistance and, as a consequence, must be operated in series with ballast resistance in a constant-voltage circuit. Secondary electrical heaters are needed to start the element because it is nonconducting when cold. It must be protected from drafts but at the same time adequate ventilation is needed to remove surplus heat and evaporated oxides (and binder).

The Globar source is a rod of sintered silicon carbide about 50 mm in length and 4 mm in diameter. It is self-starting, and is heated to 1300°–1700°C. The temperature coefficient of resistance is positive and may be conveniently controlled with a variable transformer. Its resistance increases with length of time used so that provision must be made for increasing the voltage across the element. It must be water-cooled. Maximum radiation occurs about 5200 cm^{-1} (1.9 μ). Although a less intense source than the Nernst glower, the Globar is more satisfactory for work at wavelengths longer than 15 μ (650 cm^{-1}) because its radiant energy output decreases less rapidly.

Coils or ribbons of Nichrome wire (sealed in dry inert gas) raised to incandescence by resistive heating are used in some nondispersive process analyzers. The surface temperature is about 800°–900°C.

Monochromators

Most monochromators employ the Littrow mount. The entrance slit is at the focus of a collimating mirror which is an off-axis section of a large parabolic mirror. The light from the source unit, diverging from the entrance slit, is thereby rendered parallel and sent to the dispersing device. The dispersed light is then focused onto the exit slit of the monochromator, through which it passes into the detector section. The sample (and reference) is usually placed at or near a focus of the beam, just before the entrance slit to the monochromator.

With prisms, the Littrow mount reflects the beam from a plane mirror behind the prism and returns it through the prism a second time (Fig. 5-3),

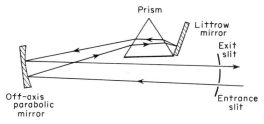

(a) Single-pass monochromator

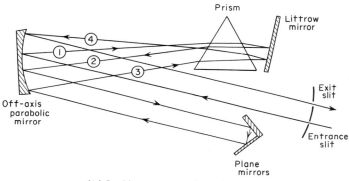

(b) Double-pass monochromator

Fig. 5-3. Traversal of light beam through a single-pass and a double-pass prism monochromator.

Table 5-1 | *Prism and Window Materials for Infrared Spectrophotometry*

MATERIAL	SUITABLE RANGE FOR WINDOWS	OPTIMUM RANGE AS PRISMS
Glass†	300 mμ to 2.6 μ (3850 cm⁻¹)	300 mμ to 2.0 μ (5000 cm⁻¹)
Fused silica†	185 mμ to 4.0 μ (2500 cm⁻¹)	185 mμ to 3.5 μ (3140 cm⁻¹)
Lithium fluoride	115 mμ to 7.0 μ (1430 cm⁻¹)	600 mμ to 6.0 μ (1670 cm⁻¹)
Calcium fluoride†	125 mμ to 10.0 μ (1000 cm⁻¹)	200 mμ to 9.0 μ (1100 cm⁻¹)
Barium fluoride†	200 mμ to 13.5 μ (740 cm⁻¹)	300 mμ to 13.0 μ (770 cm⁻¹)
Irtran 2 (ZnS)†	150 mμ to 13.0 μ (770 cm⁻¹)	
Sodium chloride	200 mμ to 17.0 μ (590 cm⁻¹)	200 mμ to 15.4 μ (625 cm⁻¹)
Silver chloride†	10 to 25.0 μ (400 cm⁻¹)	
Potassium bromide	200 mμ to 26 μ (380 cm⁻¹)	10 to 25 μ (400 cm⁻¹)
Cesium iodide	1 to 40 μ (250 cm⁻¹)	10 to 38 μ (260 cm⁻¹)
KRS-5 (TlBr-TlI)	2 to 40 μ (250 cm⁻¹)	

†Suitable window material for moist solvents and aqueous solutions.

thus doubling the dispersion produced. The double-pass system goes a step further by returning the beam through the prism again, producing a total of four passes through the prism with an attendant improvement in resolution. Materials for prism construction which are found most suitable in the infrared region are listed in Table 5-1. Large crystals of these substances are grown artificially on a commercial basis, from which blanks are cut for prisms, windows, and cell faces. The long wavelength limit is set by absorption, and the useful short wavelength limit is set by experimental circumstances such as light scattering or limited dispersion (see Fig. 5-4). The dispersive power of a prism becomes appreciable only near its transmission limit. Most instruments employ a sodium chloride (rocksalt) prism for the entire region from 4000–650 cm^{-1} (2.5–15.4 μ), with potassium bromide or cesium iodide prism and optics for the extension of the spectrum to 400 cm^{-1} (25 μ) or 260 cm^{-1} (38 μ), respectively. Prisms of

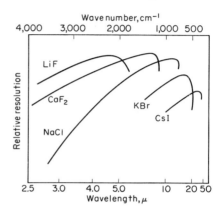

Fig. 5-4. Spectral resolution for prism materials.

lithium fluoride or calcium fluoride provide improved resolution in the region where the significant stretching vibrations are located. Quartz spectrophotometers designed for the ultraviolet-visible region also extend their coverage into the near infrared region.

Higher dispersion can be obtained from a reflection grating substituted in place of the prism in the Littrow mount. Gratings are usable only over a short spectral range, and higher diffracted orders must be eliminated by suitable filters or a fore-prism. A single, general purpose grating is ruled 75 lines/mm and 12 μ blaze. When used with a fore-prism, light from the parabolic mirror enters the fore-prism where it is dispersed so that only a relatively narrow band of wavelengths is allowed to fall on the grating. The light returning through the prism corresponds then to a range of diffracted light from only one spectral order. Since the efficiency of a grating is highest at the blaze wavelength, it is necessary to use different diffraction orders, or more than one grating, to cover the infrared region. Two gratings are often mounted back-to-back so that each need be used only in the first order. In the Perkin-Elmer model 137G instrument, one grating covers the range from 0.83 to 2.55 μ (12,000–3900 cm^{-1}); the other covers the range from 2.45 to 7.65 μ (4080–1300 cm^{-1}). In the Cary-White model 90 instrument, one grating is ruled with 50 lines/mm and 19.98 μ blaze and the other with 150 lines/mm and 6.67 μ blaze. The operation of a fore-prism grating spectrometer involves mechanical complications since prism and grating must track together over consecutive grating orders. Grating instruments incorporate a sine-bar mechanism to drive the grating mount when a wavelength readout is desired, and a cosecant-bar drive when wave numbers are desired.

In a combination prism-grating monochromator, the Littrow mirror in a sodium chloride monochromator can be replaced by a diffraction grating. When set appropriately, the instrument works from 4000 to 1430 cm^{-1} (2.5–7 μ) as a grating monochromator with a fore-prism unit and, from 1430 to 670 cm^{-1} (7–15 μ) in the Littrow position, the grating acts as a mirror and the instrument as a prism monochromator.

Detectors

Except in the near infrared, where a photoconductive cell is applicable, there is nothing better than thermal detectors. These have essentially uniform responses for all frequencies measured in terms of detector signal per watt of incident power. But since the radiant power is low for the infrared region, so will be the detector signal. To prevent the faint signals being lost in the stray (noise) signals picked up by the wires leading away from the detector, a pre-amplifier is located as close to the detector as possible. Furthermore, the radiation beam is modulated with a low-frequency light interrupter, 10–26 cps. Only the alternating signal at this corresponding frequency is measured to minimize stray light signals. This requires detectors with a short response time, and the absorbed heat must be dissipated rapidly, a difficult requirement, because heat transfer is not a rapid process.

Among thermal receivers, the thermocouple is the one most widely used. Quartz fibers are used to support the blackened gold foil receiver (0.2 × 2 mm foil pounded to less than a micron thickness), to which is fastened the "hot" junction made by welding together at their ends wires of two different semiconducting materials of high thermoelectric efficiency. The corresponding "cold" junction is kept darkened and at constant temperature in the receiver housing. An emf is produced and a small current flows whenever one junction is at a higher temperature than the other. The pair are housed in an evacuated steel casing with a KBr (or CsI) window to avoid losses of energy by convection. The response time of a thermocouple is about 60 msec, the longest of infrared receivers.

Bolometers give an electrical signal as the result of the change in resistance of a metallic conductor with temperature. One form is a thin film of noble metal evaporated on a nonconducting backing material. Two sensing elements, nearly identical, mounted close to each other with one shielded from the radiant energy, form two arms of a Wheatstone bridge. Thermistors, a fused mixture of metal oxides, show a negative thermal coefficient of electrical resistance. Two thermistors may be connected in a Wheatstone bridge circuit. Response time is 4 msec for bolometers and thermistors.

The Golay cell is pneumatic in principle. The element consists of a small metal cylinder, closed by a blackened metal plate at one end and by a flexible metallized diaphragm at the other. This cylinder is filled with xenon and sealed. The radiation falls on the blackened plate and heat is conducted to the gas, causing it to expand and deform the metallized diaphragm which separates two chambers. Light from a lamp inside the detector housing can be focused upon the diaphragm which reflects the light onto a photocell. Motion of the diaphragm moves the light beam across the photocell surface and changes the photocell output. In an alternate arrangement, the diaphragm may be used as one plate of a dynamic condenser; a perforated diaphragm a slight distance away serves as the second plate. The distortion of the solid diaphragm relative to the other alters the plate separation and hence the capacity. The alternating output with either arrangement corresponds to the chopping frequency. Response time is 4 msec. Pneumatic detectors have a sensitivity somewhat similar to that of good thermocouples and bolometers. The large area of the receiver makes a pneumatic detector suitable for instruments in which wide slits are necessary and when working at wavelengths greater than about 15 μ. On the other hand, the large size of the detector head obstructs too much energy in some spectrometer arrangements.

A nonthermal detector of greater sensitivity than any described is the photoconductive cell. The element consists of a thin layer, 0.1 μ, of lead sulfide or lead telluride supported on a backing medium, usually glass, and sealed into an evacuated glass envelope. The device depends on valence electrons in semiconductor material absorbing light and passing to an energy state in which they are free to conduct a current. Electrically a photoconductive cell is a resistor (about 200,000 Ω) which decreases in value in relation to the intensity of light striking its surface. Response time is about 0.5 msec. Unfortunately, the long wavelength sensitivity limit seems to be about 3.5 μ for lead sulfide cells and about 6 μ for lead telluride cells, but where applicable, they permit vastly improved resolution or fast scanning rates.

Single-Beam Spectrometer

In a single-beam infrared spectrometer, a blank curve of the spectral energy distribution of the light source and the atmospheric water vapor and carbon dioxide absorptions is recorded. Then, with the sample brought into the beam, the same spectrum is scanned again. The absorption bands of the sample are superimposed on the spectrum of the blank and must be obtained from the two curves by forming quotients. This is a tedious process. For qualitative use this is not particularly necessary.

In the memory method, the blank (P_0) spectrum is recorded and a slit servo operated to maintain the P_0 value constant. The slit schedule required is recorded on tape or wire. Then the sample is introduced and the spectrum rerun with the slits repeating the schedule on the tape. The optical system of a single-beam prism spectrometer is shown in Fig. 5-5; a model with a grating replacing the prism is also available from the same manufacturer.

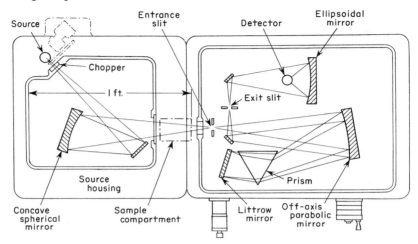

Fig. 5-5. Schematic optical diagram of a single-beam infrared spectrometer—Perkin-Elmer model 12C. (Courtesy of Perkin-Elmer Corporation.)

Double-beam instruments usually may be operated in a single-beam mode if desired.

Double-Beam Spectrophotometers

In a double-beam spectrophotometer (Fig. 5-6) two equivalent beams are taken from the source and, by means of a rotating mirror and light interrupter, in reality half of a complete circular mirror, each beam traverses the monochromator-detector system on alternating cycles. The sample is placed in one beam while the reference beam is left empty or contains a reference blank or solution. It should always be remembered that whenever more than 95 percent of the incident radiation is absorbed by the sample or solvent, the instrument is effectively inactive and the spectrum trace meaningless. This must be considered in selecting solvents, concentrations, and cell thickness.

In the optical null method, an a-c signal results when the two beams are unbalanced. The amplifier is tuned to the chopping frequency of the light beam; signals of differing frequency are not amplified. The resultant a-c signal activates a servo mechanism which moves an optical wedge or shutter comb that is mounted in the path of the reference beam, thus reducing its energy until both beams are again balanced. The optical attenuator is linked mechanically to the recorder pen which is moved across the chart paper as the equilibrium position is sought. The record traced on the chart paper is therefore the relative transmittance of the sample. The accuracy and reproducibility of the

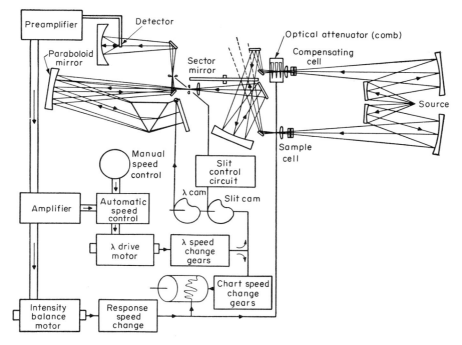

Fig. 5-6. Optical diagram of a double-beam instrument and related operating controls —Perkin-Elmer model 21. (Courtesy of Perkin-Elmer Corporation.)

spectra read out in this way depend upon the speed and sensitivity of the detector and amplifier, and the freedom from friction, inertia, and distortion of the motor driving the attenuator. Commercial versions of this popular form of prism infrared spectrophotometer include Baird-Atomic model NK-1, Beckman model IR-5, Leitz, Perkin-Elmer models 21, 137, and 221, and Unicam model SP.100. Analogous grating instruments include the Beckman model IR-8 and the Perkin-Elmer model 137G.

The direct-ratio recording system makes no attempt to achieve a physical equalization of the sample and reference beam intensities. The signals from the beams are separated after amplification, usually by microswitches operated from the shaft of the motor which drives the rotating mirror. The chopping sequence is arranged to include a dark interval between each period of illumination of the exit slit. The two separated signals, amplified independently of each other, are rectified to direct current and fed to a potentiometer recorder. The potential from the reference beam is placed across the whole slide wire, and the sample beam signal is fed to the variable contactor. By this means the transmittance ratio is automatically attained and recorded continuously. The two signals can be combined in various other ways, giving a great degree of versatility in data presentation. Representative commercial instruments include the Cary-White model 90 and the Perkin-Elmer models 13 and 13G.

Double Monochromation

A double-monochromator design employs two monochromators in series with an intermediate slit, as shown in Fig. 5-7. The optical train provides twice the dispersion and ultimate resolution of comparable single-monochromator instruments. Stray radiant energy is virtually eliminated. Two

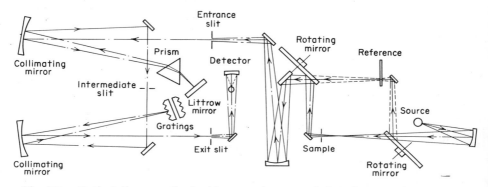

Fig. 5-7.   Optical diagram of a double-monochromator infrared spectrophotometer—Beckman model IR-9. (Courtesy of Beckman Instruments, Inc.)

prism monochromators are utilized in the Beckman model IR-4, whereas the second prism is replaced with a dual grating in the Beckman model IR-9 and the Cary-White model 90.

Process Analyzers

In process-stream analyzers, elasticity of use has been sacrificed for economy, dependability, and extreme stability. Instruments fall into two categories: dispersive and nondispersive.

A dispersive instrument is patterned after a double-beam spectrophotometer. Radiation at two fixed wavelengths passes through a cell containing the process-stream to provide a continuous measurement of the absorption ratio. At one wavelength the material absorbs selectively, and at the other wavelength the material does not absorb or else exhibits a constant, but small, absorption. The ratio of transmittance readings is converted directly into concentration of absorber and recorded. This type of instrument can handle liquid systems as well as gas streams, and has the ability to analyze quite complex mixtures.

No prisms or gratings are used in nondispersive instruments. The total radiation from an infrared source is passed through the sample, providing more signal power. By filling one or both cells containing the detector with the pure form of the gas being determined, these analyzers show high selectivity and virtually infinite resolving power although they employ a very simple optical train. Two modes of detection are employed.

A schematic diagram of a negative filter type of nondispersive analyzer is shown in Fig. 5-8(a). An infrared source sends radiation through the sample

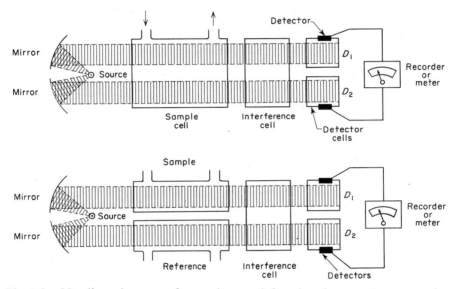

Fig. 5-8. Nondispersive types of process-stream infrared analyzers. *Above:* negative-filter arrangement; D_1 contains the gas being determined and D_2 contains a nonabsorbing gas; *below:* positive-filter arrangement in which both detector cells are filled with the gas being determined.

chamber. Half of the beam is intercepted by each detector. One cell is filled with the pure form of the gas being determined (component A); the other is filled with a nonabsorbing gas. The former absorbs all the radiation in its beam which is characteristic of component A, and a thermal detector in the cell records the temperature rise. As radiation passes through a gas stream in the sample cell which is devoid of component A, the detector filled with the nonabsorbing gas absorbs none of the radiant energy. The net difference in the two signals—the maximum difference—is the zero percent reading. When the process stream contains some of the component A, a proportionate amount of the characteristic radiation is absorbed in the sample cell and fails to reach the detectors, thus decreasing the signal from the detector which is filled with pure component A, but no change occurs in the signal from the other detector. Thus, as the concentration of component A in the process stream approaches 100 percent, the signal difference between the two detectors approaches zero.

In the positive filter arrangement, shown in Fig. 5-8(b), the beam of radiation from the source is split into two parallel beams. One beam passes through the reference cell and the other through the sample cell. Each detector, in this arrangement, is filled with the pure form of the gas being determined. When some of the latter is present in the sample beam, the sample detector receives less radiant energy by the amount absorbed by the sample component at its characteristic wavelength. The difference in signal from the two detectors is related to absorber concentration.

If some other absorbing component is present in the process stream, the analyzer is "desensitized" by filling an intermediate cell (in both light paths) with the pure form of the interfering gas or a sufficient concentration to adequately remove its characteristic wavelengths from both light paths. The analyzer operates on the remaining regions of the spectrum. Of course, this reduces somewhat the sensitivity of the analyzer toward the component being analyzed.

Sample Handling

Sample handling presents a number of problems in the infrared region. No rugged window material for cells exists which is transparent over this region and also inert. The alkali halides are widely used, particularly sodium chloride, which is transparent at wavelengths as long as 16 μ (625 cm^{-1}); potassium bromide can be used to 26 μ (385 cm^{-1}) and cesium iodide to 40 μ (250 cm^{-1}). However, the surfaces of these windows are easily fogged by exposure to atmospheric water vapor or moist samples, and require frequent repolishing when subjected to such abuse. Materials useful with moist samples, or aqueous solutions, are identified in Table 5-1. Silver chloride is often used, but it is soft, easily deformed, difficult to resurface, and darkens slowly on exposure to visible light. Teflon has only C—C and C—F absorption bands.

Gaseous samples are measured in a cell about 10 cm in length. The cell is evacuated and filled through a stopcock or needle valve. Fine rotational structure can often be resolved. Pressure broadening is troublesome in quantitative work. Multiple traversal of the cell by the light beam, using a combination of a mirror system with a beam condenser, enables the spectra of minor components to be measured.

Samples that are liquid at room temperature are usually scanned in their pure (neat) form. The sample thickness should be chosen so that the transmittance lies between 15 and 70 percent. For most liquids this will represent a very thin layer, 0.01–0.05 mm in thickness. Cells of these thicknesses are constructed with windows sealed (and separated) by thin gaskets of copper and lead which have been wetted with mercury. The whole assembly is securely clamped together. As the mercury penetrates the metal, the gasket expands, producing a tight seal. The cell is provided with tapered fittings to accept the needles of hypodermic syringes for filling. In demountable cells, the sample and spacer are placed on one window, covered with another window, and the entire sandwich is clamped together. Variable path-length cells are commercially available and provide widths from 0.002 to 3 mm. Selected types of cells are illustrated in Fig. 5-9. These small cell dimensions render it difficult to

Fig. 5-9. Infrared sample cells. (a) Fixed-thickness cell. (b) Variable-space cell. (c) Gas cell. (Courtesy Perkin-Elmer Corporation.)

repeat cell thickness accurately. Cell thickness can be measured from interference fringe patterns obtained by running a spectrum of an empty cell.[3,4] With spectrometers linear in wave numbers, the thickness b is calculated from the formula

$$b \text{ (in centimeters)} = \frac{n}{2}\left(\frac{1}{\bar{\nu}_1 - \bar{\nu}_2}\right) \tag{5-4}$$

where n is the number of fringes between wave numbers $\bar{\nu}_1$ and $\bar{\nu}_2$. Measurements are best done immediately following repolishing of the cell windows. The corresponding equation for spectrometers linear in wavelength is

$$b \text{ (in microns)} = \frac{n}{2}\left[\frac{\lambda_1 \lambda_2}{(\lambda_2 - \lambda_1)}\right] \tag{5-5}$$

Example 5-3

Calculate the thickness of a cell from the interference pattern shown:

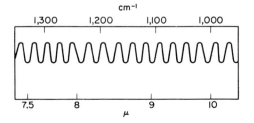

There are 12 peaks (or troughs) between 1300 and 1000 cm⁻¹. Thus, from Eq. 5-4,

$$b \text{ (cm)} = \frac{12}{2}\left(\frac{1}{300}\right) = 0.020 \text{ cm}$$

With thick cells, the average of the number of peaks and troughs between two wave numbers is taken for computation.

Whenever possible, solids are dissolved and examined as a dilute solution. However, not all substances can be dissolved in reasonable concentration in a solvent which is nonabsorbing in regions of interest. To cover the main spectral range of 4000–650 cm⁻¹ (2.5–15.4 μ) the combination of carbon tetrachloride and carbon disulfide is reasonably satisfactory, as they form a complementary pair. Carbon tetrachloride is useful even in thick layers except where it is

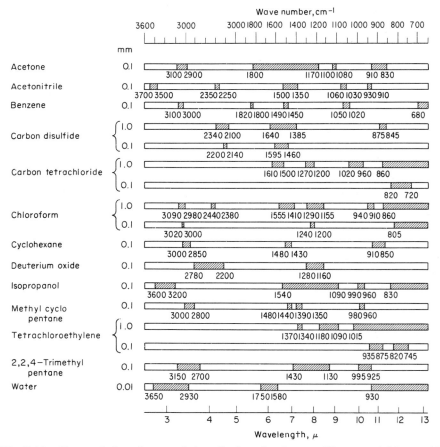

Fig. 5-10. Transmission characteristics of selected solvents. The material is considered transparent if the transmittance is 75 per cent or greater. Solvent thickness is given in millimeters.

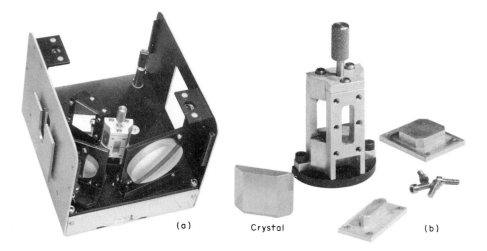

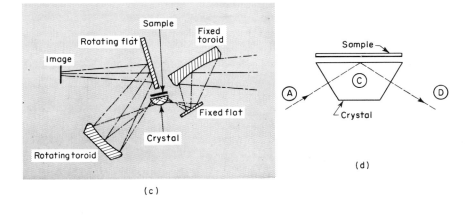

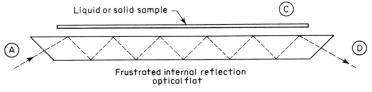

Fig. 5-11. (a) Attenuated total reflection attachment. (b) Exploded view of holder.
(c) Schematic optical diagram with the crystal and sample shown enlarged as with
(d) a trapezoidal prism. (e) With a frustrated multiple internal reflection optical
flat. (Courtesy of the Instrument Division of the Barnes Engineering Co.)

strongly absorbing between 800 and 740 cm^{-1} (12.5 and 13.5 μ), whereas carbon disulfide is useful in this region but absorbs strongly at about 2222 cm^{-1} (4.5 μ) and 1540 cm^{-1} (6.5 μ). Transparent regions of a selected group of solvents are given in Fig. 5-10. The possible influence of a solvent on the spectrum of a solute must not be overlooked. Particular care should be exercised in the selection of a solvent for compounds which are susceptible to hydrogen bonding effects. Solvents must be moisture free unless resistant windows are used in sample cells.

Attenuated total reflectance (ATR) yields spectra from thin films or surfaces of materials that can be placed in contact with an optical surface. Energy from the source enters through the edge of a trapezoidal prism—a crystal of material of relatively high refractive index—and is reflected almost totally from face C when the beam strikes it at less than the critical angle. However, radiation striking face A (Fig. 5-11) will be transmitted into (and at face D out of) the prism minus the normal reflection losses, since face A is nearly normal to the beam. Now, if another material is brought into contact with face C, the internal reflection will be reduced ("attenuated") at the sample/crystal interface at those wavelengths where the material absorbs energy. The beam penetrates only a few microns into the sample and then returns to the plate; consequently the thickness of the sample beyond the penetration depth is of no significance, so that absorption spectra of coatings and liquids (even if opaque) may be obtained. Although ATR spectra are not the same as transmittance spectra, they provide essentially the same information that conventional spectra do. In a modification of attenuated reflectance called frustrated multiple internal reflection (FMIR), energy from a source is made to travel through the edge of an optical flat from A to D by multiple reflections from the internal surface. Internal reflection will occur from 35 to 50 times down the plate, thus strengthening the absorption pattern of a material placed on one surface of the optical flat. For either reflectance method special variable area absorption cells permit precise beam balancing and spectral cancellation in the same fashion as a variable space cell. Provision is often made for varying the angle of incident radiation to permit reflectance studies of solids from any angle between 15° and 80°.

Powders, or solids reduced to particles, can be examined as a thick slurry, or mull, by grinding the pulverized solids in a greasy, liquid medium of approximately the same refractive index to reduce energy losses due to scattering of light energy. The suspension is pressed into an annular groove in a demountable cell. Liquid media include white paraffin (mineral) oil or Nujol, hexachlorobutadiene, perfluorokerosene, and chlorofluorocarbon greases (fluorolubes). The latter are used when the absorption by the paraffin oil tends to mask the presence of C—H bands. For qualitative analysis the mull technique is rapid and convenient, but quantitative data are difficult to obtain, even when an internal standard is incorporated.

The KBr pellet technique involves mixing the finely ground sample and potassium bromide, and pressing the mixture into a transparent disk in an evacuable die under high pressure. Other alkali halides may also be used, particularly CsI or CsBr for measurements at longer wavelengths. Good dispersion of the sample in the matrix is critical; moisture must be absent. Window size can be varied up to 2.5 cm and down to windows containing only 40 mg of potassium bromide and fractional milligram quantities of sample. Usual window size of 1/2 in. is obtained with 0.1 g KBr mixture. Quantitative analyses are readily performed since an accurate measurement may be made of the weight ratio of sample to internal standard in each disk.

Correlation of Infrared Spectra with Molecular Structure

Characteristic Frequencies

The infrared spectrum of a compound is essentially the superposition of absorption bands of specific functional groups, yet subtle interactions with the surrounding atoms of the molecule impose the stamp of individuality on the spectrum of each compound. For qualitative analysis, one of the best features of an infrared spectrum is that the absorption or the *lack of absorption* in

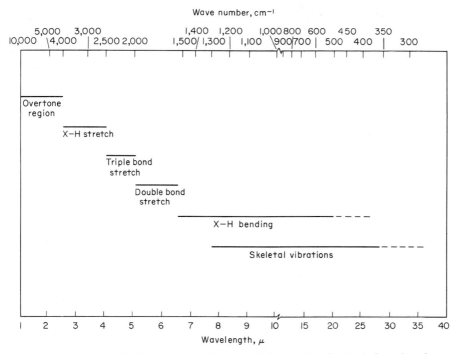

Fig. 5-12. Infrared vibrational modes and their location in the infrared region.

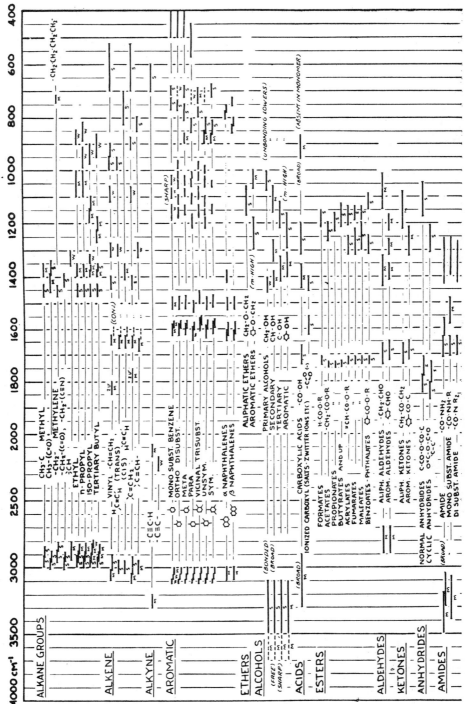

Fig. 5-13. Characteristic infrared absorption bands. After N. B. Colthup, *J. Opt. Soc. Am.*, **40**, 397 (1950).

specific frequency regions can be correlated with specific vibrational groups and bending motions and, in some cases, with the relationship of these groups to the remainder of the molecule. Thus, by interpretation of the spectrum it is possible to state that certain functional groups are present in the material and that certain others are absent. With this one datum, the possibilities for the unknown can be sometimes narrowed so sharply that comparison with a library of pure spectra permits identification.

Many useful correlations have been found in the fundamental, or "rocksalt," region of the spectrum (Fig. 5-12). This region is divided into the "group frequency" region—4000–1300 cm^{-1} (2.5–8 μ), and the "fingerprint" region—1300–650 cm^{-1} (8.0–15.4 μ). In the group frequency region the principal absorption bands may be assigned to vibration units consisting of only two atoms of a molecule; units which are more or less dependent only on the functional group giving the absorption and not on the complete molecular structure. Structural influences do reveal themselves, however, as small shifts of the absorption bands from their "normal" position. In the interval from 4000 to 2500 cm^{-1} (2.5–4.0 μ), the absorption is characteristic of hydrogen stretching vibrations with elements of mass 19 or less. When coupled with heavier masses, the frequencies overlap the triple bond region. The intermediate frequency rangé, 2500–1540 cm^{-1} (4.0–6.5 μ) is often termed the unsaturated region. Triple bonds, and very little else, appear from 2500 to 2000 cm^{-1} (4.0–5.0 μ). Double bond frequencies fall in the region from 2000 to 1540 cm^{-1} (5.0–6.5 μ). By judicious application of accumulated empirical data, it is possible to distinguish among C=O, C=C, C=N and N=O bands. The major factors in the spectra between 1300 and 650 cm^{-1} (8.0–15.4 μ) are single-bond stretching frequencies and bending vibrations (skeletal frequencies) of polyatomic systems involving motions of bonds linking a substituent group to the remainder of the molecule. This is the fingerprint region. Multiplicity is too great for assured individual identification, but collectively the absorption bands aid in identification of chain structure in aliphatics and ring substitution in aromatics as they are greatly affected by changes in the nature or position of the substituent.

The potassium bromide region (to 400 cm^{-1}, 25 μ) and the cesium iodide region (to 250 cm^{-1}, 38 μ) contain the bending vibrations of carbon, nitrogen, oxygen, and fluorine with atoms heavier than mass 19, and additional bending motions in cyclic or aromatic systems (see Fig. 5-22). These regions have not been as frequently used in analysis but are accessible with appropriate prism or grating accessories.

In the near infrared region, which meets the visible region at about 12,500 cm^{-1} (0.8 μ) and extends to about 4000 cm^{-1} (2.5 μ), are found many absorption bands resulting from overtone and combination bands associated with hydrogen atoms. Among these are the first overtones of the O—H and N—H stretching vibrations near 9100 cm^{-1} (1.4 μ) and 8500 cm^{-1} (1.5 μ), respectively, and combination bands resulting from C—H stretching and deformation vibrations of alkyl groups at 4548 cm^{-1} (2.2 μ) and 3850 cm^{-1} (2.6 μ). Thicker sample layers (0.5–10 mm) compensate for lessened absorptivities. The region is accessible with quartz optics and simple, cheap grating spectrometers.

An excellent summary of the probable positions of infrared absorption bands is shown in Fig. 5-13.

Structural Analysis

After the presence of a particular fundamental stretching frequency has been established, closer examination of the shape and exact position of an absorption band often yields additional information. The shape of an absorption band around 3000 cm^{-1} (3.3 μ) gives a rough idea of the CH group present. Alkane groups have their C—H stretching frequencies lower than 3000 cm^{-1} (3.3 μ), whereas alkenes and aromatics have them higher than 3000 cm^{-1}. Sometimes the spectrum shows a deep cleft between the bands arising from the saturated and unsaturated portions of the molecule (Fig. 5-22).

Next, one should examine regions where characteristic vibrations from bending motions occur. For alkanes a band at 1380 cm^{-1} (7.25 μ) is indicative of a terminal methyl group and, when split into a doublet at 1380 and 1365 cm^{-1} (7.25 and 7.33 μ), a *gem*-dimethyl group. The scissor motion of H—C—H at 1460 cm^{-1} (6.85 μ) indicates the presence of a methylene group, and four or more methylene groups in a linear arrangement gives rise to the rocking methylene band at about 720 cm^{-1} (13.9 μ). The substitution pattern of the benzene ring can be deduced from a series of weak but very useful bands in the region 2000–1670 cm^{-1} (5–6 μ) coupled with the position of the strong bands between 900 and 650 cm^{-1} (11.1 and 15.4 μ) which are due to the out-of-plane C—H bending vibrations (Fig. 5-14). For example, the band at 740 cm^{-1} (13.5 μ) in Fig. 5-22 is characteristic of ortho disubstitution in a benzene ring, and vibrations of the hydrogen atom toward and away from the ring cause bands in the KBr region at 580 cm^{-1} (17.2 μ) and 505 cm^{-1} (19.8 μ) for xylene; the band at 436 cm^{-1} (22.9 μ) is a deformation mode.

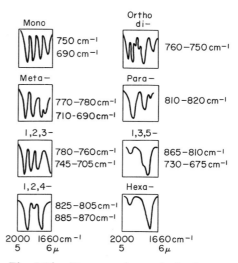

Fig. 5-14. Benzene ring substitution — pattern of combination bands between 2000 and 1670 cm^{-1} (5 to 6 μ). To the right of each curve are the approximate positions of C—H out-of-plane bending bands between 900 and 650 cm^{-1} (11.1 to 15.4 μ). After C. W. Young, R. B. Duvall, and N. Wright, *Anal. Chem.*, **23**, 709 (1951). (Courtesy of *Analytical Chemistry*.)

In the free or unassociated state a hydroxyl group will appear as a weak but sharp band at about 3600 cm⁻¹ (2.78 μ). Hydrogen bonding will greatly increase its intensity and move it to lower frequencies and, if the hydrogen bonding is especially strong, the band becomes quite broad.

The carbonyl group is not difficult to recognize; its exact position is dependent upon its environment. Aldehydes and ketones show bands between 1725 and 1690 cm⁻¹ (5.80 and 5.90 μ). If an OH group is attached, as in a carboxylic acid, the carbonyl frequency will be higher (1700–1670 cm⁻¹, 5.9–6.0 μ) than if an amide group is attached (1690–1600 cm⁻¹, 5.9–6.25 μ). Ester carbonyls are generally in the interval from 1750 to 1725 cm⁻¹ (5.72–5.80 μ). Anhydrides usually show a double absorption band, with one band between 1850 and 1800 cm⁻¹ (5.40 and 5.55 μ) and the second between 1800 and 1750 cm⁻¹ (5.55 and 5.72 μ).

The following series of spectra serve to illustrate how characteristic absorption bands are found in the spectrum of a compound. Figure 5-15 shows the

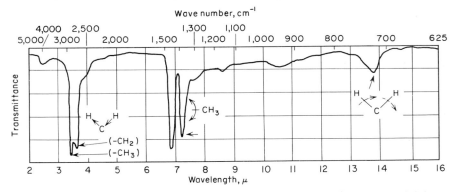

Fig. 5-15. Typical spectrum of a saturated alkane, $CH_3(CH_2)_8CH_3$. Nujol has a similar spectrum.

spectrum of a saturated alkane (Nujol), a compound which contains only carbon and hydrogen in a straight chain. The four prominent absorption bands arise from the C—H and C—C linkages: at about 2940 cm⁻¹ (3.4 μ) from C—H stretching; at 1460 cm⁻¹ (6.85 μ) from a scissors-like bending of H—C—H groups; at 1380 cm⁻¹ (7.25 μ) from a symmetrical deformation of the terminal methyl groups; and at 720 cm⁻¹ (13.85 μ) from a rocking vibration of the methylene hydrogen attached to the carbon atoms along the chain when four or more methylene groups are aligned linearly. With good resolution, the absorption bands at 2960 cm⁻¹ and 2930 cm⁻¹ (3.38 and 3.42 μ) are assignable to C—H stretchings in methyl and methylene groups, respectively. The absence of unsaturated C—H stretching at frequencies higher than 3000 cm⁻¹ (3.3 μ) and aromatic structure between 2000 and 1670 cm⁻¹ (5 and 6 μ) is noteworthy.

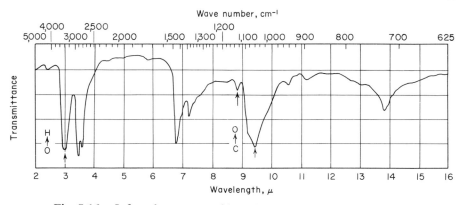

Fig. 5-16. Infrared spectrum of lauryl alcohol, $CH_3(CH_2)_{10}CH_2OH$.

Insertion of a sulfur atom in the middle of the aliphatic chain only introduces an additional band at 732 cm⁻¹ (13.67 μ) caused by a C—S—C stretching vibration which overlaps the rocking methylene band. A terminal C—Cl stretching frequency near 715 cm⁻¹ (14 μ) also often covers the methylene rocking band.

Replacing a hydrogen by a hydroxyl group on the end carbon of an aliphatic chain (Fig. 5-16) introduces two new modes of vibration: the O—H stretching at 3400 cm⁻¹ (2.95 μ) and C—O stretching at 1110 and 1060 cm⁻¹ (8.90 and 9.45 μ). The latter modes occur also in ethers (see Fig. 5-20), but reversed in intensity. Phenols will exhibit similar bands.

Introduction of a carbonyl group produces a number of new bands. Figure 5-17 shows the effect of an aldehyde group at the end of the chain. The strong C=O stretching frequency at 1730 cm⁻¹ (5.77 μ) is the usual location for aldehydes and ketones. A sharp band at 2720 cm⁻¹ (3.68 μ) is the C—H stretching frequency of the CHO group—shifted to lower frequency due to the adjacent

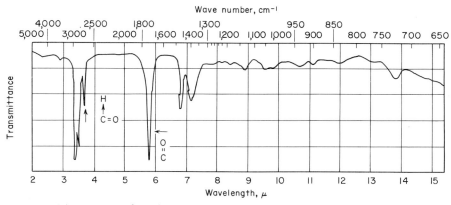

Fig. 5-17. Infrared spectrum of *n*-octaldehyde, $CH_3(CH_2)_6CHO$.

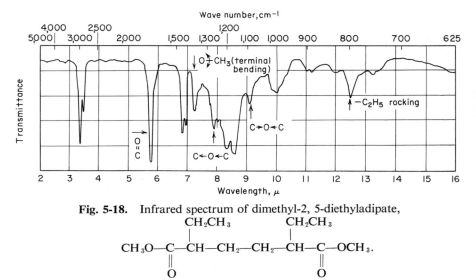

Fig. 5-18. Infrared spectrum of dimethyl-2, 5-diethyladipate,

$$CH_3O—C—CH—CH_2—CH_2—CH—C—OCH_3.$$

carbonyl group. In esters (Fig. 5-18), two bands related to C—O stretching and bending are recognizable, between 1300 and 1040 cm⁻¹ (8.3 and 9.6 μ), in addition to the strong carbonyl stretching band at 1740 cm⁻¹ (5.75 μ). The carboxyl group, in a sense, shows bands arising from the superposition of C=O, C—O, C—OH, and O—H vibrations (Fig. 5-19). Of five characteristic bands, three of these (2700, 1300, and 943 cm⁻¹; 3.7, 7.7, and 10.6 μ) are associated with vibrations of the carboxyl OH. They disappear when the carboxylate ion is formed. When the acid exists in the dimeric form, the O—H

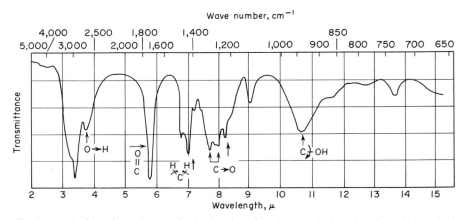

Fig. 5-19. Infrared spectrum of *n*-hexanoic acid. The methylene in-plane (scissoring) bending adjacent to COOH occurs at 1412 cm⁻¹ (7.1 μ), and the O—H stretching vibration of the carboxyl group occurs at 2700 cm⁻¹ (3.7 μ).

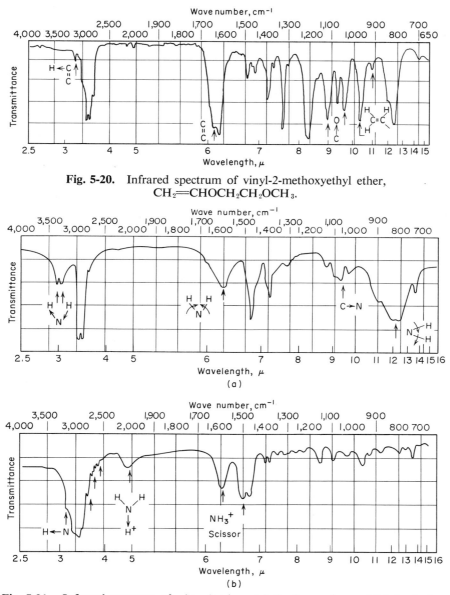

Fig. 5-20. Infrared spectrum of vinyl-2-methoxyethyl ether, $CH_2{=}CHOCH_2CH_2OCH_3$.

Fig. 5-21. Infrared spectrum of *n*-hexylamine: (a) the free amine and (b) the hydrochloride.

stretching band at 2700 cm⁻¹ (3.7 μ) disappears, but the absorption band at
943 cm⁻¹ (10.6 μ) due to OH out-of-plane bending of the dimer remains. In the
spectra of acids, aldehydes, and some aromatic hydroxyl compounds, the

amount of absorption between 3000 and 2500 cm^{-1} (3.3 and 4.0 μ) is increased, due probably to interaction among vibrational modes.

The presence of an unsaturated C=C linkage introduces the characteristic stretching frequency at 1650 cm^{-1} (6.07 μ), as shown in Fig. 5-20. Two other bands at about 990 and 910 cm^{-1} (10.1 and 11.0 μ) arise from out-of-plane hydrogen bending motions on the vinyl group. The C—H stretching frequency from the unsaturated group appears at 3080 cm^{-1} (3.25 μ).

The typical spectrum of an amine is shown in Fig. 5-21. Of particular interest are the N—H stretching vibrations around 3300 cm^{-1} (3.0 μ), actually a doublet in a primary amine, the in-plane (scissoring) bending of N—H at 1610 cm^{-1} (6.2 μ), and the out-of-plane bending of NH$_2$ at about 830 cm^{-1} (12.0 μ), which is broad for primary amines. These absorption bands also appear when acid amides are present. When the amine salt is formed, these bands, especially those due to stretching frequencies, are shifted to lower frequencies. The series of weak bands between 3140 and 2500 cm^{-1} (3.5 and 4.0 μ) and the band at 2040 cm^{-1} (4.9 μ) are due to the NH$_3{}^+$ group.

The introduction of a phenyl group, as in o-xylene, brings about several changes in the spectrum (Fig. 5-22). The aromatic and aliphatic C—H stretch-

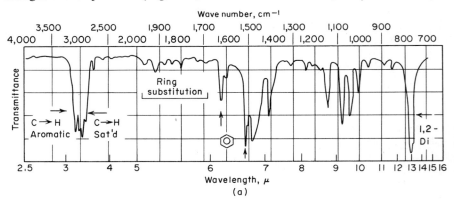

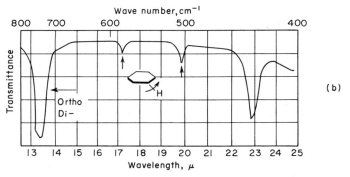

Fig. 5-22. Infrared spectrum of o-xylene: (a) the sodium chloride region and (b) the potassium bromide region.

ing frequencies, respectively, are apparent on the higher and lower frequency side of 3000 cm^{-1} (3.3 μ). Bands at 1600 cm^{-1} (6.25 μ) and at 1500 cm^{-1} (6.7 μ) are associated with the presence of the phenyl group. The ring substitution can be deduced from the spectral bands between 2000 and 1670 cm^{-1} (5 and 6 μ) (see Fig. 5-14), and the band at 740 cm^{-1} (13.5 μ), which is characteristic of *ortho*-disubstitution.

Compound Identification

In many cases the interpretation of the infrared spectrum on the basis of characteristic frequencies will not be sufficient to permit positive identification of a total unknown, but, perhaps, the type or class of compound can be deduced. Once the category is established, the spectrum of the unknown is compared with spectra of appropriate known compounds for an exact spectral match. If the exact compound happens not to be in the file, particular structure variations within the category may assist in suggesting possible answers and eliminating others.

Sufficient spectra of pure compounds must be available, and automatic sorters are needed to eliminate time-consuming matching problems. Unhappily, not enough spectra are available for a laboratory doing diversified analyses. Several collections of spectra are available commercially.[2,5]

Other physical properties should not be ignored in compound identification, and usually the history of the sample is known. Resort to NMR and ultraviolet spectral data can be very helpful.

When the question of purity of a compound arises, perhaps a new synthesis product, the infrared spectroscopist will require samples of the starting material and any chemicals used which from physical properties might be expected to be present, samples of products at intermediate steps, and some of the final product at various stages of purification. From these samples he can establish the wavelengths of characteristic absorption of any of the likely impurities and report on their absence in the final purified product.

Quantitative Analysis

The polarity and force constant of any functional group will be relatively independent of the remainder of the molecule. As a result, the intensity of absorption on a "per molecule" basis and the wavelength of absorption are essentially invariant throughout the members of a homologous series, except for the first members. Thus it is possible to determine total molar content of a particular functional group. On the other hand, resort must be made to bending motions for frequencies specific to a particular compound.

Theoretically, Beer's law is applied in infrared determinations just as it is applied in visible or ultraviolet spectrophotometric determinations. From the spectrum of each component by the use of known or constant values of cell thickness, the specific or molar absorptivity is determined at selected wavelengths where one of the components absorbs strongly and the other components have weak absorption or none. The absorbance of the unknown is determined at these selected wavelengths. A series of linear equations can be set up and solved simultaneously for the desired concentrations. Unfortunately, in many cases, the presence of scattered radiation makes the direct application of Beer's law inaccurate, especially at high values of absorbance. Furthermore, since the energy available in the useful portion of the infrared is usually quite small, it is necessary to use rather wide slit widths in the infrared spectrophotometers. Consequently, it is impossible to work with monochromatic radiation. A very slight shift of the wavelength setting of the monochromator causes a considerable change in the apparent value of the molar absorptivity. Each worker must determine this value for each compound at definitely reproducible wavelength settings of his instrument.

Empirical methods are often employed. If the spectrometer will reproduce the wavelength setting and the spectral band width, a working curve of absorbance vs concentration can be prepared. Otherwise it is necessary to use a comparison method of the unknown with knowns. The base-line method, shown in Fig. 5-23, involves selection of an absorption band of the analyte which does not fall too close to the bands of other matrix components. The value of the incident radiant energy P_0 is obtained by drawing a straight line tangent to the spectral absorption curve at the position of the analyte's absorption band. The transmittance P is measured at the point of maximum absorption. The value of $\log (P_0/P)$ is then plotted against concentration in the usual manner.

If the absorption bands of the analyte are close to those of the main constituent or an internal standard, it may be possible to measure an empirical ratio, P'_0/P', such as illustrated in Fig. 5-24. A plot of $\log P'_0/P'$ is made

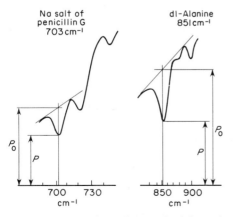

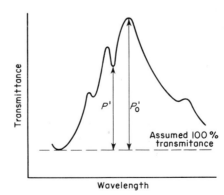

Fig. 5-23. The base-line method for calculation of the transmittance ratio in quantitative analysis.

Fig. 5-24. The empirical ratio method of determining the transmittance ratio in quantitative analysis.

against concentration. Many possible errors are eliminated by the base-line and deflection ratio methods. The same cell is used for all determinations. All measurements are made at points of the spectrum which are sharply defined by the spectrum itself, thus no dependence on wavelength settings. Use of such ratios eliminates changes in instrument sensitivity, source intensity, or changes in adjustment of the optical system. If necessary, correction for stray energy can be made by choosing as the zero point for measurements of P'_0 and P', the maximum absorption point of a nearby band of the main constituent (or solvent) where there is very intense or total absorption of all energy.

Pellets from the KBr disk technique can be employed in quantitative measurements. Uniform pellets of similar weight are essential, however, for quantitative analysis. Known weights of KBr are taken, plus a known quantity of analyte, from which absorption data a calibration curve can be constructed. The disks are weighed and their thickness measured at several points on the surface with a dial micrometer. The disadvantage of measuring pellet thickness can be overcome by the use of an internal standard. Potassium thiocyanate makes an excellent choice as internal standard. It should be preground, dried, and then reground, at a concentration of 0.2 percent by weight, with dry KBr. The final mix is stored over phosphorus pentoxide. A standard calibration curve is then made by mixing about 10 percent by weight of the analyte with the KBr-KSCN mixture and then grinding. The ratio of the thiocyanate absorption at 2125 cm^{-1} (4.70 μ) to a chosen band absorption of the analyte is plotted against percent concentration of the sample. With the same KBr-KSCN mixture, the unknown is formed into a similar pellet, its absorbance ratio measured, and the concentration read off the curve.

LABORATORY WORK

Wavelength Calibration for Infrared Spectrophotometers

A strip of polystyrene film, mounted on a handy frame, is commonly used for calibration of the wavelength (or wave number) scale. It possesses a large number of sharp absorption bands whose wavelengths are accurately known. The spectrum and a number of marked bands are shown in Fig. 5-25.

Convenient points for the near infrared region are furnished by 10-cm lengths of gaseous ammonia which has bands at these wavelengths: 1.513, 1.967, 2.264, 2.988, 6.135, 10.332, and 10.71μ.

Sample Handling

The infrared absorption cells must be handled very carefully. Do not breathe onto the window material or touch the window material with your fingers.

Liquid samples. By means of a hypodermic needle, transfer a portion of the liquid sample to the absorption cell. Wipe away any excess. Place the cell into the holder in the sample compartment; close the cover.

Nujol mulls. Place a small amount of the solid sample in a small mortar and grind to extreme fineness (about 200 mesh). Add a drop or two of Nujol (or other suitable mulling liquid) and regrind. Transfer the slurry to a sodium chloride window, placing

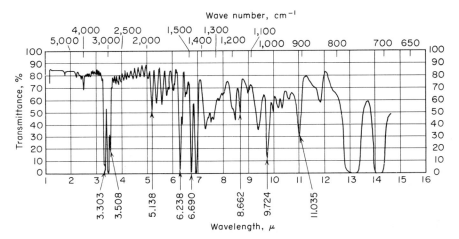

Fig. 5-25. Polystyrene film vs air; λ values after Plyler. (Courtesy Beckman Instrument Co.)

it in the cavity made by the spacer. Place the other window on top and assemble the cell. Wipe away the excess slurry that is squeezed from the cell windows. Place the cell in the sample compartment.

KBr *disk*. To produce a window having a diameter of 1.2 cm, 100 mg of powdered KBr are mixed thoroughly in a mortar and pestle with 0.05–0.5 mg of finely ground sample. Place the sample mixture within the pressing chamber of the mold so that it is contained by the polished surfaces of the top and bottom pressing dies. Attach the chamber to the vacuum line and start the vacuum pump after first applying a slight pressure to impact the powder. Apply the vacuum for $\frac{1}{2}$ min (15 mm of mercury, or less). Quickly increase the pressing force to 20,000 lb for a $\frac{1}{2}$-in. window (100,000 lb/in.² is usually sufficient). Maintain the vacuum and maximum pressure for 1 min. Release the vacuum, remove the pressure, and very carefully dismantle the die. Remove the window from the mold and place it on the sample holder. A blank KBr pellet, properly pressed, should transmit 85–90 percent of the incident light beam for wavelengths of 2 μ or longer. Successive windows should reproduce transmission curves which coincide within 1–2 percent transmittance.

No further directions will be given, since each laboratory will be equipped with specific instruments whose operating directions are contained in operating manuals supplied by the manufacturer. The instructor will assign the material to be investigated and supply detailed operating directions.

Problems

1. What is the energy, expressed in electron volts, required to raise the molecular vibration to an excited level?

2. Estimate the force constant for each pair of atoms from Gordy's rule: (a) P—S for which $N = 2$ and $d = 1.85$ Å; (b) P—O, for which $N = 2$ and $d = 1.39$ Å;

(c) C=C for which $d = 1.33$ Å; (d) C—Cl for which $d = 1.27$ Å; (e) S—S, for which $d = 2.08$ Å; (f) C≡C, for which $d = 1.20$ Å; (g) N—O, for which $d = 1.46$ Å; (h) S=O, for which $d = 1.46$ Å; (i) N=O, for which $d = 1.15$ Å. Ans. (a) 5.24×10^5 dynes cm^{-1}; (b) 9.3×10^5 dynes cm^{-1}

3. The molecular heterotope Cl^{35}Cl^{37} has a fundamental band at 554 cm^{-1} in the gaseous state. Where would one expect the 1st and 2nd overtones? What window material would be suitable? Ans. 2nd overtone at 1638 cm^{-1} in actuality.

4. Assuming a simple diatomic molecule, obtain the frequencies of the absorption band from the force constants given. Compare your answers with the tabulated positions in Fig. 5-13.
    (a) $k = 5.1 \times 10^5$ dynes cm^{-1} for C—H bond in ethane.
    (b) $k = 5.9 \times 10^5$ dynes cm^{-1} for C—H bond in acetylene.
    (c) $k = 4.5 \times 10^5$ dynes cm^{-1} for C—C bond in ethane.
    (d) $k = 7.6 \times 10^5$ dynes cm^{-1} for C—C bond in benzene.
    (e) $k = 17.5 \times 10^5$ dynes cm^{-1} for C≡N bond in CH$_3$CN.
    (f) $k = 12.3 \times 10^5$ dynes cm^{-1} for C=O bond in formaldehyde.

5. Estimate the bond order from the force constants given for the bonds in Problem 4. Obtain bond lengths and Pauling electronegativities from handbooks.

6. The apparent specific absorptivities are given for various infrared absorbers. Calculate the minimum liquid concentrations determinable (mg/ml) in 0.025-mm cells (for an absorbance reading of 0.005).
    (a) $a = 900$ for CHCl$_3$ at 1216 cm^{-1}.
    (b) $a = 1320$ for CH$_2$Cl$_2$ at 1259 cm^{-1}.
    (c) $a = 4900$ for C$_6$H$_6$ at 1348 cm^{-1}.
    (d) $a = 6080$ for COCl$_2$ at 1810 cm^{-1}.
    (e) $a = 4400$ for CH$_2$ClCOCl at 1821 cm^{-1}.
    (f) $a = 1010$ for water at 1640 cm^{-1}.

7. From the data in Problem 6, calculate the proper cell thickness when the transmittance is 0.368 for a 0.1 percent solution of each pure liquid at the analysis wavelength.

8. The incorporation of an allyl group into one or both of the side chains of a barbiturate is always associated with the appearance of strong absorption bands at 10.1 and 10.8 μ. What alteration in these absorption bands would be expected by replacement of the hydrogen atom attached to the central carbon atom of the unsaturated allyl group by bromine? *Ans.* Bands shift about 1 μ to higher wavelengths due to slowing down of allyl group vibration by a heavy atom.

9. The absorption bands at 2960 cm^{-1} (3.38 μ) and 2930 cm^{-1} (3.42 μ) are assignable to methyl and methylene groups, respectively. Identify the particular aliphatic acid from the observed ratio of absorbances—2960 cm^{-1}/2930 cm^{-1}. (a) 1:2; (b) 1:6; (c) 1:4; (d) 1:3; (e) 1:7; (f) a 6-carbon acid with 1:1 ratio, also a doublet at 1380–1365 cm^{-1}; (g) 1:2 ratio, a doublet at 1380–1365 cm^{-1}, and a band at 720 cm^{-1}. *Ans.* (b) caprylic acid, (f) 4-methyl pentanoic acid.

10. A crystalline material is believed to be either a substituted hydroxylethyl cyanamide (I) or an imino oxazolidine (II):

$$N{\equiv}C{-}NH_2{}^+{-}CH{-}CH_2OH \qquad\qquad \overset{\textstyle O}{\overset{\|}{HN{=}CH{-}NH{-}C{-}CH_2{-}}}$$
$$\mathrm{I} \qquad\qquad\qquad\qquad\qquad\qquad \mathrm{II}$$

Sharp bands are located at 3330 cm^{-1} (3.0 μ) and 1600 cm^{-1} (6.25 μ), but there are no bands at 2300 cm^{-1} (4.35 μ) or 3600 cm^{-1} (2.78 μ). Which structure fits the infrared data? *Ans.* II.

11. List all the absorption bands to be expected in the spectrum of a straight-chain six-carbon acid, along with the approximate wave number (or wavelength) assignment. Identify the bands in Fig. 5-19 with the characteristic bands enumerated.

12. Estimate the minimum concentration detectable $(A = 0.005)$ in 0.05-mm cells for each of the following compounds, given their molar absorptivities:
     (a) Phenol at 3600 cm^{-1}, $\epsilon = 5000$ (*Ans.* 2×10^{-4} *M*). '
     (b) Aniline at 3480 cm^{-1}, $\epsilon = 2000$.
     (c) Acrylonitrile at 2250 cm^{-1}, $\epsilon = 590$.
     (d) Acetone at 1720 cm^{-1}, $\epsilon = 8100$.
     (e) Isocyanate (in polyurethane foam) monomer at 2100 cm^{-1}, $\epsilon = 17,000$.

13. Calculate the thickness of the four cells from their interference fringes.

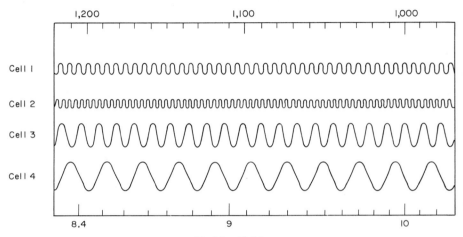

Problem 5-13.

14. Identify the particular xylene from the infrared data:
     Compound A: Absorption bands at 767 and 692 cm^{-1} (13.0 and 14.4 μ).
     Compound B: Absorption band at 792 cm^{-1} (12.6 μ).
     Compound C: Absorption band at 742 cm^{-1} (13.5 μ).
     Ans. Compound C is *o*-xylene (see Fig. 5-22).

15. A bromotoluene, C_7H_7Br, has a single band at 801 cm^{-1} (12.50 μ). What is the correct structure?

16. A chlorobenzene exhibits no absorption bands between 900 and 690 cm^{-1} (11.1 and 14.5 μ). What is the probable structure? *Ans.* Hexachlorobenzene.

17. An aromatic compound, C_7H_8O, has these features in its infrared spectrum: Absorption bands present at 3190 cm^{-1} (3.13 μ), 1060 cm^{-1} (9.45 μ), 3380 cm^{-1} (2.96 μ), 2940 cm^{-1} (3.4 μ), 1460 cm^{-1} (6.85 μ), and 690 cm^{-1} and 740 cm^{-1} (14.5 and 13.5 μ), whereas bands were absent at 1735 cm^{-1} (5.77 μ), 2720 cm^{-1} (3.68 μ), 722 cm^{-1} (13.85 μ), 1380 cm^{-1} (7.25 μ), 1182 cm^{-1} (8.45 μ) and 1038 cm^{-1} (9.65 μ). Identify the mode of each absorption band present (and absent), and write the structure of the compound.

18. The only significant absorption bands observed in the infrared spectrum were stretching of saturated C—H at 2960 and 2870 cm^{-1} (3.38 and 3.49 μ), methylene bending at 1461 cm^{-1} (6.85 μ), terminal methyl at 1380 cm^{-1} (7.25 μ), and the rocking of ethyl groups at 775 cm^{-1} (12.9 μ). Deduce the structure of this compound, C_6H_{14}. *Ans.* 3-methyl pentane.

19. Deduce the structure of C_4H_5N. Sharp, distinctive absorption bands, and virtually nothing else, occur at 3080 cm⁻¹ (3.25 μ), 2960 cm⁻¹ (3.38 μ), 2260 cm⁻¹ (4.43 μ) 1865 cm⁻¹ (5.36 μ), 1647 cm⁻¹ (6.08 μ), 1418 cm⁻¹ (7.05 μ), 990 cm⁻¹ (10.1 μ), and 935 cm⁻¹ (10.7 μ). The band at 1865 cm⁻¹ is weak.

20. An aromatic compound, C_7H_9N, has absorption bands at these wave numbers: 3520, 3430, 3290, 3030, 2925, 1622, 1588, 1494, 1471, 1442, 1380, 1303, 1268, and 748 cm⁻¹. Deduce its structure. *Ans. o*-toluidine.

21. An aromatic compound, C_8H_8O, has absorption bands at these wave numbers: 3080, 2960, 1680, 1600, 1580, 1450, 1430, 1360, 1265, 755, and 690 cm⁻¹. Deduce its structure.

22. What is the following compound that contains sodium? Mol. wt. = 144. Absorption bands occur at these wave numbers: 3060, 1599, 1549, 1415, 714, and 673 cm⁻¹. *Ans.* Sodium benzoate.

23. Deduce the structure of the compound, C_2H_4ClNO. M.p. is 118–119°C. Absorption bands occur at these wave numbers: 3350, 2940, 1644 (broad), 1615, 1430, 1404, 1274, 1250, 1102, and 774 cm⁻¹.

24. The compound, $C_{13}H_{11}N$, melts at 56°C. Absorption bands occur at these wave numbers: 3060, 2870, 1627, 1593, 1579, 1487, 1452, 1368, 1195, 759, and 692 cm⁻¹. Deduce its structure. *Ans.* Benzylideneaniline.

25. The organic compound $C_6H_{14}O$ shows no absorption bands due to C=O or O—H stretching frequencies. There is a band at 1112 cm⁻¹ and a doublet at 1380 and 1370 cm⁻¹. The NMR spectrum shows a doublet and a symmetrical heptet in the integrated ratio of 6:1. What is its probable structure?

26. Deduce the structure of the compound whose empirical formula is C_7H_5OCl. Absorbances are in parentheses after each frequency; the cell thickness is 0.1 mm. 871 (0.20), 900 (0.20), 1070 (0.14), 1196 (0.82), 1279 (0.14), 1383 (0.22), 1438 (0.22), 1470 (0.20), 1573 (0.30), 1593 (0.27), 1705 (1.0), 2720 (0.17), 2810 (0.19), 3080 (0.07).

27. Identify the compound whose spectrum is shown in the figure; cell thickness is 0.01 mm. Empirical formula is $C_{10}H_{14}$.

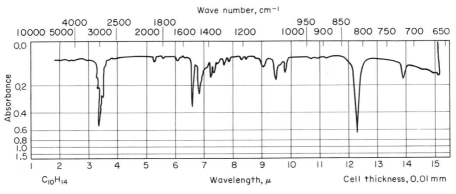

Problem 5-27.

28. An evil-smelling compound, whose molecular weight is 78, has the spectrum shown. Write its structure.

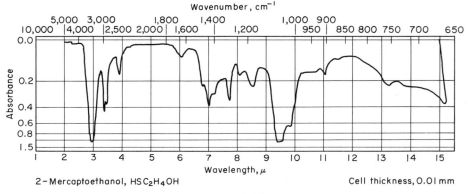

2-Mercaptoethanol, HSC₂H₄OH   Cell thickness, 0.01 mm

Problem 5-28.

29. Identify the material, empirical formula $C_4H_6O_2$, used in plastic formulations. Its spectrum is shown as obtained with a cell thickness of 0.01 mm. *Ans.* Methyl acrylate.

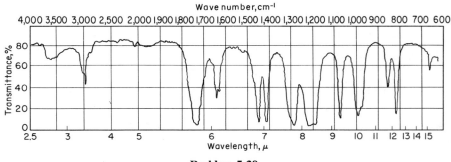

Problem 5-29.

30. A compound contains two types of unsaturation, leading to some overlap in absorption bands. Can you unravel the structure whose empirical formula is $C_{10}H_{12}O$? *Ans.* 6-allyl-*o*-cresol.

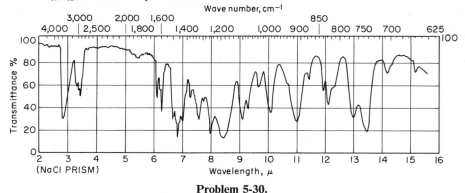

Problem 5-30.

Bibliography

Anderson, D. H., N. B. Woodall, and W. West, "Infrared Spectroscopy," in A. Weissberger (Ed.), *Technique of Organic Chemistry*, 3rd ed., Vol. I, Part 3, Interscience, New York, 1960.

Bauman, R. P., *Absorption Spectroscopy*, Wiley, New York, 1962.

Beaven, G. H., E. A. Johnson, H. A. Willis, and R. G. J. Miller, *Molecular Spectroscopy*, Heywood, London, 1961.

Bellamy, L. J., *The Infrared Spectra of Complex Molecules*, 2nd ed., Wiley, New York, 1958.

Herzberg, G., *Molecular Spectra and Molecular Structure*, Vols. I and II, Van Nostrand, Princeton, N.J., 1945.

Hoyer, H., "Infrarotspektroscopie," in E. Müller (Ed.), Houben-Weyl, *Methoden der Organishchen Chemie*, Vol. III, pp. 795–900, 4th ed., Georg Thieme Verlag, Stuttgart, 1955.

Jones, R. N., and C. Sandorfy, "The Application of Infrared and Raman Spectroscopy to the Elucidation of Molecular Structure," Vol. IX, Chapter IV, in A. Weissberger (Ed.), *Technique of Organic Chemistry*, Interscience, New York, 1956.

Silverstein, R. M., and G. C. Bassler, *Spectrometric Identification of Organic Compounds*, Wiley, New York, 1963.

Wilson, E. B., Jr., J. C. Decius, and P. C. Cross, *Molecular Vibrations*, McGraw-Hill, New York, 1955.

Literature Cited

1. Gordy, W., *J. Chem. Phys.*, **14**, 305 (1946).
2. Sadtler Catalog of Standard Spectra, Samuel P. Sadtler and Son, Inc., Philadelphia, Pa.
3. Smith, D. C., and E. C. Miller, *J. Opt. Soc. Am.*, **34**, 130 (1944).
4. Sutherland, G. B. B. M., and H. A. Willis, *Trans. Faraday Soc.*, **41**, 181 (1945).
5. Thomas, M. B. B. (Ed.), *An Index of Published Infrared Spectra*, Vols. I and II, British Information Service, New York, 1960.

Nuclear Magnetic Resonance Spectroscopy

This chapter describes a form of spectroscopy in which, as a result of the magnetic properties of nuclei arising from their axial spin, radio-frequency radiation is absorbed in a magnetic field. The method is called nuclear magnetic resonance (NMR) or nuclear spin resonance (NSR) spectroscopy. For a particular nucleus an NMR absorption spectrum commonly consists of one to several groups of absorption lines in the radio-frequency portion of the electromagnetic spectrum. The location indicates the chemical nature of the nucleus; multiplets provide information concerning the spatial positions of neighboring nuclei. Also, each nucleus in a given bonding situation contributes one unit of intensity to the resonance signal, so the number of indistinguishable nuclei of a given isotope can be determined.

Basic Principles of NMR

Nuclear Spin

About half of the known nuclei behave as if they were spinning as a whole about an axis like a child's top. They resemble a minute bar magnet, the axis of which is coincident with the axis of spin. The angular momentum of the charge created by the spinning electrons can be described in terms of spin numbers I (in units of $h/2\pi$ where h is Planck's constant). Spin numbers have integral or half-integral values from $1/2$ to at least $9/2$ for different nuclei; $I = 0$ denotes no spin.

160

The spin number is obtained by the addition of individual proton and neutron spin numbers of $1/2$ each, with the restriction that neutrons can cancel only neutrons and protons can cancel only protons. Three classes of nuclei may be distinguished: (a) Those with zero spin in which both the number of neutrons and number of protons is even—for example, C^{12}, O^{16} and S^{32}. Nuclei in this category do not give rise to an NMR signal, neither do they interfere with an NMR signal from other nuclei. (b) Those with half-integral spin in which either the number of protons or the number of neutrons is odd—for example, H^1, B^{11}, F^{19}, P^{31}, Cl^{35}, and Br^{79}. (c) Those with integral spin in which both the number of neutrons and the number of protons is odd—for example, H^2 and N^{14}.

Nuclei possessing nuclear spin values of $1/2$ act as though they were spherical bodies possessing a uniform charge distribution which circulates over their surfaces. When a probing electrical charge approaches such a nucleus, it experiences an electrostatic field whose magnitude is independent of the direction of approach. The electrical quadrupole moment is said to be zero. These nuclei include H^1, F^{19}, and P^{31}, the nuclei upon which most effort has been ex-

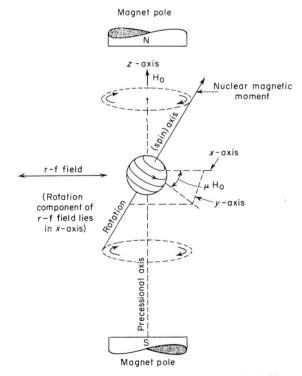

Fig. 6-1. Spinning nucleus in a magnetic field.

pended in NMR studies. Most of the other spinning nuclei possess non-spherical charge distributions over their surfaces and a corresponding electrical quadrupole moment which affects their relaxation time and their coupling with neighboring nuclei.

Nuclear Energy Levels

As the electrical charges in a spinning nucleus describe an orbit about the nuclear axis (represented by the z-axis in Fig. 6-1), the moving charges give rise to a magnetic field lying along the presumed axis of rotation. The resultant magnetic field may be represented by a nuclear magnetic moment, μ.

When a spinning nucleus is placed in a strong, uniform magnetic field H (in the z direction in Fig. 6-1), the field exerts a torque upon the nuclear magnet and the nucleus tends to assume a definite orientation with respect to the external field. The torque is a vector with its direction at right angles to the plane of μ and H. The net effect is a rotation of the nuclear axis around the direction of the external field, called precessional motion. Each pole of the nuclear axis sweeps out a circular path in the xy-plane. In effect, the applied magnetic field aligns the spinning nuclei against the disordering tendencies of thermal processes in the sample.

Each orientation of the nucleus corresponds to a different energy level or state. These energy levels are characterized by magnetic quantum numbers m, where m may take any of the values

$$I, (I - 1), (I - 2), \ldots, -(I - 2), -(I - 1), -I$$

for a total of $2I + 1$ possible energy levels. Typical energy levels are diagramed in Fig. 6-2 for nuclei of spin numbers 1/2, 1, and 3/2. For each isotope the energy levels are equally spaced, and the separation between adjacent energy levels is $\mu H/I$. The proton, for example, has two orientations or energy levels: aligned with the field ($I = 1/2$), the low-energy level; or antiparallel with the field ($I = -1/2$), the high-energy (unstable) level. The energy levels, and, consequently, the separation between adjacent levels, are a function of the magnitude of the nuclear magnetic moment and the strength of the applied magnetic field.

Resonance

When an alternating radio-frequency field, in the x direction of Fig. 6-1 and superimposed over the stationary magnetic field, rotates at exactly the frequency of an energy level, the nuclear ensemble is brought into phase coherence. Simultaneously, the nuclei will be provided enough energy to undergo a transition from a lower energy state to a higher energy state. The frequency ν of the radiation that will effect transitions between energy levels is derived by equating the Planck quantum of energy with the energy of reorientation of a magnetic dipole, namely,

$$\Delta E = h\nu = \mu H/I \qquad (6\text{-}1)$$

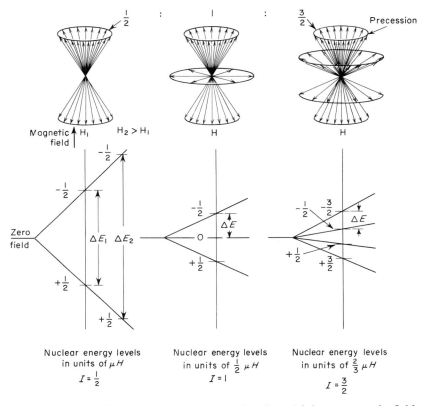

Fig. 6-2. Nuclear orientation and energy levels of nuclei in a magnetic field for different spin numbers.

Absorption of energy of the resonance frequency causes nuclei in a lower energy level to be "flipped" to the next higher energy level; a selection rule allows transitions only between adjacent levels.

The frequency of the resonance absorption can be varied by altering the value of the applied magnetic field, as indicated in Eq. 6-1. Since the strength of the absorption signal is roughly proportional to the square of the magnetic field, large values of field strength lead to a large population difference and a strong absorption signal. Considerations of magnet construction limit the applied field to approximately 23,000 gauss. An abridged table of nuclear characteristics, taken from the larger compilation by Varian Associates, is given in Table 6-1.

Example 6-1

For a proton, $\mu_p = 1.41 \times 10^{-23}$ erg gauss^{-1}. From Eq. 6-1,

$$\nu = \frac{(1.41 \times 10^{-23} \text{ erg/gauss})(14,092 \text{ gauss})}{(6.6256 \times 10^{-27} \text{ erg sec})(1/2)} = 60 \times 10^6 \text{ sec}^{-1}$$

Table 6-1	Properties of Nuclei		
ISOTOPE	RELATIVE SENSITIVITY AT CONSTANT FREQUENCY†	NMR FREQUENCY IN Mc/sec FOR 14,092 GAUSS FIELD	SPIN I IN MULTIPLES OF $h/2\pi$
H^1	1.000	60.000	1/2
H^2	0.409	9.211	1
Li^7	1.94	23.319	3/2
B^{10}	1.72	6.447	3
B^{11}	1.60	19.250	3/2
C^{13}	0.251	15.085	1/2
N^{14}	0.193	4.335	1
F^{19}	0.941	56.446	1/2
P^{31}	0.405	24.288	1/2
Cl^{35}	0.490	5.879	3/2
Br^{81}	1.35	16.203	3/2
I^{127}	2.33	12.005	5/2
Pb^{205}	0.209	8.899	1/2

†For equal number of nuclei.

That is, the protons will precess 60 million times per second (60 Mc/sec) in a fixed field of 14,092 gauss. No overlapping of signals from different nuclei occurs because the frequencies of resonance of the isotopes are widely separated.

Example 6-2

The Larmor precession theorem can be stated in terms of the angular velocity, ω, of the precessing nuclear axis, as follows:

$$\omega = 2\pi\nu = \frac{\mu H}{hI/2\pi} = \gamma H$$

where γ is the ratio of the magnetic moment to the angular momentum — the magnetogyric ratio. The magnetogyric ratio for a proton is

$$\gamma = \frac{2\pi\mu_p}{hI} = \frac{(2)(3.1416)(1.41 \times 10^{-23} \text{ erg/gauss})}{(6.6256 \times 10^{-27} \text{ erg sec})(1/2)}$$

$$\gamma = 2.674 \times 10^4 \text{ gauss}^{-1} \text{ sec}^{-1}$$

Often the expression for angular velocity will be given in terms of the nuclear magneton, μ_N, and a spectroscopic splitting factor g, namely,

$$\omega = 2\pi g \mu_N H/I$$

A nuclear magneton (cgs) is given by

$$\mu_N = eh/4\pi m_e c = 5.0505 \times 10^{-24} \text{ erg gauss}^{-1}$$

where e is the ratio of the magnetic moment to the angular momentum — the mag-electron. For a proton, $g = 5.5854$, and

$$\mu_p = gI\mu_N = 2.7927 \text{ (in multiples of the nuclear magneton)}$$

In an applied field of 14,000 gauss, it is the sad fact that only 20 protons out of each 10 million serve as the effective participating population, because of the cancellation of opposing vectors for the remainder. The population ratio is given by the Boltzmann relation

$$(n_{\text{upper}}/n_{\text{lower}}) = e^{-\mu H/IkT} \tag{6-2}$$

If an absorption signal is to persist, some mechanism must be provided for replenishing the number of nuclei in the lower energy state. Relaxation forces provide the answer. Energy may be transferred to the molecular system (or lattice in solids) by way of interactions between the nucleus and its surrounding electrons. In solids or viscous liquids, the relaxation time is in the order of hours, but in nonviscous liquids and dilute solutions the time varies from 10^{-2} to 10^2 sec, a proper duration to produce an absorption peak of usable width. Nuclei with a spin greater than $1/2$ usually possess nuclear electrical quadrupole moments which interact rather strongly with molecular electrical fields, resulting in adverse relaxation times and broad lines. Should too strong a radio-frequency field be applied, the system becomes saturated and the NMR absorption signal falls to zero—a step which is done deliberately for spin-decoupling purposes (q.v.).

Measurement of NMR Spectra

NMR Spectrometer

The NMR spectrum can be scanned either by changing the frequency of the radio-frequency oscillator or by changing the spacings of the energy levels by making a small change in the applied magnetic field. It is common practice to utilize a fixed oscillator and a variable magnetic field. A schematic block diagram of an NMR spectrometer of the "crossed coil" type is shown in Fig. 6-3.

The nonmagnetic sample holder, shown in more detail in Fig. 6-4, holds the sample that is contained in a small glass tube whose cross section is kept as small as possible. Often the internal diameter is 2–3 mm. The sample holder is spun at a rate of several hundred revolutions per minute to increase the apparent homogeneity of the magnetic field throughout the sample volume.

The sample holder is placed between the pole faces of a magnet (approximately 12 in. in diameter and spaced 1.75 in. apart). For high resolution work the magnetic field over the whole sample must be maintained uniform in space and time within about 1 part in 10^8. For an electromagnet this requires elaborate current stabilization, but this disadvantage is offset by the ability to employ different field strengths to disentangle chemical shifts from multiplet structures, and to study different nuclei. Permanent magnets are limited to 10,000 gauss and changes in field strength are not possible.

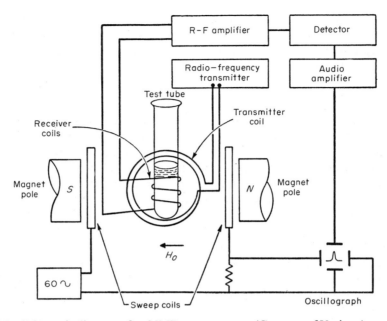

Fig. 6-3. Schematic diagram of an NMR spectrometer. (Courtesy of Varian Associates.)

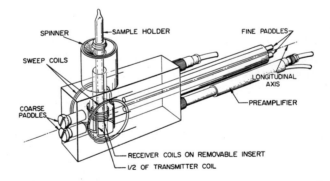

Fig. 6-4. The sample holder for the NMR spectrometer shown in detail. (Courtesy of Varian Associates.)

To flip the rotating nuclear axes with respect to the magnetic field, an oscillating radio-frequency field, supplied by a low-power, crystal-controlled oscillator, is imposed at right angles, which would be perpendicular to the plane of the paper in Fig. 6-3. The coil that transmits the radio-frequency field is made in two halves to allow insertion of the sample holder, and the two halves are placed in the magnet gap. Coils wound about the poles of the magnet, or located within the pole gap, allow a sweep to be made through the applied magnetic field which produces resonance in the range of precession frequencies anticipated from the information in Table 6-1. In the Varian HR60 instrument, the radio-frequency oscillator is set at 60 Mc/sec, and the sweep generator periodically sweeps the main magnetic field in the immediate vicinity of 14,092 gauss. The range of sweep for protons is approximately 1000 cps. A pattern of signal amplitudes is obtained when the current in the pair of sweep coils is varied periodically to provide a sweep rate of 10–50 m-gauss (0.1–0.5 ppm) per second so that a dynamic event can be observed.

A few turns of wire wound tightly around the sample tube forms a separate radio-frequency coil which picks up the resonant signal from the sample. The receiver coil is perpendicular to both the stationary field and the radio-frequency transmitter coil to minimize pickup from these fields. Even so, coupling between receiver and transmitter coils (called "leakage") persists to a small degree. It is cancelled by devices called "paddles" (Fig. 6-4), which act as inductors mutually coupled to both receiver and transmitter. Energy is absorbed from the receiver coil when nuclear transitions are induced (that is, a y component is produced in Fig. 6-1). Absorption of energy causes the radio-frequency voltage across the receiver coil to drop. This voltage change is amplified and detected by a high gain radio-frequency amplifier and diode detector tuned to the same frequency as the radio-frequency transmitter. The resulting d-c voltage is placed on the vertical plates of an oscilloscope to produce a pattern of intensity as a function of frequency—the NMR spectrum.

The Varian A60 spectrometer (Fig. 6-5) belongs in a separate category. It is designed for use with protons only over the limited chemical shift range of 2000 cps below and 500 cps above tetramethyl silane at 60 Mc/sec. The instrument is much easier to operate than the conventional high-resolution (HR60) instrument. Two samples are used, one of which is water. This is the control sample which provides a proton resonance from which a control signal is derived. Both control sample and test sample are excited by a radio-frequency field of 60 Mc/sec and by a 5-kilocycle modulation of the fixed magnetic field of 14,092 gauss. The magnetic field is adjusted for precession of the nuclei at the side band of 60.005 Mc/sec. Diode detection at the receiver of the 5-kc frequency between the 60-Mc fundamental and the 60.005-Mc upper side band is so phased that when amplified and applied to the magnet-field modulation coils in the probe it causes oscillations in the loop containing amplifier. This closed loop control provides the stability for operation with precalibrated recorder charts. The sweep system is designed so that the strong line of tetramethyl silane corresponds to the position of $\delta = 0$ $(\tau = 10)$ on the chart, and can be set exactly at this position with the fine sweep adjustment.

The Varian A-56/60 NMR spectrometer follows the design objectives of the model A-60. The instrument operates at either of two selectable radio frequencies, 56.4 Mc for F^{19} studies, or 60.0 Mc for H^1 studies. As with the A-60,

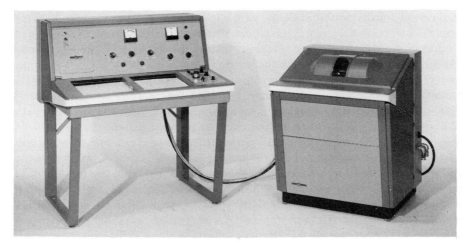

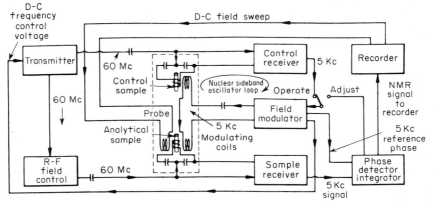

Fig. 6-5. Varian A-60 NMR spectrometer showing control console and magnet system; (*below*) schematic circuit diagram. (Courtesy of Varian Associates.)

a water resonance is part of a nuclear sideband oscillator loop which maintains a constant field frequency ratio. For fluorine studies, radio frequency is synthesized from a basic crystal oscillator which senses the operation of the control loop. The synthesized frequency is selectable in twenty 1-kc steps which bracket the resonance of the CCl_3F fluorine reference sample.

With all of the spectrometers described, variable temperature equipment will permit operation at sample temperatures from $-60°C$ to $+200°C$.

Sample Handling

Interest commonly centers about the resonance bands of protons and, to a lesser extent, those of fluorine, phosphorus, and a few other nuclei. The absorption lines of the latter isotopes appear at displacements enormous compared to the range of the proton spectrum.

At a field strength of 23,000 gauss (Varian HR100) it is possible to distinguish clearly from the noise the signal from a chemically discrete proton in a molecule which is present in a concentration of about 0.01 M. However, usual solute concentrations range from 5 to 20 percent for fields of 14,000 gauss. The actual sample size is quite small and varies from 0.01 to 0.3 ml, depending on the nature of the sample and the information needed. For other isotopes, a relative strength 0.1 on the scale employed for Table 6-1 is near the limit of usefulness with fields of 14,092 gauss (Varian HR60), and would be somewhat lower on instruments with higher applied field.*

The sample must be in the liquid state. Line width is affected by the physical state of the compound, and only when very narrow lines occur in the absorption spectrum can fine effects of multiplet couplings be measured accurately. In solids, where the positions of neighboring atoms are rigidly fixed, the physical influence of neighbors broadens the resonance line and masks any information that might be obtained from high resolution. Molecules move relatively fast in a liquid, and individual nuclear magnetic fields do not have a chance to interact strongly with other external nuclear fields because of the random tumbling of the molecule in a solution. Solid samples may be studied above their melting point, and gaseous samples below their liquification point. Viscous liquids must be diluted. Proton-free solvents include CCl_4, CS_2, $CDCl_3$, D_2O, and acetone-d_6.

Broad-Band (Wide-Line) NMR Spectrometer

Broad-band NMR stands on the same theoretical foundation as the high resolution technique. Except in special cases, however, chemical shifts and multiplet splittings do not figure prominently in its use. Line widths and shapes, as a function of temperature, and signal amplitudes, as a function of concentration, are the data sought. Naturally this leads to differences in instrumentation, particularly in the detection scheme.

An electromagnet with a field strength ranging from 1700 to 3400 gauss and a homogeneity of 1 part in 10^5 is adequate. ESR spectrometers (q.v.) may be converted to wide-line, variable-frequency, NMR spectrometers. The range of 2–16 Mc/sec suffices for studies of approximately 85 different isotopes. Because effective line widths are the same as the field inhomogeneity, all the chemical shifts are encompassed under one overlapping band for most nuclei. Sample sizes from 0.2 to 40 ml may be accommodated; the technique can be applied directly to solids.

---

*Averaging of transient signals masked by high background noise, such as with a Computer of Average Transients (CAT) manufactured by Technical Measurements Corporation, improves the detection limit 10- to 50-fold.

An early and continuing application has been the quantitative analysis of materials for proton content from the integrated area under the resonance curve. Area measurements of the dispersion signal (Fig. 6-6) are used to

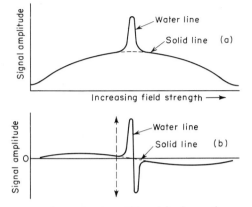

Fig. 6-6.   Resonance curves for water in solids;   (a) absorption curve and (b) dispersion curve.

construct the calibration curve, illustrated in the figure for the determination of moisture in amorphous solids or highly viscous liquids. The proton resonance appears as a greatly broadened signal, superimposed upon which is a narrow line arising from the sorbed water. In most cases the water line has a width about two or three times that of pure liquid water, whereas the width of the line of the host material may be 10–100 times greater. The determination of fluorine in chemical compounds is another area of application.

NMR Absorption Spectra

The application of NMR to chemical problems depends on the fact that the exact field experienced by the particular nucleus is not identical with the applied radio-frequency (or magnetic) field because of the diamagnetic shielding by electrons within the same molecule. The density of the extranuclear electron cloud varies with the chemical environment; each group of chemically equivalent nuclei is screened in a different degree. Thus, the magnitude of the induced field H_1 felt by each group of nuclei will be proportional to the applied field as follows:

$$H_1 = H_0(1 - \sigma) \qquad (6\text{-}2)$$

where σ is a nondimensional shielding or screening constant. The more the field induced by the circulating electrons shields the nucleus and, in effect, opposes the applied field, the higher must be the applied field to achieve resonance, if the magnetic field is varied, or the lower must be the resonance frequency if the radio-frequency field is varied. Resonance will occur in a different part of the spectrum for each chemically distinct group of a particular isotope. Because interest is highest in proton signals, subsequent discussion will be confined essentially to proton spectra, although phosphorus and fluorine spectra are also extremely useful.

The Chemical Shift

Conditions for resonance are expressed in terms of a difference (the chemical shift) between the field necessary for resonance in the sample and in some arbitrarily chosen reference compound. Typical reference compounds, each of which has only a single resonance line, are water, chloroform, cyclohexane, benzene and tetramethyl silane (TMSi) for proton spectra; perfluorocyclo-butane and trifluoroacetic acid for F^{19}; and phosphoric acid for P^{31}. For protons there appears almost universal accord to refer spectra whenever possible to TMSi used as an internal standard, with extrapolation to infinite dilution in an inert solvent such as CCl_4. Tetramethyl silane enjoys the advantage of symmetry, which reduces the possibility of specific interactions with the solvent, and its single sharp resonance line occurs at the high field end of the range of observed proton shifts where it is unlikely to obscure any other proton resonance lines arising from the sample. Reference materials may be sealed in a separate capillary, which is then placed directly in the tube which holds the sample—an external standard.

There is no accord on the value to assign to the reference or on the sign convention for expressing the chemical shift. In one system the signal from TMSi is physically placed at zero in the spectrum by the operator of the instrument. The chemical shift is expressed as a function of increasing field strength necessary to achieve the resonance condition, namely,

$$\delta = \frac{H_{sample} - H_{TMSi}}{H_1} \times 10^6 \qquad (6\text{-}3)$$

where H_{sample} and H_{TMSi} are the positions of the absorption peaks for the sample and reference material, respectively, (in cycles per second) and H_1 is the radio frequency of the signal used (usually 60 Mc/sec). One obtains a dimensionless number referred to as δ units and expressed in parts per million. A positive δ corresponds to a greater degree of screening in the sample than in the reference compound.

Example 6-3

Since it is impossible to measure the magnetic field at each absorption position with the necessary accuracy, their positions are determined relative to standard lines. Measured at 60 Mc/sec, the proton signal from benzene occurs 433 units away from the TMSi signal. Upon repeating the spectrum at 60 Mc/sec and with a 120-cps modulation of the oscillator, new peaks, termed *side bands*, appear 120 cps above and below each of the original absorption lines. Their distance apart corresponds to a separation of 240 cps, which at 60 Mc/sec equals 4.00 ppm. By simple proportion, the separation of the benzene signal from TMSi is obtained as 7.22 ppm.

In a scheme devised by Tiers,[5] TMSi is assigned an arbitrary value of 10.00. Resonance values of samples are subtracted or added as they lie at a magnetic field below or above the position of TMSi. The tau (τ) value is

$$\tau = 10.00 - \delta \qquad (6\text{-}4)$$

In the text, assignments will be made in both δ and τ values.

When comparing spectra in the older literature obtained under different field strengths and employing a reference compound other than TMSi, it will be necessary to convert chemical shifts. Table 6-2 will prove helpful.

Example 6-4

A published spectrum of n-propyl alcohol shows a peak due to the $-CH_3$ group at $+352.3$ cps with reference to benzene used as an external reference.* The radio-frequency field was 60 Mc/sec.

The shielding number, relative to benzene, is

$$352.3/60 = 5.87 \text{ ppm}$$

Since benzene lies 6.73 ppm (Table 6-2) downfield from TMSi,

$$\delta = 0.00 - (-6.73 + 5.87) = 0.86 \text{ ppm}$$
$$\tau = 10.00 - 0.86 = 9.14 \text{ ppm}$$

Had the radio-frequency field been 40 Mc/sec, the resonance peak would have occurred at 352.3 (40/60) = 234.8 cps with reference to benzene.

Table 6-2	Chemical Shifts of Reference Standards Relative to TMSi	

| | RELATIVE SHIFT | |
STANDARD	δ VALUE	τ VALUE
Chloroform	−7.25	2.75
Benzene (internal)	−7.27	2.73
(external)	−6.73	3.27
Cyclohexane	−1.49	8.51
Tetramethyl silane (TMSi)	0	10.00

As a first, very rough approximation the shift in absorption position of protons is proportional to the electron density around the nucleus, and increases linearly with decreasing electron-withdrawing power of groups attached

---

*When cylindrical sample tubes with a large length/diameter ratio are used, the correction for bulk magnetic susceptibility, in δ units, is given by

$$\delta_\kappa = 10^5(2\pi/3) (\kappa_c - \kappa_r)$$

where κ_c and κ_r are the volume susceptibilities of the compound and external reference.

to the carbon atom. Exceptions occur when electrons in neighboring bonds are magnetically anisotropic. In the case of materials with an unpaired electron, the paramagnetism associated with the net electron spin overrides the diamagnetism of the circulating paired electrons. Shielding effects seldom extend beyond one bond length except with very strong electronegative groups.

Spatial relationships with unsaturated bonds affect the proton absorption position. The induced field from π-electrons flowing in closed circuits around a benzene ring (Fig. 6-7) opposes the applied field above the faces of the ring

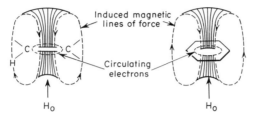

Fig. 6-7. Spatial relationships with unsaturated bonds and benzene ring.

and reinforces the signal of a proton on the edge of the ring. For carbonyl ·or olefinic bonds, the effect of the applied field is greatest along the transverse axis of the double bond. By contrast, the lines of force induced by the circulating electrons of the acetylenic bond act to shield the proton.

Protons attached to oxygen and nitrogen present special problems. Absorption positions vary over a wide range due to hydrogen bonding which, in turn, is a function of the temperature, the concentration, and the particular solvent. Another difficulty arises as a result of an exchange process in which the proton of one molecule transfers to a second at a rate that is sufficiently fast that the lifetime of a proton on any molecule is much less than the lifetime of 10^{-2} to 10^{-3} sec required for NMR to observe a single state. Were there no exchange, each site would show up as a sharp peak, but exchange averages the shielding of each environment and causes the bands to coalesce into a single peak, somewhat broader than normal, whose sharpness increases as the rate of exchange increases. Both acids and bases catalyze the exchange. Protons attached to nitrogen also have their spectra perturbed by the electric quadrupole moment of the nitrogen nucleus, resulting in a broadened absorption. Fortunately, these ambiguities due to oxygen and nitrogen can be removed by running the spectrum in deuterochloroform, then adding a few drops of deuterium oxide and shaking for several minutes. All the protons attached to oxygen and nitrogen will be replaced by deuterium ($I = 1$), which does not show up in the spectrum under the operating conditions for protons.

Band Multiplicities

In a bulk sample spinning nuclei interact with each other to cause mutual splitting of their absorption bands into multiplet structures. These multiplets arise from an indirect coupling of the nuclear spins via the bonding electrons in the molecule. This internuclear dipole effect is called *spin-spin coupling*. Coupling can take place between nuclei possessing different spin. The separation between adjacent multiplet peaks is called the coupling constant (designated by the letter *J*). The value of *J*, in cycles per second, is independent of the frequency used to make the measurement; however, the amplitude does vary in accordance with the field-strength-squared law. Values of the coupling constant for protons in various configurations are given in Table 6-3.

Table 6-3 | *Spin-spin Coupling Constants*

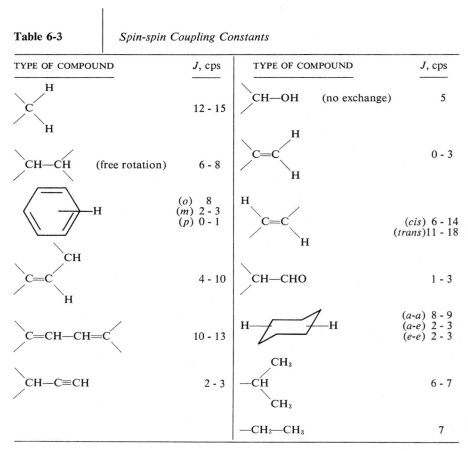

TYPE OF COMPOUND	J, cps	TYPE OF COMPOUND	J, cps
C with two H	12 - 15	CH—OH (no exchange)	5
CH—CH (free rotation)	6 - 8	C=C with two H (same side)	0 - 3
benzene ring —H	(o) 8 (m) 2 - 3 (p) 0 - 1	C=C with H and H (trans-type)	(cis) 6 - 14 (trans) 11 - 18
C=C—CH—H	4 - 10	CH—CHO	1 - 3
C=CH—CH=C	10 - 13	H— ring —H (cyclohexane)	(a-a) 8 - 9 (a-e) 2 - 3 (e-e) 2 - 3
CH—C≡CH	2 - 3	—CH with two CH₃	6 - 7
		—CH₂—CH₃	7

[From L. M. Jackman, *Applications of Nuclear Magnetic Resonance in Organic Chemistry*, Pergamon Press, London, 1959, p. 85]

Protons on the same carbon atom and on adjacent carbon atoms couple with each other, but protons on nonadjacent atoms usually do not couple unless there are intervening multiple bonds. The value of the coupling constant is very dependent on bond type and bond angles. A decrease of bond angle (on the same carbon atom, as in vinyl group) from 110^0 ($J = 12$) results in a larger coupling constant ($J = 20$ at $105°$), and an increase in this angle results in a smaller coupling constant ($J = 2$ at $120°$). The dihedral angle between planes determines the coupling constant of protons on adjacent carbon atoms (Table 6-4). Adjacent axial-axial protons, displaying a dihedral

Table 6-4	Dependence of J on the Dihedral Angle ϕ in the Saturated System H–C–C–H

$\phi°$	J, cps
0	8.2
30	6.0
60	1.7
90	−0.28
120	2.2
150	6.9
180	9.2

[From M. Karplus, *J. Chem. Phys.*, **30**, 11 (1959); M. Karplus and D. H. Anderson, *J. Chem. Phys.*, **30**, 6 (1959).]

angle of $180°$, are strongly coupled, whereas axial-equatorial and equatorial-equatorial protons are coupled only moderately. In benzene rings, splitting may extend around the ring to at least the *para* position, or may be terminated by a substituent group at almost any point.

Multiplicities can be predicted from simple first-order rules, restricted primarily to aliphatic compounds, when the difference in chemical shift between two signals (expressed in cycles per second) is much greater than the spin-coupling constant, usually $\Delta\delta \geq 2J$. This is the case in the spectrum of methyl ethyl ketone (see Fig. 6-8) where $\Delta\delta = 88$ cps and $J = 7.1$ cps. The generalized set of rules follow:

1. Equivalent protons give single, sharp peaks at the position of the unperturbed chemical shift—for example, the isolated methyl group of methyl ethyl ketone.

2. The multiplicity of the band arising from a group of equivalent nuclei is determined by the neighboring groups of equivalent nuclei. Each equivalent group splits the resonance of its neighbor into $2nI + 1$ multiplets, where n is the number of equivalent nuclei in the coupling group and I is the spin of the coupling nuclei. For protons the peaks in a multiplet are equal to the number of equivalent protons on an adjacent atom plus one. When there

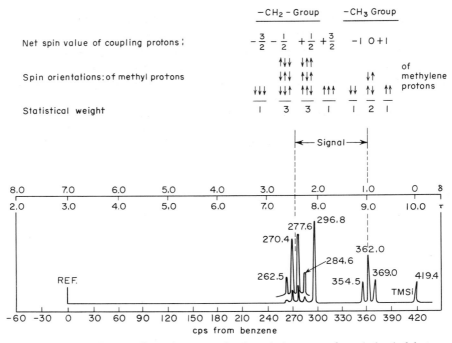

Fig. 6-8. Spin-spin coupling of protons in the ethyl group of methyl ethyl ketone. $J = 7.1$ cps. Frequency: 60 Mc/sec.

are more than two interacting groups, the multiplicity of the group split is given by $(2n_b I_b + 1)(2n_c I_c + 1)$.

Two additional facts are of value in assigning bands in overlapping multiplets.

3. Lines in a multiplet are equally spaced and, furthermore, are equal to the spacing in the multiplet which caused the splitting.

4. The intensities (areas under the bands) of the components of a multiplet are proportional to the binomial coefficients in the expansion of $(x + y)^r$ and are symmetric about the midpoint of the multiplet band. Types of multiplets and ratio of intensities of components are doublet, 1-1; triplet, 1-2-1; quadruplet, 1-3-3-1; quintet, 1-4-6-4-1; etc. Should the wings of the multiplet be lost in instrumental noise, the ratio of intensities still serves to distinguish the correct type of multiplet. However, when $\Delta\delta/J < 2$, the relative intensities of the peaks within a multiplet change, and additional lines may appear as a result of second-order splitting. Increasing the applied magnetic field separates the chemical shift values, as shown in Example 6-4, and offers a solution to this difficulty.

The application of these rules is illustrated by the spectrum of methyl ethyl ketone, shown in Fig. 6-8. Above each equivalent group of protons are given the spin orientations for the coupling protons, also their statistical weight. The three protons in the methyl group (adjacent to the methylene group) are equivalent and, as a unit, can assume four orientations with total spins of $+3/2$, $+1/2$, $-1/2$ and $-3/2$. When coupled with the protons in the methylene group, a quadruplet results whose areas bear the ratio 1-3-3-1, reflecting the statistical weight of the spin arrangements. In turn, the methyl resonance line is split into a triplet by the two protons in the methylene group. The latter can assume three orientations with total spins $+1$, 0, and -1, and this gives a statistical weighting 1-2-1.

Other nuclei with spins may also interact with protons and cause observable spin-spin splitting. Without deliberate isotopic substitution, significant numbers of only boron, fluorine, and lead nuclei occur naturally. In fact the presence of one of these elements may be deduced from an otherwise unexplained coupling effect. Deuterated compounds assist in resolving spectra. When the CH group in isopropyl benzene is replaced by CD, the doublet due to the splitting of the methyl groups collapses to a closely spaced triplet due to the difference in spin of deuterium.

Spin-Decoupling

Double irradiation solves problems introduced by complicated proton couplings. A second, relatively intense, radio-frequency field is imposed on the sample with the instrument adjusted to the resonant condition for the group whose coupling is to be eliminated. Under these conditions, the protons of the undesired nucleus are flipped rapidly enough by saturating the system so that a proton whose spin is being split cannot distinguish its individual orientations. Thus, the proton being split sees only one equivalent state and a single peak results.

Decoupling unlike nuclei is also possible through use of an appropriate precessional frequency for the second radio-frequency field.

Integral Curve

The area under an absorption band is proportional to the number of particular nuclei responsible for absorption. Instruments that are provided with an electronic integrator will trace a second curve, which consists of a series of steps whose height up to any point in the spectrum is proportional to the number of nuclei under the respective peaks. The difference in height between any two steps is likewise proportional to the number of nuclei causing the increase in elevation. Nuclei-counting with the integrator is extremely useful for identification. If the empirical formula is known, the total height (in any arbitrary units) divided by the number of protons yields the increment of height per proton. Lacking this information, but deducing the assignment of a particular absorption band, one can calculate the increment per proton from the difference in elevation for the assigned group divided by the number of protons in the particular group. Peaks hidden under other peaks can thus be detected. Unfortunately, there is no way of handling overlapping bands.

Example 6-5

An NMR absorption spectrum shows three single peaks located at δ 7.28 (τ 2.72), δ 5.00 (τ 5.00), and δ 2.00 (τ 8.00) in a field of 60 Mc/sec with TMSi as reference. The integral heights, in arbitrary units, are 42, 17, and 25, respectively.

The peak heights bear the ratio 5:2:3 and, since no splitting is observed, this must mean a group with 5 protons (probably an aromatic ring — note the value of the chemical shift), a methylene group, and a methyl group, each isolated from one another. If one had not discerned the ratio of step heights, resort could have been made to chemical shifts. The low-field position is indicative of a phenyl group, from which information the increment per proton is obtainable. If the empirical formula ($C_9H_{10}O_2$) is known, division of the total integral height (84 units) by the number of protons, gives 8.4 units as the increment per proton.

The complete structure can be deduced with a little intuition. Unaccounted for are one carbon and two oxygen atoms, obviously a carboxyl group. The placement of the carboxyl group between the methyl and methylene groups is the only way to isolate each group of protons from one another. Whether the compound is benzyl acetate or methyl phenyl acetate is answered by the chemical shifts. It is benzyl acetate.

Elucidation of NMR Spectra

It is fortunate that the majority of materials either give spectral patterns which are governed by simple first-order rules for multiplicities and intensities or give patterns sufficiently simple to be treated as first order. Improved instrumentation is, however, making the exceptions to the simple rules more common. Nevertheless, many situations exist in which one can deduce much useful information from the ability to recognize the appearance of some of the more characteristic complex patterns and qualitatively analyze them. More widespread application of spin-decoupling, particularly of nonequivalent groups of the same nuclear species, would render a great deal of the theoretical analysis superfluous for structure determination.

Extensive surveys of the chemical shifts of protons in molecules have been made.[2,4,5] Tables 6-5 and 6-6 tabulate the positions at which many groups absorb. Table 6-7 portrays this same information and indicates the range over which the three groups absorb. Similar compilations have been reported for fluorine,[1] phosphorus, and other isotopes.[3] Interpretation of the spectra of the latter elements is often much simpler because usually few nuclei are present. These tabulations can be used to predict the position of resonance bands for a known compound, and these can be compared with the sample spectrum. Conversely, one searches such compilations to ascertain groups which might occur at the positions observed in the sample spectrum. Relative position of a methyl, methylene, or methine group conforms to the general pattern of NMR spectra wherein the more highly protonated of two otherwise similar groups shows resonance at a higher field.

Table 6-5 | *Approximate Chemical Shift of Protons*

SUBSTITUENT GROUP	METHYL PROTONS δ VALUES (τ)	METHYLENE PROTONS δ VALUES (τ)	METHINE PROTONS δ VALUES (τ)
HC—C—CH₂ (or NR₂)	0.9 (9.1)	1.2 (8.8)	1.5 (8.5)
HC—C—CO	1.1 (8.9)	—	—
HC—C—C=C	1.1 (8.9)	1.7 (8.3)	—
HC—C—Ar	1.3 (8.7)	1.6 (8.4)	—
HC—C—S	1.3 (8.7)	1.5 (8.5)	—
HC—C—O—CO	1.4 (8.6)	—	—
HC—C—O	1.4 (8.6)	1.9 (8.1)	2.0 (8.0)
HC—C—Cl	1.5 (8.5)	1.7 (8.3)	1.5 (8.5)
HC—C—NO₂	1.6 (8.4)	2.1 (7.9)	—
HC—C—Br	1.7 (8.3)	1.7 (8.3)	1.8 (8.2)
HC—CH₂	0.9 (1.1)	1.3 (8.7)	1.5 (8.5)
cyclic CH₂	—	1.5 (8.5)	—
HC—C=C	1.6 (8.4)	2.3 (7.7)	—
HC—CO—O	2.0 (8.0)	2.2 (7.8)	—
HC—S	2.2 (7.8)	2.4 (7.6)	—
HC—CO—R	2.2 (7.8)	2.4 (7.6)	2.6 (7.4)
HC—NR₂	2.3 (7.7)	2.5 (7.5)	2.8 (7.2)
HC—Ar	2.4 (7.6)	2.7 (7.3)	2.9 (7.1)
HC—CO—OAr	2.4 (7.6)	—	—
HC—CO—Ar	2.6 (7.4)	—	—
HC—Br	2.7 (7.7)	3.3 (6.7)	3.6 (6.4)
HC—Cl	3.0 (7.0)	3.6 (6.4)	4.0 (6.0)
HC—OR	3.3 (6.7)	3.4 (6.6)	3.6 (6.4)
HC—OH	3.4 (6.6)	3.6 (6.4)	3.9 (6.1)
HC—O—CO—R	3.7 (6.3)	4.1 (5.9)	5.1 (4.9)
HC—O—Ar	3.8 (6.2)	4.1 (5.9)	—
HC—O—CO—Ar	4.0 (6.0)	4.3 (5.7)	5.0 (5.0)
HC—NO₂	4.3 (5.7)	4.4 (5.6)	4.6 (5.4)

Table 6-6	Approximate Chemical Shift of Miscellaneous Protons

	δ VALUES (τ)
—C≡CH	3.1 (6.9)
cyclic (ring) C=CH₂	4.6 (5.4)
>C=C< with two H	4.7 (5.3)
H$_a$ ... H$_c$ C=C H$_b$	(c) 5.9 (4.1)
	(a,b) 5.0 (5.0)
—C=CH—CO	5.9 (4.1)
—CH=C—CO	6.8 (3.2)
Ar—H	7.2 (2.8)
HCO—O	8.0 (2.0)
—CHO	9.9 (0.1)
—COOH	10–12 (0 to −2)
—SO₃H	11–12 (−1 to −2)
Ar—OH	4–7 (6 to 3)
R—OH	1–6 (9 to 4)
Ar—SH	2.8–3.6 (7.2 to 6.4)
R—SH	1.4 (8.6)
R—NH	0.5–5 (9.5–5.0)
Ar—NH	3–5 (7–5)
—NH—R	5–8 (5–2)

Table 6-7 (next page) from E. Mohacsi, *J. Chem. Educ.* **41,** 38, (1964). (*Courtesy of Journal of Chemical Education.*)

Table 6-7 | *Characteristic NMR Spectral Positions for Hydrogen in Organic Structures.*

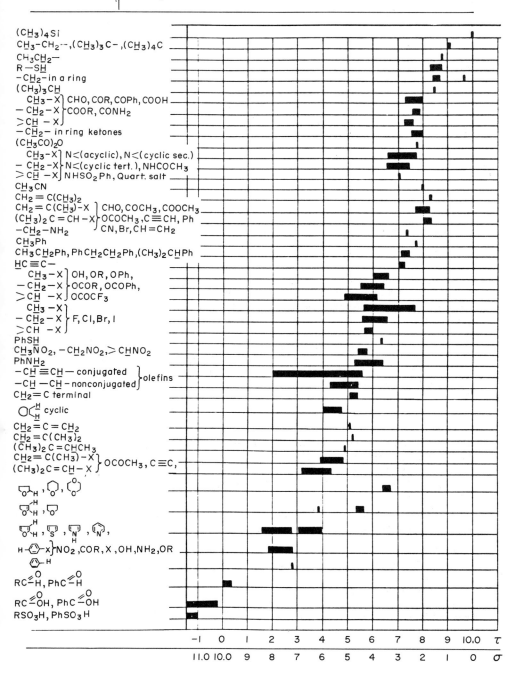

Example 6-6

The NMR spectrum shows a single peak at δ 6.83 (τ 3.17), a quadruplet at δ 4.27 (τ 5.73), and a triplet at δ 1.32 (τ 8.68). For the multiplets the coupling constant is about 7 cps. The integrator readings are in the ratio 1:2:3, respectively. Empirical formula is $C_8H_{12}O_4$.

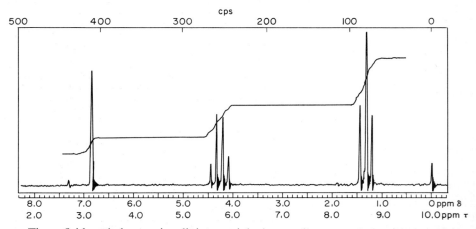

The upfield methyl group is split into a triplet by an adjacent methylene group which, in turn, is split into a quadruplet—the typical ethyl pattern. This is confirmed by the integrator readings. Assignment of the low-field group is not so simple. It is not quite in the location expected for a benzene ring, nor does it contain sufficient numbers of protons. However, an olefinic proton absorption is a possibility, although further shielding is indicated. Returning to the methylene group, its downfield position could be due to an adjacent —O—(C=O)— structure. If the olefinic proton were alongside the carbonyl group, its absorption position would be reasonable. Summarizing our present information, we have

$$CH_3—CH_2—O—\overset{\overset{\textstyle O}{\|}}{C}—CH=$$

which is exactly one-half the empirical formula. The complete structure is either diethyl fumarate or diethyl maleate. Having gotten this far we would take an NMR spectrum of each compound and would find that in diethyl maleate the low-field single peak occurs at δ 6.28 (τ 3.72). Coupling between the olefinic protons collapsed because $\delta_2 - \delta_1 = 0$.

Overlapping spectral features can be a source of difficulty in interpretation. The distribution of protons shown by the integration curve is helpful.

Example 6-7

The NMR spectrum for the compound with empirical formula $C_7H_{16}O$ shows a symmetrical heptet centered around δ 3.78 (τ 6.22) and an unsymmetrical doublet with individual peaks at δ 1.18 (τ 8.82) and δ 1.12 (τ 8.88). The integrated areas are 2 units for the heptet and 24 + 6 units for the doublet. The absence of peaks at low field indicates absence of aldehyde, unsaturation, and probably hydroxyl absorption.

The heptet spells out a probable isopropyl group whose methine proton is split by six methyl protons. Its field position indicates an adjacent oxygen. In turn, the methine proton splits the *gem*-methyl protons into a doublet. A logical presumption is an isopropyl ether group; the oxygen atom serving to isolate the methine proton from the remainder. Using the heptet proton as divisor, the integrator readings spell out nine unassigned protons in a single peak superimposed on the low-field wing of the methyl doublet in the isopropyl group. This could only mean three isolated methyl groups — a *tert*-butyl group. The compound is *t*-butyl isopropyl ether.

Problems

1. What r-f field will provide for proton resonance signals in an applied field of 23,000 gauss? Of 7,000 gauss?
2. To what value must the applied magnetic field be adjusted if the r-f field is obtained from an oscillator operating at 56.4 Mc/sec for F^{19}? For H^1?
3. Calculate the frequency required for auxiliary irradiation of a sample in order to remove unwanted multiplets arising from coupling of protons with B^{10} when the field is 10,000 gauss. Same for B^{11}.
4. The C-6 proton in $\Delta^{5,6}$ steroids absorbs at 42 cps at a field of 40 Mc/sec with reference to external benzene. Compute the position of the absorption line if the measurement had been performed at 60 Mc/sec with TMSi as the reference standard. *Ans.* At -321 cps vs TMSi.
5. In the spectrum of *p*-dimethylaminobenzaldehyde, the —CHO proton peak occurs at -174 cps and the methyl peak at $+196$ cps from benzene. The resonance position of TMSi was $+6.53$ ppm from external benzene. The r-f field was 56.4 Mc/sec. Calculate the band positions in δ and τ units for a field of 60 Mc/sec.
6. The center of a triplet due to the methyl group in a diethyl phosphonate occurs at $+204$ cps. The reference position of TMSi was $+258.0$ cps from benzene used as external reference. The r-f field was 40 Mc/sec. Calculate the band position in δ and τ units for an r-f field of 60 Mc/sec.
7. For diketene, $C_4H_4O_2$, there are five plausible structures. The NMR proton spectrum of the liquid shows two signals of equal intensity. What structure is consistent with this information? *Ans.* $CH_2{=}C{-}CH_2$.

$$O{-}C{=}O$$

8. Addition of methyldichlorosilane to vinyl acetate gives an adduct whose likely structures are

$$CH_3{-}Si(Cl)_2{-}CH_2{-}CH_2{-}O{-}CO{-}CH_3$$

or

$$CH_3{-}Si(Cl)_2{-}CH(CH_3){-}O{-}CO{-}CH_3$$

The NMR spectrum shows two bands with clearly resolved triplet splitting. Which structure is supported by the NMR evidence? *Ans.* First structure.
9. On the basis of the two peaks of equal strength found in the NMR spectrum of the sodium salt of Fiest's acid in D_2O, which structure is correct?

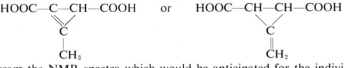

10. Diagram the NMR spectra which would be anticipated for the individual isomeric butyl alcohols. Do the same for the propyl alcohols. *Ans.* Spectrum for 2-propanol (neat liquid) contains a doublet at δ 5.12 and 5.05, a septet centered around δ 3.91 which is weakly split into doublets, and a doublet at δ 1.20 and 1.10.

11. In the spectrum of 2-propanol, given as the answer to Problem 10, deduce the individual coupling constants. *Ans.* For the methyl-methine protons, $J = 6.1$ cps; for the hydroxyl-methine protons, $J = 4.2$ cps.

12. Identify each of the multiplet structures shown for ethyl acrylate (liquid) taken at 60 Mc/sec with TMSi as internal reference.

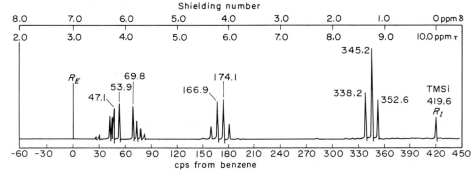

Problem 6-12.   The proton NMR spectrum of ethyl acrylate (liquid). The r-f field was 60 Mc/sec. Internal standard was TMSi; external standard was benzene.

13. The NMR spectrum contains a single peak at δ 3.58 (τ 6.42) and another single peak at δ 7.29 (τ 2.71). Integrated intensities are 8 and 20 units, respectively. From mass spectral information, the compound (mol. wt. 246) is known to contain two sulfur atoms. Deduce its structure. *Ans.* Ditolyl disulfide.

14. The NMR spectrum contains single peaks at δ 7.27 (τ 2.73), δ 3.07 (τ 6.93), and δ 1.57 (τ 8.43). The empirical formula is $C_{10}H_{13}Cl$. Deduce the structure of the compound.

15. The NMR spectrum of compound $C_4H_8Br_2$ is shown. Also shown is the trace of the integrator. Deduce the complete structure. *Ans.* 1,2-Dibromobutane.

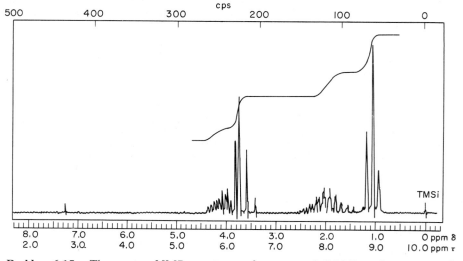

Problem 6-15.   The proton NMR spectrum of compound $C_4H_8Br_2$ taken at an r-f field of 60 Mc/sec with TMSi as internal standard.

16. Overlapping multiplets always present a challenge in unravelling an NMR spectrum, such as the one for the compound $C_6H_{11}BrO_2$ shown. Deduce the structure. Ignore the small benzene peak at δ 7.32.

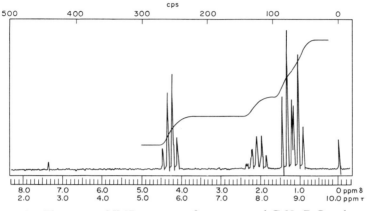

Problem 6-16. The proton NMR spectrum for compound $C_6H_{11}BrO_2$ taken with r-f field at 60 Mc/sec and TMSi as internal reference.

17. The NMR spectrum of compound $C_4H_7ClO_2$, shown, also has one obvious overlapping spectral feature. Deduce the structure. The small peak at δ 7.32 is a benzene marker. *Ans.* Ethyl chloroacetate.

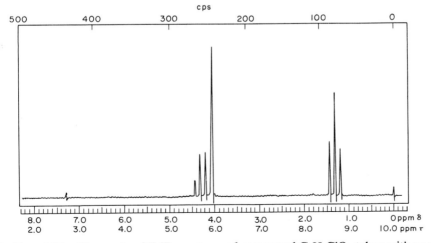

Problem 6-17. The proton NMR spectrum of compound $C_4H_7ClO_2$ taken with an r-f field of 60 Mc/sec and TMSi as internal standard.

18. Deduce the structure of the compound $C_8H_{14}O_4$ from the NMR spectrum shown. Be cognizant of the requirement for spin-spin coupling.

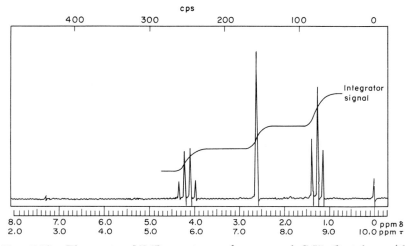

Problem 6-18. The proton NMR spectrum of compound $C_8H_{14}O_4$ taken with r-f field at 60 Mc/sec and TMSi as internal reference.

19. The compound C_3H_4 has only one peak in its NMR spectrum located at δ 1.80 (τ 8.20). Can you ascertain its structure?

20. Chart the spin-spin couplings involved in the spectrum of methyl methacrylate shown. The lower trace is an expanded scale. The resonance position of external benzene was 418.4 cps from TMSi, the internal standard, in an r-f field of 60 Mc/sec.

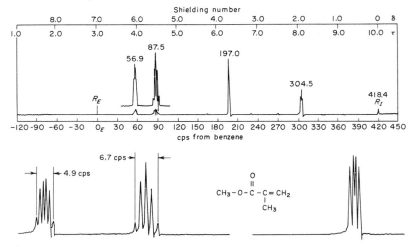

Problem 6-20. The proton NMR spectrum of methyl methacrylate (liquid) taken on Varian model A-60 spectrometer. Internal standard was TMSi; external standard was benzene.

21. The NMR spectrum of compound $C_{10}H_{13}NO_2$, isolated from a headache preparation, is shown in Fig. 6-15. Write its structure.

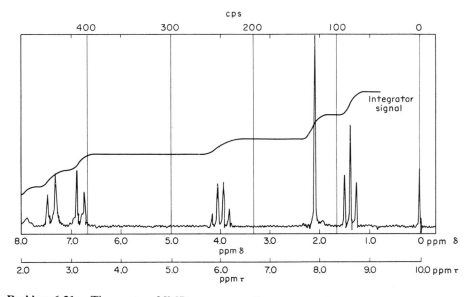

cps

Problem 6-21. The proton NMR spectrum of a compound contained in a certain headache remedy. Empirical formula is $C_{10}H_{13}NO_2$. Taken with r-f field at 60 Mc/sec and TMSi as internal reference.

22. The NMR spectrum has single peaks at δ 7.29 (τ 2.71) and δ 2.02 (τ 7.98) plus two triplets at δ 4.30 (τ 5.70) and δ 2.93 (τ 7.07). Integrated intensities are 10, 6, 4, and 4, respectively. Empirical formula is $C_{10}H_{12}O_2$. Deduce the structural formula.

23. The NMR spectrum for the compound C_3H_6O has a triplet centered at δ 4.73 (τ 5.27) and a quintet at δ 2.72 (τ 7.28). Deduce the structure.

Bibliography

Bersohn, R., *Determination of Organic Structures by Physical Methods*, edited by F. C. Nachod and W. D. Phillips, Vol. 2, Chapter 9, Academic Press, New York, 1962.

Gutowsky, H. S., *Technique of Organic Chemistry*, 4th ed., edited by A. Weissberger, Vol. I, Part IV, Interscience, New York, 1961.

Flett, M. St. C., *Physical Aids to the Organic Chemist*, Chapter 8, Elsevier, Amsterdam, 1962.

Jackman, L. M., *Applications of Nuclear Magnetic Resonance Spectroscopy in Organic Chemistry*, Pergamon, New York, 1959.

Pople, J. A., W. G. Schneider, and H. J. Bernstein, *High-Resolution Nuclear Magnetic Resonance*, McGraw-Hill, New York, 1959.

Roberts, J. D., *An Introduction to the Analysis of Spin-Spin Splitting*, Benjamin, New York, 1961.

Silverstein, R. M., and G. C. Bassler, *Spectrometric Identification of Organic Compounds*, Wiley, New York, 1963.

Varian Associates Staff, *NMR and EPR Spectroscopy*, Pergamon, New York, 1960.

Literature Cited

1. Brame, E. G., Jr., *Anal. Chem.*, **34**, 591 (1962).
2. Chamberlain, N. F., *Anal. Chem.*, **31**, 56 (1959).
3. Lauterbur, P. C., *Determination of Organic Structures by Physical Methods*, edited by F. C. Nachod and W. D. Phillips, Vol. 2, Chapter 7, Academic Press, New York, 1962.
4. Meyer, L. H., A. Saika, and H. S. Gutowsky, *J. Am. Chem. Soc.*, **75**, 4567 (1953).
5. Tiers, G. V. D., *J. Phys. Chem.*, **62**, 1151 (1958).

Electron Spin Resonance
Spectroscopy

Electron spin resonance (ESR), also called electron paramagnetic resonance (EPR), is based on the fact that atoms, ions, molecules, or molecular fragments that have an odd number of electrons exhibit characteristic magnetic properties. These arise from either the orbiting action or the spinning action, or both, of unpaired electrons about the nucleus. Unpaired electrons, relatively unusual in occurrence, are present in odd molecules, free radicals, triplet electronic states, and transition element ions. An electron possesses a spin and, associated with the spin, there is a magnetic moment.

Electron Behavior

When a strong, constant, magnetic field H is applied to the unpaired spins of an electron, there is a torque acting to make the electron dipoles line up either parallel or antiparallel to the direction of the magnetic field—the only two orientations allowed—and precess about the field axis at a frequency which is proportional to both the applied magnetic field and the electron magnetic moment, as do protons in NMR spectroscopy (q.v.). For electron spins which are parallel to the field, $E = \mu H$, whereas for those which are aligned antiparallel, $E = -\mu H$. These energy levels are illustrated in Fig. 7-1.

Because an electron bound to an atom has two distinct motions associated with it—spin about its own axis, same as for a free electron, and an orbital motion about a nucleus—the electron magnetic moment is better replaced

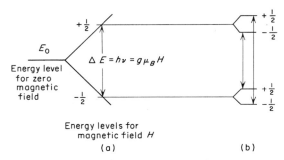

Fig. 7-1. Splitting of electron energy levels by a magnetic field. (a) Effect of electron spin only; (b) effect of adding a nucleus with spin $I = \frac{1}{2}$. Allowed transitions are indicated by arrows.

by the product $g\mu_B$, where μ_B, the Bohr magneton, is a true constant and equals $eh/4\pi\, m_e c$, and g is a variable known as the spectroscopic splitting factor. The value of g for a completely free electron is 2.0023 Mc/gauss, but when strong coupling occurs the value differs significantly.

By the Boltzmann distribution law the relative numbers of electrons in the upper and lower energy states is given by

$$n_{\text{upper}}/n_{\text{lower}} = e^{-2\mu H/kT} \tag{7-1}$$

where k is the Boltzmann constant. The absorption probability and, hence, sensitivity of the measurements increase steeply with field strength. Spectroscopic measurements become possible when the sample is simultaneously subjected to a constant magnetic field and irradiated by a much weaker radiofrequency field (in the microwave region) applied perpendicular to the fixed magnetic field and held at the frequency of precession. At resonance the absorption of energy from the rotating field causes the spins of the electrons to flip from the lower energy level to the higher level. The two levels are separated by the energy difference

$$\Delta E = 2\mu H = h\nu \tag{7-2}$$

For a free electron the frequency of absorption is given by

$$\nu = 2\mu H/h = (2.8026 \times 10^6)H \tag{7-3}$$

in megacycles per gauss. In a field of 3400 gauss, the precession frequency is approximately 9500 Mc/sec. Thus, the applied magnetic field aligns the individual unpaired electron moments against the disordering and disalignment tendencies of the thermal processes in the sample.

ESR Spectrometer

A block diagram of an ESR spectrometer appears in Fig. 7-2. In the upper portion of the figure the reflection microwave impedance bridge system is

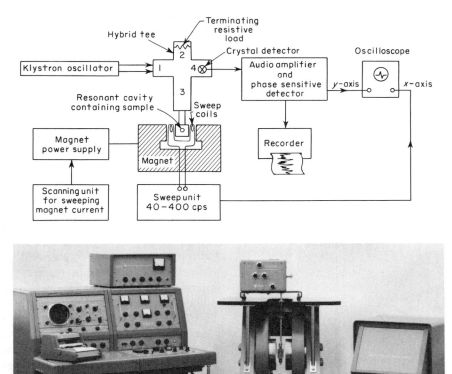

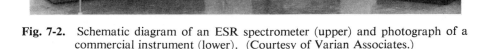

Fig. 7-2. Schematic diagram of an ESR spectrometer (upper) and photograph of a commercial instrument (lower). (Courtesy of Varian Associates.)

drawn on a larger scale. Microwaves cannot be directed by usual optical devices but can be led along rectangular metal tubes known as wave guides. The sensing element of the spectrometer is a rectangular microwave cavity constructed in such a way as to maximize the applied magnetic field along the sample dimension. A klystron oscillator, normally operated at 9500 Mc/sec, generates a microwave field. The field is applied to the resonant cavity, which is connected to one arm of the microwave bridge. The resonant cavity is placed between the pole pieces of an electromagnet, which provides a homogeneous magnetic field and which can be varied from near zero to 5000 gauss. Stability of 1 part in 10^6 is satisfactory for resolution of ESR spectra.

Provision is made for sweeping the magnetic field over a small range and through the resonant condition linearly with respect to time by varying the current in a pair of sweep coils. Standing waves are set up, the cavity serving as a very long path length cell in which waves are reflected to and fro thousands of times.

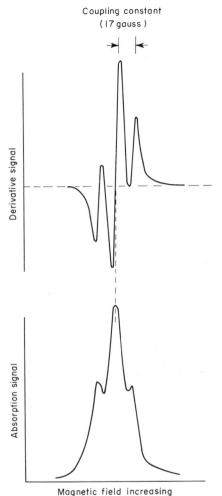

The hybrid tee is a device that will not allow microwave power to pass in a straight line from one arm to the arm opposite. Microwave power emitted from arm 1 divides equally between arms 2 and 3. Arm 3 usually contains a balancing load. When all the power is absorbed and none reflected, no power enters arm 4. Thus the crystal detector receives no energy. The detector is usually a silicon-tungsten crystal rectifier which converts microwave power to a direct-current output. At resonance, the sample absorbs energy from the microwave field. This energy change unbalances the impedance of the cavity and a signal is reflected to the crystal detector. If the d-c magnetic field is varied slowly through the value required for resonance, an absorption peak is obtained. However, a set of coils mounted on the sample cavity walls and fed by a 100-kc sweep generator provides modulation of the d-c magnetic field at the sample position. Then, if the main magnetic field is swept slowly through resonance over a period of several minutes, a dynamically recurring unbalance in the hybrid tee is detected and amplified for presentation on a recorder as the derivative of the microwave absorption spectrum against magnetic field (Fig. 7-3).

Fig. 7-3. Three-line spectrum from irradiated methanol. After M. Fijimoto and D. J. E. Ingram, *Trans. Faraday Soc.*, **54,** 1305 (1958).

tion on a recorder as the derivative of the microwave absorption spectrum against magnetic field (Fig. 7-3).

For the study of very narrow lines, frequency modulation higher than the practical limit of 100 kc/sec is achieved with a superheterodyne arrangement.

Power from a second microwave source, differing in frequency about 50 Mc/sec, is fed into the detector arm. Beats formed with the main signal (e.g., $9500 - 9450 = 50$ Mc/sec) thus become the effective output modulation frequency. A corresponding high-performance electromagnet must be incorporated in the spectrometer.

ESR Spectra

The sample may be in the form of a single crystal, solid powder, liquid or solution. Typical size of liquid samples is 0.05–0.16 ml held in pyrex tubing (3 mm i.d.). With aqueous solutions the sample volume is restricted because of the dielectric loss of water. One may detect as low as $2 \times 10^{11} \Delta H$ free radicals at a response time less than 100 μsec, where ΔH is the full width of the absorption line in gauss at one-half maximum intensity or, on the derivative absorption curve, the width between deflection points (see Fig. 7-3). If ΔH is 2.7 gauss, which is often true in the solid state, this is equivalent to 10^{-8} molar concentrations.

Although the peak height does not have much significance, the total area enclosed by either the absorption or dispersion signal is proportional to the number of unpaired electrons in the sample. Comparison is made with a standard containing a known number of unpaired electrons and having the same line shape as the unknown (Gaussian or Lorentzian). The usual standard is diphenylpicrylhydrazyl, which is completely in the free-radical state, or substandards prepared by dilution with carbon black. A dual-sample cavity allows independent and simultaneous detection of the resonances of sample and standard (under the same experimental conditions). 1,1-Diphenyl-2'-picrylhydrazyl (DPPH) contains 1.53×10^{21} unpaired electrons per gram.

Hyperfine Splitting

No counterpart of chemical shifts in NMR spectra exists in ESR, since the g-value of free radicals is always close to 2.0023 because the electron available for spin resonance is usually near or at the periphery of the species with which it is associated. Spectra must be analyzed from hyperfine splittings —interactions between the electron spin and the nuclear spins of adjacent magnetic nuclei — and from the number and relative intensities of multiplet structures.

Placed in an environment where each electron is subjected to the magnetic moments of different (spinning) nuclei, interactions are bound to occur. The magnetic field actually felt by the unpaired electron is given by

$$H = H_0 \pm H_{\text{local}} \qquad (7\text{-}4)$$

where H_{local} originates from the magnetic dipole moments of other nuclei with intrinsic spins (cf. Table 6-1 on page 164). The probabilities will be equal for an electron experiencing a magnetic field higher than the applied one (parallel alignment) or lower (antiparallel alignment with another nucleus). In the simplest case of a single electron interacting with one proton, the effective field is then $H_0 + \Delta H$ or $H_0 - \Delta H$. Therefore, instead of a single absorption line, two lines of equal intensity will occur. Each electronic energy level will be split, in general, into $2I + 1$ levels by a nucleus with spin I, giving rise to $2I + 1$ resonance lines (Fig. 7-1).

If the electron interacts with several magnetic nuclei, the situation is somewhat more complicated, since the electron experiences an interaction with each nucleus, the magnitude of which is proportional to the product of the electron density at the nucleus and the nuclear moment. A more complicated splitting pattern arises. Two general types will be considered. When two equivalent nuclei are involved, the number of possible fields is reduced. Quite generally, $2nI + 1$ lines result from n equivalent nuclei whose intensity distribution equals the coefficients of the binomial expansion.

Example 7-1

The condensation of diacetyl proceeds through a semiquinone intermediate, a free radical:

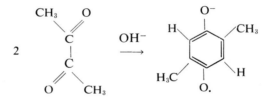

The unpaired electron is split by interaction with the six equivalent methyl hydrogens to produce a large septet with an intensity ratio of 1:6:15:20:15:6:1. Each of these lines is split again three times by the weak coupling to the two-ring protons. The ESR spectrum is shown in Fig. 7-4.

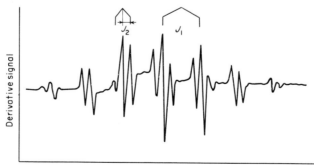

Magnetic field (increasing)

Fig. 7-4. The septet of triplets in the ESR spectrum produced by the semiquinone formed during the condensation of diacetyl.

The chlorinated benzosemiquinones illustrate a simpler case. For 2,3-dichlorobenzo-
quinone (parent quinone) the orientations of the proton axis is indicated by arrows,
from which the three-line pattern can be deduced to have an intensity ratio of 1:2:1.

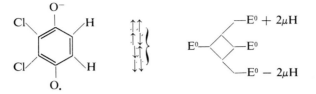

In many free radicals the unpaired electron is not rigidly attached to a
particular atom but occupies an orbital embracing several atoms. Consequently, the electron interacts to a variable extent with all these atoms.
Conversely, the magnitudes of the splittings indicate the degree of interaction
with the nuclei.

Example 7-2

When an unpaired electron couples with two nonequivalent protons, a four-line
pattern is produced whose spacing is dependent upon the magnitude of the two coupling
constants, namely,

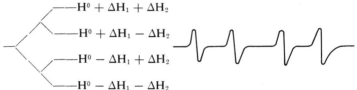

The energy-level diagram is expressed in terms of the field actually felt by the unpaired
electron.

A definite means for ascertaining beyond any question the presence of free
radicals exists in ESR spectroscopy. Other methods of detection may establish
fairly definitely the presence of some highly reactive intermediate; but ESR,
which by its very nature cannot respond unless unpaired electrons are present,
will definitely label it as a free radical.

Example 7-3

When 2,6-*di-t*-butyl-4-methyl phenol in cyclohexane was oxidized by lead dioxide,
the ESR spectrum exhibited a quartet of closely spaced triplets. The primary quartet
arises from the three protons of the 4-methyl group; the closely spaced triplets result
from weaker coupling of the electron with the two *meta*-hydrogen atoms.

After 10 min the spectrum reduced to a triplet, suggesting oxidation of the methyl
group to —CHO.

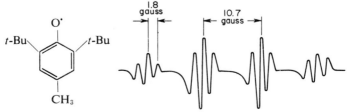

The noninteraction of the CHO hydrogen in the secondary radical is explained by the location of the CH bond being predominantly in the plane of the ring. Consequently, spin density on the ring carbon atom and on the oxygen atom will not induce spin polarization in the CH bond.

In addition to the isotropic interactions—interactions independent of the orientation of the radical—there are also anisotropic interactions, which play important roles for radicals trapped in solids or highly viscous media. The hyperfine splitting for a radical that is not spherically symmetric will depend on the orientation of the radical with respect to the magnetic field. Anisotropy often produces considerable broadening and distortion of the resonance lines and interpretation of the spectra requires extremely careful analysis.

Problems

1. What line pattern would be obtained from a 10^{-6} M aqueous solution of manganese(II) ions? *Ans.* A six-line pattern resulting from the six $(2I + 1)$ possible magnetic orientations of $Mn^{56}(I = 5/2)$ nucleus.

2. What line pattern would be expected for vanadium(IV) in vanadyl acetylacetonate? $I = 7/2$ for V^{51} nucleus. *Ans.* An eight-line pattern.

3. Predict the spectrum resulting from 1,4-benzosemiquinone and the intensity pattern. *Ans.* A five-line spectrum (1:4:6:4:1 ratios of intensities) from interaction of the odd electron with the nuclear moments of the four-ring hydrogens.

4. After irradiation with gamma rays, polythene is postulated to yield the radical
$-CH_2-C^{.}-CH_2-$, the electron interacting equally with the six protons. What
$\quad\quad\quad\quad |$
$\quad\quad\quad CH_2$
would be the ESR hyperfine pattern?

5. Irradiated glycine, H_2N-CH_2-$COOH$, gives a triplet in its ESR spectrum. Postulate the free radical responsible for the ESR spectrum.

6. The allyl alcohol spectrum after prolonged irradiation is shown. Extra components appear quite noticeably, although part of the extra spectrum is hidden

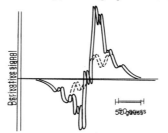

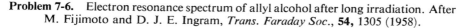

Problem 7-6. Electron resonance spectrum of allyl alcohol after long irradiation. After M. Fijimoto and D. J. E. Ingram, *Trans. Faraday Soc.*, **54**, 1305 (1958).

by the main one, which is the three-line spectrum due to $-\dot{C}H_2$. From the measurement of the spacing, deduce the extra spectrum. [See M. Fujimoto and D. J. E. Ingram, *Trans. Faraday Soc.*, **54**, 1309 (1958).]

7. Write the hyperfine spectrum which would be given by the intermediate semi-quinone formed by the oxidation of (a) 2,4,6-tri-*t*-butyl phenol; (b) 2,4-*di*-*t*-butyl-6-methyl phenol; and (c) 2,6-dimethyl-4-*t*-butyl phenol with lead dioxide in cyclohexane. *Ans.* (c) Septet of triplets.

8. The ESR spectrum of a semiquinone similar in nature to those formed in Problem 7 is shown. What is the general nature of group X?

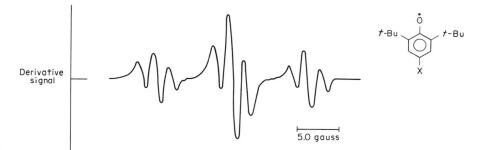

Problem 7-8. Electron resonance spectrum. After J. K. Becconsall, S. Clough, and G. Scott, *Trans. Faraday Soc.*, **56**, 459 (1960).

9. Upon irradiation, polytetrafluoroethylene gives a pattern of eight lines. Postulate the free radical formed.

10. 1,1'-Diphenyl-2'-picrylhydrazyl, in solution, gives a five-line pattern with a 1:2:3:2:1 intensity ratio. Since the spin of N^{14} is one, what conclusions may be drawn concerning the residence time of the odd electron with each nitrogen atom?

11. Which valency states of copper and silver will show a strong ESR signal?

12. Copper phthalocyanine crystals yield *g*-values of 2.045–2.165 according to the orientation of the crystal, compared with 2.14–2.45 for typical ionic copper compounds. What conclusions can be drawn about the bonds in the phthalocyanines? *Ans.* The bonds must be partly covalent.

Bibliography

Flett, M. St. C., *Physical Aids to the Organic Chemistry*, Chapter 7, Elsevier, Amsterdam, 1962.

Ingram, D. J. E.: *Free Radicals as Studied by Electron Spin Resonance*, Butterworths, London, 1959.

Varian Associates Staff, *NMR and EPR Spectroscopy*, Pergamon, New York, 1960.

X-Ray Methods

In 1913 Moseley first showed the extremely simple relation between atomic number Z and the reciprocal of the wavelength λ for each spectral line belonging to a particular series of emission lines for each element in the periodic table. This relationship is expressed as

$$\frac{c}{\lambda} = a(Z - \sigma)^2 \tag{8-1}$$

where a is a proportionality constant and σ is a constant whose value depends on the particular series.

Few absorption or emission features appear or are associated with an X-ray spectrum. The relative simplicity of characteristic X-ray spectra is explained by the limited number of energy levels in the atom, together with certain prohibited transitions, and, except in the very light elements, by the association with the inner electrons of an atom rather than with the valence electrons. The spectral features depend only on atomic number, not on any chemical properties of the elements or on the compound in which they may be present or on the physical state of the sample. There is only one K shell. The L electrons are grouped according to their binding energy into three sublevels: L_I, L_{II}, and L_{III}; the complete M shell consists of five sublevels.

The X-ray Spectrum

An X-ray tube is basically a large vacuum tube containing a heated cathode (electron emitter) and an anode, or target (Fig. 8-1). Electrons emitted by the

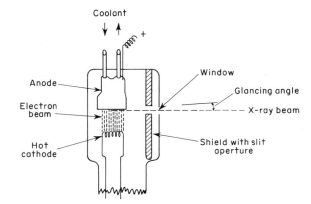

Fig. 8-1. An X-ray tube with schematic of filament and target. (Courtesy of Machlett Laboratories, Inc.)

cathode are accelerated through a high-voltage field between the target and cathode. Upon impact with the target, the stream of electrons is quickly brought to rest. They transfer their kinetic energy to the atoms of the material making up the target. Part of the kinetic energy is emitted in the form of a continuous spectrum covering a broad wavelength range (Fig. 8-2). It is due to deceleration of the impinging electrons by successive collisions with the atoms of the target material. Consequently, the emitted quanta are generally of longer wavelength than the short-wavelength cutoff; the intensity of the continuum rises to a broad maximum and falls off gradually with increasing wavelength. The short-wavelength cutoff corresponds to the voltage across the X-ray tube, given by the Duane-Hunt equation,[5] and is independent of the target element,

$$\lambda_0 \text{ (in Å)} = \frac{hc}{eV} = \frac{12,400}{V} \tag{8-2}$$

where V is the X-ray tube voltage in volts, e is the charge on the electron, h is Planck's constant, and c is the velocity of light. An increase in tube voltage

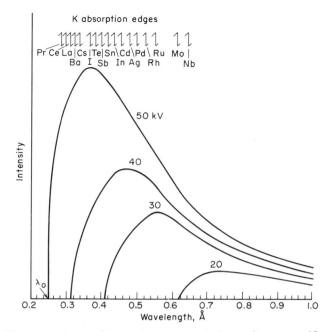

Fig. 8-2. X-ray continuum from a target operated at voltages specified. Along the top edge are indicated the wavelengths of K absorption edges for elements 41 to 59.

results in an increase in the total energy emitted and a movement of the spectral distribution towards shorter wavelengths. The wavelength of maximum intensity is about 1.5 times the short-wavelength limit. The intensity of the spectrum increases with atomic number of the target element.

If sufficient energy is available, the transfer of energy from the impinging electron beam may eject an electron from one of the inner shells of the atoms constituting the target material. The place of the ejected electron will then promptly be filled by an electron from an outer shell, whose place in turn will be taken by an electron still farther out. The ionized atom thus returns to its normal state in a series of steps, in each of which an X-ray photon of definite energy is emitted—fluorescent radiation. These transitions give rise to the line spectrum characteristic of the material in the anode or a specimen pasted on the target. When originating in an X-ray tube, these lines will be superimposed on the continuum. The characteristic X-ray spectrum of an element can also be excited by irradiation of a sample with a beam of X-rays if the primary X-radiation is sufficiently energetic to ionize an inner shell. The K series of lines is obtained when an electron in the innermost K shell is dislodged; it arises from electrons dropping down from L or M orbitals into the vacancy in the K shell. Corresponding vacancies in the L shells are filled by electron transitions from outer shells and give rise to the L series.

The energy needed to eject an electron completely from an atom is greater than that liberated as electrons from outer shells fall into the vacancy. It is related to the wavelength of the absorption edge for the particular transition. A spectral series will be excited by continuous radiation only when the wavelength limit λ_0 (Eq. 8-2) is shorter than the absorption edge of the series. Since λ_0 depends on the voltage applied to the X-ray tube, there is a critical excitation potential below which the lines of a spectral series will not be excited by primary radiation. At this critical wavelength there is a sharp rise in the absorption of X radiation impinging on the element (Fig. 8-3).

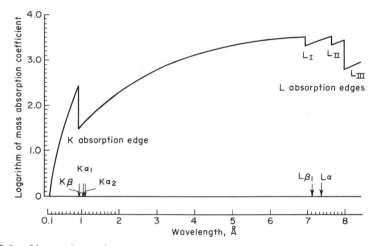

Fig. 8-3. X-ray absorption spectrum of bromine. The characteristic emission lines of the K and L series are shown with arrows.

Example 8-1

To calculate the short-wavelength limit for an X-ray tube operated at 50 kV,

$$\lambda_0 = 12,400/50,000 = 0.248 \text{ Å}$$

Europium (63), whose K absorption edge lies at 0.255 Å, would emit its characteristic K series of lines, albeit with low intensity, whereas the energy is insufficient for excitation of the K lines of gadolinium (64), whose K absorption edge lies at 0.247 Å.

As the wavelength of the incident radiation is decreased, there is successive ionization, first of electrons in the M shells, then of electrons in the L shells as the L_{III}, L_{II}, and L_I absorption edges are progressively exceeded, and finally culminating in the K shell's absorption edge. The K spectra are generally used for elements up to about neodymium ($Z = 60$) and the L spectra from lanthanum to *trans*-uranium elements when an X-ray tube is used which has a maximum rating of 50 kV and is operated at constant potential. The wavelengths of selected spectral lines and absorption edges of a number of elements are shown in Table 8-1.

Table 8-1 | *Characteristic Wavelengths of Absorption Edges and Emission Lines for Selected Elements*

ELEMENT	MINIMUM POTENTIAL FOR EXCITATION OF K LINES, kV	K ABSORPTION EDGE, Å	$K\beta$, Å	$K\alpha_1$, Å	L_{III} ABSORPTION EDGE, Å	$L\alpha_1$, Å
Magnesium	1.30	9.54	9.56	9.9		
Titanium	4.96	2.50	2.51	2.74		
Chromium	5.99	2.070	2.085	2.290	20.7	
Manganese	6.54	1.895	1.910	2.106	19.4	
Cobalt	7.71	1.607	1.621	1.789	15.9	
Nickel	8.33	1.487	1.500	1.658	14.5	
Copper	8.98	1.380	1.392	1.541	13.3	13.4
Zinc	9.65	1.283	1.295	1.435	12.1	
Molybdenum	20.0	0.620	0.632	0.711	4.91	5.4
Silver	25.5	0.484	0.497	0.560	3.70	4.155
Tungsten	69.6	0.178	0.184	0.209	1.215	1.477
Platinum	78.4	0.158	0.164	0.186	1.072	1.31

[From a tabulation of K and L emission lines and critical absorption energies for all the elements by S. Fine and C. F. Hendee, *Nucleonics*, **13** (No. 3), 36 (1955)].

Example 8-2

For a vacant orbital in a bromine atom to arise from the ejection of an electron from the innermost K shell of electrons, the energy required just to lift a K electron out of the environment of the atom must exceed the energy of the K absorption edge at 0.918 Å, or

$$V = 12,400/0.918 = 13,475 \text{ volts (13.475 kV)}$$

The K absorption edge has a wavelength always lower than that of the K emission lines. The $K\beta_1$ line at 0.934 Å arises as a result of an electron dropping from the M shell; the $K\alpha_1$ and $K\alpha_2$ lines, a closely spaced doublet at 1.048 and 1.053 Å, arise from sublevels of slightly different energies within the L shell. In energy units, the $K\alpha_1$ line represents the difference: K edge minus L_{III} edge. Thus, for bromine

$$K\alpha_1(\text{in keV}) = 13.475 - 1.522 = 11.952$$

The absorption and emission spectrum for bromine is shown in Fig. 8-3, and the energy-level diagram is shown in Fig. 8-4.

The bond character in molecules and solids affects the X-ray spectra of the light elements whose emission lines originate from the valence electron shell, and even those lines and absorption edges from the next innermost shell. In general, relative to the lines of the free element, the lines of the atom in a compound are shifted toward shorter wavelengths if the atom has a positive charge, and toward longer wavelengths if it has a negative charge in the compound. Similar fine structure may be observed at an absorption edge if a high-resolution spectrometer is employed. Mean wavelengths and shifts in the emission lines for the different oxidation states of sulfur are given in Table 8-2.

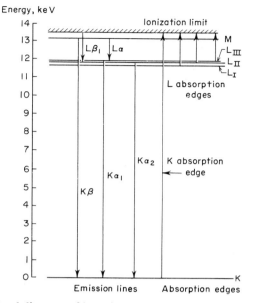

Fig. 8-4. Energy level diagram of bromine ($Z = 35$) showing the transitions that give rise to the absorption discontinuities and the emission lines.

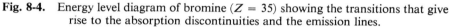

| Table 8-2 | *Mean Wavelengths and Shifts of K Lines of Sulfur for the Different Oxidation States of Sulfur* | | | |

OXIDATION STATE	λ(IN XU)† $K\alpha_1$	$K\alpha_2$	MEAN SHIFT $\Delta\lambda(XU)$	$\Delta E(eV)$
S^{6+}	5358.08	5360.89	−2.76	+1.19
S^{4+}	5358.63	5361.47	−2.20	+0.95
S^{2+}	5360.13	5362.93	−0.72	+0.31
S^0	5360.83	5363.66	0	0
S^{2-}	5361.15	6363.99	+0.33	−0.14

†One angstrom $\equiv$ 1002.02 XU, where 1 XU $= 1/3029.45$ the spacing of the cleavage planes of a calcite crystal, a former standard wavelength unit. [From A. Faessler, "X-ray Emission Spectra and the Chemical Bond," in *Proceedings of the Xth Colloquium Spectroscopicium Internationale*, 307–319, Spartan Books, Washington, 1963].

Instrumental Units

Instrumentation associated with X-ray methods in general is outlined schematically in Fig. 8-5. Many of the components will be discussed more fully in subsequent sections.

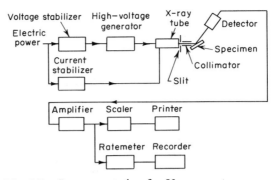

Fig. 8-5.   Instrumentation for X-ray spectroscopy.

X-Ray Generating Equipment

The modern X-ray tube is a high-vacuum, sealed-off unit, as shown in Fig. 8-1, usually with a copper or molybdenum target, although targets of chromium, iron, nickel, silver and tungsten are used for special purposes. The target is ground to a slight angle so that the focal spot may be viewed from the side. If the focal spot is a narrow ribbon, the source appears to be very small when viewed from the end, which leads to the sharper definition demanded in diffraction studies. For fluorescence work the focus is of much larger size, about 5×10 mm, and is viewed at a larger angle (about 20°). Since it becomes very hot, the target is cooled by water and is sometimes rotated when a very intense X-ray beam is generated. The X-ray beam passes out of the tube through a thin window of beryllium or a special glass. For wavelengths from 6–70 Å, ultrathin films (1-μ aluminum or cast Parlodion films), coupled with an evacuated spectrometer, separate the X-ray tube from the remainder of the equipment.

Associated equipment includes high-voltage generators and stabilizers. Voltage regulation is accomplished by regulating the main a-c supply. Current regulation is achieved by monitoring the d-c X-ray tube current and by controlling the filament voltage. Either full-wave rectification or constant high potential may be used to operate the X-ray tube. In full-wave rectification the voltage reaches its peak value 120 times a second but only persists at that value for a small fraction of the time. Constant high potential, obtained through electronic filtering, increases the output of characteristic X rays from a specimen, particularly with elements emitting at short wavelengths. With a tube operated at 50 kV the gain is two-fold for elements up to about atomic number 35 (Br), increasing to four-fold for barium (56). Commonly, X-ray tubes are operated at 50 or 60 kV. Tubes of 100-kV rating are available and extend the range of applicability both in terms of atomic numbers in the K series and in terms of sensitivity, because on increasing the voltage the intensities of all lines increase.

Collimators

Radiation from an X-ray tube is collimated either by a series of closely spaced, parallel metal plates or by a bundle of tubes, 0.5 mm or less in diameter. One collimator is placed between the specimen and the analyzer crystal in a fluorescence spectrometer to limit the divergence of the rays that reach the crystal. The second collimator, usually coarser, is placed between the analyzer crystal and the detector, where it is particularly useful at very low goniometer angles for preventing radiation that has not been reflected by the crystal from reaching the detector. Increased resolution can be obtained by decreasing the separation between the metal plates of the collimator or by increasing the length of the unit (usually a few centimeters), but this is achieved at the expense of intensity.

Filters

When two spectral lines are of nearly the same wavelength and there is an element having an absorption edge at a wavelength between the lines, that element may be used as a filter to reduce the intensity of the line of shorter wavelength. In X-ray diffractometry it is common practice to insert a thin foil in the primary X-ray beam to remove the $K\beta$-line from the spectrum while transmitting the $K\alpha$-lines with a relatively small loss of intensity. Filters for the common targets of X-ray tubes are listed in Table 8-3. Back-

Table 8-3   *Filters for Common Targets of X-ray Tubes*

TARGET ELEMENT	$K\alpha_1$, Å	$K\beta$, Å	FILTER	K ABSORPTION EDGE FILTER, Å	THICKNESS,† mm	PERCENT LOSS OF $K\alpha_1$
Mo	0.711	0.632	Zr	0.689	0.071	54
Cu	1.542	1.392	Ni	1.487	0.013	41
Cr	2.291	2.085	V_2O_5	2.269	0.01	51
	$L\alpha_1$, Å	$L\beta_1$, Å				$L\alpha_1$
Pt	1.31	1.12	Zn	1.28	—	—
W	1.477	1.282	Cu	1.380	0.035	77

†To reduce the intensity of $K\beta$ line to 0.01 that of the $K\alpha_1$ line.

ground radiation (the continuum) is reduced by the same means. Usually it makes no difference whether the filter is placed before or after the specimen unless the specimen fluoresces; if so, the filter is placed at the receiving slit of the goniometer.

Analyzing Crystal

Virtually monochromatic radiation is obtained by reflection of X rays from crystal planes. The relationship between the wavelength of the X-ray beam, the angle of diffraction θ, and the distance between each set of atomic planes of the crystal lattice d, is governed by the Bragg condition:[2]

$$m\lambda = 2d \sin \theta \qquad (8\text{-}3)$$

where m represents the order of the diffraction. The geometric relations are shown in Fig. 8-6. For the ray diffracted by the second plane of the

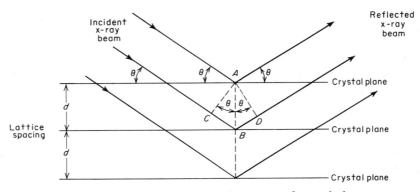

Fig. 8-6. Diffraction of X rays from a set of crystal planes.

crystal, the distance $\overline{CBD}$ represents the additional distance of travel in comparison to a ray reflected from the surface. Angles $\overline{CAB}$ and $\overline{BAD}$ are both equal to θ. Therefore,

$$CB = BD = AB \sin \theta \qquad (8\text{-}4)$$

and

$$CBD = 2(AB) \sin \theta \qquad (8\text{-}5)$$

where $\overline{AB}$ is the interplanar spacing d. In order to observe a beam in the direction of the diffracted rays, $\overline{CBD}$ must be some multiple of the wavelength of the X rays so that the diffracted waves will be in phase. Note that the angle between the direction of the incident beam and that of the diffracted beam is 2θ. In order to scan the emission spectrum of a specimen, the analyzing crystal is mounted on a goniometer and rotated through the desired angular region, as shown in the schematic diagram of a fluorescent spectrometer (Fig. 8-15).

The range of wavelengths usable with various analyzing crystals are governed by the d-spacings of the crystal planes and by the geometric limits to which the goniometer can be rotated. The d-value should be small enough to make the angle 2θ greater than approximately 8° even at the shortest wavelength used, otherwise excessively long analyzing crystals would be needed in order to prevent the incident beam from entering the detector. A small d-spacing is also favorable for producing a larger dispersion, $\partial\theta/\partial\lambda$, of the spectrum, as can be seen by differentiating the Bragg equation:

$$\partial\theta/\partial\lambda = m/(2d\cos\theta) \qquad (8\text{-}6)$$

On the other hand, a small d-value imposes an upper limit to the range of wavelengths that can be analyzed, since at $\lambda = 2d$, the angle 2θ becomes 180°. Actually the upper limit to which goniometers can be rotated is mechanically limited to a 2θ value of 150°. For longer wavelengths a crystal with a larger d-spacing must be selected. Crystals commonly used are listed in Table 8-4. These crystals are all composed of light atoms; only sodium

Table 8-4 | *Typical Analyzer Crystals*

CRYSTAL	REFLECTING PLANE	LATTICE SPACING d IN Å	USEFUL RANGE IN Å MAXIMUM†	MINIMUM‡
Topaz	303	1.356	2.62	0.189
Lithium fluoride	200	2.014	3.89	0.281
Aluminum	111	2.338	4.52	0.326
Sodium chloride	200	2.821	5.45	0.393
Calcium fluoride	111	3.16	6.11	0.440
Quartz	10$\bar{1}$1	3.343	6.46	0.466
Ethylenediamine d-tartrate (EDDT)	020	4.404	8.51	0.614
Ammonium dihydrogen orthophosphate (ADP)	200	5.325	10.29	0.742
Gypsum	020	7.60	14.70	1.06
Mica	002	9.963	19.25	1.39
Lead palmitate		45.6	78.3	6.39
Strontium behenate		61.3	121.7	8.59

†Maximum $2\theta = 150°$ mλ = 2d sin 75°
‡Minimum $2\theta = 8°$ mλ = 2d sin 4°

chloride, quartz, and the heavy metal fatty acids* have elements heavier than $Z = 9$, so that their own fluorescent X rays will not interfere with measurements. However, higher order reflections caused by the analyzing crystal may result in overlapping of lines originating from different elements.

Analyzing crystals have presented problems in the extension of X-ray analysis beyond a few angstroms. Potassium acid phthalate has made the

*The lead palmitate and strontium behenate analyzers are prepared by dipping an optical flat into the film of the metal fatty acid — Langmuir-Blodgett technique.

determination of magnesium and sodium more practical. To extend the analytical capabilities beyond 26 Å, use is made of multiple monolayer soap film "crystals." So far, a lead stearate decanoate "crystal" has proven to be superior for elements $Z = 9$ to $Z = 5$.

Detectors

In addition to photographic film, which is used in diffraction studies, the Geiger counter, the proportional counter, and the scintillation counter are used to measure X radiation. Details of their construction are given in Chapter 9. The spectral sensitivity of each detector varies with the wavelength

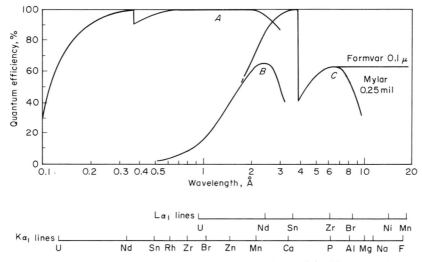

Fig. 8-7. Quantum efficiences of detectors commonly used in X-ray spectrometry. *A*, Scintillation counter with Tl activated, NaI scintillator. *B*, Argon-filled Geiger counter with Be window. *C*, Gas-flow proportional counter; 90% Ar, 10% CH$_4$; 0.00025-in. Mylar window. Lower scales indicate the wavelengths of representative emission lines.

of the X radiation, as shown in Fig. 8-7. The choice is governed by the nature of the X radiation to be detected.

The argon-filled Geiger counter, using halogen as a quenching gas, has a sensitive volume wide enough to detect nearly the entire large area beam used in some X-ray optics. The tube is relatively insensitive to scattered hard radiation and, thus, its background intensity is low. Its quantum efficiency is about 60–65 percent in the range from 1.5 to 2.1 Å, and decreases to 40 percent at 1.4 and 2.9 Å. Its principal limitation lies in its long dead time—about 270 μsec, which gives rise to counting losses at high intensities, and in its low sensitivity for the shorter wavelengths. The Geiger counter is rarely used for measuring intensities in excess of about 500 counts/sec; no practical correction is possible for coincidence losses when scanning across a peak to obtain integrated line intensities. Pulse height discrimination is impossible because pulses are all the same strength.

The proportional counter has about the same spectral sensitivity characteristics as the Geiger counter but a very short dead time—about 1.5 μsec, and its response is linear to extremely high count rates. The flow proportional counter can be equipped with an extremely thin window, usually 0.25 mil Mylar film, which naturally decreases the losses due to window absorption of the very soft X rays. Its range extends to 12 Å and is the counter of choice for long wavelength X radiation.*

Detector windows present challenging problems in work at very long wavelengths (to 70 Å), since these windows must be transparent to very low energy photons and, in addition, must be capable of supporting atmospheric pressure. Typical windows include 1-μ (sign painter's) aluminum dipped in Formvar (usable for sodium and magnesium), 1-μ hydrocarbon (cast Formvar, Parlodion, or collodion) films, and 0.1-μ hydrocarbon films. The 0.1-μ films must be supported on a 70 percent optical transmission grid or on the 0.5-mm spacing blade on a flow detector collimator. Their use is required for oxygen, nitrogen, and boron. The lifetime of unsupported, 1-μ films never exceeds eight hours.

The scintillation counter has the shortest dead time of the three counters— 0.25 μsec. It has a nearly uniform and high quantum efficiency throughout the important wavelength region—0.3 to 2.5 Å, and is usable to possibly 4 Å. Longer wavelengths are absorbed in the coating covering the crystal necessitated by the hygroscopic properties of sodium iodide.

The signal produced when an X-ray quantum is absorbed is extremely small from the proportional and scintillation counters and requires both a preamplifier and a second stage of amplification before the signal can be fed to a scaler or recorder. To diminish noise pickup, the preamplifier is located immediately after the detector in the latter's housing. However, the pulse strength produced in each counter is proportional to the quantum energy (and inversely proportional to the wavelength of the X-ray quantum). With circuits for pulse height discrimination, it becomes possible to discriminate electronically against unwanted wavelengths of different elements. Discrimination between elements eight to ten atomic numbers apart is possible with a scintillation counter. A proportional counter, because of its narrower pulse amplitude distribution, can discriminate between elements four to six atomic numbers apart. Unlike a filter, a pulse height analyzer can be used to pass either line of superposed spectral lines, serving, in effect, as a secondary monochromator. It is particularly useful for rejecting higher order scattered radiation from elements of higher atomic number when determining the elements of lower atomic number.

*Windows of 0.1-μ Formvar or "thin" nitrocellulose (often supported by screens) extend the transmission to approximately 120 and 160 Å, respectively.

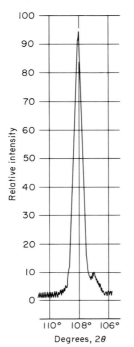

Fig. 8-8. Relative intensity of the Si $K\alpha_1$ line as a function of goniometer setting (2θ). Analyzing crystal: ethylenediamine d-tartrate.

Example 8-3

The use of a pulse height analyzer for Si $K\alpha_1$ radiation will illustrate the step-by-step operations. A relatively pure sample of silicon is inserted into the sample holder (see Fig. 8-15). Scanning with the goniometer from 106° to 110° provides the graph shown in Fig. 8-8. From an ethylenediamine d-tartrate crystal, Si $K\alpha_1$ radiation is reflected at $2\theta = 108°$. Next, with the goniometer set manually at the peak of the silicon radiation, the distribution of pulses due to the silicon X-ray quanta is obtained by scanning the pulse amplitude base-line and using a one-volt window. The integral curve of intensity versus pulse amplitude is shown in Fig. 8-9. From this information, the base of the pulse height discriminator would be set at 8.5 volts and the window width at 13.0 volts, since it is noticed that no pulses are detected until the base-line setting approaches 21 volts. In this example, the silicon radiation was peaked at 15 volts. Naturally, if the silicon pulses were peaked at a lower or higher voltage then the window and base-line settings would be different. The peak distribution (in volts) is a function of the d-c voltage on the counter and the amplifier gain.

Direct X-ray Methods

The process of exciting characteristic spectra by electron bombardment was applied many years ago in the investigation of characteristic spectra of the elements by Siegbahn and others. In this manner the element hafnium was discovered by Von Hevesy and Coster in 1923. The specimen must be plated or smeared on the target of the X-ray tube. This has disadvantages: the X-ray tube must be re-evacuated each time the specimen is changed; a demountable target is required; and the heating effect of the electron beam may cause chemical reaction, selective volatilization, or melting. These difficulties virtually prohibit the large-scale application of the direct method to routine analysis, except for electron probe microanalysis.

Electron Beam Probe

Electron probe microanalysis, developed by Castaing[3] (1951), is a method for the nondestructive elemental analysis from an area only 1 μ in diameter at the surface of a solid specimen. A beam of electrons is collimated into a fine pencil of 1-μ cross section and directed at the specimen surface exactly on the spot to be analyzed. This electron bombardment excites characteristic X rays essentially from a point source and at intensities considerably higher than with fluorescent excitation. The limit of detectability (in a 1-μ size region) is about

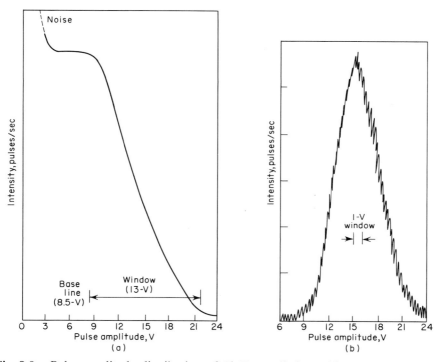

Fig. 8-9.   Pulse amplitude distribution of Si $K\alpha_1$ radiation.   (a) Integral curve and (b) differential curve.   Goniometer set at 108°.

10^{-14} g.   The relative accuracy is 1–2 percent if the concentration is greater than a few percent and if adequate standards are available.

Three types of optics are employed in the microprobe spectrometer—electron optics, light optics, and X-ray optics (Fig. 8-10).   Of these, the most complex is the electron optical system—a modified electron microscope, which consists of an electron gun followed by two electromagnetic reducing lenses to form the electron beam probe.   The specimen is mounted inside the vacuum column of the instrument and under the beam as the target.   A focusing, curved crystal, X-ray spectrometer is attached to the evacuated system with the focal spot serving as the source of X radiation.   A viewing microscope and mirror system allow continuous visual observation of the exact area of the specimen where the electron beam is striking.   Point-by-point microanalysis is accomplished by translating the specimen across the beam.

The method is used to study variations in concentration occurring near grain boundaries, the analysis of small inclusions in alloys or precipitates in a multitude of products, and corrosion studies where excitation is restricted to thin

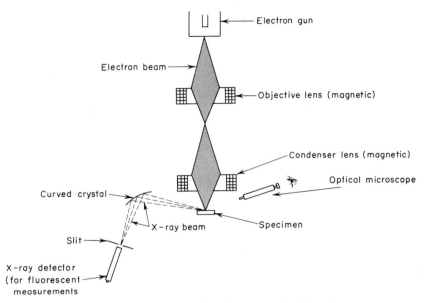

Fig. 8-10. Schematic of an electron probe microanalyzer. X-ray beam can be passed directly into detector or reflected from analyzer crystal.

surface layers, because the beam penetrates to a depth of only one or two microns into the specimen.

X-ray Absorption Methods

Since each element has its own characteristic set of K, L, M, etc., absorption edges, the wavelength at which a sudden change in absorption occurs can be used to identify an element present in a sample, and the magnitude of the change can be used to determine the amount of the particular element present. The fundamental equation for the transmittance of a monochromatic, collimated, X-ray beam is

$$P = P_0 e^{-(\mu/\rho)\rho.x} \tag{8-7}$$

where P is the radiant power of intensity P_0 after passage through x cm of homogeneous matter of density ρ and whose linear absorption coefficient is μ. The parenthetical term μ/ρ is the mass absorption coefficient, often expressed simply as μ_m. It depends upon the wavelength of the X rays and the absorbing atom; that is,

$$\mu_m = CZ^4\lambda^3(N_A/A) \tag{8-8}$$

where N_A is Avogadro's number, A is the atomic weight, and C is a constant over a range between characteristic absorption edges. It is significant that the mass absorption coefficient is independent of the physical or chemical state of the specimen. In a compound or mixture it is an additive function of the mass absorption coefficients of the constituent elements, namely,

$$\mu_{m_T} = \mu_{m_1}W_1 + \mu_{m_2}W_2 + \cdots \cdots \qquad (8\text{-}9)$$

where μ_{m_1} is the mass absorption coefficient of element 1 and W_1 is its weight fraction, and so on for all the elements present. Because only one element has a change in mass absorption coefficient at the edge, the following relationship is obtained for the ith element,

$$2.3 \log (P/P_0) = (\mu''_{m_1} - \mu'_{m_1})W_i\rho x \qquad (8\text{-}10)$$

where the term in the parentheses represents the difference in mass absorption coefficient at the edge discontinuity. Thus, the logarithm of the ratio of beam intensities on the two sides of an absorption edge depends only upon the change in mass absorption coefficients of the element characterized by this edge and on the amount of the particular element in the beam; ρx is the mass thickness of the sample in grams per square centimeter. There is no matrix effect, which gives the absorption method an advantage over X-ray fluorescence analysis in some cases.

In analogy with absorption measurements in other portions of the electro-magnetic spectrum, one would expect to obtain a representative set of trans-mittance measurements on each side of an absorption edge with an X-ray spectrometer and extrapolate to the edge. However, X-ray absorption spectro-photometers that provide a continuously variable wavelength of X radiation are not commercially available. Instead, only a single attenuation measure-ment is made on each side of the edge. A multichannel instrument is required.

The general procedure will be illustrated by the determination of lead tetraethyl and ethylene dibromide in gasoline. Four channels are required. One channel is used as a reference standard; the other three channels provide the analyses for lead, bromine, and a correction for variations of the C/H ratio and the presence of any sulfur and chlorine. Primary excitation is provided by an X-ray tube operated at 21 kV. The secondary targets for each channel are as follows, with the fluorescent X-ray lines employed:

Channel 1: RbCl, Rb $K\alpha_1$
Channel 2: RbCl, Rb $K\alpha_1$
Channel 3: SrCO$_3$, Sr $K\alpha_1$
Channel 4: NaBr, Br $K\alpha_1$

The relationship between the pertinent absorption edges and the target fluores-cent emission lines is shown in Fig. 8-11. In operation, a nominal sample is sealed in the sample cell in Channel 1; the sample to be analyzed is placed in the cells in the remaining channels. The exposure is started and automatically terminated when the integrated intensity in Channel 1 reaches a predetermined value (perhaps 100,000 counts in a time interval of 100 sec). The integrated

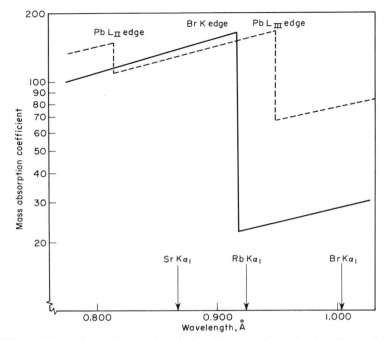

Fig. 8-11. Absorption edges and emission lines pertinent to the X-ray absorption analysis of lead tetraethyl and ethylene dibromide in gasoline.

intensities accumulated in the other channels are then recorded. Initially the four channels are adjusted to reach 100 percent transmittance with nominally pure gasoline. Results for bromine are computed from the difference in counts between Channels 3 and 2; for lead from Channels 2 and 4.

Microradiography

Another application employing the different absorbing powers of different elements towards an X-ray beam permits the gross structure of various types of small specimens to be examined under high magnification. Positions where there are elements which strongly absorb the X rays will appear light, and positions where there are elements which do not absorb the X rays will appear dark on a film placed behind the sample.

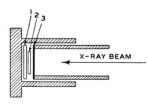

Fig. 8-12. Schematic of microradiographic camera: 1, film; 2, sample; 3, black paper.

Clark and Gross[4] developed a method employing ordinary X-ray diffraction equipment. Any of the commonly employed targets operated at 30–50kV can be used. No vacuum camera is necessary. The microradiographic camera, shown in Fig. 8-12, is designed to fit as an inset in the collimating system of any commercial X-ray equipment. Special photographic film, which possesses an extremely fine grain, makes magnifications up to 200 times possible without loss of detail from graininess. Sample thicknesses vary from 0.075 mm for steels up to 0.25 mm for magnesium alloys. Only a few seconds' exposure is necessary.

Various techniques are possible depending upon the specimen. Biological specimens may be impregnated with a material of high molecular weight to characterize particular structures. Occasionally the necessary density variations are initially present within the sample. More often, the use of various selective monochromatic wavelengths from different target elements must be employed.

Nondispersive X-ray Absorptiometer

The general arrangement of a nondispersive X-ray absorptiometer is shown in Fig. 8-13. A tungsten target X-ray tube is operated at 15–45 kV. In the

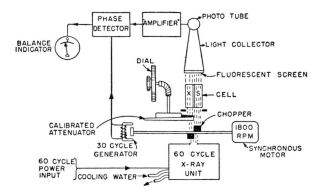

Fig. 8-13. Nondispersive X-ray absorptiometer. (Courtesy of General Electric Co.)

X-ray beam is a synchronous motor-driven chopper which alternately interrupts one-half of the X-ray beam. A variable-thickness aluminum attenuator (in the shape of a wedge) is placed between the chopper and reference sample compartment. Duplicate reference and sample cells up to 25 in. in length can be accommodated; those for liquids and gases can be arranged for continuous flow of process streams. Both halves of the X-ray beam fall on a common phosphor-coated photomultiplier tube which is protected from visible light by a thin metallic filter.

In operation, a reference sample is placed in the appropriate cell and the specimen to be analyzed in the sample tube. The attenuator is adjusted until the absorption in the two X-ray beams is brought into balance. The change in thickness of aluminum required for different samples is a function of the difference in composition. Prior calibration enables a determination in terms of the solute in an unknown. Liquids are simplest to handle. With solids, the thickness of specimen, or with powders, the density, must be uniform to a precision greater than that expected in the result.

Polychromatic absorptiometry can be used to determine chlorine in hydrogen. Sulfur in crude oil can be distinguished from the carbon-hydrogen residuum. Other examples include barium fluoride in carbon brushes, barium or lead in special glass, and chlorine in plastics and hydrocarbons. In fact, the method is applicable to any sample that contains one element markedly heavier than the others and when the matrix is essentially invariant in concentration.

X-ray Fluorescence Method

Characteristic X-ray spectra are excited when a specimen is irradiated with a beam of sufficiently short-wavelength X radiation. Intensities of the resulting fluorescent X rays are smaller by a factor of roughly one thousand than an X-ray beam obtained by direct excitation with a beam of electrons. Only availability of high-intensity X-ray tubes, very sensitive detectors, and suitable X-ray optics renders the fluorescent method feasible. The intensity is important with a view to the time that will be necessary to measure a spectrum—a certain number of quanta has to be accumulated at the detector in order to reduce sufficiently the statistical error of the measurement. The sensitivity of the analysis—i.e., the lowest detectable concentration of a particular element in a specimen—will depend on the peak-to-background ratio of the spectral lines. Relatively few cases of spectral interference occur because of the relative simplicity of X-ray spectra.

X-Ray Fluorescent Spectrometer

The general arrangement for exciting, dispersing and detecting fluorescent radiation with a plane-crystal spectrometer is shown pictorially in Fig. 8-14 and diagrammatically in Fig. 8-15. The specimen in the sample holder (often rotated to improve uniformity of exposure) is irradiated with an unfiltered beam of primary X rays, which causes the elements present to emit their characteristic fluorescence lines. A portion of the scattered fluorescence beam is collimated by the entrance slit of the goniometer and directed onto the plane surface of the analyzing crystal. The line radiations, reflected according to the Bragg condition, pass through an auxiliary collimator (exit slit) to the detector, where the energy of the X-ray quanta is converted into electrical impulses, or counts.

The primary slit, the analyzer crystal, and secondary slit are placed on the focal circle so that Bragg's law will always be satisfied as the goniometer is rotated—the detector being rotated twice the angular change in the crystal setting. The analyzer crystal is a flat single-crystal plate, 2.5 cm in width and 7.5 cm in length. The specimen holder is often an aluminum cylinder, although

Fig. 8-14. Typical X-ray fluorescence spectrometer. (Courtesy of Philips Electronic Instruments.)

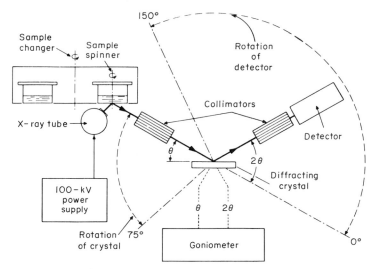

Fig. 8-15. Geometry of a plane-crystal X-ray fluorescence spectrometer. (Courtesy of Philips Electronic Instruments.)

plastic material is used for examination of acid or alkaline solutions. A thin film of Mylar supports the specimen, and an aluminum mask restricts the area irradiated (often a rectangle 18 mm by 27 mm). Intensity losses caused by the absorption of long-wavelength X rays by air and window materials can be reduced by evacuating the goniometer chamber, or the radiation path can be enclosed in a special boot which extends from the sample surface to the detector window and the air displaced by helium, which has a low absorption coefficient. Vacuum spectrometers are used where helium is scarce and for elements boron ($Z = 5$) to sodium ($Z = 11$).

Focusing spectrometers that involve reflection from or transmission through a 10-cm or 28-cm curved crystal have been described.[1] Collimators are not required, and the increase in intensity obtained by focusing the fluorescence lines makes the technique suitable for the analysis of small specimens. In the curved-crystal arrangement (Fig. 8-16) the analyzing crystal is bent to the

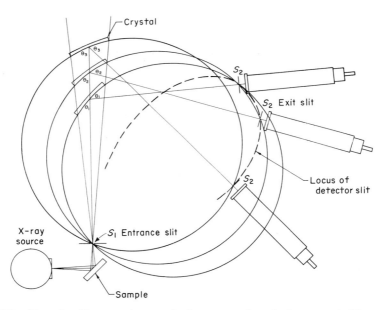

Fig. 8-16.   Focusing X-ray optics, employing a curved analyzing crystal. (Courtesy of Applied Research Laboratories, Inc.)

diameter of the focusing circle, and then the inner surface is ground to the radius of the focusing circle. A slit on the focusing circle acts as a divergent source of polychromatic radiation from the specimen. All of the radiation of one wavelength diverging from the slit will be diffracted for a particular setting of the crystal, and the diffracted radiation will converge to a line image at a symmetric point on the focusing circle (cf. Rowland circle). The angular velocity of the detector is twice that of the crystal and, as the two of them move along the periphery of the circle, the X-ray spectral lines are dispersed and detected just as in the flat-crystal arrangement.

For exciting fluorescence the primary radiation must obviously have a wavelength shorter than the absorption edge of the spectral lines desired. Continuous as well as characteristic radiation of the primary target can serve the purpose. To get a continuous spectrum of short enough wavelength and of sufficient intensity, one may calculate the voltage of the X-ray tube from Eq. 8-2, remembering that the wavelength of maximum intensity is approximately 1.5 λ_0, where λ_0 now represents the selected absorption edge of the element to be analyzed. In qualitative analyses it is usually desirable to operate the X-ray tube at the highest permissible voltage in order to ensure that the largest possible number of elements in the specimen will be excited to fluoresce. It will also ensure the greatest possible intensity of fluorescence for each element in quantitative analyses. In two cases, however, the X-ray tube voltage should be made lower than the available maximum: (1) when it is desirable not to excite fluorescence of all elements in the specimen, but rather employ selective excitation conditions, and (2) when very long-wavelength spectral lines are to be excited in order to minimize scattering of primary radiation through the system by holding down the intensity of the short-wavelength continuum.

Analytical Applications

For qualitative analysis, the angle θ between the surface of the crystal and the incident fluorescence beam is gradually increased; at certain well-defined angles the appropriate fluorescence lines are reflected. In automatic operation the intensity is recorded on a moving chart as a series of peaks, corresponding to fluorescence lines, above a background which arises principally from general scattering. The angular position of the detector, in degrees of 2θ, is also recorded on the chart. Additional evidence for identification may be obtained from relative peak heights, the critical excitation potential, and pulse height analysis.

For quantitative analysis, the intensity of a characteristic line of the element to be analyzed is measured. The goniometer is set at the 2θ angle of the peak and counts are collected for a fixed period of time, or the time is measured for the period required to collect a specified number of counts. The goniometer is then set at a nearby portion of the spectrum where a scan has shown only the background to contribute. For major elements, 200,000 counts can be accumulated in 1 or 2 min. Background counts will require much longer time—a very low background may require 10 min to acquire 10,000 counts. The net line intensity—peak minus background, in counts per second, is then related to the concentration of the element via a calibration curve.

Particle size and shape are important and determine the degree to which the incident beam is absorbed or scattered. Standards and samples should be ground to the same mesh size, preferably finer than 200 mesh. Errors from differences in packing density can be handled only by addition of an internal standard to the sample. Powders are pressed into a wafer in a metallurgical specimen press or converted into a solid solution by fusion with borax. Samples are best handled as liquids. If they can be conveniently dissolved, their analysis is greatly simplified and precision is greatly improved. Liquid samples should exceed a depth which will appear infinitely thick to the primary X-ray beam—about 5 mm for aqueous samples. The solvent should not contain heavy atoms; in this respect HNO_3 and water are superior to H_2SO_4 or HCl.

Before relating the intensity of fluorescent emission to concentration of emitting element, it is usually necessary to correct for matrix effects. Matrix dilution will avoid serious absorption effects. The samples are heavily diluted with a material having a low absorption, such as powdered starch, lithium carbonate, lampblack, gum arabic, or borax (used in fusions). The concentration, and therefore the effect, of the disturbing matrix elements is reduced, along with a reduction of the measured fluorescence also. However, the most practical way to apply a systematic correction is by the use of an internal standard. Even so, the internal standard technique is valid only if the matrix elements affect the reference line and analytical line in exactly the same way. The choice of a reference element depends on the relative positions of the characteristic lines and the absorption edges of the element to be determined, the reference element, and the disturbing elements responsible for the matrix effects. If either the reference line or the analytical line is selectively absorbed or enhanced by a matrix element, the internal standard line and analytical line ratio is not a true measure of the concentration of the element to be determined. Preferential absorption of a line would occur if a disturbing element had an absorption edge between the comparison lines. The line of longer wavelength would be preferentially enhanced by a strong disturbing line between the absorption edges of the comparison elements.

Fluorescence X-ray analysis, inherently very precise, rivals the accuracy of wet chemical methods in the analysis of major constituents. On the other hand, it is difficult to detect an element present in less than one part in 10,000. The method is attractive for elements which lack reliable wet chemical methods— elements such as niobium, tantalum, and the rare earths. It often serves as a complementary procedure to optical emission spectrography, particularly for major constituents, and also for the analysis of nonmetallic specimens, since the sample need not be an electrical conductor. To overcome air absorption for elements of atomic number below 21, operating pressure must be 0.1 torr. Even so, below magnesium the transmission becomes seriously attenuated although the method has been extended to boron.

Simultaneous analysis of several elements is possible with automatic equipment, such as the Applied Research Laboratory Quantometer. Instruments of this type have semifixed monochromators with optics mounted around a centrally located X-ray tube and sample position. Each crystal is adjusted to reflect one fluorescence line to its associated detector. A compatible recording unit permits both optical and X-ray units to be recorded with the same console.

Nondispersive Spectrometers

For some problems where only very few elements are present and their X-ray lines are widely separated in wavelength, the crystal analyzer may be eliminated and pulse height discrimination employed in its place. For compositions greater than about 1 percent, and elements separated by a few atomic numbers, nondispersive analysis is very useful because the intensities are increased about a thousand-fold.

X-ray Diffraction

Each atom in a crystal has the power of scattering an X-ray beam incident on it. The sum of all the scattered waves in the crystal results in the X-ray beam being, in effect, diffracted from each allowed crystal plane. Every crystalline substance scatters the X rays in its own unique diffraction pattern, producing a "fingerprint" of its atomic and molecular structure. The intensity of each reflection forms the basic information required in crystal structure analysis. One unique feature of X-ray diffraction is that components are identified as specific compounds.

Because different atoms have different numbers of electrons, their relative scattering varies. Consequently, the crystal structure determines the intensity and position of the diffracted beam. Even when two crystals have identical lattices, the kinds of atoms comprising them may be different. Hence, each crystal species diffracts X rays in a characteristically different way. The identification of unknown compounds from their X-ray diffraction diagrams constitutes what is probably the most widespread application of diffraction methods.

Reciprocal Lattice Concept

Diffraction phenomena can be interpreted most conveniently with the aid of the reciprocal lattice concept. As everyone knows, a plane can be represented by a line drawn normal to the plane. The spatial orientation of this line describes the orientation of the plane. Furthermore, the length of the line can be fixed in an inverse proportion to the interplanar spacing of the plane that it represents.

When a normal is drawn to each plane in a crystal and the normals are drawn from a common origin, then the terminal points of these normals constitute a lattice array. This is called the reciprocal lattice because the distance of each point from the origin is reciprocal to the interplanar spacing of the planes that it represents. Figure 8-17 considers the side view of several planes in a unit cell of a crystal, for which are shown the (100), (001), (101) and

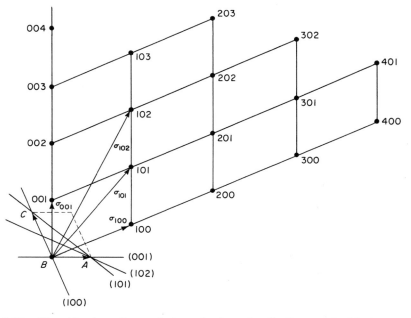

Fig. 8-17.   The side view of several planes in the unit cell of a crystal with the normals to these planes indicated.

(102) planes. The normals to these planes, also indicated, are called the reciprocal lattice vector σ_{hkl} and are defined by

$$\sigma_{hkl} = \lambda/d_{hkl}$$

In three dimensions, the lattice array is described by three reciprocal lattice vectors whose magnitudes are given by

$$a^\star = \sigma_{100} = \lambda/d_{100}$$
$$b^\star = \sigma_{010} = \lambda/d_{010}$$
$$c^\star = \sigma_{001} = \lambda/d_{001}$$

and whose directions are defined by three interaxial angles $\alpha^\star$, $\beta^\star$, $\gamma^\star$.

Writing the Bragg equation in a form that relates the glancing angle θ most clearly to the other parameters, we have

$$\sin \theta_{hkl} = \frac{\lambda/d_{hkl}}{2} \qquad\qquad (8\text{-}11)$$

The numerator can be thought of as one side of a right triangle and the denominator as its hypotenuse, Fig. 8-18(a). In view of the physical meaning of the quantities in Eq. 8-11, the construction can be interpreted as shown in

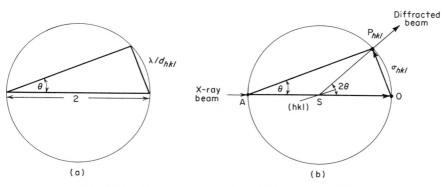

Fig. 8-18.   Representation of the diffraction condition.

Fig. 8-18(b). The diameter of the circle ($\overline{ASO}$) represents the direction of the incident X-ray beam. A line through the origin of the circle, parallel to $\overline{AP}$ and forming the angle θ with the incident beam, represents a crystallographic plane that satisfies the Bragg diffraction condition. The line $\overline{SP}$, also forming the angle θ with the crystal plane, represents the diffracted beam's direction. Then the line $\overline{OP}$ is the reciprocal lattice vector to the reciprocal lattice point P_{hkl} lying on the circumference of the circle. The vector σ_{hkl} originates from the point on the circle where the direct beam leaves the circle.

Thus, the crystal in a diffraction experiment can be pictured at the center of a sphere of unit radius, and the reciprocal lattice of this crystal is centered at the point where the direct beam leaves the sphere, as shown in Fig. 8-19. Because the orientation of the reciprocal lattice bears a fixed relation to that of the crystal, if the crystal is rotated, the reciprocal lattice can be pictured as rotating also. Whenever a reciprocal lattice point intersects the sphere, a reflection emanates from the crystal at the sphere's center and passes through the intersecting reciprocal lattice point.

Diffraction Patterns

If the X-ray beam is monochromatic, there will be only a limited number of angles at which diffraction of the beam will occur. The actual angles are determined by the wavelength and the spacing between the various planes of the crystal. In the rotating crystal method, monochromatic X radiation is incident on a single crystal which is rotated about one of its axes. The reflected beams lie as spots on the surface of cones which are coaxial with the rotation axis. If, for example, a single cubic crystal is rotated about the (001) axis, which is equivalent to rotation about the $c^{\star}$ axis, the sphere of reflection and the reciprocal lattice are as shown in Fig. 8-19. The diffracted beam directions are

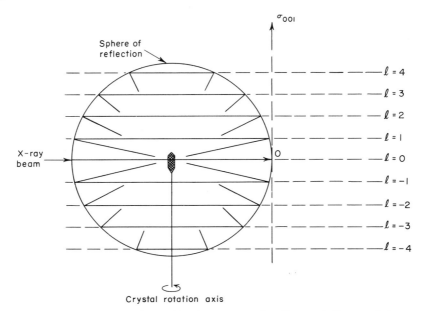

Fig. 8-19.   The reciprocal lattice construction for a rotating crystal.

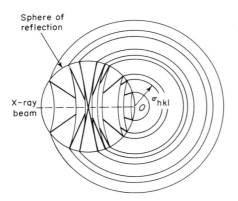

Fig. 8-20.   Origin of powder diffraction diagrams in terms of the series of concentric spheres generated from the reciprocal lattice points about the origin O of the reciprocal lattice and their intersection with the sphere of reflection.

determined by intersection of the reciprocal lattice points with the sphere of reflection. The height of the circle above the equatorial plane is proportional to the vertical reciprocal lattice spacing $c^\star$. By remounting the crystal successively about different axes, one can determine the complete distribution of reciprocal lattice points. Of course, one mounting is sufficient if the crystal is cubic, but two or more may be needed if the crystal has lower symmetry.

In a modification of the single crystal method, known as the Weissenberg method, the photographic film is moved continuously during the exposure parallel to the axis of rotation of the crystal. All reflections are blocked out except those which would occur in a single layer line.

If the crystal is replaced by a large collection of many very small crystals randomly oriented, a continuous cone of diffracted rays will be produced.

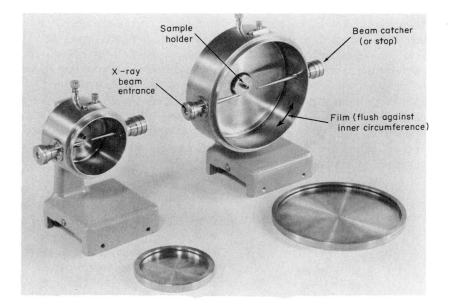

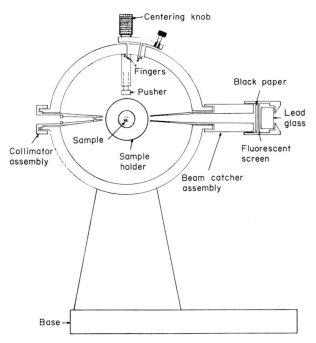

Fig. 8-21. X-ray powder diffraction cameras, 57.3-mm and 114.6-mm diameter, and schematic of internal arrangement. (Courtesy of Philips Electronic Instruments.)

There are some important differences, however, with respect to the rotating-crystal method. The cones obtained with a single crystal are not continuous because the diffracted beams occur only at certain points along the cone, whereas the cones with the powder method are continuous. Furthermore, although the cones obtained with single crystals are uniformly spaced about the zero level, the cones produced in the powder method are determined by the spacings of prominent planes and are not uniformly spaced. The origin of a powder diagram is shown in Fig. 8-20. Because of the random orientation of the crystallites, the reciprocal lattice points generate a sphere of radius σ_{hkl} about the origin of the reciprocal lattice. A number of these spheres intersect the sphere of reflection.

Camera Design

Typical cameras for X-ray powder diffraction work are shown in Fig. 8-21. Cameras are usually constructed so that the film diameter has one of the three values, 57.3 mm, 114.6 mm, or 143.2 mm. The reason for these values can be understood when one considers the calculations involved. If the distance between corresponding arcs of the same cone of diffracted rays—for example, the distance between A and B of Fig. 8-22—is measured and called S, then

$$4\theta_{\text{rad}} = S/R \qquad (8\text{-}12)$$

where θ_{rad} is the Bragg angle measured in radians and R is the radius of the film in the camera. The angle, θ_{deg}, measured in degrees, is then

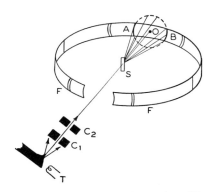

Fig. 8-22. Schematic of powder diffraction patterns. T, X-ray tube; C_1 and C_2, collimating slits; S, powdered crystalline sample; A, a line on film, left portion, and B, right portion; O, intersection of undiffracted beam with film. Angle $\overline{\text{ASO}} = 2\theta$.

$$\theta_{\text{deg}} = \frac{57.295S}{4R} \qquad (8\text{-}13)$$

where 57.295 equals the value of a radian in degrees. Therefore, when the camera diameter ($2R$) is equal to 57.3 mm, $2\theta_{\text{deg}}$ is given merely by measuring S in millimeters. When the diameter is 114.59 mm, $2\theta_{\text{deg}} = S/2$, and when the diameter is 143.2 mm, $\theta_{\text{deg}} = 2(S/10)$.

Once angle θ has been calculated, Eq. 8-3 can be used to find the interplanar spacing, using values of wavelength λ from Table 8-1. Sets of tables are available which give the interplanar spacing for the angle 2θ for the types of radiation most commonly used.

Cameras of larger diameter make it easier to measure the separation of lines provided that the lines are sharp. The sharpness of the lines depends to a great extent upon the quality of the collimating slits and the size of the sample. The slits should produce a fine beam of X rays with as small a divergence as possible. The sample size should be small so that it will act as a small source of the diffracted beam. On the other hand, smaller samples, finer pencils of incident X rays, and cameras of larger diameter all tend to require longer exposures, so that in practice a compromise must be made.

For very precise measurements of interplanar spacings, the diameter of the film and the separation of the lines must be very accurately known. Several methods of measurement have been proposed. The effective camera diameter can be determined by calibration with a material such as sodium chloride whose interplanar spacings are accurately known. Another method is to insert the film in the camera so that the ends of the film are at about 90° from the point of emergence of the beam from the camera. The developed film would then appear as in Fig. 8-23. If a_1, a_2 and b_1, b_2 represent the two sides of arcs

Fig. 8-23. X-ray powder diffraction photograph of sodium chloride. Film mounted in Straumanis method.

on the left and right sides of the film, then the two averages determine the positions of the entering and emerging beams.

Therefore,

$$\frac{b_1 + b_2}{2} - \frac{a_1 + a_2}{2} = \text{distance corresponding to } 180° \qquad (8\text{-}14)$$

or

$$360° = b_1 + b_2 - a_1 - a_2 \qquad (8\text{-}15)$$

and the angle 4θ associated with any pair of lines can then be calculated:

$$\frac{a_2 - a_1}{b_1 + b_2 - a_1 - a_2} = \frac{4\theta}{360} \qquad (8\text{-}16)$$

Choice of X Radiation

Two factors control the choice of X radiation, as can be seen by rearranging the terms of the Bragg equation

$$\theta = \sin^{-1}(\lambda/2d) \qquad (8\text{-}17)$$

Since the ratio in the parenthesis cannot exceed unity, the use of long wavelength radiation limits the number of reflections that can be observed. Conversely, when the unit cell is very large, short wavelength radiation tends to crowd individual reflections very closely together.

The choice of radiation is also affected by the absorption characteristics of a sample. Radiation having a wavelength just short of the absorption edge of an element contained in the sample should be avoided, because then the element absorbs the radiation strongly. The absorbed energy is emitted as fluorescent radiation in all directions and increases the background (which would result in darkening on a film, making it more difficult to see the diffraction maxima sought). It is obvious, then, why one commercial source provides radiation sources from a multiwindow tube with anodes of silver, molybdenum, tungsten, or copper.

Specimen Preparation

Single crystals are used whenever possible because of the relatively larger number of reflections obtained from single crystals and the greater ease of their interpretation. A crystal should be of such size that it is completely bathed by the incident beam. Generally, a crystal is affixed to a thin glass capillary which, in turn, is fastened to a brass pin, as shown in Fig. 8-24.

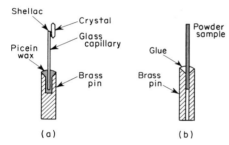
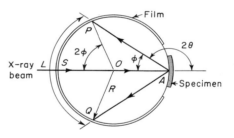

Fig. 8-24. Specimen mounts for X-ray diffraction. (a) Single crystal and (b) powdered sample.

Fig. 8-25. Geometry of the back-reflection symmetrical focusing camera.

When single crystals of sufficient size are not available, a polycrystalline aggregate is formed into a cylinder whose diameter is smaller than the diameter of the incident X-ray beam. Metal samples are machined to a desirable shape, plastic materials can often be extruded through suitable dies, and all other samples are best ground to a fine powder (200–300 mesh) and shaped into thin rods after mixture with a binder (usually collodion). The mount appears as shown in Fig. 8-24B.

Although liquids cannot be identified directly, it is frequently possible to convert them to crystalline derivatives which have characteristic patterns. Many of the classical derivatives can be used: identification of aldehydes and ketones as 2,4-dinitrophenylhydrazones, fatty acids as *p*-bromoanilides, and amines as picrate derivatives.

In order to obtain diffraction patterns from large, dense samples, a back-reflection camera can be used. The geometry of the camera is shown in Fig. 8-25. The X-rays pass through an opening in the center of the film and impinge on the sample. Beams diffracted over a range of Bragg angles extending from 59° to 88° are registered on the circular film.

Automatic Diffractometers

Results are achieved rapidly and with much better precision when automatic diffractometers are utilized. For powdered samples, the sample is spun in its own plane and, at the same time, a counter rotates with twice the angular velocity of the sample. The intensity of the diffracted beam is recorded either continuously on a strip chart or stepwise on a digital printer.

Scintillation and proportional counters, with their associated circuitry, are far superior to photographic film in regard to number of reflections per day that can be recorded. They can achieve precision of 1 percent or better. Even with the best darkroom and photometric procedures the relative degree of blackness of each spot or cone on the film cannot be estimated with an accuracy of much more than 20 percent, and often the estimation is in greater error than this. The principal advantage of photographic film over counters is that it provides a means of recording many reflections at one time.

Automatic single crystal diffractometers are quite complex. A cradle assembly provides a wide angular range for orienting and aligning the crystal under study. A precision-diffractometer assembly provides traverse of the detector on a spherical surface from longitude $-5°$ to 150° and from latitude $-6°$ to 60° on the Norelco instrument illustrated in Fig. 8-26. The complete unit provides four rotational degrees of freedom for the crystal and two for the detector. Various crystal and counter angles are set on the basis of programmed information and the resulting diffraction intensity is measured as a function of angle.

X-Ray Powder Data File

If only the identification of a powder sample is desired, its diffraction pattern is compared with diagrams of known substances until a match is obtained. This method requires that a library of standard films be available. Alternatively, d values calculated from the diffraction diagram of the unknown substance are compared with the d values of over 5000 entries, which are listed on plain cards, Keysort cards, and IBM cards in the X-ray powder data file.[9] An *Index* volume is available with the file. The cataloging scheme used to classify different cards consists of listing the three most intense reflections in the upper left corner of each card. The cards are then arranged in sequence of decreasing d values of the most intense reflections, based on 100 for the most intense reflection observed. A typical card is shown in Fig. 8-27.

To use the file to identify a sample containing one component, the d value for the darkest line of the unknown is looked up first in the *Index*. Since more

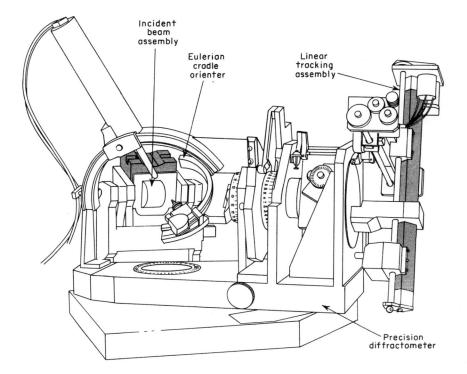

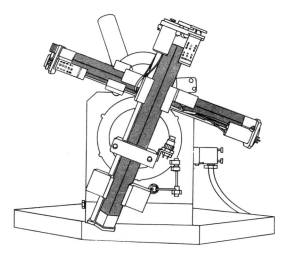

Fig. 8-26. Automatic single-crystal diffractometer. (Courtesy of Philips Electronic Instruments.)

5-0628

d	2.82	1.99	1.63	3.258	NaCl		★
I/I_1	100	55	15	13	SODIUM CHLORIDE	HALITE	

Rad. Cu λ 1.5405 Filter Dia.	dÅ	I/I_1	hkl	dÅ	I/I_1	hkl
Cut off I/I_1	3.258	13	111			
Ref. Swanson and Fuyat, NBS Circular 539, Vol. II, 41 (1953)	2.821	100	200			
	1.994	55	220			
Sys. Cubic S.G. O$_H^5$ – Fm3m	1.701	2	311			
a_0 5.6402 b_0 c_0 A C	1.628	15	222			
α β γ Z 4 Dx 2.164	1.410	6	400			
Ref. Ibid.	1.294	1	331			
	1.261	11	420			
	1.1515	7	422			
Ɛα nωβ 1.542 Ɛγ Sign	1.0855	1	511			
2V D mp Color	0.9969	2	440			
Ref. Ibid.	.9533	1	531			
	.9401	3	600			
An ACS reagent grade sample recrystallized twice from	.8917	4	620			
hydrochloric acid.	.8601	1	533			
X-ray pattern at 26°C.	.8503	3	622			
	.8141	2	444			
Replaces 1-0993, 1-0994, 2-0818						

Fig. 8-27. X-ray data card for sodium chloride. (Courtesy of American Society for Testing Materials.)

than one listing containing the first d value probably exists, the d values of the next two darkest lines are then matched against the values listed. Finally, the various cards involved are compared. A correct match requires that all the lines on the card and film agree. It is also good practice to derive the unit cell from the observed interplanar spacings and to compare it with that listed in the card.

If the unknown contains a mixture, each component must be identified individually. This is done by treating the list of d values as if they belonged to a single component. After a suitable match for one component is obtained, all the lines of the identified component are omitted from further consideration. The intensities of the remaining lines are rescaled by setting the strongest intensity equal to 100 and repeating the entire procedure.

Reexamination of the cards in the file is a continuing process in order to eliminate errors and remove deficiencies. Replacement cards for substances bear a star in the upper right corner.

Quantitative Analysis

X-ray diffraction is adaptable to quantitative applications because the intensities of the diffraction peaks of a given compound in a mixture are proportional to the fraction of the material in the mixture. However, direct comparison of the intensity of a diffraction peak in the pattern obtained from a mixture is fraught with difficulties. Corrections are frequently necessary for the differences in absorption coefficients between the compound being determined and the matrix. Preferred orientations must be avoided. Internal standards help but do not overcome the difficulties entirely.

Structural Applications

X-ray diffraction furnishes a rapid, accurate method for the identification of the crystalline phases present in a material. Sometimes it is the only method available for determining which of the possible polymorphic forms of a substance are present—for example, carbon in graphite or in diamond. Differentiation among various oxides—such as FeO, Fe_2O_3, and Fe_3O_4, or between materials present in such mixtures as KBr + NaCl, KCl + NaBr, or all four—is easily accomplished, whereas chemical analysis would show only the ions present and not the actual state of combination. The presence of various hydrates is another possibility.

In polymer chemistry a great deal of information can be obtained from an X-ray diffraction diagram. Fibers and partially oriented samples will show spotty diffraction patterns rather than uniform cones; the more oriented the specimen, the spottier the pattern. Figure 8-28 shows the fiber diagram of

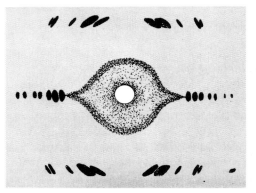

Fig. 8-28.   Fiber diagram of polyethylene. After A. Ryland, *J. Chem. Educ.*, **35**, (1958). (Courtesy of the *Journal of Chemical Education.*)

polyethylene. The center row of spots in the pattern is called the equator, and the horizontal rows parallel to the equator are called the layer lines. The equatorial spots arise by diffraction from lattice planes which are parallel to the fiber axis. The layer line spots arise by diffraction from planes which intersect the fiber axis. The repeat distance along the polymer chain can be calculated from the distances of the layer lines from the equator and their separation from one another. In the simplest cases the repeat distance will correspond to that of a fully extended chain of the known chemical composition.

LABORATORY WORK

General Instructions for Operation of X-Ray Diffraction Units

1. Read the instruction manual furnished by the manufacturer, if available. The general procedure for most X-ray units is outlined below.

2. Make sure that all unused ports are covered with lead shields and that the proper filter is in place on all ports to be used.

3. Mount and align the cameras on all ports to be used.

4. Turn on the main line switch (a key switch on some instruments).

5. Set the desired exposure on the timer.

6. Make sure that the overload relay is in the ON position.

7. Press the LINE ON button. Water should now flow through the X-ray unit.

8. Press the X-ray ON button. After a time-delay in the instrument operates, current should flow through the high-voltage circuit and be indicated on the milliammeter.

9. Adjust the voltage to the desired setting with the voltage control. For copper tubes, 30 kV is recommended, and for molybdenum tubes, 45 kV is recommended.

10. Adjust the tube current with the current control. For copper targets, 15 ma is usually suitable, and for molybdenum target tubes, 19 ma is often employed.

11. When shutting the apparatus off, follow the reverse procedure of turning the apparatus on. Turn voltage and current controls to their lowest limit and be sure these controls are in this position before starting the apparatus again.

EXPERIMENT 8-1   IDENTIFICATION OF SUBSTANCES BY THE POWDER DIFFRACTION METHOD

1. A very small sample of a crystalline material will be furnished. The sample must be very finely powdered (finer than 200 mesh) if it is not already so.

2. Prepare a small-diameter, thin-walled melting-point tube (diameter 0.7 mm or less) and fill it with the powdered sample. Place the tube in the chuck at the center of the powder camera and fix it in place with a drop of wax. Line the sample tube up so that it rotates without wobbling. Alternatively, the sample may be coated on the outside of a very fine glass rod, using collodion or vaseline or other noncrystalline material to stick it on.

3. Take the camera into the darkroom and load it with film of the proper size. A punch is available for perforating the film so that the collimator and beam trap can be inserted into the camera. Insert the collimator and beam trap and place the cover on the camera.

4. Place the camera on the X-ray unit. An exposure of 20–30 min is recommended for a first trial. If this results in too light or too dark an exposure, estimate the required time for another exposure and repeat the whole procedure.

5. Remove the film in the darkroom. Develop for four minutes in X-ray developer and fix for twice the time required for the film to clear. Wash thoroughly and dry.

6. Measure the distance between lines of the film, using the film measuring device. From the radius of the camera calculate the interplanar spacings creating the observed lines.

If the distance between corresponding arcs of the same cone of diffracted rays — for example, the distance between A and B of Fig. 8-22 — is measured and called S, then:

$$\frac{S}{R} = 4\theta_{\text{rad}}$$

where R = radius of camera, and θ_{rad} is the angle of incidence, measured in radians. The angle, θ_{deg}, measured in degrees, is then:

$$\theta_{\text{deg}} = \frac{S}{4R} \times 57.295$$

Equation 8-3 can then be used to calculate the spacing d, using the values of λ for $K\alpha_1$ from Table 8-1. The Geological Survey has prepared sets of tables[8] which give the d spacing directly if copper or iron target X-ray tubes are used and if the angle 2θ is calculated. These tables are very convenient to use.

7. For precise measurements of the camera radius and for compensation for film shrinkage during development, a pattern of sodium chloride should be taken. The main spacings in the sodium chloride pattern are 2.821, 1.99, 1.63, and 1.260 Å.

8. Estimate the relative intensity of the lines produced on the film. Refer to the A.S.T.M. X-ray tables of compounds to identify the unknown. Turn in all calculations, films, and the identification of the unknown to the instructor.

Problems

1. What is the short-wavelength limit for a 100-kV X-ray tube? What is the atomic number of the element for which insufficient energy is available for excitation?

2. Write the transition relations for each of these lines: (a) $K\alpha_2$, (b) $K\beta_1$ and (c) $L\alpha_1$.

3. Calculate the critical excitation potentials for the K and L series of these elements:

ELEMENT	K ABSORPTION EDGE, Å	L_{III} EDGE, Å
Al	7.951	—
Cr	2.070	21.6
Zr	0.688	5.58
Nd	—	1.995
W	0.178	1.215
U	0.107	0.722

Ans. Zr K-lines, 18.0 kV, Zr L-lines, 2.22 kV.

4. Calculate the wavelengths of the $K\alpha_1$ lines for the elements in Problem 3. *Ans.* Zr $K\alpha_1 = 0.786$ A.

5. For what elements will Mo $K\alpha_1$ prove sufficiently energetic to excite their L_{III} spectra? What is the limit for K spectra?

6. What causes the discontinuity in the efficiency curve of the NaI scintillation counter and of the argon-filled flow proportional counter (Fig. 8-7)?

7. Compute the goniometer setting (2θ) for each of the following emission lines when the analyzing crystal is (a) LiF, (b) CaF_2, (c) EDDT: The $K\alpha_1$ lines of Al, S, Ca, Cr, Mn, Co, Br, Sr Ag, Mo, W. *Ans.* Sr $K\alpha_1 = 25.2°$ using LiF crystal.

8. Discuss four ways that might be employed for the separation of interfering spectral lines.

9. For the determination of uranium in aluminum by measurement of U $L\alpha_1$ fluorescence, these counting relationships were obtained:

U (WT %)	COUNT RATE, CPS
2	436
5	835
10	1262
15	1533
20	1720

Determine the slope of the calibration curve (cps/% U) over each interval of uranium concentration and the counting time (in minutes) required to achieve a 95 percent confidence level for 1 percent precision. *Ans.* Slope = 165 at 2% U; time = 1.77 min at 5% U.

10. Sulfur (0.4–6.0%) has been determined in carbon materials by X-ray fluorescence using the S Kα line (5.36Å) which under a particular set of operating conditions gave 1 cps equivalent to 0.014% S. Background radiation is equivalent to 0.05% S. Select a proper analyzing crystal, the goniometer setting, the excitation conditions (X-ray tube voltage), and counting times to achieve results whose deviation does not exceed 5% at 95% confidence level.

11. What is the reflection angle (2θ) for Cu Kα_1 radiation from each analyzing crystal in Table 8-4? *Ans.* 2θ = 45.1° using LiF (200 plane).

12. The pulse amplitude distributions for these elements: Mg, Al, Si, P, S, and Ca, show a peak of pulse distribution at 11.0, 13.0, 15.0, 17.4, 19.0, and 31.8V, respectively. For each the width at one-half peak height is 2.5 V, and the base width is 9.5 V. What base line and window settings (in volts) would be employed in these situations?

   (a) The determination of Mg in the presence of P.
   (b) The determination of S is the presence of Mg.
   (c) The determination of P is the presence of Al.
   (d) The separation of calcium from all the others.
   (e) The total Al plus Si in a sample, all other elements absent.

   Ans. (e) Base line set for 8 V and the window for 11 V.

13. Suggest methods for handling each pair of overlapping X-ray spectral lines whose wavelength in angstroms are enclosed in brackets:

   (a) Mn Kα_1[2.103] — Cr Kβ[2.085]
   (b) Zn Kα_1[1.435] — Re Lα_1[1.433]
   (c) Nb Kα_1[1.494] — W Lα_1[1.476]

   Ans. (c) One possibility is to insert a nickel filter having an absorption edge at 1.48 Å selectively absorbing the Nb Kα_1 line.

14. Graphically represent these disturbing effects in the use of an internal standard element (S) for the determination of element (E), the disturbing element being (D). Plot all absorption edges and emission lines. (a) Selective absorption of "S"; (b) selective absorption of "E"; (c) enhancement of "S"; and (d) enhancement of "E". *Ans.* (b) Action of a selective filter; see Table 8-3.

15. Strontium has been determined in sediments of oil-bearing formations using yttrium as an internal standard. The spectral characteristics of these elements are

$$\text{Sr } K\alpha_1, 0.877; \quad K\beta, 0.783; \quad K \text{ edge, } 0.770$$
$$\text{Y } K\alpha_1, 0.831; \quad K\beta, 0.740; \quad K \text{ edge, } 0.727$$

(a) Compute the critical voltage for each element. (b) Using a LiF crystal, compute the Bragg angle (2θ) for the emission lines. (c) Calibration data obtained is tabulated:

Sr, wt. %	MEASUREMENT OF Y Kα_1; TIME (SEC) FOR 6400 COUNTS	MEASUREMENT OF Sr Kα_1; TIME (SEC) FOR 6400 COUNTS
0.0000	41.1	80.1
0.1000	40.1	60.4
0.2000	40.2	49.5
0.3000	40.0	41.6
0.4000	42.4	38.3

Plot intensity ratio vs concentration of strontium. Unknown samples gave these intensity ratios—Sr:Y—*A*, 0.8860; *B*, 0.7802; *C*, 0.6011. *Ans. A* contains 0.2500% Sr.

16. What is the difference in wavelength (and Bragg angle) between Hf $K\alpha_1$ and the second order of Zr $K\alpha_1$, 1.566 Å and 0.784 Å (in first order, respectively) with a LiF analyzing crystal? Suggest a method for eliminating the second-order zirconium line.

17. Oil paintings have been examined for authenticity by examining the pigment composition with the electron probe and a hypodermic needle core. With an ammonium dihydrogen phosphate crystal (101 plane), $d = 10.62$, these characteristic X-ray spectra (and relative intensity) were obtained:

TOP WHITE LAYER, 2θ	BOTTOM WHITE LAYER, 2θ
27.6° (8)	34.0° (12)
30.0° (60)	36.0° (100)
58.0° (4)	71.0° (2)
63.0° (18)	

Was the painting produced before or after the time when titanium-white pigments were available? *Ans.* See Peterson and Oglivie, *Trans. A.I.M.E.*, **218**, 439 (1960).

18. From the data given in Table 8-3, estimate the mass absorption coefficients (a) of Zr for the Mo $K\alpha_1$ radiation, (b) of Ni for the Cu $K\alpha_1$ radiation, and (c) of Cu for the W $L\alpha_1$ radiation. *Ans.* (a) Calculated to be 17 cm²/g; the literature value is given as 16 cm²/g.

19. Calculate the reduction in intensity of an X-ray beam from Mo $K\alpha_1$ line (0.711 Å) resulting from 1 ml of 1% TEL liquid in *n*-octane. The aviation mixture consists of 61.5% $Pb(C_2H_5)_4$ and 38.5% $C_2H_4Br_2$ per milliliter of TEL. The mass absorption coefficients are C, 0.64 cm²/g; H, 0.38 cm²/g; Pb, 140 cm²/g; and Br, 79 cm²/g. Density = 0.72 g cm⁻³. *Ans.* Decrease in intensity is 63% per 1 cm cell length.

20. Repeat Problem 19 using the Cu $K\alpha_1$ line (1.542 Å). The mass absorption coefficients are C, 4.6 cm²/g; H, 0.43 cm²/g; Pb, 241 cm²/g; and Br, 88 cm²/g. Note the increase in absorption by lead, but also by the carbon atoms.

21. Identify the emission lines and, from these, the base wire and plate metal in each sample. Spectrometer employed a LiF crystal and tungsten target operated at 50 kV.

SAMPLE	PLATE METAL, 2θ	BASE WIRE, 2θ
1	48.64°	41.30° (2nd)
2	99.87° (2nd)	63.88° (3rd)
3	31.19°	110.92° (2nd)
4	16.75°	110.92° (2nd)

Ans. Sample 1 is Ni ($K\alpha_1$) on Mo ($K\alpha_1$).

22. A sample ground and pelleted with lithium carbonate and starch gave these emission lines (2θ) using a LiF crystal. Identify each line.

111.0°, 100.2°, 57.8°, 48.8°, 45.1°. 44.0°, 38.0°

23. Suggest an X-ray method for each of these determinations: (a) the thickness of electroplated metal films, such as successive layers of copper, nickel, and chromium on steel (chrome plate), (b) the thickness of SrO and BaO on evaporated electrode coatings, and (c) the concentration of fillers and impregnants, such as BaF_2 in carbon brushes.

24. Iron-55 decays by K-electron capture to stable manganese-55 with the attendant emission of K-line X-rays of manganese. The half-life of iron-55 is 2.93 years For which elements would this isotope be a convenient source of X radiation for absorption analysis? *Ans.* See *Anal. Chem.*, **26**, 1889 (1954); ibid., **29**, 1631 (1957); ibid., **34**, 607 (1962).

25. An unknown material was placed in the sample holder of an X-ray fluorescence unit which used a tungsten target tube operated at 60 kV to furnish the exciting radiation. A mica crystal was used in the analyzer. The lattice spacing of mica is 9.948 Å. Reflections were observed at angles (2θ) of 9°34', 12°8', 19°12', 24°24', and 38°58'. Calculate the wavelength of the fluorescent lines and identify the elements present.

26. An unknown powder was placed in a sample tube, and the X-ray diffraction pattern was observed in a camera of radius 57.3 mm. The X-ray unit was fitted with a nickel target tube with a cobalt filter. The distances between corresponding arcs of the three strongest lines observed on the developed film were measured as 77.5, 89.9, and 130.4 mm. These lines seemed to the eye to be of about equal intensity. Calculate the spacings d of the crystal in angstrom units and identify the substance by reference to the A.S.T.M. card file.

27. In the case of polyethylene, the repeat distance obtained from the X-ray diffraction pattern of a fiber diagram was 2.54 Å. What type of chemical structure is implied? *Ans.* A fully extended planar zigzag carbon chain is indicated, since the C—C distance is essentially this value.

28. The repeat distance obtained from the fiber diagram of polytetrafluoroethylene was 19.5 Å, corresponding to 15 CF_3 units. What chemical structure is suggested?

Bibliography

Birks, L. S., *X-ray Spectrochemical Analysis*, Interscience, New York, 1959.

Birks, L. S., *Electron Probe Microanalysis*, Interscience, New York, 1963.

Buerger, M. J., *X-ray Crystallography*, Wiley, New York, 1942.

Bunn, C. W., *Chemical Crystallography*, 2nd ed., Oxford U.P., New York, 1961.

Clark, G. L., *Applied X-rays*, 4th ed., McGraw-Hill, New York, 1955.

Robertson, J. M., *Organic Crystals and Molecules*, Cornell, Ithaca, N.Y., 1953.

Literature Cited

1. Birks, L. S., E. J. Brooks, and H. Friedman, *Anal. Chem.*, **25**, 692 (1953).

2. Bragg, W. L., *The Crystalline State*, Macmillan, New York, 1933.

3. Castaing, R., *Thesis*, University of Paris,—1951.

4. Clark, G. L., and S. T. Gross, *Ind. Eng. Chem., Anal. Ed.*, **14**, 676 (1942).

5. Duane, W., and F. L. Hunt, *Phys. Rev.*, **6**, 166 (1915).

6. Hanawalt, J. D., H. W. Rinn, and L. K. Frevel, *Ind. Eng. Chem.*, *Anal. Ed.* **10,** 457 (1938).
7. Ievins, A., and M. E. Straumanis, *Z. Krist.*, **94A,** 40, 48 (1936); *see also* M. E. Straumanis, *Anal. Chem.*, **25,** 700 (1953).
8. Switzer, G., J. M. Axelrod, M. L. Lindberg, and E. S. Larsen, "Tables of Spacings for Angle 2θ, Cu Kα, Cu Kα_1, Cu Kα_2, Fe Kα, Fe Kα_1, Fe Kα_2," Circular 29, Geological Survey, U.S. Dept. of Interior, Washington, D.C., 1948; "Tables for Conversion of X-ray Diffraction Angles to Interplanar Spacings," Publication AMS 10, Govt. Printing Office, Washington, D.C.
9. "Alphabetical and Grouped Numerical Index of X-ray Diffraction Data," *Am. Soc. Testing Mater.*, *Spec. Tech. Publ.*, No. 48E (1955).

Radiochemical Methods

Until the advent of the cyclotron, and more recently the chain-reacting pile, most of the work with radionuclides was with the heavy, naturally occurring radioactive elements. It is now possible to obtain artificially produced radionuclides of most of the elements and to obtain many of these in large quantities and with extremely high activity. Quite naturally the availability of radionuclides has provided great impetus to their use.

Nuclear Reactions and Radiations

Particles Emitted in Radioactive Decay

Several different types of particles are ejected by radionuclides and, since the properties of these particles are quite different, they present different problems of measurement. The heavy, naturally occurring radioactive elements, such as thorium, uranium, and the like, emit, among other products, doubly ionized helium particles known as alpha particles. Alpha particles have only a slight penetrating power, being stopped by thin sheets of solid materials and penetrating only 5–7 cm of air. Their energies, however, are generally very high, and may exceed 10 MeV (million electron volts). As a result, the ionizing power of an alpha particle is high; that is, on passing through material a large number of ion pairs are produced along the linear path traversed by an alpha particle. For example, a 5-MeV alpha particle, which is stopped in 3.5 cm of air, produces about 25,000 ion pairs per centimeter of travel. Due to the greater ionizing power of alpha particles, they can generally be distinguished from beta or gamma radiation on the basis of pulse amplitude.

A radioactive element formed by neutron capture usually has a higher neutron/proton ratio than its stable isobars, and therefore it frequently decays by beta particle emission. A beta particle is simply a very energetic electron or positron. It will have a maximum energy, often expressed as penetrating power or range, that is characteristic of the particular decay reaction. An 0.5-MeV beta particle has a range of 1 m in air and produces about 60 ion pairs per centimeter of its path.

Gamma rays, actually high-energy photons, are emitted by the excited nuclei of atoms. When the nucleus falls from the excited to the ground state, the additional energy is given off as gamma radiation. Since only definite, discrete energy levels are possible, gamma emissions have definite energies. In many respects, the emission of gamma rays from the nucleus is similar to the emission of photons from electronically excited atoms. The penetrating power of gamma radiation is much greater than that of either alpha or beta particles, but the ionizing power is less.

A long-lived positron-emitting nucleus may decay by capturing one of its own orbital K electrons—internal conversion. The excess energy is emitted as a gamma ray, and the resulting ions with a vacant K orbital then emit X radiation characteristic of the particular element.

Interaction of Radiations with Matter

Since the radiations from radionuclides are detected by means of their interactions with matter, a brief summary of these modes of interaction is presented here.

Beta particles interact primarily with the electrons in the material traversed by the particle. The molecules may be dissociated, excited, or ionized. It is the ionization, however, which is of primary interest in the detection of beta particles. On the average, each ion pair produced represents a loss of 35 eV. Actually, the beta particle may lose a large part of its energy in a single interaction, but if it does, the ions produced have so much excess energy that they in turn produce additional ion pairs. The absorption of beta particles in matter follows approximately the exponential relation given by Eq. 9-2 for gamma radiation, up to a certain thickness where the absorption finally exceeds that predicted by the exponential law and soon becomes infinite. This maximum thickness is known as the range of the beta particle (Fig. 9-1). For energies above 0.6 MeV, the following range-energy relationship gives the maximum energy of the beta particle

$$\text{Range (in mg cm}^{-2} \text{ of absorber)} = 543 E_{\text{max}} - 160 \qquad (9\text{-}1)$$

In lower energy regions it is best to use a range-energy curve; a typical curve is shown on page 107 of the Friedlander, Kennedy, and Miller book.

Whenever a beta particle comes close to a nucleus, it may have its direction of travel greatly changed, so that the path of a single beta particle in traversing matter may be a very devious one. Scattering due to the material supporting the radionuclide, called back-scattering, increases the lower the energy of the beta particle and the higher the atomic number of the scatterer. Increasing the thickness of the support up to 0.2 range of a beta particle increases the back-scattering factor to a maximum value. Lead walls and doors of counting and shielding equipment should be lined with Lucite. Self-absorption and self-scattering also occur with beta particles. For very thin sources, 0.1–0.2 mg cm^{-2}, both factors are negligible—

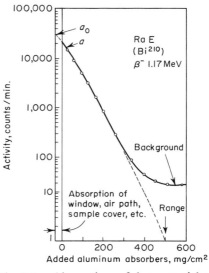

Fig. 9-1.   Absorption of beta particles.

this situation prevails with carrier-free sources mounted on thin plastic film. For thicker samples, the same amount of inert carrier must be used or a correction curve prepared for different quantities of carrier.

The continuous X radiations produced when electrons are decelerated in the coulomb fields of atomic nuclei are called *bremsstrahlung*. This type of radiation is produced whenever fast electrons pass through matter; the efficiency of the conversion of kinetic energy into bremsstrahlung goes up with increasing electron energy and with increasing atomic number of the material.

Alpha particles lose energy by the same mechanisms as beta particles. However, owing to their large relative mass and higher charge, the specific ionization is much larger than for beta particles. Since the alpha particles are emitted from the nucleus with discrete energies and since the alpha particles lose only a small fraction of energy in collision with electrons, nearly all the alpha particles from a given nucleus will traverse the same distance in an absorber. Thus a determination of the range of alpha particles is a simple matter, and the energy of the alpha particles can be found by reference to plots such as those on pages 96–97 of the Friedlander, Kennedy, and Miller book.

Gamma rays lose energy on passage through matter in three ways: by the photoelectric effect, by the Compton effect, and by pair production. The photoelectric effect is important for heavy absorbing elements and for low gamma-ray energies. In this process gamma rays are absorbed by inner electrons bound in an atom, and the energy carried by the gamma ray is transferred completely to the electron with the resultant ejection of the electron from the atom (cf. X-ray absorption). The Compton effect consists of a gamma ray interacting with an electron and transferring part of its energy to the electron. The electron is ejected from the atom and a new photon of lower energy proceeds from the collision in an altered direction. The Compton effect is important with light target elements and with gamma rays possessing energies less than 3 MeV. Pair production of a positron and an electron results when a high-energy gamma ray is annihilated following interaction with the nucleus of a heavy atom. Such a process is important with heavy elements and gamma rays of energies greater than 1.02 MeV, the energy corresponding to twice the rest mass of an electron. Conversely, when a positron and electron meet, the two are annihilated, and two gamma rays with energies of 0.51 MeV each are produced. Some of these spectral features are illustrated later in Fig. 9-12.

Each ion pair which results from the passage of radiation through air represents an average energy loss of about 35 eV. The number of ion pairs per centimeter of travel is known as the specific ionization. In the case of gamma rays, the ion pairs formed are almost entirely produced by secondary processes —the photoelectrons, the Compton electrons, and the positrons and electrons. The processes by which gamma rays lose energy when interacting with matter lead to an exponential absorption law:

$$P = P_0 e^{-\mu x} \tag{9-2}$$

where P is the fraction of incident intensity P_0 which is transmitted through an absorber of thickness x, and μ is the linear absorption coefficient. Often the energy of a gamma ray is expressed as the thickness of absorber required to diminish P to $1/2 P_0$; this half-thickness is given by

$$x_{1/2} = \frac{0.693}{\mu} \tag{9-3}$$

Absorber thicknesses are frequently given in units of surface density, grams per square centimeter; i.e., ρx where ρ is the density of the absorber. Equation 9-2 becomes

$$P = P_0 e^{-(\mu/\rho)\rho x} \tag{9-4}$$

where μ/ρ is known as the mass absorption coefficient.

Neutrons do not carry a charge and therefore they do not interact with electrons. Because of their lack of charge, neutrons can more readily enter the nucleus of an absorber element, and it is by secondary reactions that the neutron is detected and measured; for example,

$$B^{10} + n^0 \rightarrow Li^7 + \alpha \tag{9-5}$$

It is the alpha particle which is actually detected.

Radioactive Decay

The decay of a radionuclide follows the well-known first-order rate law, which may be written in differential form as follows:

$$\frac{\partial N}{\partial t} = -\lambda N \qquad (9\text{-}6)$$

where N is the number of radionuclides remaining at time t, and λ is the characteristic decay constant (in $\sec^{-1}$). The activity A is related to N by the equation

$$A = \lambda N \qquad (9\text{-}7)$$

and is usually the quantity observed or computed. The rate equation may be integrated to yield

$$A = A_0 e^{-\lambda t} \qquad \text{or} \qquad \ln A = \ln A_0 - \lambda t \qquad (9\text{-}8)$$

where A_0 is the activity at zero time.

The time required for one half of the radioactive material to decay—the half-life of the radionuclide, is generally used in describing radioactive emitters, namely,

$$t_{1/2} = \frac{1}{\lambda} \ln \frac{A}{A/2} = \frac{0.693}{\lambda} \qquad (9\text{-}9)$$

An accurate knowledge of the characteristic decay constant (λ) is essential when working with short-lived radionuclides in order to correct for the decay while the experiment is in progress. Selected decay schemes are shown in Fig. 9-2.

Units of Radioactivity

The strength of radioactive material can be expressed in a number of ways. One such term, the curie, is now defined as an activity of 3.70×10^{10} disintegrations per second. It is used as the standard unit of measurement for the activity of any substance, regardless of whether the emission is alpha or beta particles, or X or gamma radiation. Because the curie represents a very high activity, smaller units such as the millicurie and the microcurie are often used.

The unit of exposure to X or gamma radiation is the roentgen or R unit. It indicates the ionizing power of a substance. One roentgen is the amount of radiation that will, on passing through 0.001293 g of air under standard conditions, produce ions carrying one electrostatic unit of electricity, of either sign, per cubic centimeter. One roentgen produces 1.61×10^{12} ion pairs per gram of air.

The unit of specific gamma emission is the roentgen per millicurie hour at 1 cm. For measurement of energy loss of beta and other particles in tissue, the roentgen equivalent physical is sometimes used. It is that quantity of radiation which produces in tissue (per gram of tissue) ionization equivalent to the quantity of ionization from one roentgen of gamma radiation in air.

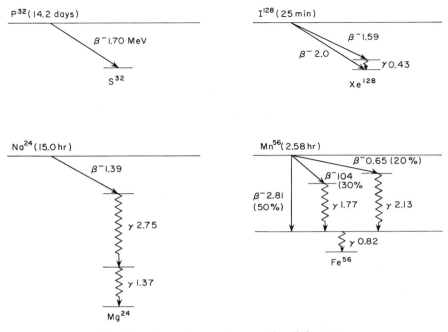

Fig. 9-2. Some decay schemes of radioisotopes.

Measurement of Radioactivity

Radiation from radionuclides can be detected and measured in many ways. The best method to employ in any particular situation depends upon the nature of the radiation and the energy of the radiation or particles involved.

Photographic Emulsion

Any ionizing particle or radiation will cause activation and, on development, darkening of a photographic plate. The intensity of the blackening can be used to measure the activity, but better methods are available. The photographic plate is useful, however, in studies of the distribution of radioactive material in a thin section of a substance—autoradiography. A slice of tissue, for example, when placed on a plate, would cause blackening at the places where uptake of a radionuclide had occurred and thus would indicate the distribution of the tracer in the biological material. Film badges are used to measure the total exposure of workers to radiation.

The Ionization Chamber

In the ionization chamber (Fig. 9-3) an electric field is applied across a volume of gas—air for alpha particles, krypton or xenon under pressure for gamma radiation. Charged particles moving through the gas undergo inelastic collisions to form ion pairs. In the absence of a field these will recombine, but

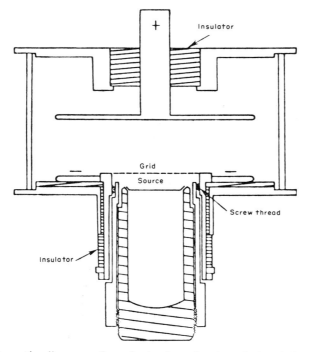

Fig. 9-3. Schematic diagram of an ionization chamber designed for insertion of sample.

at a proper field strength (Fig. 9-4) the electrons are collected at the central anode. A saturation current is obtained which is related to the number of ion pairs produced per unit time N by the equation

$$i = Ne \qquad (9\text{-}10)$$

where e is the electronic charge. The chamber therefore measures the integrated effect of a large number of ionizing events.

The change in potential of the central anode, in terms of the saturation current flowing through a very high resistance, and the voltage developed, is applied to the control grid of a vacuum-tube voltmeter or to a

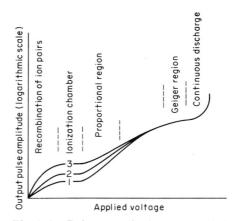

Fig. 9-4. Pulse amplitude vs applied voltage for radioactive emissions of different energy.

vibrating-reed electrometer. In the null method, the change in voltage produced across a capacitor by the ionizing current is counterbalanced by an equal
and opposite voltage supplied from a potentiometer. Commercial instruments
find this null point electronically, and a conventional strip chart recorder
registers the signal. For example, the charge associated with the 100,000 ion
pairs produced by a single alpha particle traveling approximately 1 cm in air
would amount to about 3×10^{-14} coulomb (Q). If this average charge should
pass through a resistance of $3 \times 10^{10} \ \Omega$ in 1 sec, then a difference of potential
of approximately 1 mV would exist across the high resistance. Any change in

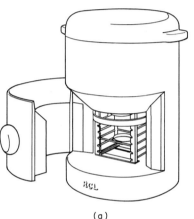

(a)

Fig. 9-5. (a) End-window type of Geiger counter.
(b) Counter and sample holder with shielding removed. (c) Schematic of counter.

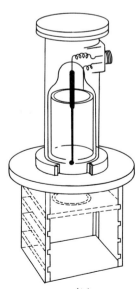

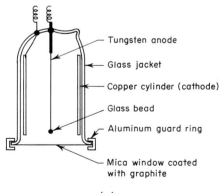

Tungsten anode

Glass jacket

Copper cylinder (cathode)

Glass bead

Aluminum guard ring

Mica window coated
with graphite

(c)

(b)

the rate of ionization in the chamber would result in a corresponding change in this voltage. The ionization system is an accurate, quick-acting detector even for very weak radiation. With a fast amplifier the total ionization of a single heavily ionizing particle passing through the sensitive volume can be measured.

The sample is placed outside a thin aluminum leaf window or inserted in a well extending into the chamber volume. Gaseous compounds containing radionuclides may be introduced directly into the chamber volume.

The Geiger Counter

The Geiger counter, also called a Geiger-Müller or G-M tube, is shown schematically in Fig. 9-5. A potential of 800–2500 volts is applied to a central wire anode surrounded by a cylindrical cathode—a glass wall which has been silvered or a brass cylinder. The two electrodes are enclosed in a gas-tight envelope typically filled to a pressure of 80 mm of argon gas and 20 mm of chlorine, methane, or alcohol. A thin end window of mica, about 2.5 cm in diameter and 2–3 mg cm⁻² in thickness, or the glass wall in dipping counters, is the point of entry of the radioactive particles. Examples of commercial counters are shown in Fig. 9-6.

When an ionizing particle enters the active volume of the Geiger counter, collision with the filling gas produces an ion pair. This is followed by migration of these particles toward the appropriate electrodes under the voltage gradient. The mobility of the electron is quite high, and under the influence of the potential gradient, it soon acquires sufficient velocity to produce a new pair of ions upon collision with another atom of argon. Under these conditions, which are repeated many times, each original ionizing particle entering the active volume of the counter gives rise to an avalanche of electrons traveling toward the central anode. Photons, emitted when the electrons strike the anode, spread the ionization throughout the tube. These processes produce a continuous discharge which fills the whole active volume of the counter in less than a microsecond. Each discharge builds up to a constant pulse of 1–10 volts regardless of the original number of ions produced by each single ionizing particle. Because of the large pulse size, very simple associated electronic circuitry is required—a principal advantage of the Geiger tube relative to other

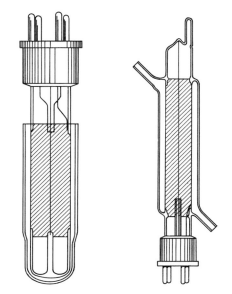

Fig. 9-6. Geiger counters: (a) dipping counter and (b) jacketed counter. (Courtesy of Radiation Counter Laboratories, Inc.)

counters. The signal is strong enough to be transmitted directly to a scaler or a ratemeter with no intermediate amplification.

During the time the electron avalanche is collected on the anode, the positive ions, being much heavier, have progressed only a short distance on their way to the cathode. Their travel time is about 200 μsec and during most of this time their presence as a virtual sheath around the anode effectively lowers the potential gradient to a point where the counter is insensitive to the entry of further ionizing particles—the dead time of the counter. Because the halogen or organic gas molecules have a lower ionization potential than argon, after a few collisions the ions moving toward the cathode consist only of these entities. In contrast to argon ions, these positive ions do not produce photons when neutralized at the cathode. Consequently, photons which could initiate a fresh discharge are prevented from forming and the counter is self-quenching. Upon being neutralized, the organic filling gas dissociates to various molecular fragments and, eventually, the quenching agent is exhausted. Counter life is limited to about 10^8 counts. However, since halogen ions do not dissociate, a halogen-quenched counter has virtually indefinite life; the operating voltage is also considerably less.

Counting rates are limited to about 15,000 counts/min because of the long dead time of 200–270 μsec. Sensitivity for beta particles is excellent, but for gamma radiation the sensitivity is less than that of the scintillation counter. There is no possibility of using pulse height discrimination with a Geiger counter because the pulses are all the same amplitude, nor is there any practical correction for coincidence losses when scanning across a spectrum.

Proportional Counters

When the electric field strength at the center electrode of an ionization chamber is increased above the saturation level, but under that of the Geiger region (Fig. 9-4), the size of the output pulse from the chamber starts to increase but is still proportional to the initial ionization. A device operated in such a fashion is called a proportional counter.

An electron avalanche is developed, as in a Geiger counter; however, in the proportional region few, if any, photons are released. Consequently, the total number of secondary electrons is proportional to the number of primary ion pairs produced by the original ionizing particle. Furthermore, the discharge is limited to the immediate environment of the entering ionizing particle and the path traversed by the ion pair plus their secondary electrons and positive ions. The dead time is thus very short, about 1.25 μsec. Multiplication factors from 10 to 10^5 are possible; they are dependent on applied voltage, gas pressures, and counter dimensions.

The source may be placed outside the counter or inside the counter, as is done with a continuous gas flow counter, thus avoiding window absorption (Fig. 9-7). An argon-methane mixture (P-10 gas) flows at atmospheric pres-

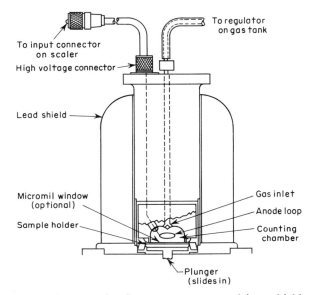

To regulator
on gas tank

To input connector
on scaler

High voltage connector

Lead shield

Micromil window
(optional)

Sample holder

Gas inlet

Anode loop

Counting
chamber

Plunger
(slides in)

Fig. 9-7. Schematic diagram of a flow counter mounted in a shield; the very thin
window is optional. The sample is inserted into the active volume by means of
the lateral slide holder. (Courtesy of Nuclear-Chicago Corporation.)

sure from a compressed-gas tank through the counter at a rate of 200 ml/min.
Counter life is virtually unlimited, since the filling gas is constantly undergoing
replenishment.

Proportional counters are useful for counting at extremely high counting
rates—50,000–200,000 counts/sec; the upper limit is imposed by the associated
electronic circuitry. The signal produced is extremely small and requires both a
preamplifier and a second stage of amplification before the signal can be fed to
a scaler. Excellent plateaus of about 100 volts can be obtained whose slopes
are as low as 0.1 percent counting-rate change per hundred volts (whereas
values of less than 1 percent variation are uncommon with Geiger counters).
Proportional counters are useful for the alpha particle counting, since their
ionizing power is so much greater than that of beta particles that one can
distinguish the two.

Scintillation Counters

When an ionizing particle is absorbed in any one of several transparent
scintillators, a flash of light of exceedingly short duration may be emitted. If
directed upon the cathode of a photomultiplier tube, a single pulse is recorded
for each particle absorbed. The combination of a scintillator and photomultiplier tube is known as a scintillation counter (Fig. 9-8).

For counting beta particles, scintillator crystals of anthracene or stilbene
affixed by a good optical liquid to an end-window photomultiplier tube are

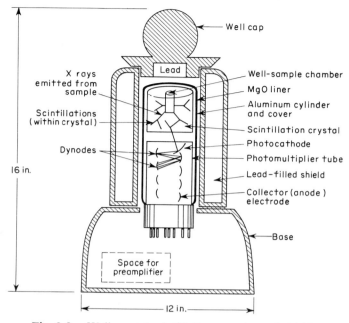

Fig. 9-8.   Well-crystal scintillation counter and shield.

used. Suitable organic scintillators consist of several aromatic rings with non-localized orbitals, linked in a manner to allow continuous conjugation and possessing a high degree of molecular symmetry. A good match should exist between the emission spectrum of the scintillator and the response curve of the

Table 9-1 | *Properties of Scintillators*

SCINTILLATOR	EFFECTIVE ATOMIC NUMBER	WAVELENGTH OF EMISSION, Å	LIGHT YIELD†	DECAY TIME, μsec
Anthracene(s)	5.8	4450	1.00	0.025
Stilbene(s)	5.7	4100	0.73	0.008
p-Terphenyl(s)	5.8	4150	0.55	0.012
Naphthalene(s)	5.8	3450	0.15	0.075
Sodium iodide (Tl)	49	4100	0.8	0.25
p-Terphenyl (liq.), in xylene	5.6	3700	0.25	0.008
2,5-Diphenyloxazole (PPO)	5.6	3800	0.46	0.006
1,6-Diphenylhexatriene	5.6	4600	0.21	0.010

†Relative to anthracene.

photocathode, and the decay time of the scintillator should be short. A number of scintillators and their characteristics are listed in Table 9-1. Owing to the low average atomic number of organic scintillators, the photoelectric and pair-production cross sections are greatly reduced, and hence such materials lend themselves primarily to the detection of charged particles and also neutrons, which produce proton recoils in the usually homogeneous material of the scintillator.

Liquid scintillators are used for assaying low-energy beta emitters, particularly H^3 and C^{14}. Self-absorption is eliminated. The compound containing the radionuclide is dissolved in toluene or xylene to which is added 1–10 g/liter of a primary scintillator plus 0.1 g per liter of a secondary scintillator to increase the pulse height (often by acting as a wavelength shifter). Combinations frequently used are p-terphenyl or 2,5-diphenyloxazole (PPO) plus 1,4-*bis*-[2-(5-phenyl-oxazolyl)]-benzene (POPOP), or p-terphenyl plus 1,6-diphenyl-1,3,5-hexatriene (DPH). The photomultiplier tube is dipped directly into the scintillator solvent. Aqueous solutions are diluted with alcohol (or dioxane), followed by toluene, in the ratio of 1:50:250. At room temperature, the pulses generated by tritium betas in liquid scintillators lie within the same range of amplitude as do pulses produced by thermionic emission in the photomultiplier tube. Discrimination is ineffective unless the temperature is $-10°C$; consequently, the entire counter and preamplifier unit are housed in a refrigerator (deep freeze unit).

For measurement of gamma emitters and the bremsstrahlung from high-energy beta emitters, a sodium iodide crystal, activated with 1 percent thallium, is most frequently used. This crystal has a large photoelectric cross section, a high density, and a high transparency to its own radiation—the optical emission lines of thallium. Its high transparency makes it possible to use it in large thicknesses to absorb gamma radiation. The crystal is sealed from atmospheric moisture and protected from extraneous light by an enclosure of aluminum foil, which also serves as an internal reflector. Roughening the crystal faces and use of a diffuse reflector such a magnesium oxide are recommended practices.

For high efficiency counting, the sample is placed in a well drilled into the crystal. Crystal size, 2–3 in. in diameter, is chosen so that it contains the entire path of the ionizing particle or radiation and so measures total energy. The dead time for scintillators is very short—0.25 μsec for a sodium iodide crystals, and 0.02 μsec or less for anthracene and other organic crystals. The signal from a scintillation counter is proportional to the energy dissipated by the radiation in the crystal so that this counter may be used with pulse height discrimination. Of the photons produced in the scintillator, the number detected depends on the geometry and the optical properties of the system, including those of reflectors and any light guides between the scintillator and the cathode of the photomultiplier tube.

Auxiliary Instrumentation

Counters require auxiliary electronic equipment including a high-voltage supply, an amplifier (often plus a preamplifier), a scaler, and a count-registering unit. The required stability of the high-voltage supply and the required sensitivity and linearity of the amplifier are dictated by both the detector and the application.

From the counter the output pulse, after amplification, is fed into a scaling circuit which, in reality, is an electronic divider. The circuit is arranged so that the output is a single pulse for each 2, 4, 8, . . . , 2^n incident particles. By a system of glow lamps the events withheld can be numbered (Fig. 9-9). In the

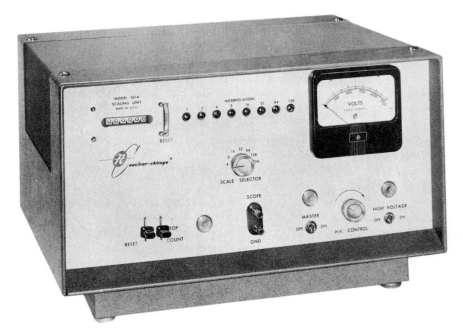

Fig. 9-9. Typical scaler, timer, and high-voltage unit. (Courtesy of Nuclear-Chicago Corporation.)

scale of two (binary) type, the overall scaling factor is 2^n, where n is the number of binary stages incorporated. More convenient and rapid reading is achieved on decade scalers. Each stage passes on every tenth pulse so that the instrument reads decimally. With either type the output from the scaler operates a mechanical register. Timing is done with built-in electric clocks which start and stop the count for a preset time interval, or, after a predetermined number of counts have been accumulated, the elapsed time is noted.

A significant amount of radiation is always present in the vicinity of a detector from natural radioactive elements and cosmic rays. Insertion of the counter into a shield of lead 2–3 in. in thickness reduces the background counting rate appreciably (Fig. 9-5). Further improvement can be achieved with anticoincidence circuits.

Pulse Height Discrimination

Whenever the amplitude of the pulse is proportional to the energy dissipation in the detector, the measurement of pulse height may be a useful tool for energy discrimination. Current pulses are fed into a linear amplifier of sufficient gain to produce voltage output pulses in the amplitude ranges of 0–100 volts.

One method of analysis of the pulse spectra is by use of a single-channel analyzer. The base-line discriminator passes only those pulses above a certain amplitude and eliminates pulses below this amplitude. It is useful for excluding scattered radiation and amplifier noise. Pulses associated with a particular radioactive emission must be amplified sufficiently so that their amplitudes exceed the discriminator setting. In practice this is accomplished by a combination of adjustment of the gain of the amplifier and the d-c voltage applied to the detector.

A pulse height analyzer also contains a second discriminator called variously the window width, the channel width, or the acceptance slit. Now all pulses above the sum of the base-line and window setting are also rejected. Only pulses with an amplitude within the confines of these settings will be passed on to the counting stages. These operations are outlined schematically in Fig. 9-10.

The analyzer slowly scans the pulse distribution with a window a few volts in

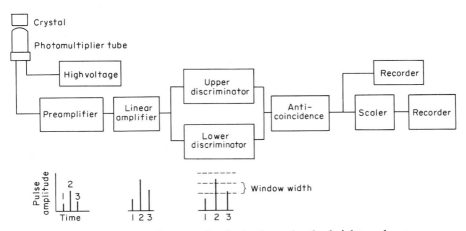

Fig. 9-10. Block diagram of a single-channel pulse height analyzer.

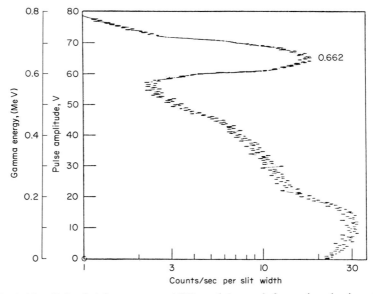

Fig. 9-11. Pulse height spectrum (differential curve) for cesium-barium-137 (γe^- 0.662 Mev).

width. For example, when the nominal slit setting is at 75 V (Fig. 9-11), there are few pulses of this amplitude in the pulse spectrum. As the slit sweeps on to the 65-V region, there are a large number of pulses which are of proper amplitude to pass the acceptance slit and be recorded. As the acceptance slit completes its scan down to zero energy, the complete pulse height distribution is plotted. The curve shown in Fig. 9-11, known as the *differential scan*, contains several features. The sharp symmetrical peak is the result of total absorption of the gamma energy by the NaI(Tl) crystal, and is normally referred to as the full-energy peak or photopeak. The continuous curve below the full-energy peak is due to Compton interaction, wherein the gamma photon loses only part of its energy to the crystal. The location of the full-energy peak on the pulse amplitude or energy axis is proportional to the energy of the incident radiation, and is the basis for the qualitative application of the scintillation spectrometer or proportional counter. The area under the full-energy peak is related to the number of photons or particles interacting with the detector, and is the basis for the quantitative application of the detector. In the analysis of gamma photons in the energy range from 0 to 100 keV, there appears to be an escape peak 28 keV below the full-energy peak. This is due to photoelectric interactions wherein the resulting iodine K X ray escapes from the crystal in a NaI(Tl) scintillation counter. Above 1.5 MeV the effect of pair production becomes apparent in a gamma scan. In addition to the full-energy peak, there are peaks in the scan at full-energy minus 0.51 MeV and full-energy minus

1.02 MeV. Also a small peak occurs at 0.51 MeV due to detection of an annihilation photon resulting from pair production in the shielding material. The manganese-56 spectrum (Fig. 9-12) shows these features.

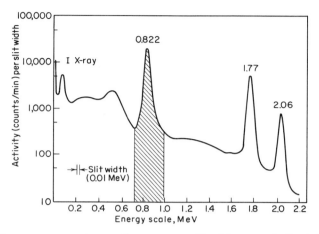

Fig. 9-12. The gamma spectrum of manganese-56. The area indicated under the photopeak at 0.822 Mev would be used in quantitative work.

With a single-channel analyzer the resulting curve is generally plotted automatically over a period of from 15 min to 2.5 hr, depending on sample counting rate and required precision. The pulse height scale is usually calibrated by the use of gamma (or beta) emitters of known energy; it is conveniently set to be a multiple of the energy peaks in the gamma spectrum. Instruments with 20 to over 1000 channels are commercially available. The multichannel analyzers of the 100- and 256-channel types all have provision for automatic analog readout.

The net area under each photopeak is directly proportional to the absolute gamma emission rate of the corresponding isotope. This is usually determined by taking the product of peak height, width at half maximum, and the normalizing factor, 1.07—based on the assumption that the full-energy peak is Gaussian. The peak area can also be integrated with a planimeter. For the analysis of mixed gamma-emitting radioisotopes, the characteristic lower energy curve of the most energetic full-energy peak must be drawn in from previously recorded standard curves detailing the Compton continuum region vs the principal full-energy peak area, as shown in Fig. 9-13. By subtraction, the net height of the second most energetic gamma photon can be established and its width measured. The Compton continuum of the second photopeak is then drawn in and the area of the third peak can be evaluated, and so on. These operations can be performed automatically on multichannel analyzers with standard curves stored on magnetic tapes.

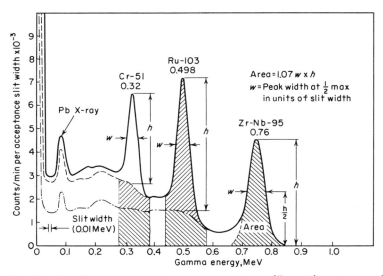

Fig. 9-13. Typical three-component gamma spectrum illustrating two methods of quantitative analysis.

Statistics in Measurement of Radioactivity

The random nature of nuclear events requires that a large number of individual events be observed to obtain a precise value of the count rate. Several factors must be considered when attempting to measure any activity. The ionizing particle may never reach the active volume of the detector; instead it may be absorbed in the walls or air path. The detector may not be perfectly efficient because of several conditions—the detector may not have recovered from a previous event (the dead time), the particle from the source may not produce an ion in the sensitive volume of the detector, and some regions of the detector are more sensitive than others.

Statistical laws will predict the magnitude of the deviations about a mean value to be expected, as well as the probability of occurrence of deviations of a given magnitude. One standard deviation, or 1σ (sigma), is the maximum deviation from the "true" value that may be expected in 68 percent of a large series of measurements. It serves as a measure of the precision of a single observation or a series of observations. In activity measurements the standard deviation in the total count is equal to the square root of the number of counts N taken:

$$\sigma = \sqrt{N} \tag{9-11}$$

The standard deviation in the counting rate r is

$$\sigma_r = \frac{1}{t}\sqrt{N} = \sqrt{\frac{r}{t}} \tag{9-12}$$

Expressed in this manner, the standard deviation is a measure of the scatter of a set of observations around their mean value. The relative standard deviation (fractional 0.68 error), often given in percent, is

$$100\sigma = \frac{100}{\sqrt{N}} \qquad (9\text{-}13)$$

It is a measure of the precision of an observation. It can be expected that one standard deviation (or smaller) will arise in about 7 out of 10 determinations. The following confidence limits apply to representative multiples of the standard deviation:

	$\pm 0.68\sigma$	$\pm\sigma$	$\pm 2\sigma$	$\pm 3\sigma$
Deviation	$\pm 0.68\sigma$	$\pm\sigma$	$\pm 2\sigma$	$\pm 3\sigma$
Population mean (limits)	$\pm 0.68\sigma$	$\pm\sigma$	$\pm 1.96\sigma$	$\pm 2.58\sigma$
Probability that observation (or confidence level) lies within this deviation, %	50	68	95	99

Example 9-1

If 8,100 counts are timed, the standard deviation is

$$\sigma = \sqrt{8100} = 90 \text{ counts}$$

Expressed as relative standard deviation,

$$100\sigma = \frac{90}{8100}(100) = \frac{100}{\sqrt{8100}} = \pm 1.11\%$$

The probable error will be 0.68σ or 0.74 percent.

Example 9-2

To ascertain the number of counts which must be taken so that the deviation in 95 percent of the determinations (2σ) will not exceed 2.0 percent, proceed in this manner.

$$\frac{2\sqrt{N}}{N} = 0.02$$

$$\sqrt{N} = 100$$

$$N = 10,000 \text{ counts}$$

If a source has an activity of 200 counts/sec, it will take 50 sec to accumulate 10,000 counts.

A counter always shows some background activity. The statistical fluctuation of the background B must be included in any estimate of the standard deviation of the source whose activity A will include any background activity recorded simultaneously. The standard deviation of the net source activity, i.e. $A - B$, is given by

$$\sigma = \sqrt{\sigma_A{}^2 + \sigma_B{}^2} \qquad (9\text{-}14)$$

Background radiation becomes significant when the peak-to-background ratio, $A:B$, is less than 20, and it becomes very difficult to measure a source accurately when the counting rate is just a little greater than the background rate. The

optimum division of available time between background and source counting
is given by

$$\frac{t_B}{t_A} = \sqrt{\frac{r_B}{r_A}} \qquad (9\text{-}15)$$

Here counting rates have to be obtained from a preliminary run. The minimum combined time necessary to achieve a predetermined precision can be
estimated from curves shown in Fig. 9-14.

Example 9-3

Suppose it is desired to determine with a precision of ± 3 percent the activity of a
sample which has a net count of 15 counts/min when the background is 30 counts/min.
Thus, the ratio, $A{:}B = 45{:}30 = 1.50$, and from Fig. 9-14 the 3-percent line intersects
the oblique line for $A/B = 1.50$ at a total count of about 18,000 to 19,000. The point
of intersection lies about three-fourths of the distance between the background-count
curves for 8,000 and 12,000. Thus, the background count should be about 11,000.
The counting periods are about 400 min for the total count and 367 min for the back-

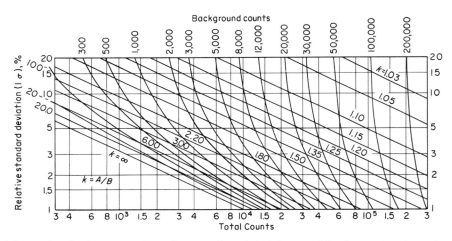

Fig. 9-14. Optimum number of counts for minimizing combined counting time when
relative standard deviation is assigned and total counter-to-background ratio
(A/B) is known. After R. Loevinger and M. Berman, *Nucleonics*, **9** (No. 1) 29
(1951).

ground count. Figure 9-14 is very valuable whenever a preset number of counts is
being accumulated.

Coincidence Correction

In order to correct for counting losses at high counting rates caused by the
finite resolution time of counters, two courses are open. One method is to
construct a calibration curve from a series of dilutions of a strong sample or
from measurements of a series of standards of known strengths. A second

procedure is to measure two samples separately and then measure the two samples together. The resolving time of the counter τ is given by

$$\tau = \frac{r_1 + r_2 - r_{1,2} - r_B}{2r_1r_2} \qquad (9\text{-}16)$$

where r_1 and r_2 represent the counting rate of source 1 plus background and source 2 plus background, respectively; $r_{1,2}$ is the measured counting rate of source 1 plus source 2 and the background r_B.

If the resolving time of the counter is greater than that of any other part of the measuring circuit, then the true counting rate r_0 is related to the observed counting rate r and the resolving time τ, namely,

$$r_0 = \frac{r}{1 - r\tau} \qquad (9\text{-}17)$$

Geometry

The arrangement of counter and source should always be reproducible so that the solid angle subtended by the counter with respect to the source remains unchanged. The "geometry" of any arrangement may be obtained by measurement of standard sources. Insertion of the source into the active volume of a counter approximates 2π-geometry; 4π-geometry is approximated in well-type detectors.

Measurement of Beta Activity

The energy of the beta particle determines its penetrating power. Above 0.4 MeV the particles have sufficient energy to penetrate the windows of most counting devices, and measurement is not difficult. Below this energy value, however, special techniques are required. Very thin-window counters may be employed, the sample may be introduced directly into the active volume of the counter, or it may be dissolved in a liquid scintillator.

High-energy beta emitters may be measured in well-type scintillation counter, either in solution or as a solid. Direct assay of liquid samples with dipping or jacketed counters usually provides geometrical conditions which enable scattering, self-absorption, and wall absorption to be controlled.

Because corrections for self-absorption, self-scattering, and back-scattering are often difficult to ascertain, beta counting should be avoided, if possible. The use of gamma radiation is preferable because of the relative freedom from all these corrections.

Measurement of Gamma Activity

Because of the low ionizing power of gamma radiation, a great proportion will pass through a tube designed for counting beta particles without producing any effect. The sensitivity of the detector must be increased by using longer chambers, by gas fillings possessing higher atomic number and under pressure, or by larger thicknesses of scintillator material. If it is desired to measure gamma radiation exclusively from a mixture of activities, a filter of sufficient thickness to absorb all beta particles may be inserted between the sample and detector.

Measurement of Alpha Activity

Because of the low penetrating power of alpha particles, self-absorption is very important. It is difficult to prepare standards and unknowns in reproducible form and such that measured activity is proportional to true activity.

The ionization chamber is the preferred detector; recently solid-state detectors in the form of silicon diodes have become available. Alpha particle activity can be measured in the presence of considerable beta activity by first measuring the total activity, then interposing a filter to absorb the alpha particles, and measuring the beta activity.

Measurement of Neutron Activity

Neutron activity may be measured by utilizing the nuclear reaction between a boron-10 atom and a neutron to yield an alpha particle and lithium-7. The reaction is quite efficient, and the ionization due to the secondary alpha particles is readily measured. Counters for this type of work simply contain very pure boron-10 trifluoride gas at a pressure of 120–400 mm of mercury.

The uranium fission reaction is involved in the silicon diode detector. On the top surface of the silicon (or germanium) diode is deposited a layer of uranium. Upon being struck by slow-speed (thermal) neutrons, the uranium fissions. The fragments and particles, energized by the enormous energy of the fission process, crash through the junction of the diode detector and upset its electrical balance. The net result is an electrical pulse that can be detected and counted.

Applications of Radionuclides

The introduction of a radioactive-labeled material into a sample system or a measurement of the natural or induced radioactivity of a system become very useful techniques for rapid and economical methods of analysis for elements or materials. Isotope dilution with radioactive tracers, labeled reagents, activation analysis, or the use of radioactive tracers for procedure development have much use in analytical chemistry.

The chain-reacting pile is without a peer as a tool for the general quantitative production of radioactivity by reason of the magnitude and spacial extent of the thermal neutron flux it is able to sustain. The pile excels the cyclotron in respect to both intensity and the magnitude of the effective flux produced. The procedure for obtaining radionuclides through the Atomic Energy Commission is described in the literature.[2]

Preformed generator sources, such as cobalt-60 source or radioisotopic-beryllium neutron sources, can be useful in meeting many analytical requirements when a pile is not conveniently near at hand.

A selection of radionuclides and their characteristics is given in Table 9-2.

Table 9-2 | *Nuclear Properties of Radioisotopes and Activation Cross Sections*

RADIO-ISOTOPE[†]	HALF-LIFE[‡]	TARGET ISOTOPE	ABUNDANCE, %	CROSS SECTION[§]	RADIATIONS AND ENERGIES IN MeV (FRACTION/DISINTEGRATION)
H^3	12.26 y				β^- 0.0176
C^{14}	5570 y				β^- 0.155
Na^{22}	2.60 y				β^+ 0.542; γ 1.277; 0.511(0.80)¶
Na^{24}	15.0 h	Na^{23}	100	0.54	β^- 1.390; γ 1.368, 2.754
Al^{28}	2.27 m	Al^{27}	100	0.21	β^- 2.865; γ 1.782
P^{32}	14.20 d	P^{31}	100	0.23	β^- 1.701
S^{35}	87.1 d	S^{34}	4.2	0.26	β^- 0.167
Cl^{36}	4.4×10^5 y	Cl^{35}	75.4	40	β^- 0.714
Cl^{38}	37.3 m	Cl^{37}	24.6	0.6	β^- 1.11(0.31), 2.77(0.16), 2.77(0.53); γ 1.60(0.43), 2.15(0.57)
K^{40}	1.2×10^9 y				β^- 1.325; γ 1.46
K^{42}	12.41 h				β^- 1.98(0.18), 3.54(0.81); γ 1.53(0.18)
Ca^{45}	164 d	Ca^{44}	2.06	0.6	β^- 0.254
Cr^{51}	27.8 d	Cr^{50}	4.31	300	γ 0.32(0.10)
Mn^{56}	2.58 h	Mn^{55}	100	13.4	β^- 0.65(0.2), 1.04(0.3), 2.81(0.5); γ 0.822(1), 1.77(0.3), 2.06(0.5); EC 0.0059
Fe^{55}	2.7 y				
Fe^{59}	45.1 d	Fe^{58}	0.31	0.9	β^- 0.27(0.46), 0.46(0.53); γ 1.097(0.57), 1.295(0.43)
Co^{60}	5.28 y	Co^{59}	100	36	β^- 0.31; γ 1.17, 1.33
Ni^{65}	2.56 h	Ni^{64}	1.2	2.6	β^- 0.60, 1.01, 2.10; γ 0.37, 1.12, 1.49
Cu^{64}	12.8 h	Cu^{63}	69.1	3.9	β^- 0.571; 0.511¶
Zn^{65}	244 d	Zn^{64}	48.9	0.5	β^+ 0.325; γ 1.11; 0.511¶
Zn^{69m}	13.8 h	Zn^{68}	18.6	0.1	γ 0.437
As^{76}	26.5 h	As^{75}	100	4.2	β^- 2.40(0.32), 2.97(0.55); γ 0.55(0.4)
Br^{80}	18 m	Br^{79}	51	9	β^- 2.0
Br^{80m}	4.4 h	Br^{79}	51	3	I.T. 0.049, 0.038
Br^{82}	35.7 h	Br^{81}	49	2	β^- 0.44(1); γ 0.55 to 1.32
Sr^{90}	19.9 y				β^- 0.61
Y^{90}	64 h				β^- 2.23
Ag^{110m}	270 d	Ag^{109}	48.7	2.8	β^- 0.53, 0.31; complex
Sb^{122}	2.8 d	Sb^{121}	47.3	6.8	β^- 1.46, 1.94; γ 0.568
Sb^{124}	60 d	Sb^{123}	42.7	2.5	β^- 0.61(0.51), 2.31(0.23); γ 0.60(0.98), 1.61(0.46)
I^{128}	25 m	I^{127}	100	6.35	β^- 1.59, 2.02; γ 0.43
I^{131}	8.05 d				β^- 0.608; γ 0.364
Cs^{137}	30 y				β^- 0.51(0.92)
Ba^{137m}	2.6 m				γ 0.66(0.81)
Au^{198}	2.69 d				β^- 0.963; γ 0.412
Tl^{204}	3.5 y				β^- 0.765

†Symbol *m* following a mass number denotes a metastable state.
‡y = years, d = days, h = hours, and s = seconds.
§For ($n\gamma$) reaction involving thermal neutrons; values given in barns (10^{-24} cm²).
¶Annihilation.

Nuclides with very short half-lives will decay too rapidly to be generally useful; on the other hand, a long-lived nuclide will be difficult to measure because disintegrations are too infrequent.

Preparation and Mounting of Samples

The active source must be free of interfering substances, in a suitable chemical and physical form, and disposed in a definite and fixed position relative to the detector. In virtually all applied radiochemistry, relative intensities of two or more samples are all that need be determined, thus making absolute measurements unnecessary. The principal requirement is reproducibility and, if this is not possible, the effects of the variable factors must be determined and a correction applied.

A chemical separation from inactive, and occasionally active, contaminants generally precedes the activity measurement. Ordinary analytical techniques and reactions form the basis for most radiochemical separations. Carrying a microconstituent by coprecipitation with a macroconstituent (a carrier), solvent extraction, volatilization, adsorption, ion exchange, electrodeposition, and chromatography are useful for handling very low concentrations of material. If the radiations are intense and penetrating, shielding and remote-control equipment are required. All work with appreciable quantities of radioactivity should be done with rubber gloves, protective clothing, and adequate ventilation to remove active vapors, dusts, and sprays. Of scarcely less importance is the danger of contamination by active materials of laboratories, equipment, and detecting instruments. Establishment and enforcement of suitable regulations and careful attention to cleanliness of operation are integral aspects of the proper technique of working with radioactivity.

The active material must be spread in a uniform layer over a definite area unless 4-π geometry is employed. Thin uniform layers of solids may be spread as slurries in water or other solvent which is later evaporated. If the deposit is not coherent but tends to fall apart and flake off, it may be stabilized by the use of a suitable binder (collodion), or it may be held in place with a covering layer of Scotch tape, aluminum foil, or similar material. The sample is frequently obtained in a solid form by precipitation from solution and separation by centrifugation. Crystalline precipitates are best, whereas flocculent precipitates, which are highly hydrated, tend to give unsatisfactory deposits because on drying they contract into a number of isolated, dense particles.

Evaporation of solutions in cup-shaped containers, or for small amounts, on flat surfaces, is convenient. The method is limited to nonvolatile activities. Electrodeposition onto a flat surface gives excellent deposits for many metals; a thin film of plastic sprayed with gold can serve as the active electrode.

Samples can be mounted on flat foils or disks; several tenths of a milliliter of a liquid can be held in place by surface tension or within a ring of silicone grease. When back-scattering by the mount is objectionable, a thin film of low atomic number may be used—mylar, polystyrene, and similar plastics. An arrangement is needed for holding samples in a definite position relative to the detector during measuring. Counters and ion chambers are generally equipped with an arrangement having one or more shelves or sets of slots in which sample holders of a standard size can be placed. Radionuclides emitting sufficiently penetrating beta and gamma radiations are conveniently assayed in solution with dipping counter tubes or counters surrounded by hollow jackets, or by insertion in the well of an ionization chamber or scintillation counter. Active gases can be introduced into proportional counters or ionization chambers equipped with stopcocks and pressure manometers.

Tagging Compounds

Since the radioactive isotopes are chemically identical with their stable isotope counterpart, they may be used to "tag" a compound. The tagged compound may then be followed through any analytical scheme, industrial system, or biological process. It is essential that a compound be tagged with an atom, however, which is not readily exchangeable with similar atoms in other compounds under normal conditions. For example, tritium could not be used to trace an acid if it were inserted on the carboxyl group where it is readily exchanged by ionization with the solvent.

It is not always true that the radionuclide will resemble exactly the normal isotope. Differences in weight do cause slight changes in the reactivity of molecules. For ordinary purposes, however, these isotope effects are slight except for the lightest elements (such as tritium). Many multiple decays are found in radio nuclides produced in chain-reacting piles. If the parent (Ba^{140}, $t_{1/2} = 12.8$ days) is longer-lived than the daughter (La^{140}, $t_{1/2} = 40$ hr), a state of radioactive equilibrium is reached after about eight half-lives (13 days). Thus, if Ba^{140} is to be used as a tracer for barium, the isolated samples either should be freed chemically of the daughter La^{140} and counted without delay, or the samples should be kept for two weeks before counting.

In biological investigations the question of purity of the isolated material is important. One must be certain that the radioactivity of the compound isolated is due to the compound itself and not to some minor contaminant which may have a high specific activity.

In ordinary analytical work, radionuclides have been used to study errors resulting from adsorption and occlusion in gravimetric methods, and to devise methods of preventing coprecipitation, adsorption, and occlusion.

Analyses with Labeled Reagents

Radiometric methods employing reagent solutions or solids tagged with a radionuclide have been used to determine the solubility of numerous organic and inorganic precipitates, or as a radioreagent for titrations involving the formation of a precipitate. In this type of application it is necessary to establish the ratio between radioactivity and weight of radionuclide plus carrier present. This may be established by evaporating an aliquot to dryness, weighing the residue, and measuring the radioactivity.

In solubility studies, the compound of interest is synthesized, using the radionuclide, and a saturated solution of the compound is prepared. A measured volume of the saturated solution is evaporated to dryness, and the radioactivity of the residue determined. From the previously established relationship between weight and radioactivity, the amount of the compound present can be calculated.

Procedures have been described for the use of radioreagents as titrants. For example, phosphorus-32 was converted into a soluble phosphate and incorporated into a standard solution of disodium hydrogen ortho phosphate. This solution was used to titrate several inorganic ions. After each addition of phosphate a sample of the clear, filtered solution was withdrawn (by means of a filter-stick) and the activity was determined. After the equivalence point was passed, the activity rose rapidly with additions of radioreagent. From the intersection of the activity curves, the end point was determined.

The efficiency of an analytical procedure can be determined by adding a known amount of a radioisotope before analysis is begun. After the final determination of the element in question, the activity of the precipitate is determined and compared with the activity at the start.

Chemical yields need not be quantitative in an analytical procedure when the results are corrected by the recovery of the radioisotope. To the mixture of ions, a known amount of radioisotope is added, or to a mixture of activities a known amount of carrier element is added, then separated in the necessary state of chemical and radiochemical purity but without attention to yield. The isolated sample is determined by any suitable method, and the activity is measured.

Isotope Dilution Analyses

This technique measures the yield of a nonquantitative process, or it enables an analysis to be performed where no quantitative isolation procedure is known. To the unknown mixture, containing a compound with inactive element P, is added a known weight W_1 of the same compound tagged with the radioactive element $P^\star$ whose activity is known (A_1). The mixture is chemically indistinguishable. A small amount of the pure compound is isolated from the mixture and the specific activity measured (A). The amount isolated need be only a very small fraction of the total amount present, merely a sufficient quantity for weighing or determining accurately. The extent of dilution of the radiotracer shows the amount W of inactive element (or compound) present, as given by the expression

$$W = W_1\left(\frac{A_1}{A} - 1\right) \qquad (9\text{-}18)$$

The method has proven valuable in the analysis of complex biochemical mixtures and in the radiocarbon dating of archeological and anthropological specimens.

Activation Analysis

The method of activation analysis depends upon the formation of radionuclides from elements in the sample when they are subjected to bombardment with neutrons or charged particles. Most elements when irradiated by slow (thermal) neutrons give rise to a radioactive species of the same atomic number but one mass unit greater than its progenitor. These radionuclides have their own characteristic radiations and modes of decay, thus making radioactivation an unusual technique for qualitative identification as well as for quantitative analysis by the comparative method.

Irradiation is accomplished by placing the sample to be analyzed in an intense flux of neutrons for a length of time sufficient to produce a measurable amount of the desired radioisotope. The capture rate will be proportional to the slow neutron flux Φ, in neutrons cm^{-2} sec^{-1}, and to the number of target nuclei N available; the proportionality constant is known as the capture cross section, σ, expressed in barns, which are units of an atomic cross section $(10^{-24}$ $cm^2)$. A correction must be made for the fractional abundance f of the target nuclide. The activity A, in disintegrations per second, after the start of the irradiation is given by

$$A = N\Phi\sigma fS \qquad (9\text{-}19)$$

where S is the saturation factor. During an activation of finite duration some of the radioisotope produced will decay according to Eq. 9-8, and the saturation factor represents the ratio of the amount of activity produced in time t to that produced in infinite time, namely,

$$S = 1 - e^{-\lambda t} = 1 - 10^{-\lambda t/2.3} \qquad (9\text{-}20)$$

where λ is the decay constant for the particular radioisotope. As irradiation proceeds, the activity grows with the saturation factor, and will reach 98 percent for irradiation times equal to six half-lives.

In terms of the weight W of the element, assuming that the rate of production of radioactivity, given by $N\Phi\sigma$, is constant during irradiation, Eq. 9-19 may be written as

$$W = \frac{A \times M}{6.02 \times 10^{23}\Phi\sigma fS} \qquad (9\text{-}21)$$

where M is the atomic weight.

Experimental samples are inserted into a chain-reacting pile, or exposed to a radionuclide-beryllium source, for suitable irradiation periods which will vary from minutes to several days and up to months, depending upon the particular induced radioisotope. A straightforward numerical calculation using Eq. 9-21 and the information listed in Table 9-2 will show that, except for the light elements, enormous sensitivities can be obtained by irradiation with thermal neutron fluxes ranging from 1.0×10^{11} to 1.0×10^{14} neutrons cm^{-2} sec^{-1}. It is not unusual to detect quantities in the order of 10^{-10} to 10^{-12} g according to the element. Service irradiations can be obtained in the national laboratories operated for the United States Atomic Energy Commission. A one-gram radium-beryllium source provides a yield of approximately 10^7 neutrons sec^{-1}; and an antimony-124 (60 days half-life)–beryllium source provides a yield of approximately 3×10^6 neutrons sec^{-1} curie^{-1}.

The most rudimentary type of analysis that may be carried out is simply to irradiate the unknown sample for a few minutes and then determine the decay of the mixture of activities produced. A resolution of the decay curve is then performed by the method of successive differences, Fig. 9-15, in an attempt to find the half-lives of the components, perhaps assisted by absorption methods. However, the most accurate method of establishing radionuclide identity is a spectral distribution study, preferably of both beta and gamma rays. Provisions are included in multichannel analyzers for the automatic subtraction of

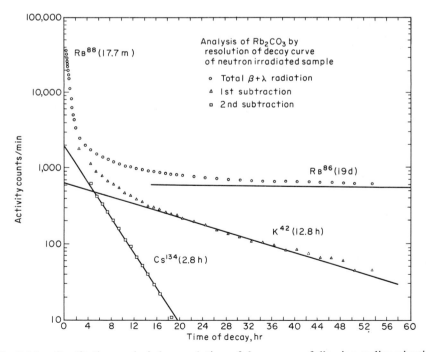

Fig. 9-15. Qualitative analysis by resolution of decay curve following radioactivation of a sample of rubidium carbonate. Impurities are cesium and potassium. After G. E. Boyd, *Anal. Chem.*, **21,** 344 (1949).

successive high-energy gamma spectra (each spectrum is stored on magnetic tape) as radionuclides are identified. These successive subtractions often enable nuclides that emit low-energy radiation to be detected and to aid in resolving overlapping spectra.

In quantitative determinations, the comparative method is used. The chemical and physical forms of the comparators should be chosen to have a low-absorption cross section. The comparators are weighed and packed in duplicate, together with samples of appropriate size, and both are irradiated in the same physical location and under the same flux conditions. Each specific element is separated from the matrix by the isotopic carrier technique. Holdback carriers are added for the remainder of the elements expected to be present. After chemical processing the chemical yield of the procedure is determined, and a comparison of the activity of a specific element in the unknown is made with that of the comparison standard. Sometimes a determination can be made by direct measurement after placing the irradiated samples directly into the well of a scintillation counter. The general procedure is well illustrated in the neutron activation analysis of aluminum-base alloys.[1] The accuracy of the method is usually better than 10 percent. The method is particularly valuable when only minute amounts of sample are available.

Example 9-4

Calculate the activity of a 0.00100-g sample of an aluminum alloy containing 0.041 percent of manganese after a 30-min irradiation in a flux of 5×10^{11} neutrons cm^{-2} sec^{-1}. Other necessary information is obtained from Table 9-2 for insertion in Eq. 9-19:

$$A = \frac{(0.00041)(0.00100)(1.00)(6.02 \times 10^{23})(5 \times 10^{11})(13.4 \times 10^{-24})(S)}{54.94}$$

where

$$S = 1 - e^{-(0.693)(30)/(2.58)(60)}$$

$$= 1 - 0.878 = 0.122$$

and therefore,

$$A = 3680 \text{ disintegrations per second}$$

About 2 hr after discharge from the reactor, all the aluminum-28 (2.3 min) and most of the other short-lived isotopes will have decayed to negligible activity. The activity of manganese-56 has dropped to

$$A = 3680e^{-\lambda t} = 2320 \text{ disintegrations per second}$$

Manganese could be determined by direct measurement of the 0.822-MeV gamma radiation. If it is, the energy region from 0.70 to 1.00 MeV is scanned: the background is taken as the base of the photopeak (see Fig. 9-12).

Example 9-5

In the determination of iron in aluminum alloys, the 1.29-MeV gamma of iron-59 was measured. A decay period of one week before chemical processing allowed for the decay of the 15.0-hr sodium-24 formed from the reaction $Al^{27}(n,\alpha)Na^{24}$.

$$A = A_0 e^{-(0.693)(168)/(15.0)} = 0.00235 A_0$$

After an interval of seven days, the sodium-24 activity has decayed to 0.00235 of its original activity. The gamma radiation from sodium-24 at 1.368 and 2.754 MeV would no longer constitute an interference.

LABORATORY WORK

Personnel Protection in Radiochemistry

When working with radioactive materials, precautions must be taken to prevent exposure of oneself and others to radiation from active sources being handled in a laboratory. Publications devoted to health physics should be consulted before engaging in extensive radiochemical operations.

Cleanliness is extremely important. Disposable paper liners should cover all working areas in order that any spills may be quickly absorbed. Work with amounts greater than mere traces of activity should be performed in well-ventilated exhaust hoods. Rubber gloves should be worn whenever active samples are handled, and the gloved hands should be washed thoroughly before the gloves are removed at the end of a laboratory period.

Distance is a great aid in decreasing exposure to radiation, since the intensity decreases as the square of the distance. Long-handled tongs and other remote control devices are used to handle the more intense sources when they are removed from a storage container and for manipulation behind a barrier. Proper shielding decreases exposure. Since radiation intensity is greatest over beakers and open containers, care should be taken to keep the hands away from such exposure. Alpha particles are easily absorbed by air and glass and are no problem unless the alpha emitter is taken internally accidentally. Beta particles from sources with energies a few tenths of a million electron volts can be absorbed by plastic or glass shields placed around the apparatus. For gamma radiation and energetic beta particles, thick lead, stainless steel or concrete shields will be required. However, for operations in the microcurie range of activity, an ordinary well-equipped laboratory will suffice.

Liquid material is transferred by pipets which are manipulated by rubber-bulb or syringe-type controls (NEVER by suction from the mouth). The micropipet and the ultra microburet are commonly used for transferring known amounts of radioactive solutions. Pipet capacities are available from 1 to 500 μl. After delivery of a sample, the pipet must be rinsed out with carrier solution several times, and the rinses added to the source when they are calibrated "to contain."

Several types of instruments are available for monitoring and surveying working areas and personnel. A portable count-rate meter is used for rapid surveys. A movable shield over the counter permits a distinction between hard and soft radiations. All workers normally wear film badges containing photographic film (often partially overlayed with various thicknesses of absorbers) to give a permanent record of general body exposure to radiation integrated over a period of time. Pocket ionization chambers, worn clipped in a pocket like a pen, consist of an inner wire carefully insulated from the case and charged to 140 or 150 V. Any radiation causes leakage of the charge. The pocket chamber can be read at any time. This is particularly useful during and at the end of an exposure to abnormal amounts of radiation.

General Directions for Operation of a Scaling Circuit

Connect the counter to the scaling circuit and, if not an integral part of the scaler, the mechanical register and timer. The positive high-voltage lead is connected to the center wire of the Geiger or proportional counter.

Be sure that all switches are in the OFF position. Then plug the cord from the scaling circuit into a 110-V, 60-cycle main. Turn the high-voltage control(s) to their counter-clockwise limit.

Turn the master switch to the ON position. After a warm-up period of 1 min, the high voltage switch is turned on. If this interval of time is not observed, the counting tube may be damaged by a surge of high voltage before the regulator tubes assume control.

When the high-voltage meter begins to indicate, slowly increase the high-voltage control (clockwise rotation) to the operating voltage of the counter. If the operating voltage is not known, follow the directions outlined in Experiment 9-1. Extinguish the interpolation lights by momentarily depressing the reset switch. Reset the mechanical register and the timing clock. A counting rate may now be ascertained.

Insert the sample in the desired geometric position in relation to the counter. For a background counting rate, simply remove all radioactive material from the vicinity of the counter. Turn the stop-count switch to COUNT. After the desired length of time, throw the stop-count switch to STOP. Multiply the number on the mechanical register by the value of the particular scaling factor used, and add the interpolation lights that are glowing.

For a preset counting rate, set the scaler to a preset count and throw the stop-count switch to COUNT. After the timer ceases to register any further time, record the elapsed time interval.

Radioactive Materials

Standards for calibration of counters can be obtained from the National Bureau of Standards (U.S.). These include RaD + E beta particle standards and Co^{60} and radium gamma radiation standards. Directions for the use of these are furnished with the standards.

Radionuclide sets of radioactive reagents are commercially available and provide a variety of radiation types and energies at AEC license-exempt quantities. One set contains the following isotopes: C^{14} as uniformly labeled fructose, P^{32} as phosphoric acid, I^{131} as the potassium salt, S^{35} as sulfuric acid, and chlorides of Zn^{65}, Na^{22}, Co^{60}, and $Fe^{55/59}$.

Two standards, easily prepared and safe to handle, involve potassium and uranium salts. Potassium-40 occurs naturally to the extent of 0.0119 percent in all potassium salts; the specific activity amounts to 0.919 disintegrations per milligram per minute. Known amounts can be weighed into planchets and covered with a layer of Scotch tape. The counter efficiency for potassium-40 is often about 25 percent.

Pure U_3O_8 is prepared by precipitating uranyl hydroxide with aqueous ammonia, filtering, and igniting the hydroxide to the oxide. The specific activity of U_3O_8 is 636 disintegrations per milligram per minute. Known amounts of the oxide are weighed, then spread out in a very thin uniform layer about 1 cm in diameter. Cover with two layers of Scotch tape (approximately 10 mg/cm^2 per layer). If the uranyl salt has not recently been separated from its daughters, Th^{234} and Pa^{234} (UX_1 and UX_2), these will be in radioactive equilibrium with the parent uranium. Uranium emits alpha particles which can be absorbed by an aluminum foil 0.025 mm in thickness. Thorium-234 emits beta particles which are absorbed by the double layer of Scotch tape. Only the Pa^{234} radiation will affect the counter.

Induced Radioactivity

Certain radioactive isotopes can be produced by irradiation with neutrons generated in a radiometric-beryllium source according to the reaction

$$_4Be^9 + {_2}He^4 \rightarrow {_6}C^{12} + {_0}n^1$$

A source containing 5 mg of radium mixed with 50 mg of beryllium provides a flux of about 10^3 neutrons cm^{-2} sec^{-1}. Activation is limited to elements with a high capture cross section ($> 50 \times 10^{-24}$ cm^2) and suitable isotopic abundance; essentially only gold-197 and indium-115. The concurrence of an appreciable number of high-energy gamma rays together with the alpha emission from radium sources introduces a considerable inconvenience in handling of this source.

An antimony-124 (60 days half-life)-beryllium source provides a convenient source whose flux is comparable to that from a radium-beryllium source. Its disadvantage is the relatively short half-life of antimony-124.

A one-curie plutonium-beryllium source provides a somewhat larger flux of 10^5 neutrons cm^{-2} sec^{-1}. A hexagonal gridwork holds uranium slugs.

Neutrons from any of these sources must be slowed down, or moderated, to thermal velocities by surrounding the source with purified water or paraffin. The sample to be activated may be mixed with, or dissolved in, the moderator or simply inserted at a favorable position in the moderator.

The Szilard-Chalmers chemical enrichment process extends the usefulness of a low neutron flux to elements with cross sections down to 1×10^{-24} cm^2. To be successful the element must be capable of existence in two or more mutually stable and separable forms which do not undergo rapid isotopic exchange, and the target molecule must be difficult or impossible to reform from the fragments produced by neutron capture.

Irradiation of aqueous permanganate solutions of pH less than 10 yields active $Mn^{56}O_2$ with high efficiency. Even the small amount of MnO_2 formed by passing the irradiated solution through filter paper is sufficient to act as carrier for the active precipitate and to retain it on the filter. [W. F. Libby, *J. Am. Chem. Soc.*, **62**, 1930 (1940).]

Successful enrichment of the antimony-122 activity is achieved through a short irradiation of triphenyl stibine dissolved in ether. A large fraction of the active antimony is ejected into an aqueous solution in contact with the ether phase. [R. R. Williams, Jr., *J. Phys. & Colloid Chem.*, **52**, 603 (1948).]

Halogen activities which yield about 10^3 disintegrations per minute per milligram of halogen can be prepared by irradiating ethyl iodide for the iodine activity or ethyl bromide or ethylene dibromide for the bromine activities. [R. H. Schuler, R. R. Williams, Jr., and W. H. Hamill, *J. Chem. Educ.*, **26**, 667 (1949).] The radioactive halogen is prepared daily (or as needed) by placing the neutron source in a spherical 1-liter flask containing the ethyl halide and a small amount of the corresponding free halogen. After three or four half-lives, or overnight, the free halogen is extracted with 5 ml of a 10 percent solution of sodium hydroxide and is converted to silver halide. The active silver halide is collected in several portions on filter paper and is given immediately to the students. [R. R. Williams, Jr., W. H. Hamill, and R. H. Schuler, *J. Chem. Educ.*, **26**, 210 (1949).]

One-inch circles of indium metal foil, weighing approximately 275 mg, can be irradiated to saturation in about 150 min with a radionuclide-beryllium source placed in a paraffin block. [W. H. Hamill, R. R. Williams, Jr., and R. H. Schuler, *J. Chem. Educ.*, **26**, 310 (1949).]

E X P E R I M E N T 9 - 1   GEIGER COUNTER CHARACTERISTICS

Connect the Geiger counter to the high-voltage supply of the scaling circuit, attaching the positive side to the central wire and the negative side (grounded) to the outer cylinder. With the voltage control set to its minimum value, turn on the electronic circuit and set the count switch to ON.

Place a radioactive sample under the counter and increase the applied voltage until impulses begin to register. Record this voltage (the starting potential). If excessive counting rates are observed ($>25,000$ counts/min), lower the voltage or remove the sample immediately to avoid damage to the counter.

Increase the applied voltage by 25 V and measure the counting rate over a period long enough to collect about 3600 counts. For reasons of convenience the activity of the source should be at least 1000 counts/min. Immediately beyond the starting potential a rapid rise in counting rate will be noticed until the "knee" of the Geiger plateau is attained. Thereafter determine the counting rate at 50-V intervals until the counting rate increases as much as 10 percent between voltage settings. The usual plateau extends over a 100- to 300-V range. Do not continue to increase the voltage beyond the plateau or else the counter will be damaged.

Express the data graphically as activity (counts per minute) versus applied voltage. All subsequent counting with this particular counter should be performed at one voltage near the middle of the plateau (the operating voltage of the tube). The slope of the Geiger plateau is expressed as the difference of two mean counting rates taken 100 V apart, and divided by the average counting rate over the particular interval.

EXPERIMENT 9-2   STATISTICAL FLUCTUATIONS IN COUNTING RATE

Choose a sample of low activity (500–1000 counts/min), or place one of higher activity on a lower shelf. Obtain 20 1-min counts.

Compute the mean counting rate, the deviations of each observation, the standard deviation of an individual observation, and the standard deviation of the mean. Evaluate the probable error, and the 2-sigma and 3-sigma variations of the mean. Tabulate your results. What percentage of the 1-min counts lies within each mode of expressing the deviation?

Determine the backgound counting rate by removing all active samples from the vicinity of the counter, and collect enough counts to give a 10 percent standard deviation about the mean. From Fig. 9-14, estimate the number of counts which must be collected from the source and the background to achieve a standard deviation equal to 2 percent.

EXPERIMENT 9-3   DEAD TIME OF COUNTER

Use two samples of small size and high activity (approximately 10,000 counts/min, if using a Geiger counter), mounted on thin Mylar.

Count sample A for a period of time sufficient to achieve 1 percent standard deviation. Without disturbing sample A, insert sample B and count again. Remove sample A, without changing the relative position of sample B, and count sample B alone. If desired, this procedure may be repeated in some other geometric arrangement, but without exceeding a counting rate of 25,000 counts/min for the combined samples.

Correct the counting rates for the background counting rate. Compute the dead time from Eq. 9-16.

EXPERIMENT 9-4   COUNTER GEOMETRY

The counting rate observed with any detector varies with the distance and the subtended angle from the detector window to the source. Since Geiger and proportional counters are usually mounted on a shelf arrangement, it is necessary to know the percentage of the activity recorded by the counter for each of the various shelf positions.

Place a radioactive standard with a known rate of disintegration on the uppermost shelf and record the activity. Repeat with the standard placed on each of the remaining shelf positions. Correct the observed activity for background and for absorption losses in the air path and window (see Experiment 9-5). Calculate the percentage of disintegrations registered by the counter for each shelf position.

EXPERIMENT 9-5   ABSORPTION CURVE FOR BETA OR GAMMA EMITTERS

Set the operating voltage of the counter at the predetermined value, and measure the background counting rate.

Place a sample of rather high activity in a fixed position; shelf 2, numbering downward, is convenient. Measure the counting rate. Add absorbers of known value in a position approximately midway between the source and the counter (uppermost shelf is convenient). Measure the counting rate for successive thicknesses of absorbers until the background counting rate or a constant counting rate is attained. With each absorber count for 5 min or until 5,000 counts have been accumulated. The absorption curve for beta emitters is obtained with aluminum foil and massive metal of various thicknesses. The absorption curve for gamma radiation and high-energy beta emitters is studied by positioning lead absorbers of varying thicknesses between the counter and source. It is preferable to use radioisotopes that are single beta or gamma emitters.

Plot the results on semilog graph paper—the net activity as counts per minute, corrected for background and dead time loss, on the ordinate logarithmic scale vs the absorber thickness in milligrams per square centimeter on the abscissa. Extrapolate the plot to zero absorber thickness. Consider the absorption of the sample itself, any mounting cover (Scotch tape, 10 mg cm^{-2}), and the air path (1 mg cm^{-2}/cm) between the sample and counter plus the window of the counter (marked on counter). Often these total approximately 50 mg cm^{-2}. From the activity at zero absorber thickness and that at 50 mg cm^{-2}, estimate the correction to be added to each measured counting rate.

Estimate by visual extrapolation the range of the beta particles having the maximum energy. From Eq. 9-1 calculate the maximum energy of the beta particles, or use the curves given in Friedlander and Kennedy's book for the energy of the gamma radiation and the maximum energy of the beta particles. From the absorption curve, determine the half-thickness in aluminum (or in lead) for the particular emitter.

EXPERIMENT 9-6   BACKSCATTERING OF BETA PARTICLES

Use a source that is mounted on a piece of cellophane (not over 1.5 mg cm^{-2}) which is cut to fit over a 2-cm hole in a sample holder. Place the source on the bottom of the holder with Scotch tape.

Measure the counting rate of the source with no added backing. Repeat with successive pieces of plastic (5.0 mg cm^{-2}) taped carefully to the back of the sample holder. Reposition the holder carefully each time to ensure reproducibility with respect to the counter.

Measure the counting rate of the source with various thicknesses of aluminum taped underneath the sample holder. Use thicknesses up to at least 0.4 range for E_{max}. Repeat with thick pieces of various metals taped to the back of the holder—aluminum, copper, silver, platinum, and lead of sufficient thickness to ensure saturation.

Plot the counting rate vs the thickness (in mg cm^{-2}) of added backing material. Separate curves will be obtained for the plastic and aluminum. Show where the saturation thickness is effectively achieved with aluminum.

Plot the percentage increase in net counting rate against the atomic number of the backing material for saturation backing. At the instructor's discretion, determine the atomic number of an unknown material by using it in a back-scattering experiment.

EXPERIMENT 9-7   IDENTIFICATION OF A RADIONUCLIDE FROM ITS DECAY CURVE

The decay of a short-lived radionuclide is followed by measuring the activity at appropriate intervals of time, always placing the sample in the same position relative to the counter each time a counting rate is determined. Suitable elements include manganese-56, antimony-122, bromine-80, iodine-128, and indium-116, methods for which have been described in the section on induced radioactivity. In addition, barium-137m ($t_{1/2}$ = 2.63 min) can be separated from its cesium-137 parent by elution from Dowex 50W-x4 (20–50 mesh) in the potassium form at pH 11 with 0.05 to 1.0% (w/v) EDTA. [R. L. Hayes and W. R. Butler, Jr., *J. Chem. Educ.*, **37**, 590 (1960).]

Longer-lived radionuclides can also be used, but it will necessitate measurements over a period of days or weeks.

Plot the net activity (corrected for background) against time on semilog paper. Determine the half-life over several time intervals and report the mean value. An unknown radioisotope (from among a restricted list) can also be identified from its absorption curve.

When a mixture of activities is present, a resolution of the decay curve is performed by the method of successive differences. First, extrapolate the linear portion (the "tail" of the decay curve) to zero time. Subtract the activity associated with the longer-lived component from the gross decay curve to obtain the activity of the shorter-lived component at different time intervals and consequently its decay curve. If the gross residual decay curve is now linear, the half-life of the longer-lived isotope can be computed; if not linear, the extrapolation process is repeated once more.

EXPERIMENT 9-8   ISOTOPE DILUTION ANALYSIS

Experiments involving isotope dilution necessarily depend on the radioisotope and sample available. Directions for the use of iron-55/59 will illustrate the possibilities.

Prepare a solution of ferric chloride with a known concentration of iron and containing a small amount of iron-55/59. Add 1 ml of this solution containing approximately 15 mg of iron, to a centrifuge tube which contains about 5 ml of water. Precipitate the iron with aqueous ammonia, centrifuge, wash with water, and recentrifuge. Transfer a portion of the precipitate to a weighed metal planchet and dry under an infrared lamp. Weigh the sample and then count with an aluminum absorber (at least 200 mg cm^{-2}) above it. Record the weight (W_1) and the activity (A_1).

Next, take 1 ml of an iron solution of unknown concentration and add to it 200 microliters of the known solution. Mix the solution thoroughly and treat the sample in the same manner as the standard. Record the final weight (W) and counting rate (A). Compute the amount of iron in the unknown solution by means of Eq. 9-18.

EXPERIMENT 9-9   SOLUBILITY OF PRECIPITATES

A 0.250-g sample of potassium iodide is spiked with 5 microcuries of iodine-131 and then precipitated with an excess of lead ion. The precipitate is filtered, washed, and suspended in 100 ml of water (or an aqueous solution with a slight excess of either common ion). After filtration the activity of the filtrate is measured and the solubility of the lead iodide calculated.

An analogous experiment could involve measurement of the solubility of strontium sulfate, using about 0.200 g of potassium sulfate that has been spiked with 50 microcuries of sulfur-35. Other experiments should suggest themselves.

EXPERIMENT 9-10   OPERATION OF A BETA-RAY THICKNESS GAUGE

Measure the counting rate of a weak beta emitter; for example, approximately 0.05 microcurie of phosphorus-32. Then determine the counting rates with varying numbers of paper sheets or layers of cardboard added between the counter and source.

Plot the counting rate versus the number of sheets as a calibration curve. Place an unknown number of cards or sheets in position and measure the counting rate. Determine the number by reference to the calibration curve. Estimate the minimum difference in thickness that could be measured and applied to monitoring paper thickness in an industrial operation (see Chapter 28).

EXPERIMENT 9-11   OBSERVATION OF THE GROWTH OF THORIUM-234
                    FROM URANIUM

U^{238} has a half-life of 4.4×10^9 years, whereas UX_1 has a half-life of 24.5 days and UX_2 of 68.4 sec. Uranyl nitrate can be freed from UX_1 and UX_2 by extraction of the uranyl nitrate into ether. If we measure the beta-ray activity of the pure uranyl salt it will be found to increase gradually, since the activity is due to UX_2 which arises from the UX_1, which in turn arises slowly from the uranium. Likewise the beta-ray activity of the $UX_1 + UX_2$ preparation would gradually decrease as the UX_1 decays. The UX_2 can be assumed to be in radioactive equilibrium and thus to decay at the same rate as the UX_1 in all of these experiments because its half-life is so much shorter than that of the UX_1.

The growth of activity in the uranium preparation can be calculated in the following manner.

Let N_1 = number of atoms of parent
  N_2 = number of atoms of product
  λ_1 = radioactive decay constant of parent
  λ_2 = radioactive decay constant of product

The rate of increase of the product is given by the rate of formation of the product minus the rate at which the product decays. Thus

$$\frac{\partial N_2}{\partial t} = N_1\lambda_1 - N_2\lambda_2$$

If $N_2 = 0$ when $t = 0$ and $\partial N_2/\partial t = N_1^0\lambda$ at time $t = 0$,

$$N_2 = \frac{N_1^0\lambda_1}{\lambda_2 - \lambda_1}(e^{-\lambda_1 t} - e^{-\lambda_2 t})$$

The activity A_2 of the product, that is, the number of atoms of the product decomposing and therefore capable of being counted, is given by $\lambda_2 N_2$, so that

$$A_2 = \frac{N_1\lambda_1\lambda_2}{\lambda_2 - \lambda_1}(e^{-\lambda_1 t} - e^{-\lambda_2 t}]$$

and for a long-lived parent and short-lived product $\lambda_2 \gg \lambda_1$ so that

$$A_2 = N_1^0\lambda_1(1 - e^{-\lambda_2 t}]$$

PROCEDURE

1. Dissolve 1 g of uranyl nitrate in 20 ml of 1:1 nitric acid. Extract in a separatory funnel with 20-ml portions of ethyl ether until the aqueous layer is quite colorless. Combine the ether layers and dry with calcium chloride.

2. Carefully evaporate off most of the ether layer. Pour the residue into water and precipitate the uranium by adding a little ammonium hydroxide. Filter on a flat piece of filter paper over a Buchner or porous glass funnel. Only a small portion of the sample should be filtered, so that only a thin layer of hydroxide will be obtained.

3. Mount the sample on the filter paper in an aluminum planchet or on a piece of cardboard or plastic which can be inserted in a reproducible manner in the counting device. Cover with a thin layer of Scotch tape or Celluloid if the counter has walls thicker than 4 mg/cm². If the counter has thinner walls than this, an aluminum foil 0.001 in. thick must be placed between the sample and the counter.

4. Count the sample, or measure the activity on an electroscope at intervals of 12–24 hr over a period of several days. At the same time, count a standard beta-ray source, preferably one of U_3O_8.

5. Calculate the activity of the sample in terms of counts per minute or divisions per minute. Each measurement should be corrected by a factor determined by multiplying by the original first-recorded activity of the standard sample divided by the activity of the standard at the time the measurement was made.

6. Plot corrected activity against time. If the uranium is first converted to a weighable form, such as U_3O_8, before measurement and if the counting efficiency and geometry of the tube are known, then N_1^0, the number of atoms of uranium at $t = 0$, can be calculated. A theoretical plot of A_2 can be made:

$$\lambda_1 = 4.9 \times 10^{-18} \text{ sec}^{-1} \quad \text{and} \quad \lambda_2 = 3.275 \times 10^{-7} \text{ sec}^{-1}$$

Problems

1. The following measurements were obtained with a proportional flow counter:

APPLIED VOLTAGE, V	OBSERVED COUNT RATE, COUNTS/MIN	APPLIED VOLTAGE, V	OBSERVED COUNT RATE, COUNTS/MIN
1200	225,000	1600	231,000
1300	231,700	1700	231,500
1400	232,400	1800	233,000
1500	231,400	1900	271,000

Plot the results on graph paper and select an operating voltage.

2. Using a gamma-emitter, these measurements were obtained with an ionization chamber:

APPLIED VOLTAGE, V	OBSERVED COUNT RATE, COUNTS/MIN	APPLIED VOLTAGE, V	OBSERVED COUNT RATE, COUNTS/MIN
1200	19,400	1470	41,000
1245	29,100	1500	40,900
1290	35,700	1545	41,100
1335	38,900	1590	41,500
1380	40,500	1635	42,200
1425	40,600	1680	45,100
		1725	48,700

Plot the results on graph paper and select an operating voltage.

3. A 50.0-mg sample of U_3O_8, compressed into virtually a point source, was placed in each of five shelf positions and the net activity recorded:

Shelf	1 (uppermost)	2	3	4	5
Activity, counts/min	11,130	2,540	1,130	478	286

    What is the geometry of each position? *Ans.* Shelf 5, 0.9 percent geometry.

4. Calculate the weight of (a) 1 curie of P^{32}, (b) 1 mc of Cl^{36}; (c) 5 mc of I^{131}, (d) 10 μc of Au^{198}, and (e) 10 mc of Co^{60}. *Ans.* (e) 8.59 μg.

5. How many microcuries are in a 50-mg sample of U_3O_8? *Ans.* 0.00145 μc

6. A sample of S^{35} contains 10 millicuries. After 174 days, how many disintegrations per minute occur in the sample? *Ans.* 5.5×10^9 disintegrations per minute.

7. How much activity of the P^{32}, the I^{131}, and the Au^{198} (in Problem 4) remains (a) after 14 days, (b) after 30 days, and (c) after 60 days?

8. Calculate the probable error, the 1-sigma, and the 2-sigma variations (in percent) for each of these total number of counts: (a) 3200, (b) 6400, (c) 8000, (d) 25,600 and (e) 102,400. *Ans.* (a) The probable error is 1.19 percent; 2 sigma is 3.54 percent.

9. Compute the dead time of the Geiger counter and the corresponding counting losses from this information: sample A gave a count rate of 9,728 counts/min sample B gave a rate of 11,008 counts/min and together samples A plus B gave a rate of 20,032 counts/min. *Ans.* Dead time is 200 μsec.

10. Assuming that the dead time of a Geiger counter is 200 μsec, and that there are no other counting losses, what is the efficiency of the counter for (a) 5000 ionizing particles per second; (b) 1000, (c) 200, and (d) 5? *Ans.* (a) Only 50 percent efficiency.

11. What is the useful range of counting rates if the dead time of the detector is (a) 0.25 μsec, (b) 1.0 μsec, (c) 5 μsec; and (d) 270 μsec?

12. A sample gave a counting rate of 200 counts/min in a 10-min count. The background gave a counting rate of 40 counts/min in a 5-min count. What is the fractional 0.95 error (2 sigma) of the sample corrected for background? *Ans.* Less than 6.6 percent.

13. For the sample in Problem 12, how much time should be devoted to counting the sample and the background if the standard deviation of each measurement, corrected for background, is to be (a) 5 percent, (b) 2 percent, (c) 3 percent? *Ans.* (b) On the sample plus background 11,500 counts should be accumulated; for the background alone, 3000 counts. This would entail a counting time of 57.5 and 37.5 min, respectively.

14. Using a RaD-E sample mounted on a thin film of plastic, the count rate in a particular shelf position was 6531 counts/min (air). When different materials were placed immediately in back of the sample, the count rate was 6755 with aluminum, 6819 with copper, and 7609 with lead. Determine the scattering effect and report it as the percent change in count rate relative to air.

15. The following experimental data were obtained when the activity of a beta-active sample was measured at the intervals shown.

TIME, MIN	ACTIVITY, COUNTS/MIN	TIME, MIN	ACTIVITY, COUNTS/MIN
10	542	80	56
20	315	90	50
30	200	100	44
40	135	120	37
50	100	140	31
60	77	160	27
70	64	180	23

    Plot the decay curve on semilog paper and analyze it into its components. What are the half-lives and the initial activities of the component activities?

16. The decay of a particular halogen, subjected to several hours of irradiation, provided the following data;

TIME, MIN	ACTIVITY, COUNTS/MIN	TIME, MIN	ACTIVITY, COUNTS/MIN
10	1800	50	650
18	1400	60	550
24	1215	80	430
32	970	120	330
36	880	180	270
40	800	240	230

Plot the decay curve on semilog paper and analyze it into its components. What are the half-lives and the initial activities of the component activities? Can you identify the particular halogen? *Ans.* Br^{80} and Br^{80m}.

17. The following data were obtained when the activity of a beta-emitter was measured at the intervals shown.

TIME, MIN	ACTIVITY, COUNTS/MIN	TIME, MIN	ACTIVITY, COUNTS/MIN
0	10,000	120	539
10	6,425	140	468
20	4,695	160	425
40	2,340	180	370
60	1,202	200	332
80	824	240	265
100	642		

Plot the results on semilog paper and analyze it into its components. What are the half-lives and the initial activities of the component activities?

18. In a certain measuring arrangement, the beta particles of Cs^{136} are absorbed as follows (correction made for gamma radiation):

THICKNESS OF ALUMINUM, mg/cm²	ACTIVITY, COUNTS/MIN	THICKNESS OF ALUMINUM, mg/cm²	ACTIVITY, COUNTS/MIN
0	10,000	53	270
12	4,700	72	30
27	1,700	85	30
41	730		

Find the maximum energy of the beta radiation. What is the aluminum half-thickness? *Ans.* Theoretical beta energy is 0.34 MeV.

19. The absorption of RaE (Bi^{210}) beta radiations produced the data below, uncorrected for counting losses or background. Dead time of counter is 200 μsec. Assume the absorption of the sample, air path, and counter window to be 60 mg/cm². Background counting rate is 30 counts/min.

THICKNESS OF ALUMINUM, mg/cm²	ACTIVITY, COUNTS/MIN	THICKNESS OF ALUMINUM, mg/cm⁻	ACTIVITY, COUNTS/MIN
0	19,100	163	1,620
25	13,680	200	850
57	8,720	265	270
90	4,820	335	82
123	3,080	1000	30

Determine the maximum energy of the beta radiation.

20. The visual range of absorber thickness, for P^{32} is 780 mg Al/cm^2. Determine the maximum energy of the beta particle.

21. Absorption data taken for Cl^{36} indicated an aluminum half-thickness of 28 mg cm^{-2}. What is its maximum beta energy?

22. To a crude mixture of organic compounds containing some benzoic acid and benzoate was added 40.0 mg of benzoic acid-7-C^{14} (activity = 2,000 counts/min). After equilibration, the mixture was acidified and extracted with an immiscible solvent. The extracted solid, following removal of solvent, was purified by recrystallization of the benzoic acid to a constant melting point. The purified material weighed 60.0 mg and gave a count rate of 500 counts/min. Compute the weight of benzoic acid in the crude mixture. *Ans.* 200 mg.

23. A fermentation broth was known to contain some Aureomycin. To a 1000-g portion of the broth was added 1.00 mg of Aureomycin containing carbon-14 (specific activity = 150 counts/min/mg). From the mixture, 0.20 mg of crystalline Aureomycin was isolated which had a net activity of 400 counts in 100 min. Calculate the weight of Aureomycin per 1000 g of broth.

24. If a 10.0-mg precipitate of $BaSO_4$ contained 0.1 microcurie of S^{35}, what fraction of the precipitate contains radiosulfur? *Ans.* 1.56×10^{-9}

25. A $BaCO_3$ precipitate containing C^{14} and weighing 10.0 mg gives a radioassay of 37 counts/sec, which is estimated to be equivalent to about 3700 absolute disintegrations per second. What fraction of the sample is barium radiocarbonate?

26. A 10.0-ml volume of a chloride-ion solution was added to a 50-ml volumetric flask and precipitated with 10.0 ml of 0.0440 N silver nitrate solution which contained silver-110. After the precipitate coagulated, the flask was filled to the mark and mixed thoroughly. A 20-ml aliquot of the clear supernatant liquid, after filtration or centrifugation, was counted and it gave a count rate of 924 counts/min. A 5.0-ml volume of the standard silver solution, diluted to 20 ml and counted, gave a count rate of 7555 counts/min. The background amounted to 100 counts/min. What is the chloride-ion concentration in the unknown solution? *Ans.* 0.079 M in chloride-ion.

27. In the analysis of mixtures of sodium and potassium carbonates, the half-lives are too nearly the same to permit a resolution of the composite gross decay curve if the total beta radiations were counted. Suggest a method for the analysis of this binary mixture. (Hint: the beta particle emitted in the decay of the sodium activity possesses a maximum energy of 1.39 MeV compared with the potassium activity, where beta particles of a maximum energy of 3.58 MeV are radiated.)

28. If a 10.0-mg sample of aluminum foil were irradiated for 30 min in a neutron flux of 5×10^{11} neutrons cm^{-2} sec^{-1}, how long should the sample be allowed to "cool" before chemical processing or counting in order that the strong aluminum activity will have decayed to less than 1 count/min? *Ans.* 69 min.

29. For the irradiation time and flux stated in Problem 28, what is the limit of detection (40 counts/sec) for traces of sodium as sodium-24 in "pure" aluminum foil after the aluminum activity has decayed to less than 1 count/min. Counting geometry is 100 percent. Assume no other activities are present and ignore corrections for absorption of sodium beta particles by the aluminum foil. *Ans.* 0.26 μg.

30. What weight of sample should be taken for the activation analysis of an aluminum alloy which contains 0.019 percent zinc if the irradiation time is 62 h with a flux of 5×10^{11} neutrons cm^{-2} sec^{-1}, followed by a cooling period of 24 hours? A counting rate of 1,000 counts/min is desirable.

31. In a particular aluminum alloy, these elements are present in the following percentages: Cu, 0.30; Mn, 0.30; Ni, 0.59; Co, 0.0053. If all samples were 10.0 mg in weight, how long should the irradiations be continued for the determination of each element? Assume a counting rate of 10,000 counts/min in a 5-min count-

ing period is desirable after a cooling period of 0.7 day. Flux is 5×10^{11} neutrons/cm²/sec.

32. Following the irradiation conditions for copper in Problem 31, how many hours should elapse before a direct determination of copper (without intermediate chemical processing) is attempted? What thickness of aluminum absorber will attenuate completely all beta radiation from other elements when measuring the gamma radiation from radiocopper?

33. With a neutron flux of 10^5 neutrons cm⁻² sec⁻¹, what activities (disintegrations per minute per milligram) can be anticipated for iodine-131, bromine-80, antimony-122, and manganese-56?

Bibliography

Choppin, G. R., *Experimental Nuclear Chemistry*, Prentice-Hall, Englewood Cliffs, N.J., 1961.

Cook, G. B., and J. F. Duncan, *Modern Radiochemical Practice*, Oxford U.P., New York, 1952.

Friedlander, G., J. W. Kennedy, and J. M. Miller, *Nuclear and Radiochemistry*, 2nd ed., Wiley, New York, 1964.

Koch, R. C., *Activation Analysis Handbook*, Academic Press, New York, 1960.

Korff, S. A., *Electron and Nuclear Counters*, 2nd ed., Van Nostrand, Princeton, N.J., 1955.

Lapp, R. E., and H. L. Andrews, *Nuclear Radiation Physics*, 2nd ed., Prentice-Hall, Englewood Cliffs, N.J., 1954.

Overman, R. T., and H. M. Clark, *Radioisotope Techniques*, McGraw-Hill, New York, 1959.

Pollard, E., and W. L. Davidson, *Applied Nuclear Physics*, 2nd ed., Wiley, New York, 1951.

Symposium on Nucleonics, *Anal. Chem.*, 21, 318–368 (1949).

Wahl, A. C., and N. A. Bonner (Eds.), *Radioactivity Applied to Chemistry*, Wiley, New York, 1951.

Weissberger, A. (Ed.), *Physical Methods of Organic Chemistry*, 3rd ed., Vol. I, Part IV, Chapter L, Interscience, New York, 1963.

Literature Cited

1. Brooksbank, W. A., Jr., G. W. Leddicotte, and J. A. Dean, *Anal. Chem.*, **30**, 1785 (1958).

2. U.S. Atomic Energy Commission, "Catalog and Price List of Radioisotopes," Isotopes Branch, P.O. Box E, Oak Ridge, Tenn.

CHAPTER | 10

Emission Spectroscopy

The spectrograph as an analytical tool has had a long period of development since the discovery of Bunsen and Kirchhoff that the spectra of flames colored from metallic salts were characteristic of the metals. Modern automatic recording spectrographs are capable of giving the percentage of a number of elements directly on dials and in only a few minutes. Qualitatively, the spectrograph is capable of detecting 0.001 percent or less of most of the metallic ions and of certain nonmetals, that is, P, Si, As, C, and B, in a sample of only a few milligrams. Quantitative determination of these elements is also readily accomplished. One spectroscopist is usually capable of analyzing as many different samples of the same type of material as five or more men by routine, wet procedures. Consequently, the spectrograph has largely replaced the older, wet analytical procedures for the routine determinations of lesser components of steels, metallic alloys, etc.

Emission Spectrography

Origin of Spectra

A complete discussion of the origin of emission spectra is beyond the scope of this book. For the present purpose, it is sufficient to understand that there are three kinds of emission spectra: continuous spectra, band spectra, and line spectra. The continuous spectra are emitted by incandescent solids and are characterized by the absence of any sharply defined lines. The band spectra consist of groups of lines that come closer and closer together as they approach a limit, the head of the band. Band spectra are caused by excited molecules. Line spectra consist of definite, usually widely and apparently irregularly spaced, lines. This type of spectrum is characteristic of atoms or atomic ions which have been excited and are emitting their extra energy in the form of light of definite wavelengths.

The quantum theory predicts that each atom or ion has definite energy states in which the various electrons can exist. In the normal or ground state, the electrons are in the lowest energy state. On addition of sufficient energy by thermal, electrical, or other means, one or more electrons may be removed to a higher energy state farther from the nucleus. These excited electrons tend to return to the ground state and in so doing emit the extra energy as a photon of radiant energy. Since there are definite energy states and since only certain transitions are possible, there are a limited number of wavelengths possible in the emission spectrum. The greater the energy in the excited source, the higher the energy of the excited electron and therefore the more numerous the lines that may appear. However, the wavelengths of the existing lines will not be changed. An abbreviated pattern is shown in Chapter 11 (Fig. 11-9).

The intensity of a spectral line depends mainly on the probability of the required energy "jump" or transition taking place. Self-absorption occasionally decreases the intensity of some of the stronger lines. Self-absorption is caused by the reabsorption of energy by the cool, gaseous ions in the outer regions of the source. When high-energy sources are used, the atoms may be ionized by the loss of one or more electrons. The spectrum of an ionized ion is quite different from that of the neutral atom; in fact, the spectrum of a singly ionized ion will bear a strong resemblance to that of the neutral atom of atomic number one less.

The constituent parts of the spectrograph, including the energy sources and the registering devices, will be considered in the following pages. A few typical, commercially available instruments are then described. Finally the various procedures used in qualitative and quantitative work are described.

Excitation Methods

The flame, an a-c arc, a d-c arc, and the a-c spark are the common methods of excitation. Each has special advantages and special applications. However, the function of each excitation unit is to introduce the sample into the source in a vaporized form and to excite electrons in the vaporized atoms to higher energy levels.

Flame. The flame furnishes a rather low energy source and excites only a few lines, but this may be an advantage. For a complete discussion of flame excitation, refer to Chapter 11.

d-c Arc

The d-c arc, produced by a voltage of from 50 to about 300 volts, is a common method for introducing the sample into the discharge. Vaporization occurs from the heating caused by the passage of current. Arc temperatures range from 4000° to 8000°K. The emission lines produced are primarily those due to neutral atoms and are indicated in tables by the symbol of the atom. (Those due to singly ionized ions are indicated by the symbol followed by II.) The necessary components for a d-c arc are a direct current power supply, a variable resistor, and a discharge gap (Fig. 10-1). Current across the discharge gap ranges from 1 to 30 amp. One difficulty with an arc is its tendency to wander and flicker, especially when struck between carbon or graphite electrodes.

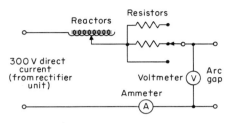

Fig. 10-1. Circuit for d-c arc.

This unsteadiness can be reduced somewhat by including a reactor in the circuit. A second difficulty involves selected volatility wherein the more volatile components may be selectively vaporized during the early portion of the arcing period. Consequently, line intensities should be monitored during the entire burning period in order to establish the optimum time for observation. To obviate this difficulty the sample may be burned to completion.

The d-c arc is a very sensitive source with a good line-to-background ratio. It is generally used for the determination and identification of substances present in very small concentrations since it can detect elements below the limit of detection of a spark. A comparatively large amount of the substance being analyzed passes through the arc, and on this account an average or more representative value of the concentration is shown, provided that the complete sample is burned. The light from the center portion of an arc is the portion usually employed, since there may be a local concentration of certain ions near the electrodes. However, since the cathode region gives higher excitation energy, especially for lines arising from unionized atoms, it is more sensitive for these atoms and is sometimes employed for illuminating the slit of the spectrograph. When an arc is operated between carbon electrodes in air, some cyanogen [$(CN)_2$] molecules are formed and, being excited by the arc, emit typical molecular band spectra in the region from 3600 to 4200 Å.

Stallwood Jet

An attachment frequently used with the d-c arc to enhance sensitivity is the Stallwood Jet, shown in Fig. 10-2. In the Stallwood Jet of Spex Industries, gas is forced into a swirl chamber and then upward through an orifice surrounding the sample electrode. As the electrode burns away, it may be advanced with respect to the curtain of gas. Instead of the gas entering the open atmosphere as it leaves the orifice, it enters a quartz enclosure where, by building up a slight positive pressure, it excludes the ambient air. Illumination from the arc is through a small window in the side of the enclosure. Gas com-

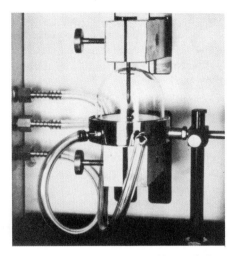

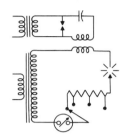

Fig. 10-2. The Spex Stallwood Jet. (Courtesy of Spex Industries, Inc.)

Fig. 10-3. Schematic diagram of a-c arc source.

positions generally used are argon-oxygen mixtures ranging from an 80-20 to a 60-40 mixture. Enhanced sensitivity arises from two causes. One is that cyanogen bands are eliminated and elements hidden in the cyanogen bands are more easily detected—these include molybdenum, the rare earths, iron, and gallium. The other reason for improved sensitivity relates to volatility. The excitation efficiency of a sample can be markedly increased if it is forced to burn slowly and is cooled with a gas stream. This is particularly helpful with volatile materials when they are placed in a deep cratered electrode.

a-c Arc

The high-voltage a-c arc employs a potential difference of 1000 volts or more (Fig. 10-3). In the illustration the transformer is equipped with two secondary windings to provide either 5 amp at 2750 volts or 2.5 amp at 5500 volts. The arc is drawn out to a distance of only 0.5–3 mm. For reproducible results the separation of the electrodes, the potential, and the current must be carefully controlled. The whole assembly must be carefully shielded so as to protect the operator from the dangerously high voltages. In comparison with the d-c arc, the a-c arc is steadier and more reproducible because reignition each half cycle on a random part of the sample provides good sampling technique.

a-c Spark

The a-c spark gives much higher excitation energies than the arc with less heating effect. The spark is produced by connecting a high-voltage transformer (10–50 kV) across two electrodes. A condenser is usually connected in parallel with the spark gap in order to increase the current. An inductor is also desirable in the circuit, since this has been found to decrease the excitation of lines and bands of the air molecules. Large values of inductance decrease the excitation energy and make the spark more arc-like in its characteristics. The relationship between the current i, potential V, capacitance C, and the inductance L, when a spark first jumps, is given by the equation

$$i = V\sqrt{\frac{C}{L}} \qquad (10\text{-}1)$$

Thus the characteristics of the spark depend upon the capacitance and inductance. Rather elaborate devices are available for allowing variations in these values. The circuit proposed by Feussner[2] (Fig. 10-4) employs an auxilia-

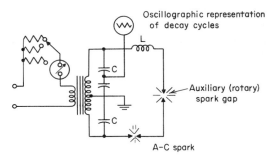

Fig. 10-4. Feussner circuit for a-c spark source.

ry rotating spark gap which is driven by a synchronous motor. The gap is closed for only a brief instant at the peak of each half-cycle, and thus the number of the decay cycles in the spark is controlled, which leads to more uniform and reproducible excitation conditions.

The spark is the preferred source whenever high precision rather than extreme sensitivity is required. Several types of spark sources have been proposed, each with its special uses. They differ mainly in the mechanism used to trigger the breakdown of the analytical gap so as to provide a series of discrete and identical breakdowns. In general, the spark source excites predominately ionic spectra. It is more reproducible and stable than the arc. Less material is consumed, and consequently the spark source is employed for higher concentrations of material than is the arc. Since the heating effect is less than that of the arc, it is well adapted for the analysis of low-melting materials. The spark source is also free from the troublesome cyanogen bands. However, the spark may strike to a particular spot on an electrode and thus give a nonrepresentative indication of the concentration of substance being determined.

The spark source is readily adapted to the analysis of solutions. The solution, rendered conducting by the addition of hydrochloric acid, is allowed to flow over a lower electrode while a spark is struck to the electrode, or rather to the thin layer of solution above the lower electrode. A bundle of fine wires may also serve as the lower electrode and draw the solution up to the top of the bundle by capillary attraction.

For the excitation of gases such as He, Ar, Kr, Ne, Xe, H_2, O_2, N_2, S_{vapor}, and Na_{vapor}, a gaseous discharge tube—that is, the common Geissler tube—is employed.

Laser Method

An optical ruby laser can be used to excite spectral emission from samples, even nonconducting materials which formerly required analysis in a cup electrode or by a graphitic pelletizing procedure. The operation of a laser microprobe is simple, requiring no sample preparation. The fundamental principle involves the absorption by the sample of the laser beam, which is concentrated onto the sample by a microscope objective lens (Fig. 10-5). Intense

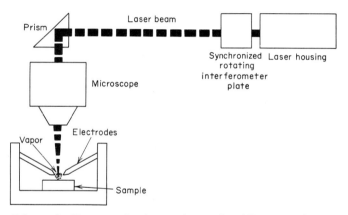

Fig. 10-5. Schematic diagram of a laser microprobe. (Courtesy of Jarrell-Ash Co.)

heat vaporizes all samples exposed to the beam and, for some of them, also achieves excitation energies in the vapor. However, the essence of the Jarrell-Ash microprobe (illustrated) is the raising of the vaporized sample to a useful spectral emission by causing the vapor to short circuit an auxiliary electrical gap positioned between the sample and microscopic objective. A sample spot as small as 50 μ may be selected.

Electrodes

The electrodes may be composed of the material being investigated if the material is a conductor and will withstand high temperatures. If not, the sample is usually placed in a small core in a carbon or graphite electrode. The upper electrode in such a case is another carbon or graphite electrode ground to a blunt point in a pencil sharpener or a special grinding tool. A variety of preformed electrode shapes have been devised in order to steady the arc or increase its temperature. Fig. 10-6(a) illustrates the usual form of the lower electrode; Fig. 10-6(b) shows a form with a center post to help prevent wandering of the arc, and Fig. 10-6(c) shows a form used to increase the arc temperature by decreasing the conduction of heat away from the crater containing the sample. Steadier arcs can be produced if the sample is mixed with pure, powdered graphite. Metallic electrodes have some advantages over graphite electrodes, but of course the lines of the electrode metal will appear in the spectrum. These may serve as a reference spectrum.

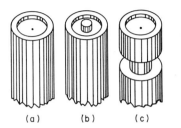

(a)   (b)   (c)

Fig. 10-6.   Several forms of carbon electrodes.

Several techniques have been employed for handling solutions. In the porous cup technique a hole about 3.2 mm in diameter is drilled in the center of a 6.5 mm diameter graphite electrode, the hole extending to within about 1 mm from the bottom of the electrode. The solution is placed in the hole, and the electrode is then employed as the upper electrode. A solid graphite rod forms the lower electrode. Either an arc or spark may be used. The solution slowly diffuses through the millimeter of graphite into the arc or spark. Still another device is to use a rotating graphite disc as the lower electrode. The disc rotates through the solution placed in a small boat and carries the liquid into the arc or spark which is struck to the upper part of the rotating disc. Solutions can also be evaporated in the craters of the electrodes. If carbon or graphite is employed, the crater is frequently waterproofed by dipping it into redistilled kerosene or collodion. Methods mentioned above for spark sources are also used.

The lower electrode is usually made the positive electrode. The arc is started by touching the two electrodes together and drawing them apart. If this does not start the arc, a graphite rod may be drawn across the gap.

Graphite is a better conductor than carbon, can be obtained in purer form, and is to be preferred in most cases for the electrode material, although carbon gives a somewhat steadier arc. The electrodes can be purified in several ways which cannot be discussed here.[4] The impurities present in Acheson spectrographic graphite electrodes generally will not cause more than a few faint lines to appear in the blanks.

Spectrographs

Every spectrograph will have a dispersing medium, either a grating or a prism, a slit, and a camera or other recording device.

The spectral lines recorded are replica images of the slit. The slit should, therefore, be straight and have parallel and sharp edges to avoid reflection from the edges. It should be kept clean and free from nicks, since dust particles or imperfections will be reproduced in the images. The slit should be adjustable, preferably continuously so, and should also be bilateral, that is, both sides should open or close rather than just one side. The center of a unilateral slit changes with width.

When using a prism and with some grating mountings, lenses are required to render the light parallel and to focus the light on the camera or detector. Since the focal length of a lens varies with the wavelength, light of different wavelengths will be brought to focus at different distances from the lens. If the lens can be constructed from two or more different materials it can be made to bring all wavelengths to focus at about the same distance; but in the ultraviolet region, where practically only quartz is available, that is not possible. The plate or film must then be tilted and curved somewhat to compensate for this characteristic of the lens. Lenses also show other errors such as spherical aberration which may require grinding of aspherical surfaces for correction or the use of only small lens apertures.

Prism Instruments

The chief distinguishing feature of the various spectrographs is whether they employ a prism or grating as the dispersing medium and in the particular type of mounting of the prism or grating.

The Cornu mounting (Fig. 10-7) requires two pieces of quartz, one of right-

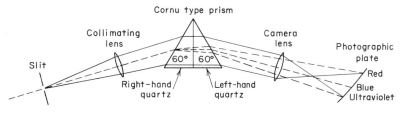

Fig. 10-7. Optical diagram of a Cornu-type spectrograph.

handed and one of left-handed circularly polarizing quartz. This is necessary since quartz possesses the property of rotating the plane of polarized light and will also separate an unpolarized beam into two beams, circularly polarized in opposite directions. Since the index of refraction for the two beams is different, two images will result unless the two different types of quartz crystals are used or unless the beam is returned in an opposite direction through the crystal. Glass, because it is isotropic, does not show this effect, and only one piece is required. It is used frequently in instruments designed for the visible and near infrared or near ultraviolet regions. Glass exhibits greater dispersion than quartz in the visible region and is often used for this reason.

The Littrow mounting employs only one piece of quartz with the back surface of the prism metallized. Since the light passes back and forth through the same prism and lens, polarization effects are eliminated. Littrow mounting results in a compact instrument (Fig. 10-8).

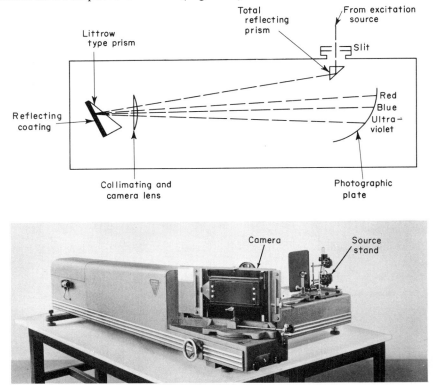

Fig. 10-8.   Illustration and schematic optical diagram of a Littrow-type spectrograph. (Courtesy of Bausch & Lomb Optical Co.)

A small prism spectrograph usually covers the range from 2000 to 8000 Å in one 7.5-cm photograph. By contrast, a large Littrow spectrograph covers the same spectral range in three photographs on 25-cm plates. The dispersion of the large type is about 0.4 mm/Å at 2500 Å and decreases to 0.10 mm/Å at 4000 Å. Sometimes an interchangeable glass prism is available for increased dispersion in the visible region.

Measures Used for the Comparison of Prism Instruments

The index of refraction of substances varies with the wavelength; over short ranges, somewhat removed from regions of anomalous dispersion, it can be expressed by Hartmann's formula:[6]

$$n = n_0 + \frac{c}{(\lambda - \lambda_0)} \tag{10-2}$$

where n = index of refraction
                        λ = wavelength
        n_0, λ_0, and c = constants

The *angular dispersion*, the change in angle of the dispersed beam with a change in wavelength, is equal to $d\theta/d\lambda$. Substances generally show greater dispersion at wavelengths near their "cut-offs" or regions of strong absorption. Glass and quartz show increasing dispersion as one moves from the visible toward the ultraviolet region. The dispersion may also be conveniently written as the *linear dispersion*, $\Delta x/\Delta\lambda$, where Δx represents the distance in millimeters on the plate between two lines $\Delta\lambda$ apart. A typical curve relating wavelength to scale reading (in millimeters) for a small Littrow prism spectrograph is shown in Fig. 10-9. This nonlinear dispersion of prismatic instruments causes some

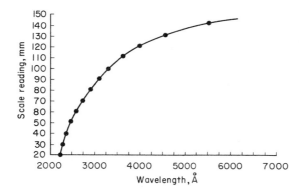

Fig. 10-9. Typical calibration curve for the small Littrow spectrograph.

extra work in calculating the wavelengths of unknown lines. The determination of wavelengths is made either from a graph constructed for the instrument or by measuring the position of three known lines and the unknown line and employing the formula of Hartmann in the form

$$\lambda = \lambda_0 + \frac{c}{(d_0 - d)} \tag{10-3}$$

in which λ_0, c, and d_0 are constants. A reference point on the spectrum plate or film is chosen near the unknown line and three lines of known wavelength. The distances from the reference point to the lines of known wavelength and the distance from the reference point to the unknown line are measured. The constants are evaluated by substitution of the known wavelengths for λ and the measured distances for d. The unknown wavelength is then easily computed from Eq. 10-3.

The *resolving power* R indicates the ability of a spectrograph to resolve two spectral lines separated by wavelength $\partial\lambda$.

$$R = \frac{\bar{\lambda}}{\partial\lambda} = t\frac{\partial n}{\partial\lambda} \tag{10-4}$$

where $\bar{\lambda}$ = the average wavelength of two lines just distinguishable from each other

$\partial\lambda$ = the difference in wavelength of these two lines

t = thickness of the base of the prism

n = index of refraction of the prism

Since $\partial n/\partial\lambda$ remains nearly constant for most prism materials, the thicker the prism, the greater will be the resolving power. Resolving power is also affected somewhat by the width and shape of the slit and by the other characteristics of the optical system.

Grating Instruments

A grating consists of a large number of parallel, equally spaced lines ruled upon a glass surface or a metal coating (often aluminum) on glass. Replica gratings made from original masters by coating the original with a plastic and then stripping off the plastic (Fig. 3-9) are in common use. A discussion of gratings and their optical properties will be found in Chapter 3 (page 40).

Commercial grating spectrographs are available with a variety of mountings. The Rowland mounting is so arranged that the film and grating are at right angles to the slit, and the length of the arms is such that the three components all lie on the Rowland circle (Fig. 10-10). The Rowland circle is a circle with radius of curvature half that of the grating itself. If the slit and grating lie on the Rowland circle, the images of the slit are brought to a focus somewhere on this circle. To scan the spectrum, both the plate and grating must be moved mechanically. This arrangement finds use mainly in X-ray spectrographs.

The Wadsworth mounting (Fig. 10-11) requires a mirror so that the grating may be illuminated by parallel light. The light-gathering power of the arrange-

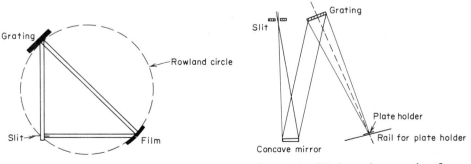

Fig. 10-10. Rowland mounting for a concave grating.

Fig. 10-11. Wadsworth mounting for a concave grating.

ment is high. Furthermore, the arrangement is stigmatic; that is, light arising from horizontal lines and from vertical lines is brought to a focus at the same distance from the grating. Most other grating mountings are astigmatic and it is then necessary to find some position beyond the slit in which to place any device which would limit the length of the lines produced by the slit. There are two positions in an astigmatic mounting in which lines will be in focus at the camera, one position for vertical lines (the slit edges) and one position for horizontal lines (slit limiting devices). An example of a Wadsworth mount is found in the Jarrell-Ash 1.5-m spectrograph. The grating has 600 lines/mm, covers the range from 2200 to 7800 Å in first order with a dispersion of 10.9 Å/mm. The camera photographs 50 cm of spectrum.

The Eagle mounting, or modifications thereof (Fig. 10-12), is very popular in spite of the fact that rather complicated adjustments are needed for the film and grating. Astigmatism is slight. This mounting is the most compact of the concave grating mountings. The Bausch & Lomb 1.5-m spectrograph employs an Eagle mounting, has fixed slits of 10, 20, and 50 μ, and provides a dispersion of 16 Å/mm in the first order. It covers the range from 2250 to 6250 Å.

The Seya-Namioka mounting (Fig. 10-13) has an angle of 70°15′ between the

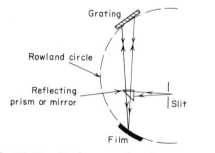

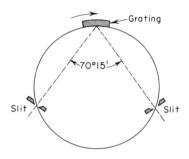

Fig. 10-12. Eagle mounting for a con- **Fig. 10-13.** Seya-Namioka mounting.
cave grating.

entrance and exit slits. Only slight defocusing occurs when the grating is rotated. This arrangement provides an excellent scanning monochromator.

The Ebert mounting (Fig. 10-14) uses a plane grating rather than a concave one, thus making the ruling of the grating easier. Also, the mounting is compact. This arrangement requires a large concave mirror to render the radiation striking the grating parallel and to intercept the dispersed beam and focus it on the plate at the camera. A modification, the Czerny-Turner mounting, has two smaller concave mirrors in place of a single large mirror. The Ebert mounting is stigmatic and also achromatic, so that the rays of all wavelengths are brought to focus at the camera without changing the camera-to-mirror distance. This makes it easy to change wavelengths merely by rotating the grating. Higher orders are readily accessible. Almost all large spectrographs (3-m instruments)

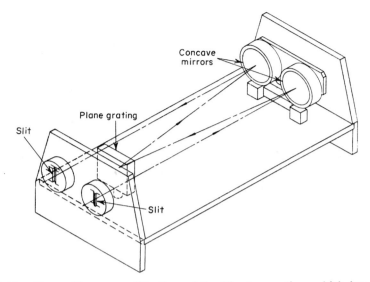

Fig. 10-14. Czerny-Turner modification of the Ebert mounting, which has a single large mirror.

now have plane gratings with modified Ebert mountings. Standard gratings will have 600 or 1200 lines/mm with resolution ranging from 5.1 Å/mm in first order to 0.7 Å/mm in third order and a range of 1800–30,000 Å. Some instruments (Jarrell-Ash) have an "order sorter"—a fore-prism arrangement which stands between the source and the main slit of the instrument and which serves to place the various orders of spectra one above another on the photographic plate.

A combination of an echelle grating with a Littrow prism provides a high-resolution spectrograph. The principle of operation is illustrated in Fig. 10-15, and a schematic diagram of the optical system is shown in Fig. 10-16. Fig. 10-15 shows what an echelle grating does. The iron triplet at 3100 Å is shown as it would appear when resolved by the Littrow prism. The slit is then rotated 90° to the horizontal position and placed across the spectrum. When all sections of the line images that will not pass through the horizontal slit are removed, the image looks like the third section of the illustration. Now if this image is passed to an echelle grating (78 lines/cm), vertical dispersion is introduced with a result about 10 times superior to that of the prism alone. With this arrangement it is possible to obtain resolution better than 0.5 Å/mm in a compact, eight-foot instrument.

Measures Used for the Comparison of Grating Instruments

The dispersion, both angular and linear, is defined in the same manner as that for a prism instrument. For a grating, however, the dispersion is constant

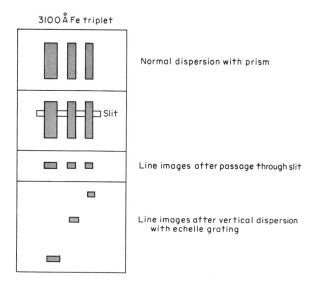

Fig. 10-15. How an echellogram is produced. (Courtesy of Bausch & Lomb Optical Co.)

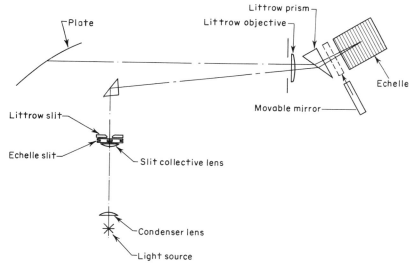

Fig. 10-16. Bausch & Lomb Littrow-Echelle system. (Courtesy of Bausch & Lomb Optical Co.)

or very nearly so and does not vary with wavelength as it does for a prism. The dispersion is said to be "normal." This is a decided advantage when it comes to identifying lines.

The resolving power R of a grating can be shown to be

$$R = nN \tag{10-5}$$

where n is the order of the spectrum, and N is the number of lines in the illuminated portion of the grating. Resolving power also depends upon the quality of a grating. A grating may show faint displaced images of lines—"ghost lines"—due to imperfections in the ruling. It usually will also show some faint higher-order spectra overlapping the desired spectrum.

The particular spectrograph to be used in any situation depends on the type of material and the nature of the work to be performed. For materials with fair amounts of iron, cobalt, nickel, manganese, uranium, chromium, and the like, an instrument with high dispersion is required, since the spectra of these elements consist of a very great number of closely spaced lines. For alloys of aluminum, lead, tin, copper, silver, magnesium, etc., an instrument with reciprocal dispersions of only 10-20 Å/mm will suffice, since only a few lines appear.

The Photographic Process

In all spectrographs except the direct readers, the intensity of the spectral lines is registered on a photographic emulsion. The nature of the photographic process is therefore of considerable importance.

Photographic materials consist of a light-sensitive emulsion coated on a support (glass plate or plastic film). This emulsion contains light-sensitive crystals (grains) of silver halides suspended in gelatin. When the material is exposed in a camera of the spectrograph, it shows no visible effect, but an invisible change occurs—a latent image is produced. Treatment of the material in a developer solution converts the exposed silver halide crystals into metallic silver, which forms a visible and usable image. After development, the emulsion still contains the sensitive silver halides which were not utilized in producing the image, and on exposure to light these undeveloped crystals would eventually darken and obscure the image. Therefore, in order to make the image permanent, the material is "fixed" in a solution which dissolves the undeveloped silver halides but does not appreciably affect the silver image. After fixing, the material must be washed thoroughly to remove the chemicals used in developing and fixing. The entire series of operations must follow rigidly controlled conditions in respect to time, temperature, and chemicals. Recommended developing times and temperatures are given in data sheets supplied by the manufacturer of the film. Many types of automatic processing machines, most of which produce a quality superior to random manual agitation, are in use in spectrographic work.

If one plots the density of a film, that is, the logarithm of the ratio of the intensity of a beam of light passing through a clear portion of the film to the intensity of the same beam after passing through an exposed portion of the film, as a function of the logarithm of the exposure, curves such as the one shown in Fig. 10-17 result. It will be noted that there is a region *B-C* over which the density is directly proportional to the logarithm of the intensity of exposure. This is the useful range of the film. The slope of this straight portion of the curve is known as the γ of the emulsion.

$$\gamma = \tan \theta \qquad (10\text{-}6)$$

High values of γ indicate a high degree of contrast, and low values of γ indicate low contrast.

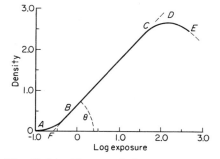

Fig. 10-17. Characteristic curve of a photographic emulsion: *A*, threshold exposure; *B-C*, linear portion of curve; *D-E*, reversal region; *F*, inertia of emulsion.

The density of a film can be measured by passing a beam of light through a clear portion of the film and measuring the intensity of the transmitted beam by a phototube. The beam is then passed through the blackened portion of the film and the intensity is recorded. The logarithm of the ratio of the intensity of light passing through the clear film and through the blackened film is computed. An example of a commercial densitometer is shown in Fig. 10-18, and a schematic of the optical system is shown in Fig. 10-19. Essential parts include a source of light (tungsten lamp), a slit to detect the desired portion of the emulsion, a holder for the photographic plate (or film), a phototube, and a circuit and meter (or recorder) for reading the photocurrent. A projection system provides visual inspection of a portion of the spectrum. A racking mechanism provides a means of moving the plate horizontally (scanning) and vertically (from one spectrum to another).

The shape of the characteristic curve of a photographic emulsion varies from emulsion to emulsion, with wavelength, and with the conditions of development. In order to determine the curve for any given emulsion, it is first necessary to standardize the conditions of development, that is, the time, the type of developer, the temperature, etc. A step-wedge transmitting known relative intensities of light through the various steps may be placed directly on the film and the film exposed through the wedge. After development the densities of the steps are measured and plotted against the known intensities. In order to calibrate at several wavelengths it is better to place the wedge in front of the slit of the spectrograph and expose with a metallic arc, such as a copper arc. Each line will then show a reproduction of the wedge.

Instead of a wedge or a series of filters with known transmittancies, a rotating step-sector disc or a log-sector disc (Fig. 10-20) may be placed just in front of the slit of a stigmatic spectrograph or at the second (horizontal) focus position of an astigmatic spectrograph. The different parts of the lines will show definite

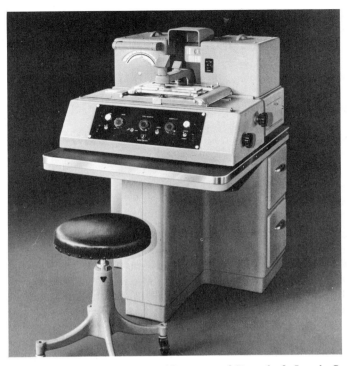

Fig. 10-18. Densitometer-comparator. (Courtesy of Bausch & Lomb Optical Co.)

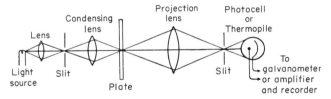

Fig. 10-19. Typical optical system of a microdensitometer.

graduated intensities depending upon the construction of the sector. Photographic emulsions, however, show what is known as an *intermittancy effect;* that is, several short exposures may not produce the same effect as one long exposure. In other words, the relationship

$$\text{Exposure} = Pt \qquad (10\text{-}7)$$

(where P = intensity, t = time of exposure) breaks down if intermittent exposures are employed. If the frequency is high, this effect may be negligible.

Therefore, sectors are run by high-speed motors. The particular emulsion employed should always be studied to discover its behavior in this respect.

A photographic emulsion is sensitive basically to radiation which is absorbed by the silver salts, that is, basically to blue, violet, and shorter-wavelength radiation. However, an emulsion can be sensitized optically by the addition of suitably chosen dyes that absorb radiation of longer wavelengths. By this means it is possible to extend the sensitivity through the green (orthochromatic film), through the green and red (panchromatic film), and into the infrared regions of the spectrum.

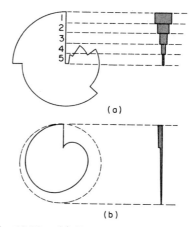
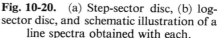

Fig. 10-20. (a) Step-sector disc, (b) log-sector disc, and schematic illustration of a line spectra obtained with each.

Qualitative Identification

The elements present in a sample can be determined by comparing the spectrum of the unknown with that of pure samples of the elements or by measuring the wavelengths of the lines and looking up the corresponding elements in tables. If only certain elements are being sought, the spectra of these elements may be taken on one film along with the spectrum of the unknown. It is then easy to compare lines in the known samples with lines in the unknown. It is usually considered sufficient proof that an element is present in an unknown if three or more sensitive lines of the element in question can be definitely identified in the spectrum of the unknown sample. Elements shown in Fig. 10-21 are readily detectable using a d-c arc as source of excitation. To detect the sensitive arc lines of carbon, phosphorus, and sulfur, air must be excluded from the optical path of the instrument either through use of a vacuum or displacement of air by helium.

R.U. Lines and R.U. Powder

Those lines of each element which are the last to disappear as the concentration of the element is gradually decreased are known as R.U. (*raies ultimes*) or persistent lines. These are the lines most useful in detecting small concentrations of impurities. The Johnson-Mathey Company, London, England, prepares a powder containing more than fifty elements in such concentrations that only the R.U. lines of most of the elements appear in the arc spectrum. A spectrogram of this powder taken on each spectrograph and with all lines identified is a useful aid in identification of elements.

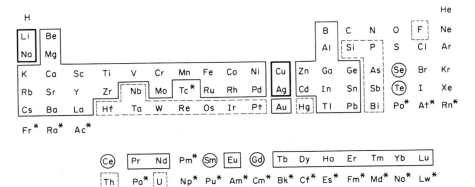

Fig. 10-21. Elements detectable using a d-c arc source. In the range of 2000–9000 Å elements detectable in the <1 ppm limit are enclosed in heavy solid lines; those in the 1–10 ppm limit are enclosed in solid lines; those in 10–100 ppm range enclosed in dashed lines; and those in the 100–1000 ppm range are circled. Elements identified with an asterisk occur only as radioactive isotopes.

Wavelength Measurement and Tables

The wavelength of unknown lines may be determined by linear interpolation between lines of known wavelengths if the dispersion of the instrument is "normal." For prismatic dispersion, the formula of Hartmann (Eq. 10-1) must be employed. Many instruments have wavelength scales which may be impressed on the film. Such scales are useful for rough identification of the wavelengths of lines.

For exact measurements of the distances of lines on a film, a magnifying glass with a built-in scale is useful. For distances greater than a few millimeters, a measuring microscope is useful.

There are many tables available which list the wavelengths of the spectral lines and the corresponding elements. Many of these tables are listed in the selected references at the end of this chapter. Once an element is definitely located by identification of three or more lines, the tables which list the lines under each element are useful in eliminating the remainder of the lines due to that element before proceeding with the identification of the second constituent, etc.

Quantitative Methods

Early workers in spectrography attempted rough estimations of the concentration of elements in various ways. Hartley[5] correlated the concentration of solutions with the number of lines appearing in the spark spectrum.

De Gramont[1] and later Meggers, Kiess, and Stimson[7] employed a series of standard electrodes with known concentrations of the substance to be determined. Spectra of the various standards and of the unknown are photographed alternately on the same plate and under the same conditions. The concentration of the desired constituent can then be estimated by comparing the blackening of the lines of this constituent with the same lines in the standards. Photometric or simple visual comparison of the blackening of the lines is possible. The accuracy depends on the number of standard samples available and on maintaining constant excitation and exposure conditions.

Internal Standards

In the above-mentioned methods—and in any procedure that depends on the measurement of the intensity of only the lines of the unknown element—the excitation conditions, the time and nature of the exposure, and the conditions of development must all be carefully controlled. In order to eliminate the effects of variations in these factors, the modern methods of spectrographic analysis measure the intensity of an unknown line relative to that of an internal standard line. The internal standard line may be a weak line of the main constituent, or it may be a strong line of some material added in a definite concentration to the sample. The ratio of the intensities of these lines—the analysis line and the internal standard line—will be unaffected by exposure conditions and development conditions. Gerlach and Schweitzer[3] were the first to propose this method of "internal standards."

Homologous Pairs

In order that variations in excitation conditions may not affect the relative intensities of the two lines, it is necessary that the two lines constitute what is known as a "homologous pair." Such pairs are lines that respond in the same way to changes in excitation conditions. Both lines should arise from the same type of excitation, that is, atoms or ions. Homologous pairs may be selected by experiment or be chosen on the basis of recommendations of others as recorded in the literature. Two lines which change intensities quite differently with variations in the conditions of excitation are called a "fixation pair" and such a pair of lines is sometimes observed as a check that the excitation conditions remained constant during each exposure.

Gerlach and Schweitzer prepared tables listing homologous pairs of lines which had equal blackening at given concentrations of the desired element. Such a table for the determination of cadmium in tin is shown in Table 10-1. This method suffers from the defect that only definite limited steps are available.

The most obvious and the best method of comparing the intensities of the unknown and the internal standard lines is to measure the density of the two lines on the film or plate by means of a densitometer. The intensity of the light striking the plate and creating the two lines is then calculated by means of the characteristic curve for the emulsion under the chosen conditions. Either the ratio of the intensities of the homologous pair of lines is plotted against concentration, or the log of the ratio is plotted against the log of the concentration.

Table 10-1	Homologous Pairs for Determination of Cadmium in Tin	

CADMIUM LINE, Å	TIN LINE, Å	EQUAL INTENSITY AT Cd CONCENTRATION, %
3404	3331	10
3404	3656	2
3404	3142	1.5
3404	3219	0.5
3466⎫ 3468⎭	3656	0.3
3611⎫ 3615⎭	3656	0.2
3404	3224	0.1
3466⎫ 3468⎭	3224	0.05
2288	2282	0.01

Either plot should result in a nearly straight line, since intensity of light is proportional to the concentration of the responsible atom or ion in the source. A less precise method would be to plot the ratio of the densities of the lines directly against the log of the concentration—assuming, of course, that one is working on the strictly straight-line portion of the characteristic curve of the emulsion.

Log and Step Sector Methods

There are other methods of comparing the relative intensities of two lines when a densitometer is not available. If a step-sector or a log-sector is run in front of the slit during the exposure, the resulting lines will have different lengths (Fig. 10-22). The strong lines will be long, since even at small exposure

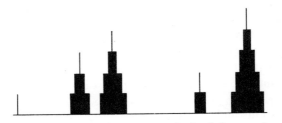

Fig. 10-22.   Schematic diagram of line-spectra obtained from a log-sector in front of the slit.

times sufficient light will reach the film to cause a visible blackening. On the other hand, the weak lines will be short, because a visible blackening of the film will result only where the sector allows radiation to pass onto the slit for a

long time. A measurement of the length of the lines indicates the intensity.
Thus, if C = concentration, D = density, P = intensity of characteristic line
in the source, and h = height of line image on the photographic plate, then

$$\log C \text{ is proportional to } \log P \text{ or } D \qquad\qquad (10\text{-}8)$$

and if the sector is logarithmic, that is,

$$h \text{ is proportional to } \log P \qquad\qquad (10\text{-}9)$$

then,

$$h \text{ is proportional to } \log C \qquad\qquad (10\text{-}10)$$

Actually, the difference in height of the internal standard and unknown lines
is plotted against the logarithm of the concentration. A nearly straight line
should result (Fig. 10-23). The main difficulty with this procedure is the
determination of the exact length of the lines. It is very difficult to judge just
when a line disappears.

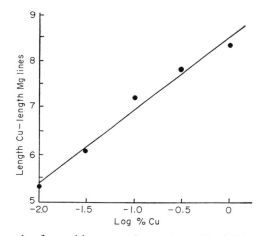

Fig. 10-23. Example of a working curve, log-sector method: Determination of copper
in an alumina-silica mixture; magnesium, 1%, added as internal standard. Lines
compared: Cu 3275 and Mg 2852.

The step-sector method and the photometric measurement of density method
can be combined for very precise work. If a step-sector is employed, the
densitometer can be used to measure the densities of the two lines at steps
where the two lines are of nearly equal blackening. The densitometer measurements are more precise when the densities are nearly equal. Since the ratios of
intensities of the various steps are accurately known, one can easily calculate
the original intensities of the lines.

In any case a series of several standard samples must be run to establish
points on the "*working curve.*" Once this working curve has been established,

similar unknown samples can be quickly analyzed. A new working curve must be established for each type of material. The presence of elements not originally present in the standards from which the working curve was established will usually affect the determination.

Direct Readers

Optical direct readers can be used whenever spectrographic methods are applicable. The essential difference between a spectrograph and a direct reader is that with the latter the photosensitive emulsion is eliminated (and thus the need for developing equipment, comparator densitometers, and calculating equipment) and replaced by multiplier phototubes and electronic circuitry. Basically, the receiver system is an arrangement of semifixed slits on the focal circle of the spectrometer with cylindrical mirrors to focus the light coming through the slits onto multiplier phototubes, as illustrated in Fig. 10-24. Although the photographic technique is inherently more versatile, the direct reading technique is faster and more precise.

Direct readers are usually custom built for a specific analytical requirement by carefully placing exit slits and multiplier phototubes to measure specific lines of elements of interest. Of course, physical size of the receiver system limits the number of individual lines which can be monitored. Instruments generally measure from eight to 24 elements in a single matrix. The receivers are often grouped into several bridges—one for each type of matrix—so that the instrument can be used to analyze several types of samples successively.

Photomultiplier readout is accomplished in several ways. In one method the photomultiplier outputs are integrated by charging individual capacitors during a fixed exposure period. Although the resulting voltages are a function of the concentrations of the elements in the sample, simple voltage measurement is not enough to obtain good precision of analysis. Rather the internal standard method is used, in which the voltage ratio of each of the unknown lines is measured relative to an internal standard line. The voltage ratio measurement is performed during the period immediately following the exposure period; the mechanism of turning off the spark at the end of the exposure and of beginning the measure period is entirely automatic. At the beginning of the measure period, the capacitors, which have been charged by the photomultipliers, are rearranged in the circuit and are connected through sensitive amplifier-trigger circuits to individual dial indicators (or digital readout tapes). In the measure period, the capacitors for unknown elements maintain their voltages and do not discharge; only the internal standard capacitor discharges through a fixed resistance. At the beginning of the measure period all the indicators start to run, but whenever the reference capacitor reaches the voltage of an element capacitor, the indicator associated with that capacitor stops. The time that any dial indicator will run can be expressed as

$$t = RC \ln (E_s/E_x) \qquad (10\text{-}11)$$

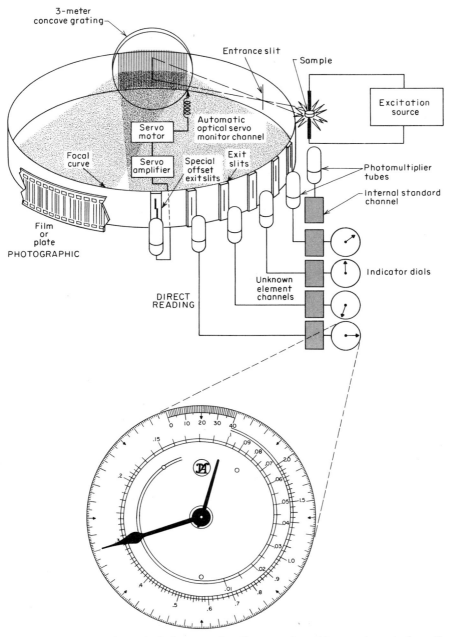

Fig. 10-24. Schematic optical diagram of a direct reader with an enlarged view of a dial-indicator. (Courtesy of Baird-Atomic, Inc.)

where R is the resistance through which the capacitor C is discharged, and E_s, E_x are the voltages to which the reference and unknown capacitors are charged. Thus the time scale can be replaced by a scale reading directly in percent concentration for a particular element.

To standardize the direct reader the operator places a standard sample in the electrode holder and pushes the start button. After the dial-indicator hands are stopped, the operator notes whether or not the dials indicate the known analysis of the standard. If any hand does not point to the correct scale reading, the operator rotates the scale so that it does so. Thus, any change in sensitivity causes a parallel displacement of the calibration curve but not a change in its slope (the constant RC in Eq. 10-11).

Other methods devised for presentation of results involve recording a fixed number of counts by the multiplier tube monitoring the internal standard line. At this point the excitation period is terminated. The ratio of counts accumulated in the phototubes receiving lines of individual elements to the fixed number in the reference tube is correlated with the known analysis of standards (by varying the sensitivity of individual counters).

Direct readers present the results of an analysis in a matter of 1–2 min. About 30 min is usually required for a quantitative analysis of about five elements by spectrographic procedures. Direct readers with the optical system sealed in pipe are available for production floor installation.

Visual Spectroscope

The Fisher Duo-Spectranal is an inexpensive spectroscope that provides a quick, easy way to make qualitative and semiquantitative analyses for elements whose emission lines lie in the visible portion of the spectrum. The sample is usually dissolved in dilute nitric acid with a small amount of potassium nitrate added. Two platinum electrodes are immersed in about 2 ml of the acid solution: one, the excitation electrode, is submerged to a depth of no more than 2 mm; the other, more deeply. When 115-V alternating current is passed between the electrodes, a sparklike discharge appears on the surface of the shorter electrode. This discharge consists of a rapid series (60/sec) of microscopic hydrogen-oxygen explosions, taking place in the film of mixed gases produced by electrolysis at the surface of the excitation electrode. Thus, essentially an electrically generated oxygen-hydrogen flame is the excitation source.

The instrument employs a plane reflection grating (55 Å/mm) and a stigmatic optical system brings the spectra of two sources to a focus, side by side, in the field of a five-power Ramsden-type eyepiece. The field of view covers about 700 Å; by tilting the grating, the operator can sweep spectra and eyepiece scale through the field of view. An optical schematic and typical view through the eyepiece is shown in Fig. 10-25).

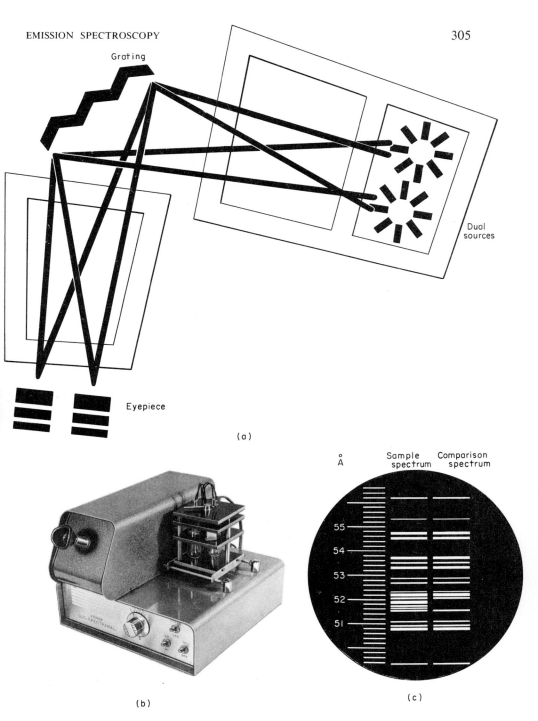

Fig. 10-25. The Fisher Duo-Spectranal, showing (a) the schematic optical diagram, (b) the instrument and electrode jig, and (c) a view through the eyepiece. (Courtesy of Fisher Scientific Co.)

LABORATORY WORK

It would be foolhardy to attempt to teach a student all the intricacies of spectrographic methods in a few laboratory periods. However, individual instructors, endowed with specific pieces of equipment, may wish to devise specific experiments.

As a starter, one should purchase and study the latest edition of A.S.T.M.'s "Methods for Emission Spectrochemical Analysis," American Society for Testing Materials, Philadelphia, Pa., 1964. A useful spectrochemical primer has been published in The Spex Speaker, **9** (No. 2) (June, 1964), a house organ of Spex Industries, authored by R. F. O'Connell and A. J. Mitteldorf.

Problems

1. Calculate the wavelength of the unknown line from the following data taken from a spectrogram recorded on a prism spectrograph: Distances, in millimeters, from reference point to lines of wavelength 3247.54, 3262.33, and 3273.96 Å, were respectively 0.50, 6.42, and 11.00 mm. The distance from the reference point to the unknown line was 8.51 mm.

2. What is the theoretical resolving power of a spectrograph equipped with a 2.5-in. grating of 15,000 lines/in. when used in the first order? Theoretically, what order would have to be employed to resolve the iron doublet at 3099.90 and 3099.97 Å?

3. A sample of an unknown light-metal alloy was placed on a spark stand and a spectrum was recorded. Observation of the spectrogram revealed lines at the following wavelengths : 6438, 5184, 5173, 4810, 4722, 4680, 3838, 3832, 3829, 3611, 3466 and 3403 Å, plus many lines of aluminum. What elements, besides aluminum, are present?

4. In the spectrographic determination of lead in an alloy, using a magnesium line as internal standard, these results were obtained:

SOLUTION	DENSITOMETER READING		CONCENTRATION OF LEAD, mg/ml
	Mg	Pb	
1	7.3	17.5	0.151
2	8.7	18.5	0.201
3	7.3	11.0	0.301
4	10.3	12.0	0.402
5	11.6	10.4	0.502
A	8.8	15.5	
B	9.2	12.5	
C	10.7	12.2	

(a) Prepare a calibration curve on log-log paper. (b) Evaluate the concentrations for solutions A, B, and C. *Ans.* Solution B contains 0.335 mg/ml.

5. A step-sector with arc lengths (or angle subtended by each step at the center) in the ratio of 1 : 2 : 4 : 8 : 16 : 32 was rotated in front of the slit of a spectro-

graph while a sample of a tin alloy containing lead was being arced in the source unit. After the plate was developed, fixed, and dried, the density of a suitable tin line was measured at each step with a microphotometer.

The values of I_0/I obtained for each step were 1.05, 1.66, 4.68, 13.18, 37.15, and 52.5. Plot the characteristic curve for the film and determine the γ and the inertia of the emulsion.

6. Several standard samples of the tin alloy mentioned in Problem 5 were prepared by chemical analysis for the lead content. These alloys were then employed as electrodes as in Problem 5. The ratio of the density of the tin line at 2761 Å and the density of the lead line at 2833 Å were measured on the microphotometer. The results are listed below:

SAMPLE NO.	% LEAD	$D_{\text{tin line}}$	$D_{\text{lead line}}$
1	0.126	1.567	0.259
2	0.316	1.571	1.013
3	0.708	1.443	1.546
4	1.334	0.825	1.427
5	2.512	0.447	1.580

Using the results of Problem 5 above, plot a "working curve" of log percent Pb as abscissa and log $(I_{\text{Pb}}/I_{\text{Sn}})$ as ordinate. An unknown tin alloy sample was treated in the same way as the standards. The 2761-Å tin line had a density of 0.920 on the photographic plate, while the 2833-Å lead line had a density of 0.669. What was the percentage of lead in the alloy?

Bibliography

Ahrens, L. H., and S. R. Taylor, *Spectrochemical Analysis*, 2nd ed., Addison-Wesley, Reading, Mass., 1961.

ASTM, "Methods for Emission Spectrochemical Analysis," American Society for Testing Materials, Philadelphia, Pa., 1964.

Brode, W. R., *Chemical Spectroscopy*, 2nd ed. Wiley, New York, 1943.

Gerlach, W., and E. Schweitzer, *Foundations and Method of Chemical Analysis by the Emission Spectrum.* (Authorized translation of *Die chemische Emissionspektralanalyse*, Vol. I, L. Voss, Leipzig, 1929.) Adam Hilger, Ltd., London.

Gibb, T. R. P., *Optical Methods of Chemical Analysis*, McGraw-Hill, New York, 1942, pp. 1-69.

Harrison, G. R., R. C. Lord, and J. R. Loofbourow, *Practical Spectroscopy*, Prentice-Hall, Englewood Cliffs, N. J., 1948.

Meggers, W. F., C. H. Corliss, and B. F. Scribner, "Tables of Spectral-line Intensities," Parts I and II, *Nat. Bur. Std.* (*U.S.*), *Monograph 32*, 1961, 1962.

Nachtrieb, N. H., *Principles and Practice of Spectrochemical Analysis*, McGraw-Hill, New York, 1950.

Sawyer, R. A., *Experimental Spectroscopy*, 2nd ed., Prentice-Hall, Englewood Cliffs, N.J., 1946.

Twyman, F., *Metal Spectroscopy*, C. Griffin, London, 1951.

Literature Cited

1. De Gramont, A., *Compt. rend.*, **159,** 6 (1917); **171,** 1106 (1920).
2. Feussner, O., *Arch. Eisenhuttenw.*, **6,** 551 (1921).
3. Gerlach, W., and K. Schweitzer, *Foundations and Methods of Chemical Analysis by the Emission Spectrum*, Adam Hilger, Ltd., London, 1929.
4. Gibb, T. R. P., *Optical Methods of Chemical Analysis*, McGraw-Hill, New York, 1942, p. 10.
5. Hartley, W. N., *Phil. Trans. London*, **175,** 326 (1884).
6. Hartmann, J., *Astrophys. J.*, **3,** 218 (1898).
7. Meggers, W. F., C. C. Kiess, and F. S. Stimson, *Nat. Bur. Std. (U.S.), Sci. Papers* 444 (1922).

CHAPTER | 11

Flame Photometry

Probably everyone at some time has observed the characteristic yellow light emitted when a small quantity of sodium salts is introduced into a flame. Emission of such characteristic radiation by each element and the correlation of the emission intensity with the concentration of that element form the basis of flame photometry.

The sample to be analyzed is prepared in solution and sprayed under controlled conditions into a flame. The radiation from the flame enters a dispersing device to isolate the desired region of the spectrum. A phototube and some type of meter or electronic amplifier measure the intensity of the isolated radiation. After carefully calibrating the photometer with solutions of known composition and concentration, one can readily correlate the intensity of a given spectral line of the unknown with the amount of an element present that emits the particular radiation. The use of a solution spray permits the distribution of the sample throughout the body of the flame, and the entire sample or a representative portion is introduced into the flame. Many of the difficulties encountered with arc or spark sources are thus avoided.

The Flame Photometer

The flame photometer consists essentially of six parts: (1) the pressure regulators and flow meters for the fuel gases, (2) the atomizer, (3) the burner, (4) the optical system, (5) the photosensitive detector, and (6) the instrument for indicating or recording the output of the detector. The components are

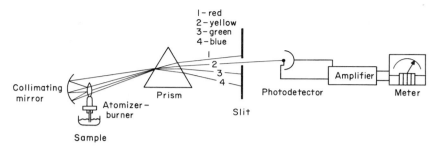

Fig. 11-1. Schematic diagram of a flame photometer.

schematically shown in Fig. 11-1. In the following sections each of these parts is discussed in some detail.

Pressure Regulators and Flow Meters

Suitable gauges must be provided to indicate the pressures and flow rates actually prevailing when the instrument is in operation, so that proper adjustments may be made each time the photometer is used. A 10-lb gauge for the fuel and a 25-lb gauge for the oxygen or air supply are generally satisfactory. Double diaphragm valves are recommended, and they should be followed by some additional control such as a needle valve.

Although gas pressures can be adjusted to the same gauge reading each time the instrument is placed in service, sometimes there is a change in the quantity of gas, particularly oxygen (or air), flowing to the burner, because of a clogging of the orifice. In addition, a capillary flow rate meter or rotameter should be inserted in the line from the tank gas to the burner. A knowledge of the individual flow rates of the fuel and oxygen enables the operator to choose various fuel-oxygen mixtures ranging from lean flame mixtures through stoichiometric mixtures and even to fuel-rich types of flames. Flow rates vary between 2 and 10 ft³/hr.

Atomizers

The most exacting problem in flame photometer design is presented by the atomizer. This deceptively simple little device must introduce the liquid sample into the flame at a stable and reproducible rate. It must remain unattacked by corrosive solutions and must be rugged and easily cleaned. Atomizers can be classified as (1) those which introduce the spray into a condensing chamber for removing large droplets and (2) those which introduce the spray directly into the flame.

The first type is made with two capillary tubes sealed into the walls of the atomizer chamber in such a way that their bores are perpendicular to each other as shown in Fig. 11-2. The sample is poured into the funnel, or drawn up from a container, and the blast of air from the tip of the other capillary atomizes the solution as a coarse spray against the side of the chamber. The larger droplets condense on the walls of the chamber and helical tube

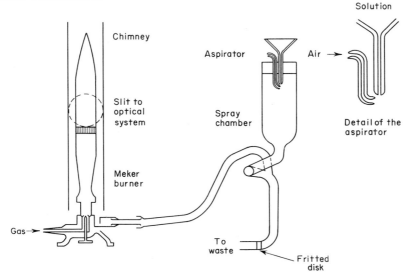

Fig. 11-2. Discharge type of atomizer (with condensing chamber) and burner.

leading to the burner. The condensate flows off to the waste drain. The smaller droplets, constituting a virtual fog, are carried by the air stream into the burner, where they are thoroughly mixed with the normal burner gases and carried into the region of active combustion. Two removable hypodermic needles constructed of stainless steel or glass are commonly used. This type of atomizer consumes between 4 and 25 ml of sample per minute. Of this amount, less than 5 percent actually reaches the flame. Most of the less expensive instruments incorporate this style of atomizer.

A second type of atomizer is constructed of two concentric tubes, shown as the two inner tubes of Fig. 11-3. The sample is introduced through the innermost, a vertical palladium capillary. A concentric channel provides oxygen, and its tip is constricted to form an orifice. The passage of oxygen from this orifice causes the solution to be drawn up to the tip of the inner capillary. There the liquid is sheared off and dispersed into droplets. Usually the atomizer and burner are an integral unit, and an outer annulus supplies the combustible gas to the flame. All the droplets, large and small, are introduced directly into the flame. A

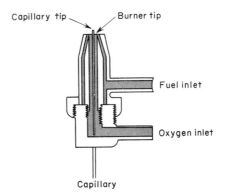

Fig. 11-3. Integral-aspirator burner. (Courtesy of Beckman Instruments, Inc.)

slurry of powdered material in isopropanol-glycerine solvent can be sprayed directly into a flame if a wide-bore capillary is used.[10]

Each atomizer, regardless of type, requires separate calibration and is not strictly interchangeable with another of the same type.

The Burner

The main requirement of the burner is that when supplied with fuel and oxygen or air at constant pressures it should produce a steady flame. For low-temperature flames the Meker burner is commonly employed. The fuel gas issues from a small orifice and passes through a venturi throat where considerable air is entrained. The mixture of gas and entrained air passes up the burner tube and burns at the top of the burner, the combustion being assisted by the surrounding air. A deep grid of metal across the mouth of the burner prevents the flame from striking back down the tube. A chimney often surrounds the flame to protect it from air drafts and to safeguard the operator (Fig. 11-2).

The combination of burner and aspirator introduces the sample solution directly into the flame. A concentric channel provides oxygen to operate the atomizer and the flame. An additional concentric channel provides the fuel for the flame. This type of burner is shown in a cutaway drawing in Fig. 11-3.

The Optical System

The function of the optical system is to collect the light from the steadiest part of the flame, render it monochromatic, and then focus it onto the surface of the photosensitive detector. A concave mirror is frequently placed behind the flame, with its center of curvature in the flame. In this way the intensity of the emitted light is nearly doubled. It is important to focus the mirrors and lenses so that the light is distributed over the entire surface of the detector.

Less expensive flame photometers use an absorption or interference filter to isolate the radiation characteristic of a given element. These instruments are limited in application to those samples and to those elements which, upon excitation by a flame, provide a simple spectrum. The usual absorption filters transmit a rather wide spectral band (see Chapter 3). They are incapable of absorbing radiation arising from lines of elements that lie in close proximity to the analytical line. Interference filters improve the resolution. Nevertheless, with filters it is difficult to eliminate interfering radiation completely, to obtain the degree of resolution required for complex systems, and to measure background radiation adjacent to an analytical line.

Better isolation of spectral energy can be obtained by the use of instruments which incorporate a monochromator. By using sensitive detecting circuits and narrow slit widths, quite narrow bands of radiant energy can be isolated. Dispersing media can be a quartz prism or a diffraction-grating replica. The combination of adjustable slit of good optical quality, adequate gain control in the amplifier of the detecting circuit, and a wavelength drum enables an operator to select the most favorable ratio between background and analytical line radiation and to isolate more effectively the radiation due to the test element. Flame spectrometers expand the field of application of flame methods to approximately 70 elements. Large dispersion and high resolving power in monochromators will stress the importance of spectra with discrete lines, whereas continua and bands show up more clearly with instruments of small dispersion. A test of an instrument's resolving power concerns the separation of the manganese line at 403.3 mμ, the potassium line at 404.4 mμ, and the lead line at 405.8 mμ from each other. Quartz optics enable many atomic lines to be used that occur in the far ultraviolet portion of the spectrum—for example, lines from magnesium at 285.2 mμ, copper at 324.7 and 327.4 mμ, and silver at 328.0 and 338.3 mμ, to enumerate only a few. Naturally the cost is considerably higher for instruments of this type.

Photosensitive Detectors

In the flame photometer any photosensitive device may be used as a detector of the radiant energy provided that it has a response in the part of the spectrum to be used and has a sensitivity high enough for the particular task at hand. A barrier-layer cell is the simplest and requires little additional equipment, but its response is difficult to amplify. Consequently, its use is restricted to systems emitting a large amount of radiant energy and to instruments with an optical system that permits a wide band of radiant energy to strike the detector. Filter flame photometers often use barrier-layer cells as detectors. However, the barrier-layer cell has a high temperature coefficient. It must be placed at a cool part of the photometer and sufficient time must be allowed for the body of the instrument to reach ambient temperature before readings are taken.

Flame photometers that restrict the bandwidth of the radiant energy reaching the detectors employ phototubes and amplifier units to boost the output signal. In this respect, the electron multiplier phototube provides the maximum signal and permits applying flame photometry to systems that are weak in emission, either because of a small concentration of test element or because of difficulty in exciting any appreciable fraction of the test element under the excitation conditions existing in the flame. The RCA 1P28 or EM-1 tube is used over the range 200–700 (or 800) mμ and enjoys a high quantum efficiency and low dark current. For longer wavelengths, no completely satisfactory photomultiplier tube is currently available. Excessive dark current is a problem.

Commercial Flame Photometers

It was not until the classic studies by Lundegårdh,[11] that the attention and interest of chemists were drawn to the advantages of flame excitation for quantitative analysis. His procedure involved using photographic plates to record the spectra, followed by some method of measurement of the blackening of the selected lines on the photograph. The use of a photocell for detection of radiant energy was first incorporated in 1935 in several German instruments. Real impetus was given to flame photometry in the United States with the advent of the work of Barnes and co-workers.[2] In 1948, Beckman Instruments, Inc., made available a flame attachment for their well-known quartz spectrophotometer; subsequent versions incorporated an integral aspirator-burner and photomultiplier tube, with recording accessories optional. The photomultiplier tube provided the sensitivity and, consequently, the selectivity needed in direct-reading flame spectrometry.

Modern flame photometers or flame spectrometers are essentially of two basic designs which can be designated as either single- or double-beam arrangement. Table 11-1 contains a partial listing of current instruments.

Table 11-1 | *Commercial Flame Photometers*

CLASSIFICATION	NAME
Direct-reading, absorption filters, barrier-layer cell	Coleman† Evans Electroselenium Ltd. (EEL) Lange models 2 and 3 Schuhknecht
Internal-standard, interference filters, barrier-layer cells	Analytical Instruments‡ Baird, model KY-2§ Electro-synthese Janke¶ Lange model 4 Norelco Patwin (Barclay)¶
Prism monochromator, direct-reading or recording, photomultiplier tube	Beckman model B (DB)# Beckman model DU Unicam SP.900 Hilger UVspek
Grating monochromator, recording, photomultiplier tube	Jarrell-Ash Ebert 0.5 meter Hitachi Perkin-Elmer model 139

†Phototube used.
‡CdS photocells used.
§Photomultiplier tube used.
¶Absorption glass filters used.
#Glass prism.

Single-Beam Instruments

A single-beam instrument contains only one set of optics. Light emitted from the center of the flame just above the inner cone(s) is collected by a reflector and focused by a lens of heat-resistant glass through interchangeable optical filters onto a single photodetector, or light from the burner passes into a monochromator and radiation leaving the exit slit is focused onto the detector. The photocurrent produced by the radiant energy of a test solution is compared directly with a predetermined calibration curve of intensity vs element concentration.

For barrier-layer cells a light-spot galvanometer which possesses a maximum sensitivity ranging from 0.007 to 0.0004 μa/mm scale division, a coil resistance of approximately 400 Ω, and a period of 3–4 sec is a suitable measuring device for the output photocurrent. Direct-reading flame photometers, which use barrier-layer photocells as photodetectors, are designed similar to the one in Fig. 11-4. The photoelectric current produced by the light signal divides at B,

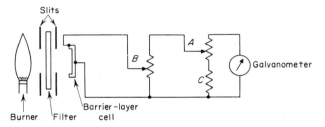

Fig. 11-4. Typical circuit diagram for direct-reading flame photometer employing a barrier-layer cell. Although actual value of the components depends on the characteristics of the galvanometer, one set is $B = C = 5A = 20,000\ \Omega$. Galvanometer, 0.00065 μa/mm. Adapted from J. W. Berry, D. G. Chappell, and R. B. Barnes, *Ind. Eng. Chem., Anal. Ed.*, **18**, 19 (1946). (Courtesy of *Analytical Chemistry*.)

part flowing through the galvanometer. In Fig. 11-4, B is the coarse sensitivity control and A is the fine sensitivity control. Their settings are chosen to produce a desirable galvanometer reading when the strongest standard solution is sprayed into the flame. If desired, a zero suppressor circuit (Fig. 11-5) could be incorporated. The barrier-layer cell exhibits no "dark current"

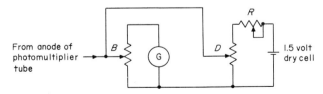

Fig. 11-5. Zero suppressor circuit. B, sensitivity control; D, zero suppressor control; $B = D$; $R = 10D$.

which would require suppression, but a suppressor circuit might be useful in bucking out a reading resulting from the flame background.

The output of a multiplier phototube for some solutions and higher ranges of concentration permits use of a light-spot galvanometer in circuits similar to that in Fig. 11-4. In many practical applications, however, the phototube currents are so small that one or more stages of amplification must be used.

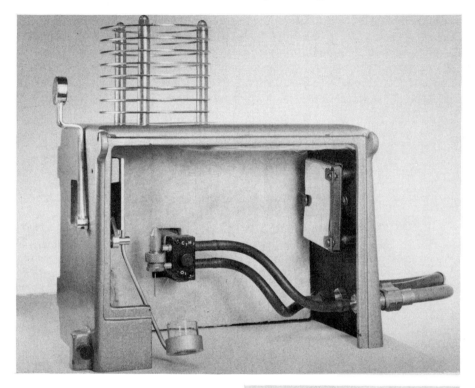

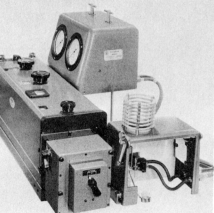

Fig. 11-6. Beckman model DU flame spectrometer, with closeup of burner housing. (Courtesy of Beckman Instruments, Inc.)

Since vacuum-tube amplifiers are voltage-operated devices, the changes of phototube current must be converted into voltage changes by means of a resistance in series with the phototube. The circuit of the Beckman model DU spectrometer, a potentiometric null-point system, is shown in Fig. 11-6. For ordinary phototubes, the photoelectric current flows through a 10,000 MΩ resistance, the grid resistance. With photomultiplier tubes the potential developed by cascade emission from the last dynode and the coupling resistance is applied to the control grid of the first amplifier tube. The response of the photomultiplier tube is fully linear with a 22–110 MΩ coupling resistor. A separate zero-adjustment circuit, called the "dark current" control, enables the operator to balance out any incoming signal which might result from the background-noise level in the phototube, the steady component of plate current in the amplifier tubes, or the background reading of the flame. The range of the dark-current control can be enlarged by the addition of an auxiliary zero suppression circuit (Fig. 11-5).

A long time constant (approximately 1 sec) is incorporated in the measuring circuit to render the meter or recorder unresponsive to sudden flashes of light in the flame. For recording purposes, the wavelength dial on the mono-chromator is replaced by a drive mechanism synchronized with the chart drive of a pen-recording potentiometer (full-scale response, 1 sec). In a-c measuring systems, radiation leaving the exit slit of the monochromator is chopped with a rotating disk and amplified by an a-c amplifier, which is stabler than its d-c counterpart.

Double-Beam Instruments

In double-beam instruments a second light path is provided for the light emitted by the internal standard element that is added in a fixed amount to each test solution and calibration standard. The internal standard and analytical wavelengths are isolated by means of optical filters in a dual optical system, and each beam is focused on a separate photoelectric cell. The signal of one detector opposes that of the other through a galvanometer (Fig. 11-7).

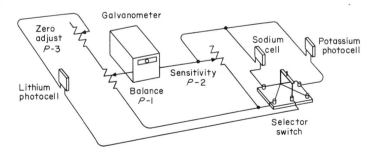

Fig. 11-7. Circuit diagram for double-beam flame photometer. *P*-1 is a precision 10,000-Ω potentiometer; *P*-2 is a 10,000-Ω potentiometer; *P*-3 is a 500-Ω potenti-ometer. Barrier-layer cells.

By means of an accurate, linearly wound potentiometer (P-1) in this circuit the opposing photoelectric currents can be balanced. The readings of the potentiometer required to produce balance are calibrated in terms of known solutions. The calibration curves so obtained are used for measurement of the unknown. Sensitivity adjustments are made with P-2 by shunting current generated by the measuring cell; this makes it possible to read more concentrated solutions of the test element without changing the concentration of the internal-standard used. A small resistor P-3, in series with P-1 across the internal-standard cell, facilitates bringing the reading for the zero standard solution near zero on the balance dial (P-1). These last two controls may not always be found on commercial instruments but are useful accessories.

Light usually leaves the flame through two apertures on different sides of the flame and thence through the respective optical paths. Alternate circuit arrangements are suggested by those used for absorption photometers (q.v.).

On multichannel instruments, a number of exit slits at the focal plane of a monochromator are used to isolate several wavelengths and to present the radiant energy to individual measuring circuits for simultaneous readout. One circuit is commonly reserved for the internal standard element.

Theoretical Principles

Flames and Flame Temperatures

A flame is used (1) for transforming the sample to be analyzed from the liquid or solid state into the gaseous state, (2) for decomposing the molecular compounds of the investigated element into simpler molecules or atoms, and (3) for exciting the latter particles to light emission. The function of light excitation is not a requisite of flames in absorption flame photometry.

In flame photometry many different combustible gases have been utilized. These have been ably reviewed by Mavrodineanu.[12] The two main requirements of a satisfactory flame are that it has the proper temperature (or chemi-excitation conditions) to carry out the enumerated functions of the flame and that the spectrum of the flame itself does not interfere with observation of the light emission being measured.

The diagrammatic structure of a flame is shown in Fig. 11-8. Emerging from region A, the unburned gas mix-

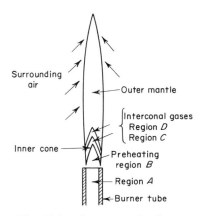

Fig. 11-8.   Structure of a flame.

ture passes into a region of free heating about 1 mm in thickness (zone B), in which it is heated by conduction and radiation from reaction zone C and by diffusion of radicals into it, which initiate the oxidation. Gases emerging from zone C consist mainly of CO, H_2, CO_2, and H_2O (and N_2, if air is one of the original gases), with lesser amounts of the species H, O, and OH. The actual composition of the gases varies with the initial mixture composition. In general, they are not in thermal equilibrium, the amounts of the radicals being too high (the precursors of chemi-luminescent reactions). Thermal equilibrium will be almost completely reached in zone D. When speaking of a flame, we have in mind generally the burned gas mixture—the outer mantle or plume. However, the reaction zone of hydrocarbon flames provides a rich source of emission lines. A detailed study of the structure and characteristics of flames can be found in the book by Gaydon and Wolfhard.[8]

The energy liberated in a flame is best represented by the adiabatic flame temperature, values of which are listed in Table 11-2 for various fuels burning

Table 11-2   *Maximum Flame Temperatures with Various Mixtures of Fuels*

	FLAME TEMPERATURE, °C	
FUEL	IN AIR	IN OXYGEN
Illuminating gas	1700	2700
Propane	1925	2800
Butane	1900	2900
Hydrogen	2100	2780
Acetylene	2200	3050
Cyanogen	2330	4550

in air and in oxygen. An ordinary air-gas flame, because of its relatively low temperature (about 1700°C), is only energetic enough to excite about a dozen elements, chiefly the alkali and alkaline earth metals. Mixtures of hydrogen or acetylene with oxygen produce much hotter flames and correspondingly greater excitation. Compared with an arc or spark source, flames excite fewer lines of each element—one of the advantages of flame photometry. It is also less difficult to establish reproducible conditions of excitation in flames and, therefore, to obtain accurate quantitative evaluation.

Emission Spectra

When an aerosol is uniformly delivered into a flame, the following sequence of events occurs in rapid succession.

1. The water, or other solvent, is vaporized, leaving minute particles of dry salt.

2. At the high temperature of the flame, the dry salt is vaporized, and part or all of the gaseous molecules are progressively dissociated to give neutral atoms, which are the potentially emitting species.

3. Some of the free metal atoms unite with other radicals or atoms present in the flame gases, or they are introduced into the flame concomitantly with the test element.

4. The vapors of the neutral metal atoms, or of molecules containing the metal atom, are then excited by the thermal energy of the flame, or by chemi-excitation mechanism. Ionization and excitation of the neutral atoms may occur to some degree.

5. From the excited levels of the atom, or molecule, or ion, a reversion takes place to the ground electronic state—partly by impacts with other species, partly spontaneously by emission of light.

The processes occurring after the formation of gaseous salt molecules can be formulated as follows, taking as our example calcium chloride:

$$\begin{array}{c} \text{-----} + \text{OH (from flame gases)} \rightleftarrows \text{CaOH} \\ \text{-----} + \text{O (from flame gases)} \rightleftarrows \text{CaO} \end{array}$$

Gaseous molecules $\rightleftarrows$ neutral atoms $\rightleftarrows$ ionized atoms
$CaCl_2$ $\qquad\qquad$ $Ca^0 + Cl^0$ $\qquad$ $Ca^+ + e^-$

Subsequently, the neutral atoms and ionized atoms of calcium, and the molecules of CaOH and CaO will be excited and their characteristic spectra will appear in emission. It should be obvious that the equilibrium quantities are a function of many variables such as flame temperature, gas-phase components, free-electron concentration, and other anionic species in addition to OH radicals and oxygen atoms.

Spectra of the elements fall into two classes—those consisting of lines originating from excited atoms or ions, and band spectra resulting from molecules. In many instances a third general type of spectra, continuous radiation, is observed.

The process of excitation results in the raising of an electron to a higher energy level and is followed by the loss of a discrete amount of energy in the form of radiant energy as the electron falls back into its original position or a lower energy level. In neutral-atom spectra, the emission of radiation occurs as discrete lines when an excited electron from the upper energy levels of the neutral atom falls back into a lower energy level or the ground state of the atom. The relation between the frequency ν of the radiation emitted to the energies E_1 and E_2 of the two states of the atom is given by the expression: $E_1 - E_2 = h\nu$. The emission does not necessarily occur as radiation of a single wavelength. The electron may pass back in one step or in a series of steps corresponding to intermediate orbitals, the return to the ground state being accompanied by the emission of several spectral lines.

Energy-level diagrams can be constructed for all atoms. The student is referred to the texts by Grotrian[9] or Mavrodineanu and Boiteux[13] for a fairly complete set of diagrams. As an illustration, the partial energy-level diagrams for lithium, sodium, potassium, and calcium are given in Fig. 11-9. The most

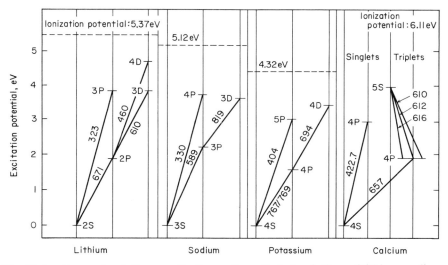

Fig. 11-9. Energy-level diagrams for the easily excited atomic lines of lithium, sodium, potassium, and calcium. Wavelengths are given in millimicrons for the spectral lines produced by transitions between the different levels. The ionization potential is indicated by the dashed line above the respective diagrams.

prominent line in each case is the line resulting from the transition between the lowest excited level and the ground state. These transitions give rise to the red lithium line at 671 mμ, the unresolved yellow sodium doublet at 590 mμ, the red potassium doublet at 767/769 mμ, and the blue calcium singlet at 422.7 mμ. Next in intensity are the lines ending in the same ground state but originating in the level immediately above the preceding lines. Far less intense are the lines arising from the transitions involving an excited state and a still higher excited state. Nevertheless, lines originating from these transitions are important when high concentrations of the elements are present in the flame. Interferences can often be traced to these lines. By controlling the flame temperature, the number of elements excited and the type of energy-level transitions may be regulated. In an illuminating gas-air flame only the transitions involving the lowest excited state and the ground state will be observed.

In a flame most of the lines emitted are from the neutral atom, but for the alkaline earth metals, emission lines arising from singly ionized atoms are also observed, particularly in high-temperature flames. The spectrum of the ion is completely different from the spectrum of the neutral atom and resembles the spectrum emitted by the element of preceding atomic number. However, because of the additional positive charge on the nucleus, the zero energy level is higher than for the element of preceding atomic number, and consequently the emission lines are displaced toward the ultraviolet. Typical ionic lines are those found at 455.5 and 493.4 mμ in the spectrum of barium, at 407.8 and 421.6 mμ in the spectrum of strontium, and at 393.3 and 396.8 mμ in the spectrum of calcium. Of course, the alkali metals ionize also, which is a source of difficulty in their determination.

Band spectra arise from electronic transitions involving molecules. Molecules possess energy of internal vibration (and rotation) as well as electronic excitation levels and, for each electronic transition, there will be a whole suite of vibrational levels involved. This causes the emitted radiation to be spread over a portion of the spectrum rather than being concentrated in a discrete line. The position of the band spectra may be centered about the wavelength associated with the electronic transition, but more often the vibrational contribution leads to asymmetrical bands with sharp edges or heads on one side and degraded on the other side. Only the envelope is observed with the dispersion obtainable with the optics of the Beckman model DU, whereas the Jarrell-Ash 0.5 meter Ebert monochromator resolves the individual lines, but so weak are their individual intensities that they are useless for analyses. Band systems of triatomic hydroxides are often observed: CaOH, SrOH, BaOH, MnOH, etc.; along with band systems from monoxides of the rare earths, LaO, CaO, etc. Band systems often are due to molecules that have no independent existence outside the flame. The background radiation of the flame itself arises from the excited molecular emitters—OH, CO, O_2, CH, C_2, and H_2O. Figure 11-10 shows the emission spectrum of aluminum, including the molecular band systems.

Flame Background

No characteristic spectrum can be associated with the flame of a given fuel. The spectrum is very dependent on flame conditions, principally the fuel-oxygen ratio and the temperature. The hydrogen flame gives the best combination of metal-to-background signal. Prominent OH band structures occur between 280 and 295, 306 and 320, and 340 and 348 mμ. Between 800 and 1250 mμ there is a broad emission resulting from the pure rotation-vibration spectrum of water, one of the products of combustion. Hydrogen flames do not show any obvious signs of an inner cone.

The acetylene flame shows, like the outer cones of most organic flames, principally the OH band spectrum and the continuum of dissociating CO molecules. Superimposed on this background may be seen the faint bands of the CH radical at 431.5 and 438.4 mμ, and several heads of diatomic carbon C_2 in the green (see background in Fig. 11-10). With rich mixtures the acetylene-oxygen flame shows a luminous mantle surrounding the inner cone which

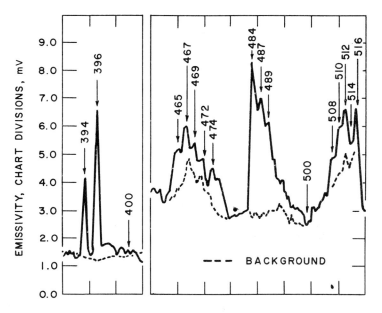

WAVE LENGTH, mμ

Fig. 11-10. Flame emission spectrum of aluminum. Present, 25 μg aluminum per ml in methyl isobutyl ketone. Spectral (effective) bandwidth is 0.3 mμ at atomic lines and 0.5 mμ at band systems. After H. C. Eshelman, J. A. Dean, O. Menis, and T. C. Rains, *Anal. Chem.*, **31**, 183 (1959). (Courtesy of *Analytical Chemistry*.)

may be a few millimeters in thickness. The CH, C_2, and other hydrocarbon flame bands are very strong in the spectrum of the reaction zone. In the far ultraviolet region of the spectrum, the reaction zone exhibits the atomic emission line of carbon at 247.8 mμ and a continuous background due to the incandescent carbon particles, on which is superimposed the molecular band system of CO. Figure 11-11 shows typical flame background spectra.

Intensities of Atomic Spectral Lines

The measured intensity of a given spectrum line is determined in general by the following factors:[1]

1. The fraction of introduced salt that is evaporated.
2. The fraction of salt molecules that are dissociated.
3. The fraction of the atoms formed by dissociation that are not ionized.
4. The fraction of the nonionized atoms that are excited.
5. The probability of a transition from the excited state to a lower state.
6. The energy of the light quantum.
7. The self-absorption factor that accounts for the fraction of emitted energy that is lost by self-absorption.

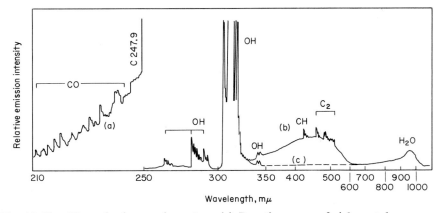

Fig. 11-11. Flame background spectra. (a) Reaction zone of rich acetylene-oxygen flame. (b) An acetylene-oxygen flame containing an organic aerosol. (c) A hydrogen-oxygen flame containing an aqueous aerosol.

The evaporation factor and the self-absorption factor will be discussed in subsequent sections.

When dissociation is rather complete and ionization not yet important, the variation of emission power with temperature is mainly controlled by the excitation, or Boltzmann, factor $e^{-E_j/kT}$, which depends exponentially on temperature T (with k = Boltzmann constant, and E_j = excitation energy of excited state). For a given emission line, the occupational number of an excited energy level, N_j, is related to the number in the ground state (essentially proportional to the number introduced into the flame gases), N_0, by the relation

$$N_j = N_0 \frac{g_j}{g_0} e^{-E_j/kT} \tag{11-1}$$

where the g terms are the statistical weights for the particular energy levels. Values of N_j/N_0 for the lines of several elements at different temperatures are given in Table 11-3. The fraction of atoms in the first excited level is a small

Table 11-3 | *Values of N_i/N_0 for Various Resonance Lines*

RESONANCE LINE	g_j/g_0	N_j/N_0		
		2000°K	3000°K	4000°K
Cs 852.1 mμ	2	4.44×10^{-4}	7.24×10^{-3}	2.98×10^{-2}
Na 589.6 mμ	2	9.86×10^{-6}	5.88×10^{-4}	4.44×10^{-3}
Ca 422.7 mμ	3	1.21×10^{-7}	3.69×10^{-5}	6.03×10^{-4}
Zn 213.9 mμ	3	7.29×10^{-15}	5.58×10^{-10}	1.48×10^{-7}

fraction of the total number of atoms introduced into the flame and becomes appreciable only at high temperatures and for states of low energy.

Obviously, ionization reduces the content of neutral metal atoms in the flame, and as a result, it decreases the emissivity of the atomic spectral lines. The ionization of an atom A to its positive ion A^+ and a free electron e^- may be treated like a diatomic dissociation process, basically governed by the equation

$$A = A^+ + e^- \tag{11-2}$$

and the corresponding equilibrium constant K_1:

$$K_1 = \frac{[A^+][e^-]}{[A]} = \frac{x^2}{1 - x^2}P \tag{11-3}$$

where x is the degree of ionization and P is the partial pressure of metal in all forms in the burned gases, in atmospheres. The change in the degree of ionization with temperature is given by the Saha equation

$$\log K_1 = \frac{-5050E_i}{T} + 5/2 \log T - 6.50 + \log \frac{g_{A^+} + g_{e^-}}{g_A} \tag{11-4}$$

where E_i is the ionization potential in electron volts, T is the absolute temperature, and the g terms are the statistical weights of the ionized atom, the neutral atom, and the electron. For alkali metals the final term is zero; for the alkaline earth metals the final term is 0.6. Assuming the partial pressure of metal atoms in the flame to be 10^{-6} atm, the percent ionization for the alkali and alkaline earth metals at various operating flame temperatures is shown in Table 11-4. The influence of concentration of potassium atoms upon the fraction ionized is shown in Table 11-5.

When the energy required for the dissociation of metal compounds into their constituent atoms is not very different from the ionization potential of

Table 11-4			*Percent Ionization of Alkali and Alkaline Earth Metals in Flames*	

ELEMENT	IONIZATION POTENTIAL, eV	AIR-PROPANE, 2200°K	HYDROGEN-OXYGEN, 2450°K	ACETYLENE-OXYGEN 2800°K
Lithium	5.37	<0.01	0.9	16.1
Sodium	5.12	0.3	5.0	26.4
Potassium	4.32	2.5	31.9	82.1
Rubidium	4.16	13.5	44.4	89.6
Cesium	3.87	28.3	69.6	96.4
Calcium	6.11	<0.01	1.0	7.3
Strontium	5.69	<0.1	2.7	17.2
Barium	5.21	1.0	8.6	42.8

Table 11-5 | *Fraction of Potassium Atoms Ionized*

P, atm	10^{-2}	10^{-4}	10^{-6}
1500°K	2.7×10^{-6}	2.7×10^{-5}	2.7×10^{-4}
2000°K	2.5×10^{-4}	2.5×10^{-3}	0.025
2500°K	4.7×10^{-3}	0.047	0.42
3000°K	0.028	0.27	0.94
3500°K	0.11	0.75	0.99

the metal atoms, there is only a rather narrow region of temperature and concentration in which the dissociation is nearly complete and the ionization is still small. This poses a unique problem for rubidium, cesium, and barium. For these elements the dissociation energy is 0.3 to 0.6 eV higher than the ionization energy. Accordingly, there is no temperature and concentration range in which complete dissociation and negligible ionization take place. Both emission and absorption signals will be affected.

Variations of Emission Intensity Within the Flame

The intensity of the spectrum lines varies in different parts of the flame. Among the alkali metals, sodium and potassium are similar and their maximum intensity occurs at a considerable distance from the inner cone. The maximum intensity of the other alkali metals occurs nearer the inner cone. These differences are related to the formation of metal hydroxide in the flame gases. Ionization is minimized when the emission, or absorption, is observed close to the outer boundary of the inner cone where there is a relatively high concentration of flame electrons.

Lines of a number of elements that are absent or very weak in the plume of an oxygen-hydrogen or an oxygen-acetylene flame appear in unusual strength in the spectrum of the reaction zone of a rich acetylene-oxygen flame.[6] These are primarily elements of high excitation potential and high ionization potential. The region of maximum intensity is rather sharply localized from 2 mm below to 3 mm above the inner cone of the flame (Fig. 11-12). The analyte must be dissolved in a hydrocarbon solvent.

Adjustable burner mounts are required. They can be constructed from rack-and-pinion movements.

Emissions from Fuel-Rich Hydrocarbon Flames

A fuel-rich, oxygen-acetylene flame provides an environment more favorable for the existence of free atoms of those elements which have a strong predilection to form stable monoxide (or hydroxide) molecules in stoichiometric flames.[7] The analyte is dissolved in a hydrocarbon solvent. These flames are

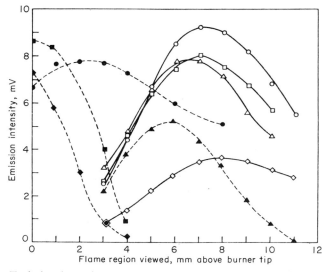

Fig. 11-12. Emission intensity as a function of flame region viewed. Individual analytes contained 200 $\mu g/ml$ of arsenic, 80 $\mu g/ml$ of antimony, 500 $\mu g/ml$ of bismuth, and 100 $\mu g/ml$ of tin, each in methyl isobutyl ketone. $\bigcirc$, 235.0-mμ arsenic line; $\square$, 252.8-mμ antimony line; $\triangle$, 223.1-mμ bismuth line; $\Diamond$, 243.0-mμ tin line; $\bullet$, 306.7-mμ OH band head; $\blacksquare$ 431.5-mμ CH band head; $\blacklozenge$, 516.5-mμ C_2 band head; $\blacktriangle$, 247.8-mμ carbon line. After J. A. Dean and W. J. Carnes, *Analyst*, **87,** 743 (1962). (Courtesy of *The Analyst*.)

saturated with carbon vapor and provide an environment favorable for existence of free atoms in the flame gases owing to the strong chemical reducing action of carbon as expressed by the reaction

$$C + MO \rightarrow CO + M^0 (\text{or } M^*) \qquad (11\text{-}5)$$

Since ΔH_f of CO is 11.1 eV, and the dissociation energy D_{MO} for many monoxides seldom exceeds 7 eV, the reaction expressed by Eq. 11-5 will always be exothermic by the amount $\Delta H_f - D_{MO}$, the energy available for excitation of metal atoms (M^*). In this environment the line spectra of vanadium, niobium, titanium, molybdenum, rhenium, tungsten, and the rare earths have been elicited.

Organic Solvents

The emission intensity is enhanced significantly when elements are aspirated into the flame from an organic solution instead of an aqueous solution.[3,5] A number of water-organic-solvent mixtures have been used. The general relation between organic-solvent concentration and the increase in emission intensity of some elements is shown in Table 11-6. Increases in emission intensity ranging from three- to sevenfold are usual. Significantly larger

Table 11-6 | *Relation between Solvent Composition and Intensification of Flame Emissions*

The enhancement is expressed as a ratio of emission readings in the water-organic-solvent mixture to the reading in water.

ELEMENT	WAVELENGTH, mμ	SOLVENT	VOLUME PERCENT OF ORGANIC SOLVENT PRESENT WITH WATER									TYPE OF ATOMIZER†
			10	20	30	40	50	60	70	80	90	
Barium	455.4	Methanol	1.6		3.1		4.8		7.8		14	A
	553.6	Methanol	1.5		2.2		2.7		4.8		10	A
	488	Methanol	1.5		1.8		2.0		2.9		9	A
Boron	518	Methanol		2.4			6.8			11	17	A
Calcium	422.7	Methanol					2.0	2.3			4.6	A
		Methanol	1.4		1.7		2.1		2.3		2.6	B
		Acetone			2.0	2.2	2.5	3.0	4.2	5.5	6.2	A
Copper	324.7	Methanol		2.5		2.7				4.0	7	A
Magnesium	383	Methanol		1.7		2.3				5.0	6	A
		Ethanol		2.0		2.2				3.9	5	A
		Propanol-1		2.3		2.0				2.9	4	A
		Acetone		2.3		3.3				5.6	5.6	A
Potassium	767	Methanol	1.3	1.7	2.5	2.9	3.0	3.8		5.2	6.8	B
Sodium	589.6	Methanol	1.3	1.6	1.6	1.7	1.7	1.8		2.4	2.6	B

†A: integral aspirator-burner. B: discharge type with condensing chamber.

increases are found for group IIIB elements. The degree of enhancing action depends somewhat upon the atomizing system employed. Although pure organic solvent produces the greatest net emission, this concentration is not usually practical when starting with an aqueous solution. An 80 percent solvent concentration is more desirable because it contains sufficient water to facilitate the preparation of samples for analysis. Combinations of organic solvents often provide greater enhancement.

More spectacular enhancements (Table 11-7) are found for elements that

Table 11-7	Emission Intensity of Certain Elements in Water and Organic Solvents				
ELEMENT	WAVELENGTH, $m\mu$	EXCITATION POTENTIAL, eV	SENSITIVITY, μg $ml^{-1}(\% T)^{-1}$		ENHANCEMENT
			WATER	ORGANIC†	
Al	396.2	3.14	67.0	0.5	134-fold
AlO	484	2.60		0.5	
BO₂	518		17	1.0	17
Ca	422.7	2.93	0.08	0.01	8
Cr	425.4	2.91	5.0	0.1	50
Cu	324.7	3.81	0.6	0.06‡	10
Fe	372.0	3.3	2.5	0.125	20
Pb	405.8	4.37	14	1.3§	11
Li	323.3	3.83	46	2.1	22
	460.3	4.52	12.5	0.7	18
	610.4	3.87	4.4	0.6	7
	670.8	1.85	0.067	0.007	9
Mg	282.5	4.34	1.0	0.1	10
K	767	1.61	0.02	0.0012	8
YO	597		100	0.5	200

†Methyl isobutyl ketone.
‡Chloroform.
§Gasoline.

are aspirated into a flame from essentially a nonaqueous solvent. The degree of intensification varies for different emission lines of a single element and is quite dependent upon the nature of the solvent, the flow rate of the organic solvent, the type and flow rate of fuel and oxygen, the type of atomizer employed, and the observation point within the flame. Liquid-liquid extraction techniques can be exploited to accomplish analytical separations and then the organic phase can be aspirated directly into the flame to take advantage of the enhancement of emission intensity. Rather specific extractants are useful for isolating one metal from other elements in the sample, among which may be interferences. Numerous possibilities exist for the simultaneous extraction and successive determination of several elements in a sample matrix. In addition, it is possible to concentrate a small amount of one metal, and coupled with the increased emission intensity, the determination of metals with relatively weak flame spectra is feasible. Many extractive colorimetric methods, including many dismissed formerly as unsatisfactory, are directly applicable for flame photometry. Cleaner's naphtha, alone or as a 1:1 mixture with isopropanol, is an excellent solvent for metal naphthenates and petroleum products in general. Methyl isobutyl ketone or amyl acetate is ideal for many metal complex extractions.

The gain factor obtained with the substitution of organic solvents for water depends in a complicated and subtle way on the combined action of many factors. The cooling effect of the organic solvent is less than that of water (which may lower the flame temperature 200°–300°). The feed rate is generally larger. Smaller mean-drop diameters and more rapid and complete evaporation of spray droplets are directly helpful. The organic ligand in a metal-organic complex will burn and leave the free metal atom unfettered by a shell of hydrated water (or OH or O). The increase in absorption signals can be attributed largely to these factors, and also to the more commonly encountered emission enhancements of three- to twentyfold, but not to the unusually large enhancements observed for the elements of group IIIB or the appearance of many high energy lines in the spectra from the reaction zone of flames.

The use of organic solvents minimizes variations of the physical properties of the aspirated solution, such as viscosity, droplet size, and volatility. The presence of an organic solvent is essential if one wishes to elicit chemiluminescence or to work with incandescent fuel-rich flames.

Selection of Optimal Working Conditions

There are many operational variables that affect the effective light flux that actually reaches the photodetector. With filter photometers many of these variables are fixed, which simplifies the operation of the instrument. However, the more versatile flame spectrometers allow the operator to select the optimal working conditions for each problem. A choice has to be made of the best wavelength from any of the usable wavelengths of spectral emission lines or bands. Measurements should be conducted with varying oxygen and fuel flows, and the region of maximum emission should be localized in the flame. Flame-photometric methods are often limited, not by the recording of the spectrum lines, but by the accuracy with which the solutions are prepared and the steadiness and control of the flame and atomizer. Various solvents should be investigated.

Resolution and Slit Width

The choice of mechanical slit width or of the bandwidth of a filter affects the ratio of signal-to-flame background and also the interference ratio of two closely spaced emission lines. The signal-to-background ratio, which is the line or band emission diminished by the background and divided by the background reading, should be as large as possible. With a filter type of flame photometer this variable is fixed. However, with a monochromator equipped with adjustable entrance and exit slits, the operator can select an optimum ratio for each analysis line. The response to the flame background (and to band spectra) varies as the square of the slit width, whereas the response to a spectral line is linear with slit width. The net effect of decreasing the slit width (or band pass) is to produce a larger signal-to-background ratio when working with spectral lines. However, the net emission of an analysis line must be sufficiently large to be distinguishable from the blank and to provide adequate sensitivity in analyses for the test element. On direct-reading instruments the signal-to-background ratio is less important. As long as the flame background emission is steady, a zero suppression circuit will depress the background to any position on the reading scale.

The choice of slit width also affects the separation of closely spaced emission lines from the same element in some cases, or from other constituents in the sample. The composite effect is measured as the concentration of each desired element which gives the same deflection as a high concentration of each interfering element. For example, a solution containing 1,000 μg/ml of sodium gave a deflection of 0.5 division under the conditions used to isolate potassium radiation at 767 mμ. At the same wavelength, 10 μg/ml of potassium gave a deflection of 45 divisions, so that 0.11 μg/ml of potassium would have given a deflection of 0.5 division. The interference ratio would be 1 in 9,000.

Optimum Gas Pressures and Flow Rates

The pressures and flow rates which produce maximum emission intensity of an emission line or band vary considerably, depending upon the element, its concentration, and the wavelength used for measurement. Pertinent excitation conditions for individual elements must be sought in the literature.[4] Lacking specific information, suitable pressures and flows are found experimentally by scanning the emission line and adjacent background and adjusting the fuel and oxygen (or air) flows (or pressures) independently until maximum line emission associated with a steady background is obtained. Figure 11-13 is a plot of the emission of the iron line at 372.0 mμ as reading above background, the latter taken at 371.0 mμ. Next, the optimum oxygen pressure was found as illustrated in Fig. 11-14. The fuel pressure was maintained constant at the optimum value previously ascertained while the oxygen pressure was varied. The resultant iron emission attained its maximum value at slightly lower oxygen pressures than did the flame background emission. For other elements the emission may show a steady increase as the fuel pressure is increased, with little or no indication of a plateau. Such is the case for aluminum (Fig. 11-15).

Better attainment of proper flame conditions can be achieved through the

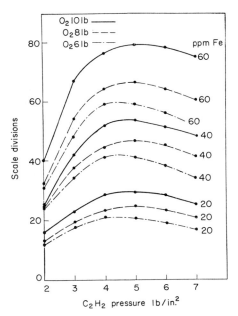

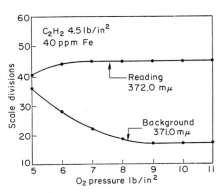

Fig. 11-13. Emission of iron at 372.0 mμ as a function of acetylene pressure, with oxygen pressure and iron concentration as parameters. After J. A. Dean and J. H. Lady, *Anal. Chem.*, **27,** 1533 (1955). (Courtesy of *Analytical Chemistry.*)

Fig. 11-14. Intensity of iron emission and flame background reading as a function of oxygen pressure. After J. A. Dean and J. H. Lady, *Anal. Chem.*, **27,** 1533 (1955). (Courtesy of *Analytical Chemistry.*)

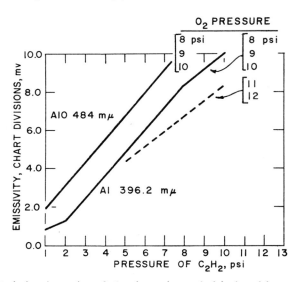

Fig. 11-15. Emission intensity of aluminum in methyl isobutyl ketone as a function of acetylene pressure, with oxygen pressure as parameter. Present, 40 μg/ml aluminum. After H. C. Eshelman, J. A. Dean, O. Menis, and T. C. Rains, *Anal. Chem.*, **31,** 183 (1959). (Courtesy of *Analytical Chemistry.*)

use of flow meters inserted in the fuel and oxygen lines. Optimal flows are ascertained in the same manner as for gas pressures. However, once the optimum ratio of fuel (plus any organic solvent) to oxygen is established, the same ratio can be quickly used on any other burner. Only the actual quantity of fuel and oxygen and the pressure of the aspirating gas stream remain as additional parameters. The emission of the 338.3-mμ silver line as a function of the acetylene flow, with the oxygen flow as a parameter, is shown in Fig. 11-16. Larger flow rates, while maintaining the ratio fixed, will alter the flame dimensions, and a higher flow of oxygen will aspirate a greater volume of solution per unit of time. This results in an increase of the available number of ions of the test element, which should increase the emission intensity. However, an increase in the volume of water aspirated into the flame decreases the flame temperature. This results in a lower emission for a given number of atoms of the test element and may also bring about a shift in any equilibria involving molecular compounds $\rightleftarrows$ neutral atoms $\rightleftarrows$ ionized atoms. Consequently, an optimal flow exists at which the observed intensity of a given spectral line exhibits a maximum, falling off rapidly with increase or decrease in flow rate. For the silver line, whatever the oxygen and acetylene flows, the optimum ratio of oxygen/acetylene flows is approximately 1.1, as shown in Fig. 11-17. The fuel mixture is very rich, in fact much richer than a stoichiometric ratio (equal to 2.5 and corresponding to a burned gas composition which consists of $CO_2 + H_2O$).

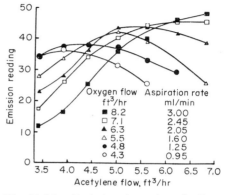

Fig. 11-16. Emission intensity of silver line at 338.3 mμ as a function of acetylene flow at various oxygen flows. Present, 200 μg/ml of silver. After J. A. Dean and C. B. Stubblefield, *Anal. Chem.*, **33**, 382 (1961). (Courtesy of *Analytical Chemistry*.)

Optimum flows of oxygen and combustible gas are different when a combustible solvent is aspirated. This would be anticipated, since the organic solvent would require additional oxygen for combustion. At high ratios of oxygen to acetylene, the aspirated solvent becomes the major source of fuel. At too low a ratio, insufficient oxygen is provided for combustion of the acetylene and solvent, and an unsteady flame background results. Of course, fuel-rich flames will be incandescent and the oxygen/fuel ratio will exceed only slightly the value at which carbon formation is initiated.

Because the location of the different zones in a flame varies with changing oxygen/fuel ratios, the profile of emission intensity as a function of these ratios requires investigation if the burner height can be adjusted.

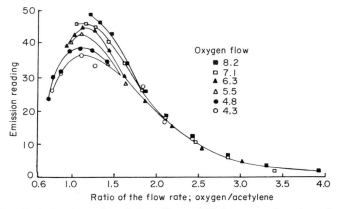

Fig. 11-17. Emission intensity of silver line at 338.3 mμ as a function of ratio of flow rate, oxygen/acetylene, at various oxygen flows. Data same as for Fig. 11-16. After J. A. Dean and C. B. Stubblefield, *Anal. Chem.*, **33,** 382 (1961). (Courtesy of *Analytical Chemistry*.)

The internal-standard method does not completely eliminate the effect of variations in gas and oxygen pressures at any range. Although the magnitude of the effect is considerably reduced, absolute pressure (and flow) regulation remains necessary for the best results.

Interferences

Flame photometry is subject to numerous disturbances, some of which are understood and can be dealt with, whereas others remain obscure. The term interference is intended to cover all types of difficulties that affect the flame emission of a test element. These include spectroscopic interferences and interferences that arise from variations in the physical properties of the test solution. Even the test element, when sufficiently concentrated, may interfere with its own spectral emission. One should give careful consideration to the history and probable composition of every sample analyzed before proceeding with the analysis.

Spectral Interference

Interference of this category is especially prevalent when filters are used to isolate the desired radiant energy. With monochromators, interference is much less. For example, the emission of the orange band of CaOH interferes with the sodium line at 590 mμ. With absorption filters, interference is so serious that various expedients have been proposed to eliminate the calcium radiation. Although progressively less serious when the sodium line is isolated by means of interference filters or by means of a prism or grating monochromator, the problem remains because the calcium band system overlaps the sodium wavelength. Difficulties in determination of copper arise from the remnants of the strong OH band systems in the vicinity of the two copper lines. The lithium line at 670.8 mμ suffers interference from the orange-red band system of SrOH. These are but a few examples among many. It is fortunate that most of the spectral lines useful in flame photometry occur in the blue and ultraviolet, while most of the molecular band systems and continua occur in the green and red regions.

Spectral interference may be caused by adjacent line emissions when the analysis element and the interferent have nearly the same wavelength. In this case, the two lines overlap partially or completely and will be read together in proportion to the degree of overlap. If the interference cannot be obviated by increased resolution, the difficulty must be overcome by selecting other spectral lines where mutual interference does not occur, or by prior removal of one element, perhaps by selective solvent extraction.

Background Emission

The emission reading of a spectral line and band always includes any contribution from the flame and sample matrix. Failure to correct properly for the background reading can be a source of serious error. The manner by which correction for the background reading is handled depends on the behavior of the background and the type of flame photometer employed.

When the background results solely from the flame gases, it may be measured by aspirating the pure solvent into the flame and subtracting the resultant emission reading from subsequent sample readings. Alternatively, the flame photometer may be adjusted to give a reading of zero while water or other solvent is being aspirated. The contribution of matrix elements can be eliminated by the use of a synthetic blank, but unless routine samples are being handled, this begs the question.

With instruments embodying a monochromator and thus a choice of contiguous narrow bands of radiant energy, it is possible to read directly the background radiation in the presence of the test element. First, the line-plus-background intensity is measured in the normal manner at the peak of the line or the crest of the band system. Next, the wavelength dial is rotated slowly until the emission readings decrease to a minimum at a wavelength setting off to one side or the other of the emission line or band system. The background reading is then subtracted from the line-plus-background reading. If the background reading is essentially the same on either side of the line or band head, one background reading will suffice; if not, an interpolated value should be used. When a recorder is employed, the background can be estimated by means of a line drawn across the base of the emission line or band system—the *base-line* method.

Self-Absorption

As discussed earlier, the process of excitation is followed by the loss of a discrete amount of energy in the form of radiation as the electron falls back to its original position or to a lower energy level. The radiant energy usually has to travel from some part in the interior of the flame to the outside. During its passage through the outer fringes of the flame mantle, the radiant energy is subject to absorption through collision with atoms of its own kind present in the ground energy level. If some of the radiant energy is self-absorbed, the strength of the spectral line is weakened. The effect is most noticeable for resonance lines—those arising from the lowest excited level.

The influence of concentration on the sodium emission at 590 mμ is evident from the calibration curves in Fig. 11-18. In cool flames, the curve can be

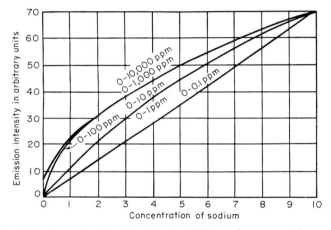

Fig. 11-18. Emission intensity of sodium at 590 mμ in an acetylene-oxygen flame, rectilinear coordinates. (By permission, from Bulletin 334, Beckman Instruments, Inc.)

considered essentially linear up to 10 μg/ml of sodium, whereas in hot flames curvature becomes evident above concentrations of 2 μg/ml. Above 40 μg/ml, readings are nearly proportional to the square root of the sodium concentration.

Self-absorption is primarily determined by the number of atoms present in the ground state, essentially the concentration of atomized solution, and by the probability that these atoms (see oscillator strengths) will be excited by the incident radiation from excited atoms of its own kind. At very low concentrations of a test element, self-absorption is insignificant, usually because the vapor density of absorbing atoms is low and, consequently, the line intensity will initially be proportional to the concentration of the atomized solution. The onset of self-absorption is easy to ascertain. A plot of the emission intensity on a logarithmic scale vs the concentration of the test element, also on a logarithmic scale, gives the best representation of the onset of self-absorption. The data for sodium are shown in Fig. 11-19 replotted on logarithmic coordinates.

In work with internal-standard lines, caution must be exercised in the amounts of test element and internal-standard element used because of differences in self-absorption between them. For example, at a concentration of 60 μg/ml of sodium there is only a small amount of reabsorption of sodium light in a propane-air flame, but there is enough reabsorption of lithium light, when 1,000 μg/ml of lithium is present, to make a proportional increase in the concentration of both elements appear as a relative increase in the amount of sodium.

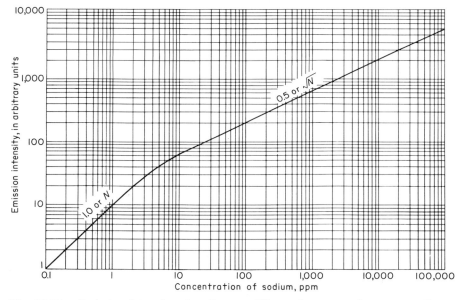

Fig. 11-19. Emission intensity of sodium at 590 mμ in an acetylene-oxygen flame, logarithmic coordinates. (By permission, from Bulletin 334, Beckman Instruments, Inc.)

Ionization

An oxygen-gas flame possesses sufficient energy to ionize the alkali and alkaline earth metals (Table 11-4). The consequence is a depletion of the number of available neutral atoms that can be excited, with the result that the intensity of the atomic spectrum is weakened whereas any ionic spectrum is strengthened. When small but increasing quantities of easily ionized metals are added to a flame, the tendency is for the number of neutral atoms to increase more rapidly, in comparison with ionized atoms, than proportionally

Table 11-8	Effect of Sodium on Emission Intensity of Potassium

CHANGE IN EMISSION INTENSITY, %, UPON ADDITION OF SODIUM

POTASSIUM, μg per ml	20 μg per ml OF SODIUM	100 μg per ml OF SODIUM	500 μg per ml OF SODIUM	1,000 μg per ml OF SODIUM	2,000 μg per ml OF SODIUM	5,000 μg per ml OF SODIUM
			An Acetylene-Air Flame			
5	+17	+56		+92	+96	+97
10	+13	+31	+48	+71		+78
40	+1	+7	+14	+21	+26	+25
100	0	+1	+1	+2	+2	+1
			An Illuminating-Gas-Air Flame			
2		+13				
5	+3	+5				
10	+2					
40	+1	0				

to the concentration of metal sprayed into the flame. As a result, the curve of intensity vs concentration may initially be concave upward.

The partial pressure of free electrons in the flame gases is increased by the addition of a second ionizable element. Thus, equilibrium is shifted in the direction of an increased partial pressure of neutral atoms. The calibration curve tends to be straightened, and the intensity of spectral lines from the neutral atom is enhanced. The increase in percent enhancement is greatest in hot flames, in which a higher proportion of ionizable metal atoms are normally ionized, and is least in relatively cool flames, in which a negligible fraction of atoms are ionized. The data in Table 11-8 illustrate the mutual-cation-enhancement effect for potassium when sodium is added to the solution. The effect is not proportional to the concentration of interferent. Thus, if an analyst wished to determine potassium and did not know the concentration (or type) of interferent in the sample, he might add a large amount of an easily ionizable element (but an element devoid of direct spectral interference) to both the sample and the standards. In this manner the effect of any easily ionizable element which might have been originally present in the sample would be minimized. This is called the *radiation-buffer* technique. A smaller quantity of cesium would be as effective in brightening the potassium lines as a much larger quantity of sodium.

Influence of Anions

In general, the emission of elements is lowered when relatively large amounts of acids and their salts are introduced into the flame concomitantly. There is usually no interference with concentrations less than 0.1 M. Above this concentration, sulfuric, nitric, and phosphoric acids, in particular, show a marked effect in lowering metallic emission.

The strong depression of the calcium emission (and other alkaline earth elements) in the presence of phosphate, aluminate, and other similar anions has been known for some time. In fact, over limited intervals of concentration, the depression is linear and forms the basis for indirect determination of the depressant in the presence of a standard amount of calcium. In interference of this type a compound of the element sought, crystallizing out of the evaporating droplets of spray, is not fully vaporized on passing through the flame. That is, for the equilibria

$$AX\ (s) \rightleftarrows AX\ (g)$$

$$AX\ (g) \rightleftarrows A^0\ (g) + X^0\ (g)$$

a slow step is involved. Salts of high-melting compounds will not be converted rapidly into the gaseous state, and the apparent concentration of neutral atoms will be limited by the incomplete volatilization. Inhibition is less in hotter flames and becomes progressively less the farther the observation area recedes from the inner cone.

The use of releasing agents or protective chelating agents circumvents this type of interference. A releasing agent preferentially combines with the interferent or simply by mass action denies the test element the interfering anion, thereby leaving the test element free to vaporize in the flame. In protective chelation, the element sought is masked to prevent it from combining with the interferent in the solution phase, although, of course, the masking agent must be promptly decomposed in the flame. Various polyhydroxy alcohols or EDTA chelate with calcium; control of pH is also important.

Solution Properties

Various solution properties affect the observed emission intensities, particularly in the case of an atomizer with a condensing chamber. Vapor pressure and surface tension influence droplet size. Added salts and acids hinder the evaporation of solvent; larger droplets result in a diminished quantity of aerosol reaching the burner because the larger droplets are more likely to settle out upon the walls of the condensing chamber. A high concentration of any one of a number of salts or acids may be added to both the test solution and comparison standards to minimize the effect of the others. Lithium chloride is often added for this purpose.

Anything which lowers the surface tension contributes to the production of smaller spray particles. In this respect, variable amounts of an organic solvent would be an interferent. Nonionic surfactants in small amounts are helpful.

Viscosity also influences the rate at which aerosol reaches the flame through its effect on aspiration rate. It is essential that the viscosities of standard solutions approximate as closely as possible those of the sample solutions. This is done conveniently by dilution with miscible solvents, for example, in the case of lubricating oils.

Evaluation Methods

The selection of standards is of primary importance. Spectrographically pure salts should be used. Generally, a set of concentrated stock solutions, each containing, for example, 1,000 $\mu g/ml$ of a single element, is prepared. From them, dilutions to any desired concentration are made as needed. For storage it is advisable to use bottles of polyethylene or of resistant-glass composition. Care must be exercised in the handling of diluted samples and standards, in particular, solutions of sodium, potassium, and calcium, to avoid contact with the operator's hands, losses from adsorption on the surface of the storage container, and contamination from soap powder, tobacco smoke, and dust particles in the air and detached from the floor or clothes.

In Table 11-9 are listed the wavelength and useful emission sensitivity of a representative group of lines and bands. Wavelengths of unresolved multiplets are given for the center of the multiplet.

Table 11-9 | *Flame Spectra of the Elements†*

ELEMENT	WAVELENGTH, mμ	TYPE OF EMISSION	TYPE OF FLAME	EMISSION SENSITIVITY, μg ml$^{-1}(\% T)^{-1}$
Aluminum	396.2	L	OA*n*	0.5
	484	B	OA*n*	0.5
Antimony	252.8	L	OA*nn*	1.0
Arsenic	235.0	L	OA*nn*	2.2
Barium	455.5	I	OH	3
	553.6	L	OH	1
Bismuth	223.1	L	OA*nn*	6.4
Boron	249.8	L	OA*nn*	7
	518	B	OA	3
Cadmium	326.1	L	AH	0.5
Calcium	422.7	L	OA	0.07
	554	B	OA	0.16
	622	B	OA	0.6
Cesium	455.5	L	OH	2.0
	852	L	OH	0.5
Chromium	425.4	L	OA	5.0
Cobalt	242.5	L	OA*nn*	1.7
	353.0	L	OA	4.0
Copper	324.7	L	OA	0.6
Gallium	417.2	L	OA	0.5
Indium	451.1	L	OH	0.07
Iron	372.0	L	OA	2.5
	386.0	L	OA	2.7

Table 11-9 | *Flame Spectra of the Elements†* *(Continued)*

ELEMENT	WAVELENGTH, mμ	TYPE OF EMISSION	TYPE OF FLAME	EMISSION SENSITIVITY, μg ml^{-1}($\%$ T)$^{-1}$
Lanthanum	442	B	OA	0.7
	741	B	OA	4.5
Lead	405.8	L	OA	14
Lithium	670.8	L	OA	0.067
Magnesium	285.2	L	OA	1.0
	383	B	OA	1.6
Manganese	403.3	L	OA	0.1
Mercury	253.6	L	OA*n*	2.5
Molybdenum	379.8	L	OA*n*	0.5
Neodymium	555	B	OH*n*	0.2
	702	B	OH*n*	1.0
Nickel	352.4	L	OA	1.6
Niobium	405.9	L	OA*n*	12
Palladium	363.5	L	OH*n*	0.1
Phosphorus	253	B	OH*n*	1.0
Platinum	265.9	L	OA*n*	15
Potassium	404.4	L	OH	1.7
	767	L	OH	0.02
Rhenium	346.1	L	OA*n*	3
Rhodium	369.2	L	OH*n*	0.7
Rubidium	780.0	L	OH	0.6
Ruthenium	372.8	L	OA	0.3
Scandium	604	B	OH*n*	0.012
Silicon	251.6	L	OH*n*	4.5
Silver	328.0	L	OH	1.0
	338.3	L	OH	0.6
Sodium	590.0	L	OH	0.001
Strontium	460.7	L	OA	0.06
Tellurium	238.6	L	OA*n*	2.0
Thallium	377.6	L	OH	0.6
Tin	243.0	L	OA*n*	1.6
Titanium	399.9	L	OA*n*	5
Vanadium	437.9	L	OA*n*	3
Yttrium	597	B	OA*n*	0.3
Zinc	213.9	L	OA*n*	77

†The symbols used in this table and their meanings are as follows:

B = molecular band emission
I = ionic-line emission
L = atomic-line emission
AH = air-hydrogen flame

OA = oxygen-acetylene flame
OH = oxygen-hydrogen flame
n = organic solvent (usually methyl isobutyl ketone)
z = reaction zone of fuel-rich flame

Emission Intensity vs Concentration

When interferences are absent, the procedure for calibrating the flame photometer for a given metal is as follows:

With the flame burning properly and the correct filter in place, or the

INSTRUMENTAL METHODS OF ANALYSIS

monochromator set at the correct wavelength, deionized water is introduced into the atomizer and the background emission is recorded or zero suppression controls are adjusted to bring the instrument reading to zero. Next, the most concentrated comparison standard is introduced and the sensitivity adjusted so that the maximum scale reading (or any predetermined reading) is attained. The zero reading is rechecked and any necessary adjustments are made. These two steps are repeated until duplicate readings are within one scale division out of 100 total divisions. Then several standards of lower concentration are introduced in turn and the respective readings noted.

The instrument readings, plotted on the axis of ordinates, vs the concentrations in micrograms per milliliter on the axis of abscissas produce the calibration (or analytical) curve. On nonlinear portions of the curve, interpolation within limited portions of the curve suffices. Standards should always bracket the sample closely.

When interferences are encountered, it is necessary to use standard solutions containing all the important constituents of the specimen in exactly equivalent amounts. If this step is insufficient or not feasible, self-compensating methods of evaluation must be employed or prior chemical separation made. However, when all the constituents in the unknown are exactly reproduced in the comparison standards, no other evaluation method is capable of providing such freedom from disturbing influences.

Standard-Addition Method

In the method of standard addition, net emission readings are obtained on two solutions: solution A, containing an aliquot of the unknown solution, and solution B, containing the same quantity of unknown solution plus a measured amount of a standard solution of the element. The quantity of test element in each of these solutions is then determined from their measured emission intensities and the standard calibration curve. Subtracting the quantity of unknown found in solution A from that found in solution B yields an amount of test element equal to that added when there is no depression or enhancement. When one of these effects is present, however, the quantity of the test element found by subtraction is greater or less than that added. In such cases, the true metal content of solution A is found by multiplying the observed metal content by a factor which corrects for the interference. This factor is found by dividing the quantity of metal added to solution B by the amount of metal found by subtracting the observed metal content of solution B from that of solution A.

The concentration of an unknown is found from the following relationships:

$$(L_1 - H)_A = kX_{found}$$
$$(L_2 - H)_B = k(X + S)$$
$$L_2 - L_1 = kS_{found}$$

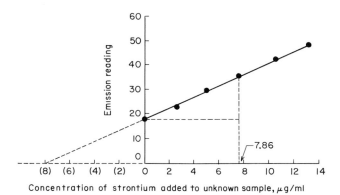

Fig. 11-20. Graphic representation of the standard-addition method of evaluation (see Table 11-10).

$$X_{\text{found}} \frac{S_{\text{added}}}{S_{\text{found}}} = X_{\text{actually present}}$$

where L_1 = emission reading of unknown (solution A)
$\quad L_2$ = emission reading after addition of standard (solution B)
$\quad H$ = background reading
$\quad S$ = amount of standard added (considering any dilution factor)
$\quad X$ = concentration of unknown

Improved results can be obtained by using a series of standard additions. Normally additions which are equal to, twice, and one-half the original amount are optimum. The resulting net emissions are plotted against the concentration of the increments of the standard solutions that were added to the unknown. The extrapolated line intersecting the response axis indicates the emission of the test element in the unknown sample (Fig. 11-20). Typical emission readings for strontium in sea water are given in Table 11-10, third

Table 11-10 | *Evaluation by Method of Standard Addition*

The net emission readings are given for a series of pure strontium standards and for a series of solutions containing equal volumes of sea water and added standard solution of strontium. Sample contained 7.86 μg/ml of strontium.

METER READINGS, STRONTIUM STANDARDS	STRONTIUM, μg per ml, PRESENT OR ADDED	METER READINGS, SEA WATER SAMPLE
0	0	18
16.0	2.62	24
32.5	5.24	30
47.1	7.86	36
63.7	10.50	42
79.2	13.10	48

column. For comparison, a series of readings obtained with pure strontium solutions equal to the added increments of strontium "spike" are given in the first column.

The method of standard addition is well established as an evaluation method. By its use a number of radiation interferences can be overcome; it is particularly suited for residual matrix effects and in trace analysis. However, limitations exist which must be recognized. The calibration curve must be linear over the range of concentrations employed and it must pass through the origin. Proper correction for background radiation must be made on both the sample and the sample plus added standard solution. Ionization effects must be stabilized by means of a radiation buffer. It is desirable that all the solutions be diluted to the same final volume, for then any interfering substance will be present at the same concentration in all solutions and will affect equally the radiation from the test element either originally present or added as the standard increment.

Internal-Standard Method

A fixed quantity of internal-standard element is added to samples and standards alike. Upon excitation, radiant energy emitted by the latter and by the test element is measured simultaneously by dual detectors or by scanning successively the two emission lines. The ratio of the emission intensity of the analysis line to that of the internal-standard line is plotted against the concentration of the analysis element on log-log paper to prepare the calibration curve for a series of standards. The intensity of each line is corrected for the background radiation in which it lies. The plot of log (emission ratio) vs log (concentration of test element) will give a straight line whose slope ideally is 45° over limited concentration intervals. On most double-beam instruments, the ratio is given by the reading of the balancing potentiometer. Calibration curves on linear coordinate paper suffice.

The choice of a suitable element and spectral line as an internal standard is rather limited in flame photometry because of the small number of lines excited. Lithium is frequently used, particularly when analyzing for sodium, potassium, and sometimes calcium. The characteristics of lithium, in respect to excitation and ionization potentials and the influence of anions on its emission in air-gas flames, are almost identical with those of sodium, with some variation in respect to potassium and considerable deviation for calcium. The method is most effective when the content of the reference element is of the same order of magnitude in emission intensity as the test element. In any event, for dual-beam instruments, the concentration of the internal standard should be adequate so that, when the current produced by the internal-standard photocell is fully amplified, it will exactly balance the current output from the photocell that is measuring the test element.

When light-intensity ratios rather than absolute light intensities are measured, disturbing effects due to variation in spray rates, changes in droplet size, variations in viscosity and surface tension, and fluctuations in pressure of the fuel gases are greatly minimized. The technique possesses particular merit with atomizers in series with a condensing chamber. Unsuspected errors may arise, however. If the test sample were to contain some of the reference element, a corresponding error would result. More serious is the fact that the emissivity of the standard and analysis lines is usually influenced differently with respect to ionization and excitation and by variations in flame temperature. Seldom will an interferent affect the internal-standard and test elements in precisely the same manner, although the effect is often similar among members of a family in the periodic table of elements. Changes in background radiation must also be considered for instruments that provide no means for independent measurement. The presence of other radiating species, including the added reference element, may increase the background more at one wavelength than at the other.

Absorption Flame Photometry

Principle of the Method

The basis of the method is the measurement of the light absorbed at the wavelength of a resonance line by the unexcited atoms of the element. Thus, elements not themselves excited to emission by a flame may nevertheless be determined in a flame by absorption *provided* that the atomic state is capable of existence. At the temperature of a normal air-acetylene (or similar) flame, only a very small fraction of all atoms is excited to emission in a flame; 99 percent remain unexcited (Table 11-4). Therefore, the absorption due to a transition from the ground electronic state to a higher energy level is virtually an absolute measure of the number of atoms in the flame, and hence the concentration of element in a sample.

The flame can be treated as if it were a trough of absorbing gas, as in spectrophotometry. The number of atoms capable of absorbing any transmitted light of appropriate wavelength is proportional to the product of the concentration of these atoms in the flame and the length of the light path through the flame. The relationship between the integrated absorption and operating parameters is given by the expression

$$\int K_\nu \partial\nu = (\pi e^2/m_e c)N_0 f$$

where K_ν is the absorption coefficient, e is the electronic charge, m the electronic mass, c the velocity of light, N_0 the number of metal atoms per cubic centimeter capable of absorbing radiation of frequency ν, and f the oscillator strength (the oscillator strength is inversely proportional to the lifetime of the excited state). The degree of self-absorption to be observed in emission flame photometry provides a good indication of the magnitude of the f value (Table 11-11) and, therefore, the sensitivity of the absorption method.

An important advantage of the absorption method lies in the fact that it consists of measuring the ratio of two intensities: the intensity of the monochromatic line source in the presence of and in the absence of absorbing atoms.

Table 11-11 | *Limits of Detectability by Absorption Flame Photometry*

ELEMENT	RESONANCE LINE, mμ	LIMIT OF DETECTABILITY, μg per ml†	OSCILLATOR STRENGTH (f VALUE)
Antimony	231.1	1.5	
Barium	553.6	8.0	2.21
Bismuth	306.8	2	
Cadmium	228.8	0.03	
	326.1	2	
Calcium	422.7	0.08	2.27
Cesium	852.1	0.15	0.66
Chromium	357.9	0.15	
	425.4	50	0.03
Cobalt	240.7	0.2	
	353.3	5	
Copper	324.7	0.1	0.32
Gallium	287.4	250	
Gold	242.8	0.3	
	267.6	2	
Iron	248.3	0.1	
Lead	283.3	0.5	
Lithium	670.8	0.03	0.71
Magnesium	285.2	0.01	1.74
Manganese	279.5	0.05	
	403.4	1.0	0.052
Mercury	253.7	10	
Molybdenum	313.3	0.5	
Nickel	232.0	0.2	
	341.5	5	0.19
Palladium	247.6	0.8	
Platinum	265.9	5	
Potassium	766.5	0.03	0.70
Rhodium	343.5	0.3	
Rubidium	785.0	0.1	
Silver	328.1	0.05	0.39
	338.3	2	
Sodium	589.0	0.03	0.70
Strontium	460.7	0.15	1.20
Thallium	276.8	0.8	
Tin	286.3	5	
Zinc	213.9	0.03	

†Concentration giving 1 percent absorption.

Ratios may be much easier to measure accurately than are emission intensities in absolute units.

Because the absorption line has a finite width (of the order of 10^{-2} Å), the value of the absorption coefficient varies with frequency. Fortunately, it is not necessary to measure the profile of an absorption line as long as the source provides a sharp, narrow line, centered exactly, and whose half width is small as compared with that of the absorption. Several factors cause broadening of the emission and the absorption line, the chief being Doppler broadening and pressure broadening.[14] Doppler broadening is caused by the thermal motion of the atoms and is proportional to $\sqrt{(T/M)}$, where T is the temperature and M the mass of the atom. Pressure broadening is due to collisions of the atoms with one another and between the atoms and molecules constituting the flame itself. The low pressure employed in a hollow-cathode tube lessens this effect in the source.

Design of an Absorption Flame Photometer

The general arrangement of an absorption flame photometer is no different from an emission flame photometer except for the addition of a light source.[15] An aerosol is introduced into a flame which is placed on the optical axis between the entrance slit of the monochromator and the monochromatic light source. Energy of the wavelength absorbed by the analyte is provided by a source lamp whose emitting cathode is made of that element. This energy is passed through the flame and then through a dispersing device. A detector measures the absorbed and unabsorbed exciting radiation.

The atomic-line source is the critical component. Because the width of absorption lines is extremely small, it is difficult to measure the absorption accurately against the background of a continuous spectrum. The source must therefore be sensibly monochromatic. Also, the source must not exhibit erratic fluctuations in intensity or self-absorption. For metals such as alkali metals and mercury, vapor lamps are satisfactory, provided they are underrun to prevent self-absorption. For other elements a hollow cathode lamp is the most useful source for sharp resonance lines. These lamps can be used for a wide range of elements and can be made or purchased commercially. Generally, lamps containing more than one element are unsatisfactory. However, lamps are quickly interchanged. The hollow-cathode discharge tube consists of an anode and a cylindrical cathode enclosed in a gas-tight chamber. In some models the cathode liner is removable and may be of any conducting material desired. An inert carrier gas (helium or argon) is introduced at 1–2 mm pressure. When a potential of 600–1000 volts is applied to the electrodes, a discharge is created which fills the cathode crater. The inert gas ions formed by this discharge are accelerated toward the cathode and upon collision with the element in the cathode cavity, sputter it into the discharge zone. The highly energetic carrier gas ions then excite the sputtered atoms to emission through collisions. Lamps are operated at low currents to improve linearity of response and maintain narrow emission lines.

Constant feed rate of sample into the burner is critical. Although solids have been volatilized directly using induction heating or electron bombardment, the most common practice involves use of a solution which is introduced into a flame by an atomizer. Atomizer design and construction follow practice in emission spectrometry. The burner has two principal functions to perform: (1) It must introduce the sample into the flame and (2) it must reduce the metal to the atomic state. Flame shape is important. The flame should have a long path length (but a narrow width, such as a fishtail flame) so that the source traverses an increased number of atoms capable of contributing to the absorption signal. The effective length of the flame may be increased by multiple passages through the flame with a reflecting mirror system, or by alignment of several burners in series. To perform adequately its second function, the flame temperature need only be high enough to dissociate molecular compounds into the free metal atoms.

The dispersing device has two tasks: to reject resonance lines of other elements, and to prevent the detector from being overloaded with light, e.g., from the carrier gas in the discharge tube. Usually the spectrum line is isolated with a monochromator and its intensity measured by a photomultiplier tube and conventional amplifier. For some purposes the arrangement of an appropriate filter and photocell is adequate. The resolution of the method is implicit in the width of the emission and absorption lines.

Single- or double-beam circuits may be adopted. For work with a single-beam instrument, results are directly dependent upon source and detector stability. Both must be powered by separate power supplies. In a double-beam system small variations in the source signal are compensated automatically. A modulated source with a tuned amplifier in the detecting circuit will largely overcome the effects of emission from the flame. Modulation can be accomplished by chopping the light beam. When the emission from the source is steady and relatively intense, it may be sufficient to suppress electrically the signal from the matrix and flame emissions.

Attachments, designed for use with existing spectrophotometers, consist of a hollow-cathode discharge lamp, attendant power supply, and flame vaporizer (Hilger Uvispek). The Perkin-Elmer model 303, shown in Fig. 11-21, is a double-beam, time-shared spectrophotometer. The emission from the source is split into two beams by a rotating sector mirror that has alternate reflecting and transparent sectors separated by opaque portions. The sector rotates at a synchronous speed of 1800 rpm, which is the chopping frequency of 60 cps. One beam is directed through the flame at the sampling burner, while the other bypasses it. The two beams, after being recombined by a semitransparent mirror, pass through the grating monochromator to a detector and preamplifier, after which the signal is separated into sample and

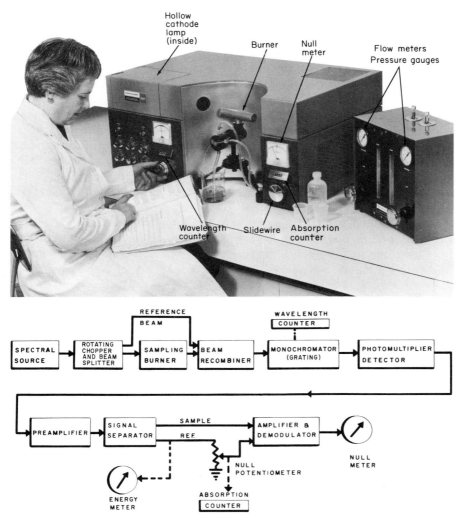

Fig. 11-21. Double-beam, time-shared, grating spectrophotometer for atomic absorption photometry and block diagram of the instrument. (Courtesy of Perkin-Elmer Corp., Norwalk, Conn.)

reference channels by a vibrating-reed chopper. The reference voltage is then attenuated by a slidewire, the null potentiometer, and recombined with the sample voltage in such a way that only the difference between them remains. This difference voltage is amplified, rectified, and fed to a microammeter. The operator turns the slidewire until the meter reads a null—the amount of attenuation required is equivalent to the percent absorption in the sample beam. Manual conversion to absorbance by means of tables of logarithms (i.e., log (100 — percent absorption)), completes the operations needed to prepare calibration curves of absorbance vs concentration.

Choice of Absorption Line

To realize the full potentialities of the method, the strongest absorption line must be used. For elements with simple spectra, the resonance line arising from the lowest excited state is usually the line exhibiting strongest absorption. With complex spectra the best spectral lines are not always the most persistent lines, although they are always lines resulting from transitions ending in the ground state. The light passing through the flame, with and without the analysis element, should be scanned over all the prominent emission wavelengths of the source.

To extend the dynamic range of absorption flame photometry when dealing with solutions containing widely varying amounts of the analyte, it is sometimes desirable to switch to a weaker absorption line, if one is available.

Calibration curves depart from linearity at much lower concentrations in absorption work as compared with emission work. Curvature results partly from increased pressure broadening as the concentration of salts rises, but also depends on source characteristics, particularly self-absorption, and on the nature and homogeneity of the flame.

Interferences

Absorption flame photometry is free of some of the interferences suffered by emission methods. Insofar as effects observed in emission are due to variations in the distribution of atoms over the various excited states, they would have no counterpart in absorption where this is due to a transition from the ground state. Absorption will not be critically dependent on the temperature of the flame except to ensure reduction to the atomic state and provided the number of ionized atoms is small. Some elements, however, tend to form refractory compounds in the flame, so that molecules rather than atoms are present. Stability of oxides is the chief factor preventing the detection of all the elements which have accessible resonance lines. Dissociation will be more complete in oxygen-acetylene flames.

Condensed-phase interference affects each method equally. Use of releasing agents or protective chelation works in absorption as in emission with the advantage that absorption will not be troubled with the spectrum of the releasing agent.

Spectral interference is lessened in absorption methods because the band width of the monochromator is essentially the width of the source emission line, namely 0.001 mμ. Thus, closely spaced lines such as Mg 285.21 and Na 285.28 present no problem in absorption work.

Physical interference may result from the effect of solute or solvent characteristics on the efficiency or rate of transport of analyte into the flame. Generally organic solvents enhance the degree of absorption—atomization efficiency is improved and the viscosity and density of the solvent are controlled. Signal enhancement is about threefold.

LABORATORY WORK

General Instructions

Read the instruction manual accompanying the particular instrument to be used before attempting any laboratory operations.

Lighting the flame. Turn on the air (or oxygen) pressure and then the fuel (city gas, propane, hydrogen, or acetylene) pressure. Immediately bring a lighted match alongside the burner and slightly above the tip of the burner. The flame makes a loud noise when lighted and while burning. Allow the flame to burn several minutes before proceeding. **When extinguishing the flame, always turn off the fuel before turning off the oxygen or air.**

Optimum fuel and oxygen (or air) pressures. Adjust the oxygen (or air) and fuel pressure to the value recommended in the instruction manual furnished by the manufacturer. Spray a solution of the analyte into the flame. Vary the fuel pressure in steps of 0.5 lb/in.^{2} and measure the emission of the analyte and of the solvent alone when each is sprayed into the flame. Plot the net emission of the analyte against the fuel pressure.

If a maximum value is attained, set the fuel pressure at this value and vary the oxygen (or air) pressure in steps of 1 lb/in.^{2}. If no maximum is attained for fuel pressure, choose an intermediate value of fuel pressure and use it throughout the remainder of your work. Plot the emission as a function of the oxygen (or air) pressure.

Repeat these steps for each test element and at each wavelength of the test element, particularly if the emission originates from an atomic line in one case, but from a molecular species in another. See Figs. 11-13 through 11-17 for typical examples.

Slit width. With flame spectrometers the slit width may be varied. For emissions emanating from atomic lines, the slit width is usually set at 0.02–0.05 mm. For band spectra, the slit width can sometimes profitably be set at values as large as 0.2 mm. For prism spectrometers, consult the dispersion curve supplied by the manufacturer.

Wavelength setting. With filter photometers, insert the proper filter or filter combination in the holder and rotate the units into the light beam.

With monochromators, it is necessary to find the exact wavelength-drum setting at which the instrument gives maximum response. Spray a solution of the test element into the flame and scan the wavelength region where the spectral lines or bands are located (see Table 11-9). Slowly vary the wavelength until the maximum signal is obtained. If possible, use a different slit width, and rescan.

Summary. Select the optimum working conditions after considering the emission intensity, the resolution of the spectral lines (or bands) from each other and from adjacent spectral features of other sample constituents, the magnitude of the background radiation, and the steadiness (noise) of readings.

E X P E R I M E N T   1 1 - 1   DETERMINATION OF SODIUM AND POTASSIUM

Standard solutions. Dissolve 2.5416 g of sodium chloride in deionized water and dilute to 1 liter. Dissolve 1.9070 g of potassium chloride or 2.586 g of potassium nitrate in deionized water and dilute to 1 liter. Each solution contains 1,000 $\mu g/ml$ of the respective cation.

Weigh out 2.473 g of lithium carbonate and transfer to a 1-liter volumetric flask. Add approximately 300 ml of deionized water and then add slowly 15 ml of concentrated hydrochloric acid. After the CO_2 has been released, dilute the solution to 1 liter. This solution contains 1,000 $\mu g/ml$ of Li_2O. Most samples of lithium salts are contaminated with considerable sodium and some potassium, and therefore the same batch of stock lithium solution should be used in preparing the working standards used in the internal-standard method.

Working standards. Prepare a set of six standards that contain 5, 10, 25, 50, 75, and 100 $\mu g/ml$ of potassium (or sodium). These solutions will be used in the direct-intensity method.

Prepare a set of seven standards that contain 0, 5, 10, 25, 50, 75, and 100 $\mu g/ml$ of potassium (or sodium), with each solution also containing 100 $\mu g/ml$ of Li_2O. This series will be used in the internal-standard method.

PROCEDURE

Determine the calibration curve for potassium using the direct-intensity method. Use deionized water and the strongest standard solution to adjust the reading scale to zero and 100 divisions (or full scale). Without changing the instrument controls, determine the emission reading for the other concentrations. These directions presuppose that a single-beam flame photometer is available. If not, use the internal-standard method.

When using the internal-standard method, set the instrument zero with the standard containing 100 $\mu g/ml$ of Li_2O but with potassium absent. Be sure any reading scale knob is positioned at the zero mark. Next, set the 100-division (full-scale) reading with the strongest standard aspirating; again be sure the reading dial control is positioned at 100 mark. Recheck each reading once again. Without changing the instrument controls, determine the emission reading for the other concentrations.

At the instructor's discretion, unknown samples may be compared by either or both procedures.

Plot emission intensity vs concentration of potassium from the direct-intensity data on rectilinear graph paper and also on log-log graph paper. Mark the regions where the calibration curve is linear and the log-log plot has a slope of unity.

EXPERIMENT 11-2   INFLUENCE OF FUEL AND OXYGEN (OR AIR) PRESSURE

Use one of the solutions prepared for Experiment 11-1.

Adjust the instrument to read zero when deionized water is aspirated, and to read near midscale when the standard solution is aspirated (direct-intensity method); or use the appropriate zero solution and standard solution, each containing lithium, when using the internal-standard method. Insert the standard solution whose concentration lies immediately below and one whose concentration lies above the original standard solution; measure the emission intensity of each.

Change the fuel pressure by 0.5 lb/in.^{2} but do not change any other instrument controls. Measure the emission intensity of the three standard solutions. Continue to vary the pressure in 0.5-lb/in.^{2} increments over a range of 2–3 lb/in.^{2} and measure the emission of these three solutions.

Plot the emission readings vs the fuel pressure. Explain the difference between the results obtained for the direct-emission and the internal-standard methods.

If provisions are available for varying the air, or oxygen, pressure, this might be done while keeping the fuel pressure at a fixed value. Since this is usually also the aspirating gas, the range of pressures over which the aspirator and burner will operate properly will be limited.

EXPERIMENT 11-3 INFLUENCE OF SOLVENT

Standard solutions. Prepare a set of standards, each containing 25 μg/ml of potassium (or sodium), and 0, 10, 30, 50, and 70 volume percent of isopropyl alcohol (or ethanol). Also prepare a solution that contains 30 volume percent glycerine. Include lithium if using an internal-standard method.

PROCEDURE

Adjust the instrument to read zero with the appropriate solution (water or 100 μg/ml Li$_2$O) and to a scale reading of 20 divisions with the aqueous potassium standard. Now measure the emission intensity of each of the alcoholic standards and the glycerine standard solution.

Plot the emission intensity (direct-reading method) vs the volume percent of alcohol. Explain why little change in emission is noted in the internal-standard method. Does the viscosity of a solution exert an influence on the emission intensity?

With a single-beam photometer a number of organic solvents may be investigated (see Table 11-6 for suggestions).

EXPERIMENT 11-4 DETERMINATION OF IRON

Standard solution. Prepare a stock solution of iron containing 1000 μg/ml by dissolving 1.000 g of iron wire in 11 ml of 6 M HCl. Dilute with about 25 ml of water, add 5 ml of concentrated nitric acid, and boil for 10 min. Cool and dilute to 1 liter with distilled water.

Working curve. Transfer 20, 40, 80, 120, 160, and 200 μg of iron to individual separatory funnels. Add sufficient 12 N HCl to adjust the concentration of HCl to 6 M. Add exactly 10.0 ml of methyl isobutyl ketone to each solution (or *n*-amyl acetate) and equilibrate for at least 2 min at the rate of 30 inversions per minute. Allow the phases to separate. Aspirate the organic phase into an oxygen-acetylene or an oxygen-hydrogen flame. Measure the emission intensity of the atomic line at 372 mμ. To obtain the net emission intensity, subtract the flame background reading taken at 368 mμ. Plot the net emission intensity against the iron concentration.

Suggestions for the further work. Copper-base alloys are suitable samples for unknowns. Weigh samples containing 0.1 to 0.4 mg of iron into 150-ml beakers. Dissolve with 20 ml of 6 N HCl plus a few drops of nitric acid. Transfer the solutions to 50-ml volumetric flasks and dilute to the calibrated volume with 6 M HCl. Transfer aliquots of the sample solutions which contain from 20 to 200 μg of iron to separatory funnels. Dilute to approximately 10 ml with 6 M HCl. Add exactly 10.0 ml of methyl isobutyl ketone and proceed as above to prepare the working curve.

The extraction of iron(III) as a function of hydrogen-ion concentration and of chloride-ion concentration, each independently or merely as total HCl concentration, can be studied over the range 0.01 to 6 M HCl. The percent extraction varies from 100 percent at 6 M to 2.5 percent at 1 M, and less at lower concentrations.

Problems

1. For the analysis of cement samples, a series of standards were prepared and the emission intensity for sodium and potassium was measured at 590 mμ and 768 mμ, respectively. Each standard solution contained 6300 μg/ml of calcium as CaO to compensate for the influence of calcium upon the alkali readings. The results are shown below:

CONCENTRATION,	EMISSION READING	
μg/ml	Na$_2$O	K$_2$O
100	100	100
75	87	80
50	69	58
25	46	33
10	22	15
0	3	0
Cement A	28	69
Cement B	58	51
Cement C	42	63

For each cement sample 1.000 g was dissolved in acid and diluted to exactly 100 ml. Calculate the percent of Na$_2$O and K$_2$O. *Ans.* Cement A contains 0.14% Na$_2$O and 0.62% K$_2$O.

2. In Problem 1, what contributed to the emission reading of the blank at the analytical wavelength for sodium, but did not for potassium? A Beckman model DU spectrometer was employed to obtain the results. Would the blank reading be larger, smaller, or the same if a filter photometer equipped with glass absorption filters had been employed? [See *Anal. Chem.*, 21, 1296 (1949).]

3. Indium has a strong emission line at 451.1 mμ. Using the Beckman model DU with a slit aperture of 0.02 mm, the background read 5.5 units and the line read 350 units, whereas for a slit aperture of 0.05 mm, the background read 35 units and the line read 1400 units. (a) What is the line-to-background ratio for each slit setting? (b) Estimate the dependence of line emission and background reading (due to molecular band systems) upon the slit aperture?

4. Boron gives a series of fluctuation bands due to the radical BO$_2$ which lie in the green portion of the spectrum. Although the overlapping band systems present a problem in the measurement of the flame background, the minimum between adjacent band heads can be used. These results were obtained:

BORON PRESENT,	EMISSION READING	
μg/ml	518-mμ PEAK	505-mμ MINIMUM
0	36	33
50	44	36
100	52	39
150	62	42.5
200	70	45.5

What are the concentrations of boron in these unknowns?

A	45	36.5
B	85	65
C	66	50

[See *Anal. Chem.*, 27, 42 (1955).] *Ans.* Unknown B contains 155 μg/ml.

5. A calibration curve for strontium, taken at 460.7 mμ, was obtained in the presence of 1000 μg/ml of calcium as CaO and also in the absence of added calcium. These results were

STRONTIUM PRESENT,	EMISSION READING	
μg/ml	NO CALCIUM	CALCIUM ADDED
0	0	13
0.25	2	18.5
0.5	6	24
1.0	16	36
2.5	44	70
5.0	94	125
7.5	150	181
10.0	200	238

(a) Graph the calibration curve on rectilinear graph paper and also on log-log paper. (b) What might be the cause of the upward curvature in the region of low concentrations on the rectilinear graph when calcium is absent? (c) Why does the addition of calcium straighten the calibration curve and increase the net emission reading for strontium?

6. Typical emission readings for magnesium at its atomic line are as follows, each reading corrected for background:

MAGNESIUM,	EMISSION IN	MAGNESIUM,	EMISSION IN
μg/ml	SCALE UNITS	μg/ml	SCALE UNITS
1.25	3.5	50	41
2.5	7.0	75	50
5.0	12.4	100	57
10	19.6	150	69.5
15	24.2	200	80
25	30.8	250	87

Plot the data on log-log graph paper. Note the slope of the graph at very low concentrations and also at concentrations above approximately 10 μg/ml of magnesium. What is the explanation for the shape of the log-log plot?

7. In the determination of manganese at 403.3 mμ, solution A, containing an aliquot of the unknown solution, gives a meter reading of 45. Solution B, containing the same quantity of unknown solution plus 100 μg/ml of added manganese, gives a meter reading of 83.5. Each reading has been corrected for background. Calculate the quantity of manganese in solution A. *Ans.* 117 μg/ml

8. Under the same conditions as Problem 7, solution A gave a net reading of 31. Solution B, with 75 μg/ml of added manganese, gave a net reading of 68. Calculate the quantity of manganese in solution A.

9. A sample of mineral ash gave a meter reading of 37. Solutions B and C, containing the same quantity of unknown solution plus 40 and 80 μg/ml of added potassium, respectively, gave net meter readings of 65 and 93. Calculate the quantity of unknown potassium in the original solution. *Ans.* 53 μg/ml.

10. A metal naphthenate sample, ashed, and diluted to a fixed volume, gave a reading of 29. Solutions B and C, containing the same quantity of unknown solution plus 25 and 50 μg/ml of barium gave readings of 53 and 78, respectively. Calculate the quantity of barium in the original solution.

Bibliography

Dean, J. A., *Flame Photometry*, McGraw-Hill, New York, 1960.

Elwell, W. T., and J. A. F. Gidley, *Atomic-Absorption Spectrophotometry*, Pergamon, New York, 1961.

Herrmann, R., and C. Th. J. Alkemade, *Flammenphotometrie*, 2nd ed., Springer-Verlag, Berlin, 1960. English translation: P. T. Gilbert, Jr., "Flame Photometry," Vol. 14 in *Chemical Analysis*, P. J. Elving and I. M. Kolthoff (Ed.), Interscience, New York, 1963.

Mavrodineanu, R., and H. Boiteux, *Flame Spectroscopy*, Wiley, New York, 1965.

Literature Cited

1. Alkemade, C. Th. J., *Spectrochim. Acta*, **11**, 7 (1957).
2. Barnes, R. B., D. Richardson, J. W. Berry, and R. L. Hood, *Ind. Eng. Chem. Anal. Ed.*, **17**, 605 (1945).
3. Dean, J. A., *Flame Photometry*, Chapter 5.
4. Dean, J. A., *op. cit.*, Chapters 11–19.
5. Dean, J. A., *Am. Soc. Testing Mater., Spec. Tech. Publ.*, **238**, 43 (1958).
6. Dean, J. A., and W. J. Carnes, *Analyst*, **87**, 743 (1962).
7. Fassel, V. A., R. B. Myers, and R. N. Kniseley, *Spectrochim. Acta*, **19**, 1194 (1963).
8. Gaydon, A. G., and H. G. Wolfhard, *Flames: Their Structure, Radiation and Temperature*, Chapman & Hall, London, 1953.
9. Grotrian, W., *Graphische Darstellung der Spektren von Atomen and Ionen, mit ein, zwei und drei Valenzelektronen*," Part II, Springer-Verlag, Berlin, 1928.
10. Gilbert, P. T., Jr., *Anal. Chem.*, **34**, 1025 (1962).
11. Lundegardh, H., *Die Quantitative Spektralanalyse der Elemente*, Vols. 1 and 2, G. Fischer Verlag., Jena, 1929, 1934.
12. Mavrodineanu, R., "Colloquium spectroscopicum internationale VIII," 15 (1959); *Spectrochim. Acta*, **17**, 1016 (1961).
13. Mavrodineanu, R., and H. Boiteux, *L'Analyse Spectrale Quantitative par La Flamme*, Masson et Cie, Paris, 1954, Chapter XIV.
14. Mitchell, A. C. G., and M. W. Zemansky, *Resonance Radiation and Excited Atoms*, Cambridge U. P., New York, 1961.
15. Walsh, A., *Spectrochim. Acta*, **7**, 110 (1955).

Raman Spectroscopy

Since its discovery in 1928, the Raman effect has been important as a method for the elucidation of molecular structure, for locating various functional groups or chemical bonds in molecules, and for the quantitative analysis of complex mixtures, particularly for major components. Although Raman spectra are related to infrared absorption spectra, a Raman spectrum arises in a quite different manner and thus provides complementary information.

Theory

The Raman effect arises when a beam of monochromatic exciting radiation passes through a transparent medium that contains molecules capable of undergoing a change in polarizability. Some of the incident photons collide with molecules in the sample. Most of the collisions are elastic (Rayleigh scattering) in the sense that the frequency of the scattered light is unchanged from the frequency of the incident radiation. However, a small fraction of the collisions are inelastic and involve an exchange of energy between the scatterer and the incident photon. The fundamental equation for the energy interchange is

$$h\nu_1 + E_1 = h\nu_2 + E_2 \tag{12-1}$$

or

$$\Delta E = h\nu_1 - h\nu_2 = \pm h\Delta\nu \tag{12-2}$$

357

where ν_1 and ν_2 are the frequencies of the incident photon and the scattered radiation, respectively, and E_1, E_2 are the initial and final energy states of the scatterer. The incident photon elevates the scattering molecule to a quasi-excited state having a height above the initial state equal to the energy of the exciting radiation (Fig. 12-1). On the return to the ground electronic state, a

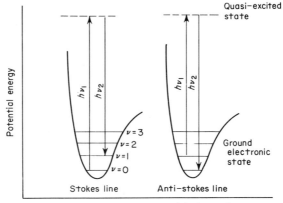

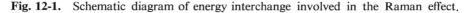

Fig. 12-1. Schematic diagram of energy interchange involved in the Raman effect.

vibrational quantum of energy may remain with the scatterer, and hence there is a decrease in the frequency of the re-emitted (scattered) radiation. If the scattering molecule is already in an excited vibrational state, a vibrational quantum of energy may be taken from the scatterer, leaving it in a lower vibrational energy state and thus increasing the frequency of the scattered radiation. These scattered lines, called Raman lines, are characteristic of the vibrational modes of the substance irradiated and therefore a "fingerprint" of that substance.

The frequency of the exciting line must have less energy than the minimum energy required to elevate the molecule being irradiated into the lowest lying excited electronic state; otherwise absorption may be followed by fluorescence or photodecomposition (or both) and no Raman spectrum will be the result.

The shift in frequency of the scattered Raman lines is proportional to the vibrational energy involved in the transition, and thus the shift is a measure of the separation of the two vibrational energy states of the molecule. It is independent of the frequency of the incident radiation; in fact, a suite of Raman lines will be associated with each exciting radiation when several different wavelengths simultaneously irradiate a sample. The normal process, a decrease in energy of the incident photon, results in scattered radiation known as Stokes lines; the reverse process gives anti-Stokes lines. The former will be stronger because of the relatively small number of molecules in a higher vibrational level of the ground state at room temperature. The frequency difference is subject to the selection rule $\Delta\nu = \pm 1$, which, however, does not hold strictly for an anharmonic oscillator.

It is the polarizability of the molecule which determines whether the Raman effect will be observed. Polarizability, it will be recalled, is a measure of the elastic deformation of the vibrational (or other quantized) configuration of a molecule and, in the Raman effect, measures the dipole moment induced in the scatterer by the incident electromagnetic radiation. If the polarizability of the molecule changes with the vibrational mode, the molecule will be Raman active.

Raman Spectrum

A Raman spectrum consists of a group of lines lying on the long wavelength side of the very intense exciting line. Figure 12-2 is the Raman spectrum for *o*-xylene obtained with 4358-Å exciting radiation. Compare the spectrum with the infrared absorption spectrum shown in Fig. 5-22 (page 150). The spacings between the Raman lines are related to the vibrational-rotational spacings in the infrared absorption spectrum. However, the relative intensities of the Raman lines and infrared absorption bands often differ, and some transitions may be weak or absent in one of the spectra.

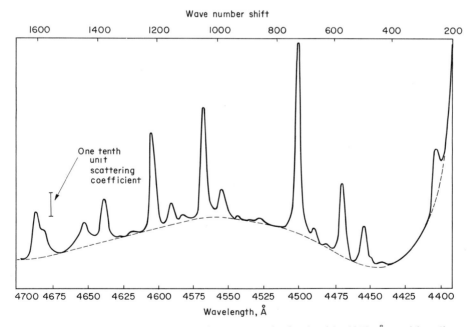

Fig. 12-2. Raman spectral trace of *o*-xylene obtained with 4358 Å exciting line.

Example 12-1

Suppose, for example, that the blue 4358-Å line of the mercury arc (22,937 cm⁻¹) is passed through a sample of carbon tetrachloride. The Raman spectrum contains the exciting line and, displaced from it, a series of comparatively weak Raman lines at 4401, 4420, and 4449 Å, and a feeble pair at 4510 and 4515 Å. The frequency difference from the exciting line (λ_i), or Raman shift ($\Delta\bar{\nu}$), expressed as wave numbers, is given by

$$\Delta\bar{\nu} = = \frac{10^8}{\lambda_i} - \frac{10^8}{\lambda_R}$$

For the Raman lines of carbon tetrachloride, the frequency differences of the displaced lines and the relative intensities of the lines are given in Table 12-1.

Table 12-1 | *Raman Lines Observed for Carbon Tetrachloride*

WAVELENGTH OF RAMAN LINE, Å†	WAVE NUMBER SHIFT OF RAMAN LINE, cm⁻¹	RELATIVE INTENSITY OF LINE‡	DEPOLARIZATION FACTOR
4401	218	7	0.857
4420	314	9	0.857
4449	459	10	0.046
4510	762	4	0.84
4515	790	4	0.83

†Exciting light is 4358Å (22,937 cm⁻¹) mercury-arc line.
‡On a relative scale with 10 the strongest line in intensity.

In general a sample is scanned from about 4000–150 cm⁻¹, which in angstrom units extends from 5260 to 4385 Å when the incident radiation lies at 4358 Å. Raman shifts are not confined to vibrational changes, but have also been observed for rotational changes. These Raman shifts, however, are seldom greater than 75 cm⁻¹; consequently the Raman lines are very much closer to the wavelength of the unscattered line. Great care is required to resolve them from the intense unscattered line.

The most frequently used system of intensity measurements is to correlate the various lines on a basis of 0–10, where 0 is the intensity of the weakest and 10 the intensity of the strongest line in each spectrum. For correlation of molecular structure and different Raman spectra this method is satisfactory. For analytical work, however, this method does not allow the intensity comparison of a line in one spectrum with a line in another. A reproducible method for expressing scattering intensities involves employing a reference standard. Usually the 459-cm⁻¹ line of carbon tetrachloride is scanned before and after the spectral trace of each sample. Scattering intensities (peak heights on the trace) are then converted to scattering coefficients by dividing the recorded height of the sample peak by the average of the heights of the two traces of the carbon tetrachloride peak. Both the standard and sample must be recorded in cells of the same dimension.

Instrumentation

The observation of a Raman spectrum entails illumination of the sample with monochromatic light and observing the light scattered at right angles to the incident radiation. Raman intensities are roughly 0.01 percent of that of the incident radiation. Consequently, intense irradiation, sensitive detection, and high light-gathering power coupled with freedom from extraneous scattered incident light, must be built into a Raman spectrometer. Figure 12-3

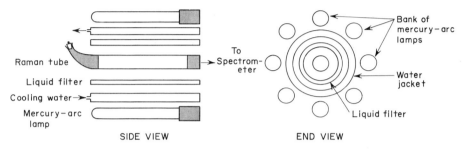

Fig. 12-3. General arrangement of excitation source and Raman sample tube.

shows the typical arrangement of source and sample and the handling of the scattered light. The horn shape of the sample cell reduces direct reflection of the source from the back of the cell.

The sample tube is irradiated longitudinally with monochromatic light to excite only one Raman spectrum rather than a number of superimposed spectra. A helix Toronto-type mercury lamp or a bank of four to eight individual tubular mercury-arc lamps of the H-type surround the sample tube. The Raman tube is protected from the heat generated by the lamps by means of a glass water jacket through which tap water is circulated. Useful lines in the mercury-arc spectrum include the ultraviolet 2537 and 3650 Å, the violet 4047 Å, the blue 4358 Å, and the green 5461 Å. Choice of the line is governed by several factors. The intensity of the Raman spectrum is proportional to the fourth power of the frequency of the exciting line. Thus, it is advisable to use as high an excitation frequency as possible without engendering photodecomposition. On the other hand, the resolution required for a separation of 5 cm^{-1} at 2500 Å is 0.25 Å, and at 5000 Å it is 1 Å. Also, the interval between mercury-arc lines should be sufficient to obviate overlap from each suite of Raman shifts unless appropriate filters are employed to remove unwanted lines. Where it can be used the mercury 4358 Å line is usually chosen. Raman shifts up to 4000 cm^{-1} overlap only one other weak arc line at 4916 Å, and Raman shifts arising from the 4047 Å line can be reduced in intensity by filters if the overlap proves troublesome.*

---

*A helium-neon laser beam (6328 Å) is employed in the Perkin-Elmer Raman spectrometer It provides extreme monochromaticity. Excitation energy is conserved by coating the cell windows with multilayer dielectric, reflective films, tuned to the laser output.

Liquid filters are placed between the source and the sample tube in order to remove high-energy radiation that might cause fluorescence or photo-decomposition, to isolate a single exciting line, and to remove the continuous spectrum in the region occupied by the Raman lines. For 4358 Å excitation a saturated solution of sodium nitrite is used to remove the ultraviolet lines and the violet line at 4047 Å; a saturated solution of praseodymium chloride removes the continuum to the long wavelength side out to 4850 Å; and a 3-cm thickness of 0.002 percent Rhodamine 5GDN Extra and 2 percent p-nitro-toluene in ethanol removes the blue-green and green light. Too much heat is involved to use glass absorption filters.

The Raman spectrum can be photographed with an ordinary spectrograph, but so weak are the Raman lines that long exposure times are required. Modern instruments have photomultiplier tubes for direct measurement and automatic scanning of a spectrum. Scattered light is gathered through a

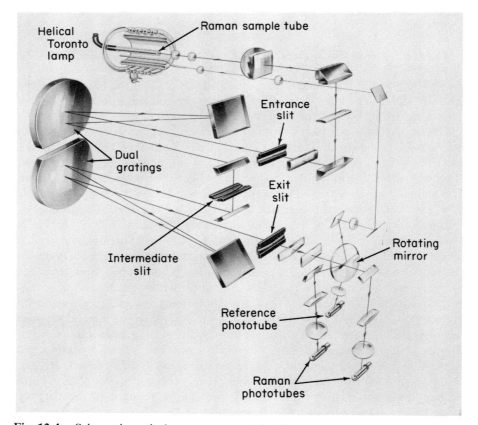

Fig. 12-4. Schematic optical arrangement of the Cary model 81 Raman spectropho-tometer. (Courtesy of Applied Physics Corp.)

plane window at the end of the Raman tube and is focused into the front slit of the spectrograph.

The optical system is designed so that the maximum amount of scattered Raman radiation is accepted by the spectrometer and so that stray light is rejected. A suitable prism or grating instrument has a wide aperture and a medium dispersion, sufficient to provide a resolving power of 20,000, needed to separate two lines 1 cm^{-1} apart at 1000 cm^{-1} when using 4358 Å exciting radiation. The stray light problem from scattering by dust particles in the sample is best countered by the use of a double monochromator.

Instruments have been assembled by adding attachments to existing spectrographs. An example is the scanning attachment and Raman source unit supplied with the large-aperture Hilger two-prism spectrograph. The Lane-Wells spectrometer (Applied Research Laboratories) contains three prisms in series. The Perkin-Elmer model 12 spectrometer, modified to accept a grating, has also been adapted to Raman spectroscopy.

The Cary model 81 Raman spectrophotometer, the optical schematic of which is shown in Fig. 12-4, exemplifies an instrument designed specifically to record the Raman effect. Radiant energy from the Raman tube is focused by a lens near the sample cell on an image slicer. The image slicer is a unique arrangement of optical elements which convert the rectangular apertures at the Raman tube into a series of 20 thin slices which are later reassembled end-to-end so as to match the entrance slit of the monochromator. In this way most of the available Raman radiation at the cell is passed into the monochromator. The Raman light is then directed by two right-angle prisms and associated lenses to the entrance slit of the monochromator. A double monochromator with two gratings of 1200 grooves/mm is used. They are

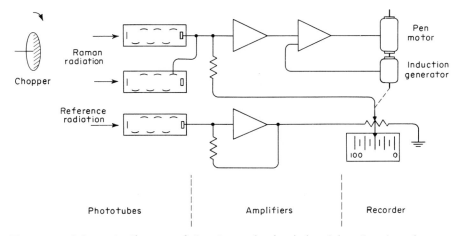

Fig. 12-5. Schematic diagram of the electronic circuit involving the photodetectors and read-out device. (Courtesy of Applied Physics Corp.)

blazed for high efficiency in the first order at 4500 Å, and arranged in a
Czerny-Littrow mount. Two spherical mirrors collimate the light falling on
the gratings. A wavelength drive rotates the gratings linearly in wave numbers,
the wave-number setting being read on a Veeder counter. Scanning speeds
can be varied from 0.005 to 50 cm^{-1}/sec in 12 steps. The entrance, intermediate, and exit slits are in reality double slits. Energy emerging from the
exit slit falls on a rotating semicircular mirror which directs the radiation
alternately to two photomultiplier tubes at 30 cps. The outputs of these
phototubes are of opposite phase, but when the last dynode of one tube is
connected to the anode of the other (Fig. 12-5), the signals are combined in
phase. This twin phototube arrangement avoids the loss in energy (50 percent)
that would otherwise occur during the chopping of a beam. An alternate
optical path brings a portion of the exciting radiation to a reference phototube so that, after amplification, the reference and Raman beams are compared
in an electronic-null system.

Structural Characteristics

Since the Raman spectrum is characteristic of the scattering molecule,
both in wave number shift and the intensities of the various lines, it can be
used like any other physical property as a means of identification. A valuable
feature of a Raman spectrum from the point of view of the shape of the molecule in structural determination is the behavior toward polarized light. By
placing a suitable polarizing device, often Polaroid sheets surrounding the
Raman tube, first with the plane of polarization vertical and then horizontal,
each Raman line can be divided into a strong part (I_h, the horizontal component of the electric vector in the scattered beam) and a weak part (I_v,
the vertical component). The ratio of the two intensities

$$p = I_v/I_h \qquad (12\text{-}3)$$

is called the depolarization factor. The horizontal (parallel) vector is always
preponderant and, according to theory, the depolarization factor approaches
the value of zero for highly symmetrical types of vibrations. The theoretical
maximum for p is 0.857 (6/7), when the line is said to be depolarized. Quantitative data are difficult and time-consuming to obtain, but qualitative results
often are of value in assigning frequencies to particular modes of vibration.
A vibrational frequency that is antisymmetrical or degenerate to one or more
symmetry elements will be depolarized if observable or else will be inactive.
Depolarization factors are given in Table 12-1 for the Raman lines of carbon
tetrachloride.

A qualitative identification of a Raman spectrum consists in the evaluation
of the wavelengths or frequencies of the lines, their intensities, and state of

polarization, although the latter is needed only in investigations of molecular structure. These data are then compared with spectra obtained for pure compounds. Correlations exist between the presence of certain functional groups in a molecule and Raman lines at certain frequencies, as in infrared absorption spectra (q.v.). The spectrum of the unknown is compared with that of pure compounds until a match is obtained. For polyatomic molecules, only fundamental changes in the vibrational contributions to the energy are ordinarily observed in the Raman effect. Combination and overtone shifts are very weak. The strongest Raman transitions are from totally symmetrical vibrations, which are weak or nonexistent in infrared work. Thus, sharp lines are observed in the Raman spectrum for molecules such as CH_4 and CCl_4 in which the motion of the nuclei is symmetrical to the center of symmetry. Other examples of differences between Raman and infrared spectra are found in the C-S stretching frequency near 650 cm^{-1} and the *trans*-olefin bands at 1675 cm^{-1}, both strong in Raman but absent or very weak in the infrared.

Covalently bonded inorganic compounds are Raman active. Raman spectra have found application in the determination of the degree of dissociation of strong electrolytes in aqueous solution.

Quantitative Analysis

For mixtures in which the components are all of the same molecular type, there is a direct proportionality between the scattering coefficient and the volume fraction of the compound present. For mixtures of dissimilar type, Raman displacements will vary among the various compounds, and a broad band is recorded at the position characteristic of these bond types. Scattering coefficients based on recorded peak height cannot be employed under these conditions. How-

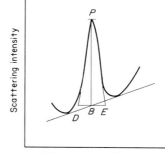

Fig. 12-6. Quantitative analysis by means of the scattering area.

ever, the area under the recorded peak can be used as a measurement of scattering intensity. A recorded trace is handled as shown in Fig. 12-6, where

$$\text{Scattering area} = (\text{scattering coefficient})(\text{base width})$$

$$= \left(\frac{\overline{PB}}{\text{height of CCl}_4 \text{ peak}}\right)(\overline{DBE}) \qquad (12\text{-}4)$$

Although Raman spectroscopy is not useful for the determination of components at low concentrations, it is ideal for major components.

Applications

Until recently, the sample volume used to be 10–50 ml. With modern instruments, sample volumes as small as 0.25 ml are used, although perhaps 2 ml is an average sample size. Solutions need to be at least 0.1 M in strength. Water is a satisfactory solvent, since the Raman spectrum of water is very weak when excited by visible light.

The samples examined must be free of dust, turbidity, colored material, and fluorescing impurities. Dust and suspended matter, for example, cause an increase in background because of the Tyndall effect, the suspended material scattering the light of the mercury continuum. Colored samples, where the absorbing region lies in the wavelength region of their Raman spectrum, will give distorted Raman intensities. One of the most satisfactory methods for removal of these materials is a simple distillation where the distillate is collected directly in the Raman tube. Mixtures must be distilled to dryness to avoid any effects of fractionation.

Raman spectra have been obtained with gases and solids, but liquids are by far the easiest to handle. The diffuse nature of gases requires the use of large sampling tubes if weak lines are to be observed, thus complicating the design of the irradiation system. With solid samples, difficulties due to excessive general scattering are severe.

Investigation of bond angles, bond stiffness, and other structural confirmation require Raman data in addition to infrared studies. Raman spectroscopy has been applied to the analysis of strong acids and other aqueous solutions, and to the determination of the degree of dissociation of strong electrolytes and the corresponding activity coefficients.

LABORATORY WORK

General Directions

With photographic recording, the following are required: plates, darkroom equipment, microphotometer, means of plate calibration, means of wavelength measurement, contrivances for depolarization measurements, and apparatus for purifying samples. Stamm has described the use of a calcite Wollaston prism and quarter-wave plates for depolarization measurements [R. F. Stamm, *Ind. Eng. Chem., Anal. Ed.,* **17,** 322 (1945)].

A spectrometer of aperture about $f/16$ gives quite satisfactory results with a slit width of 0.1–0.2 mm and slit height of 18–20 mm.

For 4358 Å excitation 103-J Eastman spectroscopic plates are suitable, ordered with antihalation backing. For 5461 Å excitation Eastman 103-F plates are useful for an overall survey. The plates are developed in Eastman D-19 for 4 min at 18°C, rinsed for 20–30 sec, and fixed for 15 min in Eastman F-5, all at 18°.

Exposure times range from 4 to 8 min generally, but the exact time should be obtained from the instructor.

Widely used reference lines for quantitative work, or wave number calibration, are the 459 cm⁻¹ and the 313 cm⁻¹ lines of carbon tetrachloride, and the 801 cm⁻¹ line of cyclohexane.

Liquid filters for isolation of the 4358 Å mercury-arc line are described in the text. The green line at 5461 Å can be isolated by a solution of 0.15 g malachite green and 0.3 g tartrazine in 1 liter of water.

Unless a double monochromator is used, it is advisable to distill all solutions directly into the Raman tube.

Production of Spectrograms

Place in the apparatus a tube containing pure carbon tetrachloride (or other reference standard). Scan the short section of the spectrum which includes the 459 cm^{-1} Raman shift of this material. Then insert the tube containing the sample for analysis and scan the spectrum from 4000 to 150 cm^{-1} (5270–4385 Å). A second carbon tetrachloride calibration mark is recorded for a check on the first calibration and if, after the recording is processed, the two standard deflections of carbon tetrachloride, before and after the determination of the spectral scan of the sample, are found to agree within 2 to 3 percent, the spectrogram of the sample is used for analytical work.

Problems

1. For exciting light of 4358 Å, the spectral trace of benzene shows Raman lines for $\Delta\nu = 606, 850, 992, 1176, 1584, 1605, 3047,$ and 3063 cm^{-1}. At what wavelengths would these Raman lines appear if benzene is irradiated with monochromatic light of these wavelengths: (a) 5461, (b) 4358, (c) 4047, (d) 2537, and (e) 3888 Å (helium arc)?

2. If unfiltered mercury-arc radiation were used to excite the Raman spectrum of benzene, to what extent would each suite of Raman lines overlap?

3. What would be the relative scattering intensity of the 992 cm^{-1} Raman line for each of the exciting wavelengths listed in Problem 1?

4. Raman spectral traces for the three trimethylbenzenes are given in the figure. Select Raman shifts for the determination of each component. There are two sets of wave numbers. *Ans.* 1,3,5-trimethylbenzene could be determined at either 1298 or 570 cm^{-1}.

5. For each unknown mixture of the trimethylbenzenes, compute the volume percent of each. The scattering coefficient of the pure compound at each analytical wave number is tabulated:

	1,2,3-		1,2,4-		1,3,5-	
	652 cm^{-1}	0.627	716 cm^{-1}	0.208	570 cm^{-1}	0.555
Unknown A		0.209		0.069		0.185
B		0.251		0.054		0.189
C		0.157		0.077		0.211

Ans. Unknown A contains 33.3 percent of each component.

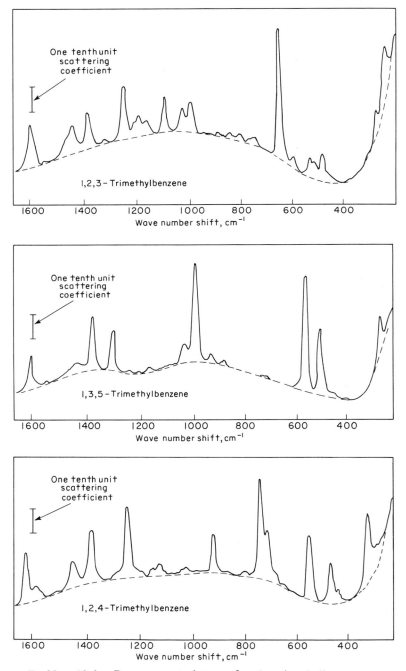

Problem 12-4.   Raman spectral traces for the trimethylbenzenes.

Bibliography

Fenske, M. R., W. G. Braun, R. V. Wiegand, D. Quiggle, R. H. McCormick, and D. H. Rank, *Ind. Eng. Chem., Anal. Ed.*, **19**, 700 (1947).

Herzberg, G., *Molecular Spectra and Molecular Structure*, 2nd ed., Vols. I and II, Van Nostrand, Princeton, N.J., 1950, 1951.

Hibben, J. H., *The Raman Effect and Its Chemical Applications*, Reinhold, New York, 1939.

Stamm, R. F., *Ind. Eng. Chem., Anal. Ed.*, **17**, 318 (1945).

CHAPTER | 13

Fluorescence and
Phosphorescence Methods

This chapter examines the ways in which a molecule can get rid of its excess energy following absorption of electromagnetic radiation. When dissipation of energy takes place by re-emission of radiation in random directions, the behavior is known as photoluminescence. If there is a measurable time interval between absorption and re-emission, the phenomenon is called phosphorescence. The lifetime for phosphorescence varies from 10^{-4} sec to 10 sec or more, whereas that for fluorescence is of the order of 10^{-4} to 10^{-8} sec. Phosphorescence and fluorescence can be distinguished also by their spectra.

The exciting radiation and re-emitted radiation may lie in the visible, ultraviolet, or more energetic regions of the spectrum. The case in which the exciting radiation lies in the X-ray region and the fluorescent radiation is also in the X-ray region is considered in Chapter 8. This chapter is concerned with the cases where the exciting radiation and resultant photoluminescence lie in the ultraviolet or visible region of the spectrum. Fluorescence methods will be considered first, followed by phosphorescence methods.

Fluorescence Methods

The fluorescence process is characterized by two spectra. A fluorescent molecule emits its *fluorescence spectrum* after it absorbs radiation anywhere within its *excitation spectrum*, which may differ from the usual absorption

370

spectrum of the molecule as a result of instrumental artifacts. The spectral distribution of the fluorescence radiation is a physical and absolute character-istic of a given substance and is useful for qualitative considerations. The emission intensity of fluorescence at a given wavelength is useful for quantita-tive analysis with a given instrument after careful standardization.

Fluorescence Spectrum

Before fluorescence emission can occur, a fluorescent species must be exposed to radiation in the portion of the spectrum where the molecule is capable of absorbing energy. When a quanta of light impinges on a molecule, it is absorbed in about 10^{-15} sec. If the energy of the molecule is thereby increased sufficiently, an electronic transition will take place to an upper electronic state. A schematic energy-level diagram for a diatomic molecule is shown in Fig. 13-1. The abscissa represents the internuclear distance between the two atoms,

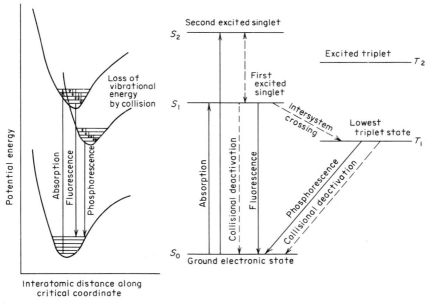

Fig. 13-1.   Schematic energy-level diagram for a diatomic molecule.

and the ordinate represents potential energy. The absorption is a highly specific phenomenon, and radiation of a particular energy can be absorbed only by characteristic structures. The absorption transitions originate usually in the lowest vibrational level of the ground electronic state (denoted G or S_0). Now in the ground state of most molecules each electron is paired with another; i.e., in each orbital there are two electrons whose spins are opposed and cancel each other. Such a state is called a singlet state and given the symbol S. When radiant energy of a frequency within a normal absorption band of the molecule is absorbed, one of the paired electrons is raised to an upper excited singlet state, S_1 or perhaps even S_2. These singlet transitions were responsible for the visible and ultraviolet absorption spectra discussed in Chapter 4.

The excited singlet state persists for a finite time of the order of 10^{-8} to 10^{-4} sec. During this time interval any absorbed energy in excess of the lowest vibrational energy level of the first excited state is rapidly dissipated. Dissipation of vibrational energy may involve transfer of energy by intermolecular collisions with other molecules or by partition of vibrational energy to other modes of rotation and vibration within the molecule until the lowest vibrational level ($\nu = 0$) of the excited singlet state S_1 is attained (see small arrows, Fig. 13-1). The probability for return of the electron to the ground electronic state is highest at this point. If all the excess energy is not dissipated further by collisions with other molecules, then, after a short period of time which is characteristic of the molecule (10^{-8} to 10^{-4} sec), the electron returns to the ground electronic level. The transition from the excited singlet state to one of the vibrational levels within the ground state leads to a release of energy and gives rise to fluorescence emission. The fluorescence emission spectrum will appear on the low frequency (longer wavelength) side of the absorption band of longest wavelength, and it will appear as a series of emission bands, usually rather diffuse unless observed in a rigid medium.

The fluorescence emission spectrum of a material must be determined before the wavelength for the measurement of fluorescence can be selected. The excitation spectrum must also be determined. To obtain these spectra a fluorescence spectrometer (q.v.) is desirable, although the fluorescence spectrum can be observed with a visual spectrometer or photographed with a spectrograph of high light-gathering power.

Excitation Spectrum

The excitation spectrum is represented by a plot of the exciting wavelength against the intensity of the fluorescence at the wavelength of some fluorescence maximum. If the fluorescence spectrum is strong enough, one can determine the excitation spectrum by placing a cuvette with the solution in a spectrometer and observing the fluorescence visually or photometrically while slowly varying the wavelength of the exciting light from the spectrometer. Examination of the excitation spectrum will reveal those portions of the absorption spectrum that give rise to fluorescence emission. As an example, the absorption, fluorescence emission, and excitation curves for the aluminum complex with acid alizarin Garnet R are illustrated in Fig. 13-2. The excitation spectrum possesses band peaks at 350, 430 and 470 mμ (but none at very short wavelengths), whereas the absorption spectrum exhibits peaks at 270, 350, and 480 mμ.[16]

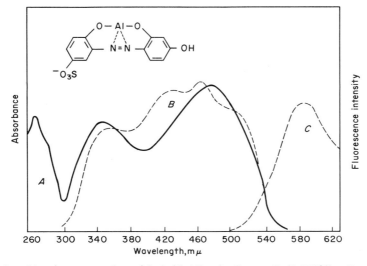

Fig. 13-2. Aluminum complex with Acid Alizarin Garnet R (0.008%). Curve *A*, the absorption spectrum; curve *B*, the fluorescence excitation spectrum; and curve *C*, the fluorescence emission spectrum. From Ref. 16.

When a fluorescence spectrometer is used at constant slit width, the "apparent" excitation and fluorescence spectra obtained are a function not only of the absolute fluorescence characteristics of the substance being measured, but also of the characteristics of the particular instrument. For purely routine work, the uncorrected spectra are often adequate, but it is desirable to correct the spectra if the information is to be of maximum value to other workers. The "true" spectrum is a plot of fluorescence intensity (measured in quanta per unit frequency interval) against frequency. To determine this, the apparent curve has to be corrected for the changes with frequency of (a) photomultiplier sensitivity, (b) the band width of the monochromator, and (c) the changing transmission of the monochromator.[8,9,11] The point-by-point correction is tedious, and it is a great advantage to have an instrument that records directly the true spectrum.

Molecular Structure

The first requirement for fluorescence is an absorbing molecular structure —the greater the absorbance of a molecule the more intense will its fluorescence be. For many materials the true excitation spectrum is proportional to the molar absorptivity of the compound; hence this spectrum resembles the absorption spectrum. Fluorescence may be expected generally in molecules that contain multiple-conjugated double bonds with a high degree of resonance stability, although substituents may alter greatly the degree of fluorescence. At least one electron-donating group, such as —NH₂ or —OH, should be on the resonating nucleus. A fruitful field is that of aromatic and heterocyclic compounds, both simple and complex. On the other hand, electron-withdrawing groups, such as —COOH, —NO₂, —N=N—, and halides, diminish or even destroy fluorescence.[17]

Ring closure is conducive to the fluorescence of aromatic compounds. Compare, for example, fluorescein (I) with phenolphthalein (II). Metal

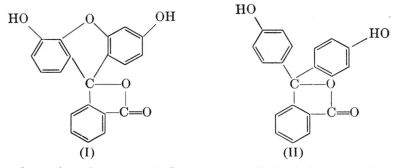

(I)   (II)

chelate formation also promotes fluorescence.[16] In both instances, the structures induce rigidity into the molecule as a whole and minimize internal vibration. Also, fluorescing structures are coplanar with respect to the chromophore, whereas nonfluorescing structures exhibit a molecular crowding which interferes with coplanarity of the chromophoric structure. In the chelate structure from which the data in Fig. 13-2 were obtained, the aluminum ion combined with the cis isomer of the 0,0'-dihydroxyazo benzene dye and held the molecule in a rigid planar position.

Charge status of the chromophore has an important influence on fluorescence emission. Sharp changes of fluorescence occur both in intensity and in position with pH of the solution, although little effect on the absorption spectrum is noticed. Dissociations which lead to increased resonance energy enhance fluorescence. For example, in neutral or alkaline solution, the violet fluorescence of aniline base (III) extends into the visible, corresponding to the long wavelength absorption band associated with the resonating structures (IV) and (V). In sufficiently acid solution, the fluorescence loses its long wavelength band and becomes similar to that of benzene. The anilinium cation (VI) has only the same resonance possibilities as benzene. The fluorescence of naphthalenediols, as a function of pH, is shown in Fig. 13-3. The curve shown for the molecular form of 2,6-diol is typical of most curves

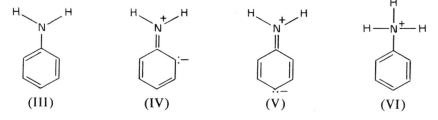

(III)   (IV)   (V)   (VI)

obtained, the break in the curve at the lower pH corresponding to the pK_a of the excited state of the molecule, and the second, to the pK_a of the ground state. In the curve for 1,5-diol, the third break is due to the pK_a for excited-state dissociation of the hemi-ion.[2]

Some substances are so sensitive to pH that they can be used as indicators in acid-base titrations. They will fluoresce in ultraviolet light and change in color or have their fluorescence quenched with change in pH. The merit of such indicators is that they can be employed in the titration of colored (even intensely colored) solu-

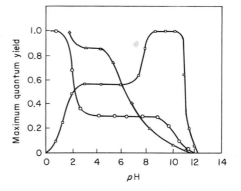

Fig. 13-3. Quantum efficiency as a function of pH for some selected naphthalenediols: O, molecular 2,5-diol; △, molecular 1,3-diol; □, hemi-ionic 1,5-diol. From Ref. 2.

tions. The solution to be titrated is simply placed in a dark box, illuminated with a mercury lamp equipped with a black glass envelope, and the progress of the titration observed visually. Some fluorescent indicators for acid-base titrations are listed in Table 13-1. Photofluorometric titrations are as feasible as regular photometric titrations. Even complexometric titrations are possible. When EDTA plus calcein is used as indicator, and calcium ion as titrant, the solution does not fluoresce prior to the end point, but upon reaching the end point the solution becomes highly fluorescent due to formation of the calcium complex with the indicator.

Fluorescence is not as widespread as light absorption because competing "quenching" processes tend to decrease the quantum yield of fluorescence. If all the excited molecules finally emit fluorescence, the efficiency of the process is unity. The quantum efficiency is usually less than unity because some of the excited molecules return to the ground state by other mechanisms than the

Table 13-1	Typical Fluorescence Indicators

NAME OF INDICATOR	pH RANGE	COLOR CHANGE
3,6-Dihydroxyphthalimide	0.0– 2.5	Colorless to yellow-green
Erythrosin B	2.5– 4.0	Colorless to green
Chromotropic acid	3.0– 4.5	Colorless to blue
Fluorescein	4.0– 6.0	Colorless to green
β-Naphthoquinoline	4.4– 6.3	Blue to colorless
Umbelliferone	6.5– 8.0	Faint blue to bright blue
o-Coumaric acid	7.2– 9.0	Colorless to green
Naphthol AS	8.2–10.3	Colorless to yellow-green

emission process responsible for fluorescence. If the absorption process leads to an electronic state in which the energy is greater than the bond strength of one of the linkages, then excitation energy is lost by molecular dissociation before fluorescence can take place. Deactivation can also occur when there is a crossing of potential-energy surfaces of the excited and the ground electronic states of two portions of the same molecule or with another solute or solvent molecule. The former may lead to phosphorescence but at room temperature it is not an efficient process. The latter would lead to thermal degradation. Sometimes, of course, quenching effects can be used to determine the concentration of the inhibiting substance.

Intermolecular transfer between the fluorophor and other molecules does not operate if the solute concentration is sufficiently low so that average distance between molecules is considerably greater than 30 Å. Suitable dilution may therefore lessen quenching. The probability of external conversion transfer of energy tends to be reduced when working at low temperatures and in a medium of high viscosity in which the rotational relaxation time of the solute molecules is much longer than the lifetime of the excited state. Hence substances fluoresce more brightly in a rigid state or in glycerol as compared with alcohol or water solutions. Degradation is also less rapid in the rigid state, and for this reason, glasses are often prepared and measured at liquid nitrogen temperature (Fig. 13-4). Low-temperature fluorescence is also characterized by a shift to higher frequencies, which is believed due to fluorescence emission from a solute molecule without solvent reorientation at the low temperature.[3]

Fluorescence Intensity as Related to Concentration

The magnitude of the total fluorescence will depend on the population of fluorophors in the solution. This forms the basis of the quantitative use of fluorescence measurements in analysis. Beer's law states that in a solution of an absorbing substance the absorbance is directly proportional to the concentration. The fraction of light transmitted is

$$\frac{P}{P_0} = e^{-\epsilon b C} \tag{13-1}$$

The corresponding fraction of light absorbed is then

$$1 - \frac{P}{P_0} = (1 - e^{-\epsilon b C}) \tag{13-2}$$

When Eq. 13-2 is rearranged, the amount of light absorbed is

$$P_0 - P = P_0(1 - e^{-\epsilon b C}) \tag{13-3}$$

The total fluorescence intensity will be equal to the rate of light absorption (quanta per unit time) multiplied by the quantum efficiency of fluorescence, ϕ,[13]

$$F = (P_0 - P)\phi \qquad (13\text{-}4)$$

whence

$$F = \phi P_0 (1 - e^{-\epsilon bC}) \qquad (13\text{-}5)$$

For very dilute solutions in which only a small fraction of light is absorbed, i.e., the term ϵbC is not greater than about 0.05, Eq. 13-5 reduces to

$$F = k\phi P_0 \epsilon b C \qquad (13\text{-}6)$$

where k is an instrumental constant to handle instrumental artifacts and the fact that fluorescence will be emitted in all directions but will be viewed only through a limited aperture.

Thus, for very dilute solutions of the order of a few parts per million or less, the fluorescence intensity is proportional to the concentration. However, when the concentration increases, the form of the plot of fluorescence intensity against concentration tends towards kP_0 asymptotically (Fig. 13-4). The fluorescence becomes noticeably concentrated near the entrance of the cuvette and there is less and less through the remainder of the cuvette. Although the exciting light does penetrate the solution, it is not evenly distributed along its path. Absorption of the fluorescence emission by substances in the solution may even cause the curve to bend downward at high concentrations.

· With multiplier phototubes and high-gain amplifiers, very low fluorescence intensities can be measured. It is therefore advantageous to make the exciting intensity as large as possible, except when photodecomposition is likely to occur. This is the fundamental difference from absorption spectrometry, in which the detection limit is set by the minimum detectable difference in intensity between the incident and transmitted light. Often fluorescence

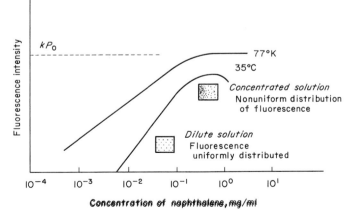

Fig. 13-4. Dependence of fluorescence upon concentration of fluorophor and temperature. From Ref. 9.

offers a sensitivity at least two orders of magnitude greater than absorption spectrometry. Measurements down to 0.0001 $\mu g/ml$ are often feasible and linearity obtains up to 10 $\mu g/ml$ or higher. Then there is the additional specificity inherent in two spectral requirements instead of one. Because a finite signal is always measured, the limit of sensitivity is only approached when the fluorescence signal strength falls to the noise level of the detector circuit.

The development of elegant methods for separating complex mixtures, such as chromatographic methods, makes it possible to utilize fluorescence methods in instances formerly thought impossible. Analytical methods have been described for the determination of phenols, aromatic amines, polycyclic compounds, conjugated polyenes, steroids, tocopherols, desoxyribonucleic acid, alkaloids, reserpine and derivatives, estrogens and flavins, and flavones. In inorganic chemistry the most frequent application is the determination of metal ions after complexation with organic reagents. For details the reader should consult the reviews by White.[15] By observing the guiding principles outlined when discussing structural characteristics, nonfluorescent compounds can oftentimes be converted into fluorescing substances by suitable reactions which produce a fluorophor.

Filter Fluorometers

Photoelectric instruments for measuring fluorescence are termed fluorometers (fluorimeters in Britain). Every fluorometer, or fluorescence spectrometer, no matter how simple or complicated, contains three basic items:

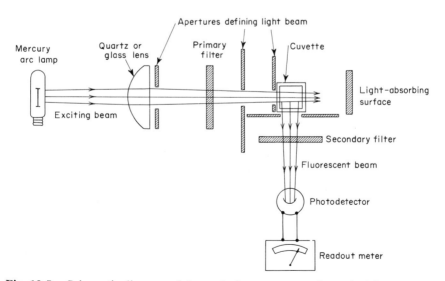

Fig. 13-5. Schematic diagram of the optical components of a typical fluorometer.

(a) a source of radiant energy with which to irradiate the sample, (b) a sample holder, and (c) a detector to measure the fluorescence. They are designated filter fluorometers or fluorescence spectrometers, according to the method of selecting the exciting wavelength and fluorescence emission. There are also relatively simple visual instruments. The components of a typical fluorometer are usually arranged as shown schematically in Fig. 13-5. Appropriate arrangement for dissipation of heat from the source is required.

Unsophisticated filter fluorometers are quite satisfactory for measuring a relatively intense blue or green fluorescence, except when there is more than one fluorophor in the solution. A mercury discharge lamp with glass or fused silica envelope is commonly the excitation source. By isolating one of the principal lines at 366, 405, 436, 546 or 578 mμ, high intensities with good spectral purity can be obtained. Selection of the exciting wavelength is made by inserting a (primary) filter in the incident beam before the sample cuvette. The transmittance curves of two groups of primary filters are shown in Fig. 13-6. One of each

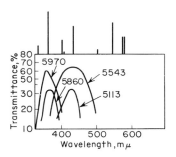

Fig. 13-6. Transmission characteristics of some primary filters. The position of the emission lines from the mercury arc lamp is represented by the vertical lines whose height indicates relative intensity. Numbers are Corning filters.

pair is considered to be a narrow-band pass filter. Interference filters would be superior. Quartz or fused silica for lenses and cuvette wall facing the exciting beam enable ultraviolet radiation below 320 mμ to be used in exciting fluorescence.

To compensate partially for the relatively weak fluorescence of many samples, two photocells or phototubes are connected in parallel, or a reflecting mirror is used to increase the signal strength. Photomultiplier tubes are almost invariably used at the present time because of their superior characteristics. In a position at right angles to the incident beam, and with masking slits, the detector views only the illuminated liquid and not the illuminated cuvette faces, which minimizes reflection of any of the intense exciting radiation. To protect further the detectors from reflected or scattered exciting radiation, (secondary) filters are placed in front of the photodetectors. The transmittance of several secondary filters is included in Fig. 13-7. Secondary filters, usually a short wavelength cutoff type, must be selected so that they will absorb any scattered primary radiation but transmit the fluorescent light. When the excitation and fluorescence maxima are widely separated, this is readily accomplished with filters, an example being shown in Fig. 13-2.

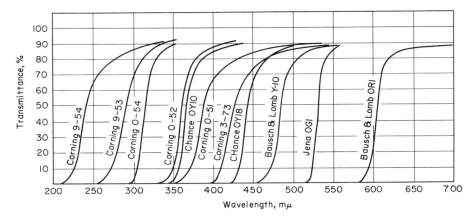

Fig. 13-7. Transmission characteristics of secondary filters. Corning Glass Works (U.S.A.); Chance Pilkington Optical Works (U.K.); Bausch & Lomb Optical Co. (U.S.A.); Jena Glaswerke (Germany).

Since it is difficult to measure an absolute fluorescence intensity, measurements are usually made by reference to some arbitrarily chosen standard substance. A standard solution of the latter is placed in the instrument and the circuit balanced with the reading scale at any chosen setting. Without readjusting any circuit components, the standard solution is replaced by additional standard solutions of lesser concentration and, lastly, the fluorescence of the solvent and cuvette alone is measured to establish a true zero concentration. Some fluorometers are equipped with a zero-adjust circuit. For specific details of a particular instrument, the manufacturer's directions should be consulted.

A plot of scale readings against concentration in the standards furnishes the fluorescence-concentration curve (Fig. 13-4). The initial standard solution often represents the highest concentration anticipated. In order to readjust the instrument quickly to some definite setting for routine analyses, it is convenient to use reference glasses or some stable solution such as dilute quinine in 0.1 N H_2SO_4 or dichlorofluorescein as secondary standards. With filter fluorometers, standard test tubes can be used once they have been matched. Tubes which have become scratched through usage will scatter light excessively. Different varieties and grades of quartz exhibit different amounts of fluorescence in the far ultraviolet, and care must be given to the selection of sample cuvettes.

For opaque solids and concentrated solutions, for which light absorption is large at some or all frequencies of interest, some form of frontal illumination must be used. Examples are solid fluorophors, zones of a chromatographic column or paper chromatogram, and studies of whole cells.

Commercial Filter Fluorometers

Commercial instruments differ from each other in the various components which are utilized and in the manner in which these are assembled. Character-

Table 13-2 | *Characteristics of Some Typical Fluorometers*

INSTRUMENT	OPTICS	DISPERSING DEVICE	PHOTO-DETECTOR	CIRCUIT
Coleman model 12C	Glass	Glass filters	Phototube	Single beam, direct reading
Photovolt model 540	Quartz	Filters	1P21 photo-multiplier	Single-beam, direct reading
Klett	Glass	Glass filters	Barrier-layer cells	Double-beam, potentiometric balance
Lumetron model 402-EF	Glass	Glass filters	Barrier-layer cells	Double-beam, bridge circuit
Farrand	Quartz	Interference, glass filters	1P21 photo-multiplier	Single-beam
Turner model 110	Quartz	Glass filters	1P21 photo-multiplier	Double-beam, optical balance
Hilger Spekker	Glass	Glass filters	Photomulti-plier	Double-beam, optical balance
Hitachi type FPL-2	Glass	Interference filters	Photomulti-plier	—
Beckman ratio	Vycor	Glass filters	Photomulti-plier	Double-beam, ratio recording

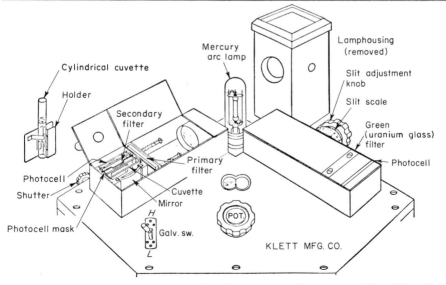

Fig. 13-8. Schematic diagram of the Klett fluorometer. (Courtesy of Klett Mfg. Co.)

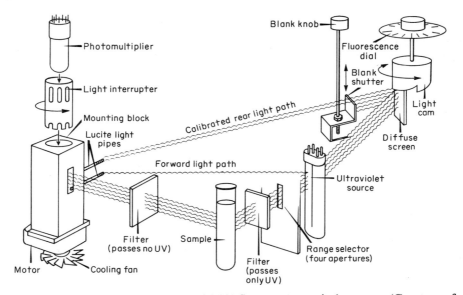

Fig. 13-9. Details of the Turner model 110 fluorometer optical system. (Courtesy of Turner Instrument Co.)

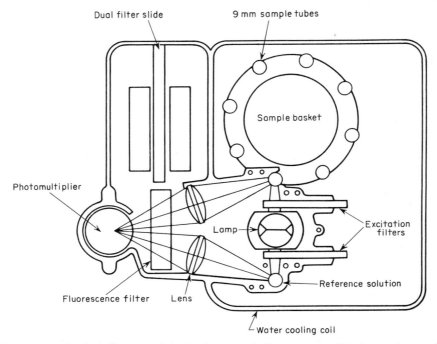

Fig. 13-10. Optical diagram of the Beckman ratio fluorometer. The lamp alternately illuminates the reference and sample solutions. (Courtesy of Beckman Instruments, Inc.)

istics of some fluorometers are summarized in Table 13-2. The Coleman model 12C, the Photovolt model 540, and the Farrand fluorometers possess a single-beam circuit similiar to Fig. 13-5, whereas the Klett, the Lumetron model 402-EF, and Hilger Spekker instruments utilize some sort of a null-indicating circuit for nulling lamp fluctuations. A typical circuit diagram is shown in Fig. 13-8.

An optical bridge circuit is illustrated by the Turner model 110 fluorometer (Fig. 13-9). A single photomultiplier with light interrupter is used to measure the light differential between the fluorescent emission and a standard calibrated (rear light path) beam. Rotation of the reading (fluorescence) dial and connected diffuse screen adjusts the calibration beam to equal the sample emission intensity. When balanced, the photomultiplier detects no difference in signal intensity and thus provides a null-balance instrument. This circuit arrangement cancels out variations in line voltage, light source, and photomultiplier sensitivity.

A true ratio fluorometer (Fig. 13-10) places the reference solution in one beam while the sample solution is irradiated by the second beam. This makes the fluorometer insensitive to temperature changes affecting instruments using fluorescent radiation in the sample beam and radiation of a different wave-length in the reference beam. A special lamp irradiates alternately each solution, and a discriminator circuit presents the ratio signal (reference usually set at 100) to the meter.

Fluorescence Spectrometers

Individual commercial spectrophotometers have been adapted to fluorescence measurements, usually by arranging to pass the emitted fluorescent light through the spectrometer for analysis, excitation usually being carried out by a mercury arc lamp with appropriate filters. Fluorescence attachments housing the light source, a filter, sample holder, and the optics needed to reflect the emitted fluorescence into the spectrometer are available for the Beckman model DU (Fig. 13-11) and model DK, the Cary, the Unicam SP. 500, and the Zeiss model PMQ 11 spectrometers. In these in-

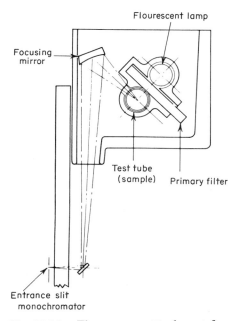

Fig. 13-11. Fluorescence attachment for the Beckman DU or DK spectrometers. (Courtesy of Beckman Instruments, Inc.)

struments no provision is made for measuring excitation spectra although, of course, two monochromators could be suitably arranged.

A true fluorescence spectrometer is an instrument in which two monochromators are used, one to supply the excitation radiation and the other to analyze the fluorescence emission. With dual monochromators the wavelength of the excitation as well as the fluorescence peaks can be determined and utilized selectively. With such an apparatus, one can (a) choose any frequency of exciting light and measure the spectrum of the fluorescence emitted by the sample or (b) set the fluorescence monochromator on the wavelength of the fluorescence band of the substance and observe how the intensity of this fluorescence varies with the frequency of the exciting light used.

The components of the Aminco-Bowman fluorescence spectrometer[1,5] are shown in Fig. 13-12. Because only a limited portion of the light from the

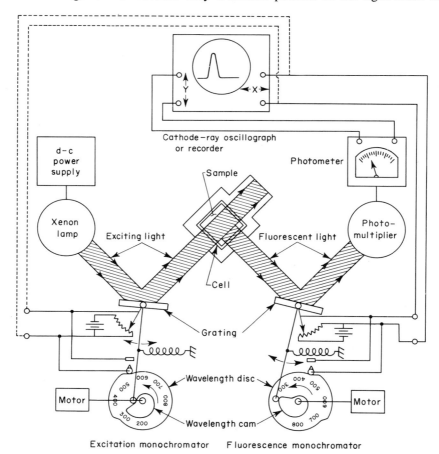

Fig. 13-12. Schematic diagram of the Aminco-Bowman fluorescence spectrometer· (Courtesy of American Instrument Co.)

source finds its way into the excitation monochromator and, of this light, only a narrow band of frequencies is selected for exciting the sample, an intense continuous source is required. Equally obvious, very sensitive detectors and high light-gathering monochromators must be used. The source is a xenon-arc lamp whose spectral output extends from 150 mμ to above 1500 mμ, and is continuous except for a few lines between 800 and 1000 mμ. An appropriate blue- or red-sensitive photomultiplier tube measures the spectral signal. After amplification the output is coupled to the vertical axis of an oscillograph or is indicated by a recorder. The two gratings are moved by motor-driven cams to which are coupled graduated discs for visual observation and adjustment of wavelength. Potentiometers coupled to the gratings supply wavelength information in the form of a d-c signal to the x-axis of the recorder. When the recorder x-input is connected to the scanning fluorescent monochromator and the excitation monochromator is set at a wavelength for maximum excitation, a fluorescent spectrum is plotted. Similarly, when the recorder x-input is connected to the scanning excitation monochromator and the fluorescent monochromator is set at a wavelength for maximum fluorescence, an excitation spectrum is plotted.

The Farrand spectrofluorometer is a two-grating monochromator which is based on a design suggested by the experimental instrument developed by Bowman and coworkers.[1] The compact, direct-reading instrument, made by Baird-Atomic and shown in Fig. 13-13, uses two double grating monochromators. On the other hand, the Zeiss spectrofluorometer is made up of a series of prism monochromators. With the latter instrument a more powerful xenon lamp is used to conpensate for the larger light losses in a prism monochromator.

None of the foregoing fluorescence spectrometers contains circuitry to convert the instrument spectra to "true" spectra. This is done on the Perkin-Elmer instrument.[12] The circuit involves a beam splitter so that a small proportion of the light is deflected to a fluorescent screen viewed by a monitoring photomultiplier. The outputs from the fluorescence photomultiplier and the monitoring photomultiplier are fed to a ratio recorder, and compensation for fluctuations in the light intensity is thereby automatically made. When the fluorescent screen is suitably chosen so that its fluorescence output is proportional to the quantum intensity of the exciting beam, irrespective of frequency, the instrument will record a true excitation spectrum. When the balancing beam is permitted to fall on a thermopile, spectra are recorded in terms of energy rather than quantum units. The instrument incorporates servo-operated slits on the fluorescence monochromator and, as the emission spectrum is scanned, automatic correction is made for the spectral sensitivity of the photomultiplier-monochromator combination. A true emission spectrum is thus recorded.

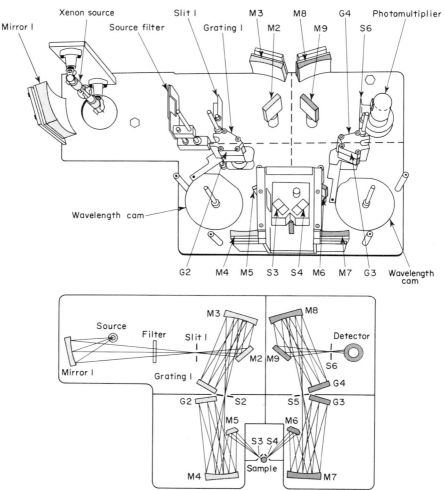

Fig. 13-13. Schematic optical diagram of a fluorescence spectrophotometer with two double gratings—the Fluorispec model SF/1. The sequence of numbers denotes the path followed by the incident and fluorescent light. (Courtesy of Baird-Atomic, Inc.)

Phosphorescence Methods

Phosphorescence methods are based upon the nature and intensity of light emitted by excited molecules in the triplet state. Unfortunately, because of the relatively long lifetime of the triplet state, molecules in this state are much more susceptible to deactivation processes and only when the substance is dissolved in a rigid medium can phosphorescence emission usually be observed.

Phosphorescence emission is unique in regard to its frequency, lifetime, quantum yield, and vibrational pattern. Such properties are used for qualitative identification. The correlation of intensity with concentration serves as a basis for quantitative measurement.

Excitation Conditions

Most important phosphorescence emissions arise from transitions between the first excited triplet state and the ground electronic (singlet) state.[6,7] These are states of different multiplicities. When a phosphor absorbs radiant energy of a frequency within the normal absorption bands of the molecule, one of the electrons in the ground electronic state is elevated to the first (or higher) excited singlet electronic state. All electrons are spin-paired in both electronic states and the multiplicity, given by the term $2S + 1$ where S is the spin quantum number, is one. These are denoted singlet states. As described under fluorescence, internal conversion and collisional deactivation drop the potential energy of the excited molecule from any higher excited singlet state to the first excited singlet state. This is followed by rapid vibrational cascade (radiationless transitions) to the vicinity of the zero-point level of the first singlet state. At this point, if the potential energy curve of the singlet state crosses that of the triplet state, it is possible for electrons to pass from a vibrational level of the first singlet state by an intersystem crossing, which does not absorb or emit radiation, to the triplet state (Fig. 13-1). Although singlet-triplet transitions are forbidden processes, the internal conversion from the excited singlet to the triplet state may occur with some probability, since the energy of the lowest vibrational level of the triplet state is lower than that of the singlet state. The probability of intersystem crossing is greater when the potential energy curves cross at the lowest point on the excited singlet curve. Collisional deactivation will ensure a more populated zero-point vibrational level than any elevated vibrational level.

The triplet state is characterized by a pair of unsaturation (pi) electrons, each occupying a different orbital and aligned with unpaired spins. The unpaired spinning electrons give rise to three slightly different energy levels, one in each molecule, but three when averaged over all molecules. Once a triplet state is formed, further vibrational energy will be lost and the molecules will occupy the zero-point vibrational level of the triplet state. Return from here to a vibrational level of the ground state constitutes phosphorescence emission, a transition which will occur with low probability. Consequently, the triplet state persists for a relatively long average lifetime and phosphorescence emission will continue over relatively long periods of time. Spin-orbit coupling, which is a magnetic perturbation capable of flipping spins, is believed to be the main source of phosphorescence transitions back to the ground electronic state. Competing degradation processes via collisions are minimized by keeping the sample in a rigid state at low temperatures. The role of the rigid medium is to remove triplet state vibrational energy above the zero-point level but not to remove the triplet state electronic energy by thermal deactivation.

Constitutive Effects

Pi electrons, which are above the resonance plane, are involved in the postulated change of molecular configuration in excitation of the triplet state. Several examples are (crudely) represented below.[6] Exact locus of excitation is decided on the basis of phosphorescence characteristics obtained for competing parts of the molecule when studied separately.

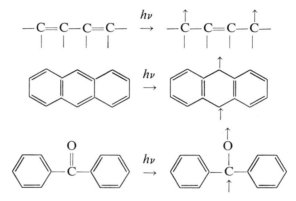

Charge status of the phosphor has an equally important influence on phosphorescence yield as it does on fluorescent emission (q.v.). Introduction of paramagnetic metal ions, such as copper(II) and nickel, gives rise to phosphorescence but not fluorescence. On the other hand, magnesium and zinc compounds show only strong fluorescence. With the lighter members of a group of atoms with two optical electrons, there will be a very low probability of triplet-conversions, whereas in atoms of higher atomic number, the interaction between the spin and orbital motions becomes relatively large, so that during an electronic transition the perturbation can change the spin. The ratio of fluorescence intensity to phosphorescence intensity also varies greatly from one metal complex to another.

Phosphorescence lifetimes are also affected by molecular structure. Unsubstituted cyclic and polycyclic hydrocarbons and their derivatives containing $-CH_3$, $-NH_2$, $-OH$, $-COOH$, and $-OCH_3$ substituents have lifetimes in the range of 5–10 sec for most benzene derivatives and 1–4 sec for many naphthalene derivatives. The nitro group diminishes the intensity of phosphorescence and the lifetime of the phosphorescent state to about 0.2 sec. Aldehydic and ketonic carbonyl groups diminish the lifetime to about 0.001 sec. Introduction of bulky substituents which force a planar configuration to become nonplanar markedly shortens lifetimes.

Phosphorescence Spectrum

Each phosphorescence spectrum is characterized by four qualitative parameters:

1. The mean emission lifetime τ, which is the length of time required for the phosphorescence intensity to decrease to $1/e$ of its initial value, may be in the order of seconds in the rigid medium and in the order of 10^{-4} to 10^{-3} sec in fluid medium. Mechanical methods on phosphorescence spectrometers distinguish different time delays. Similar phosphorescence emissions may be resolved if the lifetimes differ sufficiently.

2. The frequency of the vibrationless transition ($\Delta\nu = 0$) characterizes the transition from the zero-point level of the triplet state to the zero-point level of the ground state. It will be the highest frequency band of the phosphorescence spectrum, but it will occur at lower frequencies than a fluorescence band originating from a corresponding transition from the first excited singlet state. There is a gap between the highest phosphorescence frequency and the lowest absorption frequency.

3. The vibrational pattern represents the spacings of the vibrational levels of the ground electronic state.

4. The quantum efficiency is the ratio of the quanta of light phosphoresced to the quanta absorbed. This parameter is too difficult to measure for use in qualitative identification, but as high a value as possible is desirable in quantitative work.

Quantitative Factors Affecting Phosphorescence

The population of the triplet state depends on how quickly molecules reach it, how efficiently the light is absorbed, and how fast the triplet state decays through undesired routes. As in fluorescence, the expression relating phosphorescence intensity to concentration is

$$I = kP_0\phi(2.3\epsilon bC) \qquad (13\text{-}7)$$

which is valid for low concentrations, i.e., when the terms in parentheses are less than 0.01 the initial light intensity.

Examination of Eq. 13-7 points out that the radiant power of the excitation source should be as large as possible and the length of time of excitation should be as long as possible to populate fully the triplet state. The interval of time following cessation of excitation is an important factor in phosphorescence. The influence of impurity molecules, leading to deactivating collisions, and the need for a rigid medium have been discussed earlier.

The solvent frequently used is a mixture of ethyl ether, isopentane, and ethanol in a volume ratio of 5:5:2, respectively. It is referred to as the EPA mixed solvent. When cooled to liquid nitrogen temperature it gives a clear transparent glass.

Phosphorescence Spectrometer [1, 5, 10]

A phosphorescence spectrometer is identical to the fluorescence spectrometer described earlier with the addition of a resolution phosphoroscope. Excitation light from a xenon lamp, after dispersion by an excitation monochromator, is admitted to the sample via a fixed slit system and rotating set of slotted disks with equally spaced ports, driven by a variable speed motor. The sample cuvette is located on the axis of rotation and between the rotating blades of the disks. The blades are so arranged that openings in one are in line with uncut portions of the second. Thus the sample is first illuminated and then darkened; while it is dark its phosphorescence is allowed to pass the second disk and go thence to the phosphorescence monochromator. The cuvette is a small Dewar flask made of fused quartz and silvered, except in the region where the optical path traverses the Dewar.

The resolution time of the instrument is the length of time between the cutoff of each pulse of excitation light admitted to the sample and the clearing of the optical path by the second blade to allow the phosphorescence emission to enter the phosphorescence monochromator. The time is a function of the motor speed, the size and spacing of the cuts, the relative radial positions of the cuts to each other, and the size of the slit openings.

A phosphorescence spectrum is obtained by setting the excitation monochromator at the wavelength which corresponds to a phosphorescence maximum, and allowing the emission monochromator to sweep throughout its wavelength range. An excitation spectrum is produced by setting the emission monochromator at the wavelength which produces the maximum emission of a sample, and allowing the excitation monochromator to sweep throughout its wavelength range.

Decay curves can be recorded if the instrument is equipped with an oscillograph. The decay in the intensity of phosphorescence emission at a selected wavelength with time after removal of an exciting radiation is followed.

LABORATORY WORK

EXPERIMENT 13-1   DETERMINATION OF QUININE

Standard solution of quinine: Dissolve 0.100 g of quinine bisulfate in 0.1 N H_2SO_4 solution and dilute to 1 liter with additional acid solution. Dilute 10.0 ml of the foregoing solution to 1 liter with 0.1 N acid solution. The resulting solution contains 0.00100 mg/ml of quinine bisulfate.

Dilute sulfuric acid, 0.1 N: Add 3 ml of concentrated sulfuric acid to 100 ml of water and dilute to 1 liter in a graduated cylinder.

PROCEDURE

Pipet 10.0, 25.0, 35.0 and 50.0 ml of the dilute standard quinine solution into a set of 100-ml volumetric flasks. Dilute to the mark with 0.1 N H_2SO_4 solution. Treat the unknown sample similarly. Measure the fluorescence and prepare a calibration curve.

The fluorescence of quinine is constant in the concentration interval from 0.01 to 0.2 N H_2SO_4. Proper primary and secondary filters, or wavelengths for excitation and fluorescence measurement, can be ascertained from Fig. 13-14.

EXPERIMENT 13-2   DETERMINATION OF ALUMINUM[14]

Standard solution of aluminum. Dissolve 1.760 g of potassium aluminum sulfate $(K_2SO_4 \cdot Al_2(SO_4)_3 \cdot 24H_2O)$ crystals in distilled water, add 3 ml of concentrated sulfuric acid, and dilute to 1 liter in a volumetric flask. Pipet 10.0 ml of this solution into a 1-liter flask, add 3 ml of concentrated sulfuric acid, and dilute to the mark with distilled water. This solution contains 0.00100 mg/ml of aluminum.

Dye solution. Prepare a 0.1 percent solution of a 0,0'-dihydroxyazo dye in ethanol. Suggested dyes include Pontachrome (also Eriochrome or Solochrome) Blue Black R (C.I. 202), Pontachrome Violet SW (C.I. 169), and Acid Alizarin Garnet R (C.I. 168).

Ammonium acetate solution. Dissolve 50 g of the salt in distilled, freshly boiled water. Dilute to 500 ml in a graduated cylinder. Prepare a fresh solution daily.

PROCEDURE

Into 100-ml volumetric flasks, each containing 10 ml of ammonium acetate solution, 1.0 ml of dilute (1 + 9) sulfuric acid solution, and 3.00 ml of the dye solution, pipet 10.0, 20.0, 30.0, 40.0, and 50.0 ml of the dilute standard aluminum solution. Dilute each solution to the mark and allow to stand 1 hr. On a small portion of each solution, check the *pH*, and, if necessary, adjust the *pH* to 4.6 ± 0.2. Measure the fluorescence of each solution and prepare a calibration curve. Appropriate excitation and fluorescence wavelengths can be deduced from Fig. 13-2 for Acid Alizarin Garnet R. For the other dyes, the excitation conditions are similar, but the fluorescence is orange with Pontachrome Violet SW and red with Pontachrome Blue Black R.

EXPERIMENT 13-3   DETERMINATION (SIMPLIFIED) OF RIBOFLAVIN[4]

Standard riboflavin solution. Dissolve 10.0 mg of riboflavin in 1 liter of 1 percent acetic acid solution, Keep the solution in a cool, dark place. This solution contains 10.0 μg/ml of riboflavin.

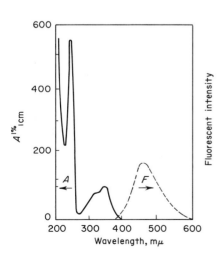

Fig. 13-14. Absorption and fluorescence spectra of quinine bisulfate in 0.1 N H_2SO_4.

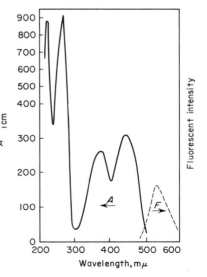

Fig. 13-15. Absorption and fluorescence spectra of riboflavin in water.

PROCEDURE

Prepare a series of standard riboflavin solutions, the strongest of which does not contain more than 1.0 μg/ml of riboflavin. Prepare a calibration curve. Appropriate excitation and fluorescence wavelengths can be deduced from the spectra in Fig. 13-15. One suggested set of filters is Corning 3–73 plus 5–58 ($\frac{1}{2}$ standard width) in the primary beam and Corning 3–69 in the secondary beam.

E X P E R I M E N T 1 3 - 4   SELECTION OF A PROPER PAIR OF FILTERS

Prepare a series of standard fluorescence solutions. Insert a primary and a secondary filter into the fluorometer. Balance the fluorometer at about 50 percent of the normal full-scale reading when the strongest standard solution is employed. Preliminary selection of a primary filter is made by observing visually the fluorescence of the strongest standard solution when different primary filters are inserted in the exciting beam. Likewise, secondary filters can be selected by holding them between the eye and the top of the cuvette when the sample is irradiated with the exciting beam.

Measure the fluorescence reading of each of the remaining solutions in the series. Include a blank in the series. Plot your results.

Now remove the primary filter and replace with another. Without changing any instrument settings, measure the fluorescence of each member of the standard series of solutions, including the blank. Plot your results. Repeat these operations until all available primary filters have been used.

From the preceding results, select the primary filter which yields the steepest slope (and perhaps the smallest reading for the blank), and change the secondary filters, one at a time. For each secondary filter measure the fluorescence of the series of standard solutions. Plot your results.

On the basis of the complete sets of data, choose the optimum pair of filters. Factors to be considered include linearity of the calibration curve, slope of the curve, and minimal fluorescence of the blank.

E X P E R I M E N T 1 3 - 5   EFFECT OF pH UPON FLUORESCENCE

Into a series of 150-ml beakers, each containing 10 ml of 10 percent ammonium acetate and 3.00 ml of 0.1 percent dye solution (see Experiment 13-2 for details of solution preparation), pipet 50.0 ml of the dilute standard aluminum solution. Adjust the pH to these approximate values: 3.0, 4.0, 4.5, 4.8, 5.0, 5.5, and 6.0. Allow the solutions to stand 1 hr, then measure the pH carefully. Transfer the solutions quantitatively to a series of 100-ml volumetric flasks and dilute to the mark with distilled water. Mix thoroughly.

Balance the fluorometer at about 80 percent of full-scale reading with the pH 4.8 solution in the cuvette. Measure the fluorescence of the remaining solutions. Plot your results as fluorescence reading vs pH.

At the discretion of the instructor, alternate systems may be studied. These include quinine over the pH range from 0 to 7, and various naphthalenediols over the pH range from 0 to 12 (see Fig. 13-3).

Problems

1. A 1.00-g sample of a cereal product was extracted with acid and treated so as to isolate the riboflavin plus a small amount of extraneous material. The riboflavin was oxidized by the addition of a small amount of $KMnO_4$, the excess of which was removed by H_2O_2. The solution was transferred to a 50-ml volumetric flask and diluted to the mark. A 25-ml portion was transferred to the sample holder and the fluorescence measured. Initially the fluorometer had been adjusted to read 100 scale divisions with a solution of quinine bisulfate. The solution read 6.0 scale divisions. A small amount of solid sodium dithionite was added to the cuvette to convert the oxidized riboflavin back to riboflavin. The solution now read 55 scale divisions. The sample was discarded and replaced in the same cuvette by 24 ml of the oxidized sample plus 1 ml of a standard solution of riboflavin which contains 0.500 μg/ml of riboflavin. A small amount of solid sodium dithionite was added. The solution read 92 scale divisions. Calculate the micrograms of riboflavin per gram of cereal.

2. Solutions of varying amounts of aluminum were prepared, 8-quinolinol was added and the complex was extracted with chloroform. The chloroform extracts were all diluted to 50 ml and compared in a fluorometer. These readings were obtained:

ALUMINUM, μg/50 ml	FLUOROMETER READING	ALUMINUM, μg/50 ml	FLUOROMETER READING
2	10	12	53
4	19	14	60
6	28	16	66
8	37	18	71
10	45		

Plot the fluorometer reading vs the aluminum concentration. Does the calibration curve follow the relationship predicted by Eq. 13-6? Over what concentration range is the approximation of Eq. 13-6 valid?

3. From the information given in Fig. 13-2, select the optimum wavelength for excitation and for fluorescence emission. Do the same for the quinine and riboflavin systems, Figs. 13-14 and 13-15.

4. Repeat Problem 3, but assuming this time only a filter fluorometer is available. Select the optimum primary and secondary filters from the information given in Figs. 3-4, 13-6, and 13-7.

5. From the appropriate spectra for naphthalene (Fig. 13-16), phenanthrene (Fig. 13-17), and 1,2,3,5-tetramethylbenzene (Fig. 13-18), devise a method of analysis for each component assuming that a fluorescence spectrometer and a phosphorescence spectrometer is available. *Ans.* Excitation at 340 mμ produces only phenanthrene emissions. Excitation at 275 mμ gives distinguishable phosphorescence for tetramethylbenzene. Excitation at 275 mμ maximizes the naphthalene fluorescence, which is spectrally quite distinct.

6. In Fig. 13-19 are given the phosphorescence emission spectrum of 4-nitrobiphenyl ($\tau = 0.080$ sec), benzaldehyde ($\tau = 0.006$ sec), and benzophenone ($\tau = 0.006$ sec). Outline a scheme of analysis for each component based on considerations of wavelength of phosphorescence and the phosphorescence lifetimes.

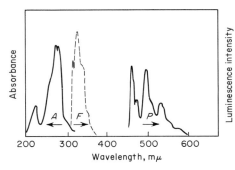

Fig. 13-16. Absorption, fluorescence emission, and phosphorescence emission spectra of naphthalene at 77°K in EPA. From Ref. 9.

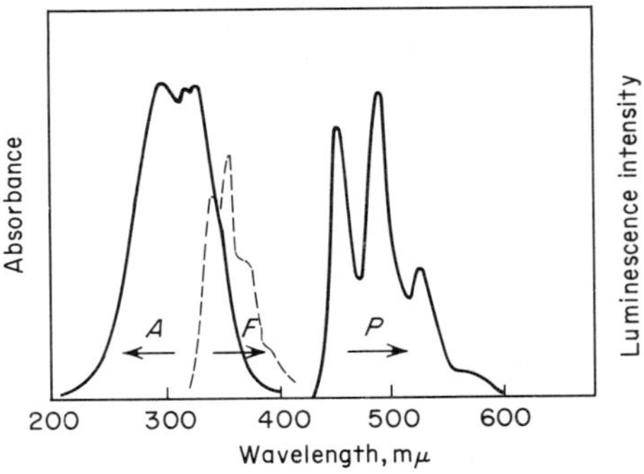

Fig. 13-17. Absorption, fluorescence emission, and phosphorescence emission spectra of phenanthrene at 77°K in EPA. From Ref. 9.

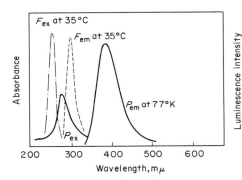

Fig. 13-18. Excitation and emission spectra of 1,2,4,5-tetramethylbenzene. Not shown is the fluorescence excitation spectrum (λ_{max} = 285 mμ) at 77°K. From Ref. 9.

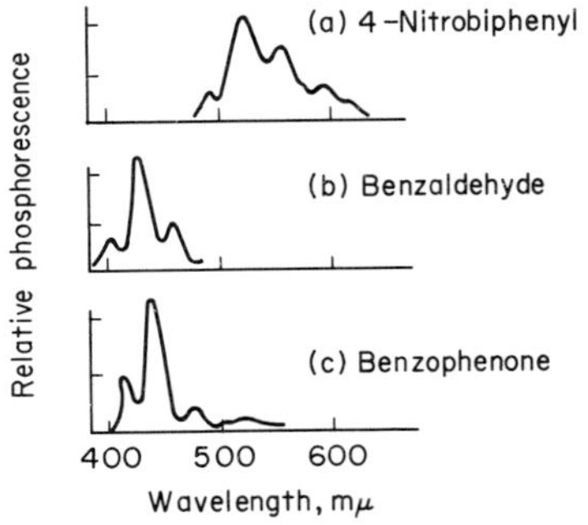

Fig. 13-19. Phosphorescence emission spectra for (a) 4-nitrobiphenyl, (b) benzaldehyde, (c) benzophenone, each at 77°K in EPA. From Kiers et al.

7. From the spectra shown in Fig. 13-16 for naphthalene at 77°K, construct an approximate energy level diagram for the fluorescence and phosphorescence transitions to the vibrational levels in the ground electronic state. For the fluorescence spectra, the emission maximum is 320 mμ and the excitation maximum is 275 mμ. Similarly, for the phosphorescence spectra, the emission maximum is 475 mμ and the excitation maximum is 310 mμ.

8. From the spectra shown in Fig. 13-17 for phenanthrene at 77°K, construct an approximate energy level diagram for the fluorescence and phosphorescence transitions to the vibrational levels in the ground electronic state. For the fluorescence spectra, the emission maximum is 300 mμ, as is also the excitation maximum. For the phosphorescence spectra, the emission maximum is 465 mμ and the excitation maximum is 340 mμ.

Bibliography

Udenfriend, S., *Fluorescence Assay in Biology and Medicine*, Academic Press, New York, 1962.

Keirs, R. J., R. D. Britt, Jr., and W. E. Wentworth, "Phosphorimetry, A New Method of Analysis," *Anal. Chem.*, **29**, 202 (1957).

Literature Cited

1. Bowman, R. L., P. A. Caulfield, and S. Udenfriend, *Science*, **122**, 32 (1955).
2. Hercules, D. M., and L. B. Rogers, *Spectrochim. Acta*, **15**, 393 (1959).
3. Hercules, D. M., and L. B. Rogers, *J. Phys. Chem.*, **64**, 397 (1960).
4. Hodson, A. Z., and L. C. Norres *J. Biol. Chem.*, **131**, 621 (1939).
5. Howerton, H. K., *J. Instrument Soc. Am.*, **6**, 50 (October 1959).
6. Kasha, M., *Chem. Revs.*, **41**, 401 (1947).
7. Lewis, G. N., and M. Kasha, *J. Am. Chem. Soc.*, **66**, 2100 (1944).
8. Mehluish, W. H., *J. Phys. Chem.*, **64**, 762 (1960).
9. Nebbia, G., in *Proceedings of the Xth Colloquium Spectroscopicum Internationale*, p. 605, Spartan Books, Washington, 1963.
10. Parker, C. A., and C. G. Hatchard, *Analyst*, **87**, 664 (1962).
11. Parker, C. A., and W. T. Rees, ibid., **85**, 587 (1960).
12. Slavin, W., R. W. Mooney, and R. W. Palumbo, *J. Opt. Soc. Am.*, **51**, 93 (1961).
13. Weber, G., and F. W. J. Teale, *Trans. Faraday Soc.*, **53**, 646 (1957).
14. Weissler, A., and C. E. White, *Ind. Eng. Chem.*, *Anal. Ed.*, **18**, 530 (1946).
15. White, C. E., *Anal. Chem.* **21**, 104 (1949); **22**, 69 (1950); **24**, 85 (1952); **26**, 129 (1954); **28**, 621 (1956); **30**, 729 (1958); **32**, 47R (1960); **34**, 82R (1962) and subsequent biannual reviews.
16. White, C. E., D. E. Hoffman, and J. S. Magee, Jr., *Spectrochim. Acta*, **9**, 105 (1957).
17. Williams, R. T., *J. Roy. Inst. Chem.*, **83**, 611 (1959).

Refractometry and Interferometry

When a ray of light passes obliquely from one medium into another of different density, its direction is changed on passing through the surface. This is called *refraction*. If the second medium is optically denser than the first, the ray will become more nearly perpendicular to the dividing surface. The angle between the ray in the first medium and the perpendicular to the dividing surface is called the angle of incidence, i, while the corresponding angle in the second medium is called the angle of refraction, r. Sine i and sine r are directly proportional to the velocities of the light in the two media. The ratio sin i/sin r is called the *index of refraction, n*. If the incident ray is in the denser medium, n will be less than 1; if in the rarer, greater than 1. Commonly, n is taken as greater than 1, the ray passing from the optically rarer medium (usually air) to the denser.

The index of refraction for two given media varies with the temperature and the wavelength of light and also with the pressure, if we are dealing with a gas. If these factors are kept constant, the index of refraction is a characteristic constant for the particular medium and is used in identifying or determining the purity of substances and for determining the composition of homogeneous binary mixtures of known constituents.

The refractive index is theoretically referred to vacuum as the first medium, but the index referred to air differs from this by only 0.03 percent and, for convenience, is more commonly used. The symbol n_D^{20} means the index of refraction for the D lines of sodium* measured at 20°C.

When the beam of light passes from a denser to a rarer medium, the angle r will be greater than the angle i. As angle i increases, the ratio sin i/sin r remain-

*The yellow doublet at 5890/5896 Å.

ing constant, the angle r must also increase and remain greater than i. If angle i is increased to the value where r becomes 90°, the beam of light will no longer pass from the first medium to the second, but will travel through the first medium to the dividing surface and then pass along this surface, thus making 90° with the perpendicular to the surface (Fig. 14-1). This is called the *critical ray*. In the figure, i and r would then be interchanged, and the direction of the arrows would be reversed. If i is smaller than this particular value, light will pass through the second medium; if greater, all light will be reflected from the surface back into the first medium. This furnishes the basis for the

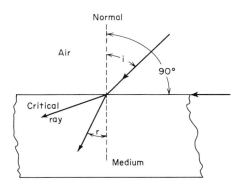

Fig. 14-1.   Angles of incidence (i) and refraction (r).

reference line used in several refractometers. Total reflection can occur only when light passes from the denser to the rarer medium.

The refractive index of a liquid varies with temperature and pressure, but the specific refraction, r_D,

$$r_D = \frac{n^2 - 1}{n^2 + 2} \cdot \frac{1}{\rho} \tag{14-1}$$

where ρ is the density, is independent of these variables. The molar refraction is equal to the specific refraction multiplied by the molecular weight. It is a more or less additive property of the groups or elements comprising the compound. Tables of atomic refractions are available in the literature; an abridged set of values is given in Table 14-1. Thus, specific refraction is valuable as a means for identification of a substance and as a criterion of its

Table 14-1 | *Atomic Refractions*

GROUP	Mr_D	GROUP	Mr_D
H	1.100	Br	8.865
C	2.418	I	13.900
Double bond (C=C)	1.733	N (primary aliphatic amine)	2.322
Triple bond (C≡C)	2.398	N (*sec* aliphatic amine)	2.499
O (carbonyl) (C=O)	2.211	N (*tert* aliphatic amine)	2.840
O (hydroxyl)(O—H)	1.525	N (primary aromatic amine)	3.21
O (ether, ester)(C—O—C)	1.643	N (*sec* aromatic amine)	3.59
S (thiocarbonyl)(C=S)	7.97	N (*tert* aromatic amine)	4.36
S (mercapto)(S—H)	7.69	N (amide)	2.65
F	1.0	—NO₂ group (aromatic)	7.30
Cl	5.967	—C≡N group	5.459

purity. In a homologous series of compounds the specific refraction of higher members generally increases fairly regularly with increase in length of the carbon chain.

The values of refractive index for organic liquids range from about 1.2 to 1.8, those for organic solids from about 1.3 to 2.5.

Example 14-1

The refractive index of acetic acid at 20°C is 1.3698, the density at 20° is 1.049 g cm^{-3}, and the molecular weight is 60.0. From Eq. 14-1 the specific refraction is found

$$r_D = \frac{[(1.3698)^2 - 1]}{[(1.3698)^2 + 2]} \cdot \frac{1}{1.049} = 0.2154 \text{ cm}^3 \text{ g}^{-1}$$

The molar refraction is

$$Mr_D = (60.0)(0.2154) = 12.93 \text{ cm}^3 \text{ mole}^{-1}$$

The molar refraction is a constitutive property depending upon the structural arrangement of the atoms within the molecule. From the atomic and group refractions in Table 14-1, the molar refraction of acetic acid can be computed and compared with the experimental value as follows:

Acetic Acid			*Methyl Formate*		
2 carbons	=	4.836	2 carbons	=	4.836
4 hydrogens	=	4.400	4 hydrogens	=	4.400
1 carbonyl oxygen	=	2.211	1 carbonyl oxygen	=	2.211
1 hydroxyl oxygen	=	1.525	1 ester oxygen	=	1.643
		12.972			13.090

Methyl formate possesses the same empirical formula as acetic acid and differs only slightly in structure. This difference is apparent in the molar refraction values, although the difference only amounts to about 0.85 percent. To distinguish between the two compounds would require a precision of ±0.006 in refractive index and ±0.005 in density. For methyl formate, $n_D^{20} = 1.344$ and $d^{20} = 0.974$.

Refractometers

There are three types of refractometers—the Abbe, the immersion or dipping and the Pulfrich instruments. The last named is used infrequently and will not be discussed.

The Abbe Refractometer

The range of available models is from $n = 1.30$ to 1.71 and from 1.45 to 1.84. Except on some of the newer models, the range cannot be changed. The reproducibility of the individual readings is ±0.0002 in refractive index. The instrument reads the refractive index directly, is durable, requires only a drop of sample, and gives a good approximation of partial dispersions. Except for precision models, however, it is not well suited for accurate measurement of solutions with a volatile component or of powders. Solid samples can be attached to the lower surface of Abbe prism. The clear plane face of the specimen is brought into optical contact with the prism face by placing a drop of liquid on the prism surface and carefully pressing the solid into place. As contacting liquid 1-bromonaphthalene (n_D = 1.68) is commonly used.

White light is used, and to prevent a colored, indistinct boundary between the light and dark fields due to the differences in refractive indices for light of different wavelengths, two direct-vision prisms, called *Amici prisms*, are placed one above the other in front of the objective of the telescope. These are constructed of different varieties of glass and are so designed as not to deviate a ray of light corresponding to the sodium D line. Rays of other wavelengths are, however, deviated, and by rotating these Amici prisms it is possible to counteract the dispersion of light at the liquid interface.

The instrument and its essential parts are shown in Fig. 14-2. Light reflected from a mirror passes into the illuminating prism P_1, the upper surface of which is rough ground. This rough surface acts as the source of an infinite number of rays which pass through the 0.1-mm layer of liquid in all directions.

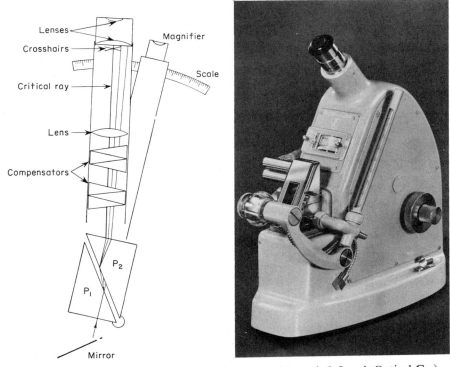

Fig. 14-2.   The Abbe refractometer. (Courtesy of Bausch & Lomb Optical Co.)

These rays then strike the surface of the polished prism P_2 and are refracted. The critical ray forms the border between the light and dark portions of the field when viewed with the telescope which moves with the scale. The scale is provided with a reading telescope.

The temperature should be controlled within $\pm 0.2°C$. The instrument is fitted with hollow prism casings through which water may be passed. A short thermometer is inserted into the water jacket. The most satisfactory temperature control is obtained by using a small circulating pump to pass water from a thermostat through the prism casing.

Improved reproducibility is obtained with a precision Abbe refractometer. Three ranges are available: 1.30–1.50, 1.40–1.70, and 1.33–1.64. Refractive index readings are reproducible within $\pm 2 \times 10^{-5}$ to $\pm 6 \times 10^{-5}$ when the temperature is maintained within $\pm 0.02°C$. Improved precision is obtained by dispensing with compensating prisms and by use of unusually large and precise Abbe prisms mounted on a long, vertical, taper bearing. The instrument is usually calibrated with known standards when one is working a few degrees above or below the calibration temperature, as corrections for changes in prism index and in the state of the reference medium become very important.

The Immersion Refractometer

This type is the simplest to use but requires 10–15 ml of sample. It uses white or artificial light and contains an Amici compensator as already described. The single prism is mounted rigidly in the telescope containing the compensator and eyepiece as shown in Fig. 14-3. The scale is mounted below the eyepiece inside the tube. The lower surface of the prism is immersed in a small beaker containing the sample with a mirror below to reflect light up through the liquid. The complete instrument in position with the water bath for maintaining a constant temperature is also shown.

The scale, situated at the focal plane of the eyepiece, is graduated from −5 to +105. The field will be partly dark and partly light, separated by a sharp line as already explained (Fig. 14-1). The position of this line is read on the scale, and the tenths of a division are found by turning a micrometer screw at the top of the instrument, which slides the scale toward the border line until it covers the lower numerical scale division previously noted. The figure on the micrometer drum then shows the decimal to be added. A change of 0.01 division corresponds to ± 0.000037 in n_D. The immersion refractometer therefore gives greater precision in its readings than any other type except the interference refractometer.

Since the refractive index changes with the temperature, a standard temperature must be chosen. This, unfortunately, is 17.5°C, which is rather difficult to maintain. The solution to be tested is placed in a very small, specially designed beaker placed in a rack in a water bath illuminated through the bottom. A current of water at the proper temperature is passed through the bath. This

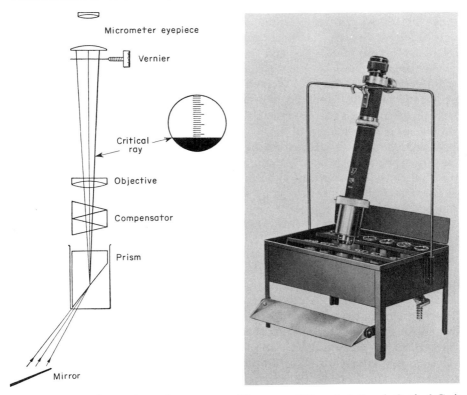

Fig. 14-3. The immersion refractometer. (Courtesy of Bausch & Lomb Optical Co.)

may be done by running tap water from a constant-level tank into the bath at the proper rate; or various types of constant-temperature baths may be used.

The correctly adjusted refractometer should show for distilled water at various temperatures the following readings:

15°	15.5	18°	14.9	22°	14.0
16°	15.3	19°	14.7	23°	13.75
17°	15.1	20°	14.5	24°	13.5
17.5°	15.0	21°	14.25	25°	13.25

The temperature should not vary more than 0.1°C, because readings are reported to an estimated 0.01 scale division. In order to be of any value the reading must be converted into concentration by means of published tables, the most comprehensive of which are those by Wagner, obtainable from suppliers of the instrument. These tables apply only to 17.5° and there is no formula for converting them to other temperatures. There are, however, tables for methyl and ethyl alcohol at other temperatures. Leach and Lythgoe[3] have published complete data for 20°C. The table by Andrews[1] covers only the range 70–100 percent ethyl alcohol at 25°C. In all tables, readings are given only in scale divisions. Readings may be converted into index of refraction by reference to tables furnished with the instrument.

The range of the instrument with prism 1 is 1.325–1.367. This covers all ordinary salt solutions and alcohols. For higher values, special auxiliary prisms are furnished extending the range to 1.492. Thus the range of this refractometer is much narrower than that of the Abbe, but this gives it the advantage of greater sensitivity.

A disadvantage of refractometric analysis is the necessity for carefully regulating the temperature. An attempt has been made by Clemens[2] to avoid this, but considerable precision was necessarily sacrificed.

The refractometer measures concentration more accurately and readily than can be done by ordinary density measurements with a hydrometer. For example, assuming a sufficiently accurate temperature control, 0.02 scale division (which is about the best one can do in reading the instrument, estimating the nearest 0.01 division) corresponds to the following weight of substances per 100 ml: methyl alcohol, 24 mg; ethyl alcohol, 12 mg; ammonium chloride, 4 mg; perchloric acid, 10 mg.

If both density and refractometer readings are determined, it is possible to determine each of two components, such as methyl and ethyl alcohol, with a fair degree of accuracy if nothing else is present. It should be noted that both density and refractive index are measures of the total amount of substance in solution, no matter how many different ones there may be.

Applications

The immersion refractometer is especially useful in determining the concentration of aqueous and alcoholic solutions. Wagner[5] describes precautions to be used, such as constancy of temperature, rinsing the prism with water of the same temperature, wiping lightly, and allowing two minutes before reading.

Shippy and Barrows[4] showed how the index of refraction could be used to determine the composition of solutions of sodium chloride and potassium chloride. A curve was constructed by plotting percentage of sodium chloride against index of refraction. A fair degree of accuracy was attained.

In physiological chemistry the refractometer is very important. In only 2 ml of serum it can be used to determine nonalbuminous constituents, total globulins, insoluble globulins, albumens, and total albumen, with great accuracy. The action of ferments can be followed with the refractometer. The refractometer is also useful in controlling the analysis of commercial products, in identifying unknown substances, and in distinguishing substances of the same boiling point and compounds of the same nature, such as halogenated hydrocarbons.

Recording Refractometers

Instruments have been designed for continuous and automatic recording of refractive indices (or differences between a reference and specimen). These instruments utilize servomechanisms which track the position of a slit image, or critical boundary, or operate a compensating mechanism to maintain a constant position of the image or boundary. Figure 14-4 is a schematic repre-

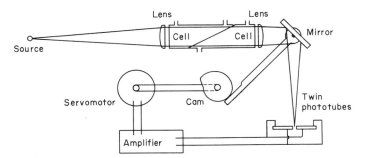

Fig. 14-4. Schematic optical system of a recording refractometer.

sentation of the latter type of instrument. Light from the source is defined by a slit and chopped by a rotating sector (not shown), then passes through the double-prism cell. The refracted beam then strikes a mirror (or beam-splitting arrangement) which focuses the light on twin detectors. Imbalance is removed by the servomotor which is geared to the mirror. The amount of rotation, which is proportional to the refractive index, is correlated with known standards. The instrument may be used to compare the refractive index of two process streams.

The Interferometer

Refractometers are dependent upon the refraction of light when passing from one substance to another. The finest measurement of refractive index, however, is based upon the interference of light. In this method there is no diffraction. The light enters and leaves the solution at right angles. The interferometer, reduced to its simplest terms, may be represented by Fig. 14-5.

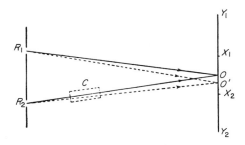

Fig. 14-5. Optical principle of an interferometer.

Parallel light passes through two small openings, R_1 and R_2 in Fig. 14-5. Since R_1O and R_2O are of equal length, the two beams arrive at O in phase and a bright spot results. At other points on the screen the lengths of the two beams are not the same. Thus at some point X_1 the two beams differ by half a wavelength. Interference of the two beams produces a dark spot here. At a point a little farther along, Y_1, the difference is one wavelength and a bright spot is formed. With monochromatic light, this succession of light and dark spots (maximum and minimum) continues indefinitely. Now, if a substance of slightly greater refractive index be placed at C, the optical length of the beam R_2O is increased by an amount Δb because the velocity of light through C is decreased. The magnitude of this increase depends on the thickness of C and upon its refractive index, where

$$\Delta b = b(n - n_0) \tag{14-2}$$
$$b = \text{thickness of } C$$
$$n = \text{refractive index of } C$$
$$n_0 = \text{refractive index of medium (air)}$$

The velocities of light in two media are proportional to their indices of refraction.

The two beams will no longer arrive in phase at O, but at some other point O', which is now optically equally distant from R_1 and R_2. The entire band system will be shifted by this amount. For light of wavelength λ, the distance between O and O', measured in numbers of fringes, N (each made up of a dark and a light band), is

$$N = \frac{\Delta b}{\lambda} \tag{14-3}$$

or

$$N = \frac{b(n - n_0)}{\lambda} \tag{14-4}$$

If N is greater than 1, it is impossible to tell how many whole numbers of bands greater it is, since all bands are alike. This difficulty is avoided by using white light instead of monochromatic. Now the central band is the only one which is pure white. The bands on either side of this maximum of the first order are fringed with blue toward the center of the system and with red along the outer edge. This is due to the different wavelengths which go to make up white light. The next adjacent bands are even more highly fringed. After six or seven bands, the diffusion is so great that the rest of the field is again uniformly white. Thus, with substance C in the path of one of the beams, by counting the number of bands which the central band has been shifted, we may determine the value of $b(n - n_0)$. Any one of these terms can then be calculated if the others are known. If two plates of equal thickness were placed in the two beams, the number of bands that the central band shifts would be a means of calculating the refractive index of one of the plates, provided that the value of the other one was known. The interferometer is, however, not used primarily for measuring index of refraction but for comparing and measuring concentrations of solutions and gases.

In one type of instrument, shown in Fig. 14-6(a) the optical length of the two beams is equalized by means of a glass plate in the path of each beam

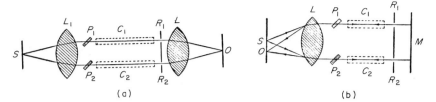

Fig. 14-6. Optical schematic of interferometers: (a) extended version and (b) folded type.

(P_1 and P_2) at an angle of about 45° to the beam, one plate being fixed and the other attached to a lever by which it can be rotated, thus increasing or decreasing its effective thickness. The movement is measured by a micrometer screw. This is turned until the central achromatic bands of the two systems correspond, that is, the optical path of the two beams is the same length. It is possible to match them to one-twentieth of a band, corresponding to a reading of about one scale division on the micrometer screw. This instrument was originally used for measuring changes in the composition of gases, and when the gas chambers are 1 m long, one scale division corresponds to a change in n_D of 0.000000015. It is capable, therefore, of measuring quantities of such substances as CO_2 and CH_4 present in air in amounts as low as 0.02 percent.

In a later type of portable gas-and-water *interferometer*, made by *Zeiss* and shown in Fig. 14-6(b), the light is reflected by the mirror M so that it passes twice through the chambers, and the bands are observed at the same end as the light source. In this way it is possible to obtain the same precision with half the length. The light is furnished by a small electric lamp and is focused on a slit. The interference bands are not as brilliant as those of the other instrument but are just as plain and as easily set. The chambers can be jacketed with an air thermostat or with water, and gases as well as liquids can be used. With the latter, the cells vary from 1 to 40 mm in length. The scale reading is proportional to the thickness of the liquid, so that the range and precision of the instrument may be varied by changing the length of the cell.

A diagram in plan and elevation of the Zeiss water interferometer is shown in Fig. 14-7. White light is furnished by the small 4-V tungsten lamp F. By means of the lens A, a mirror, and the totally reflecting prism K, the image of the filament F is focused on the narrow slit S (see Fig. 14-7, lower half); this slit acts as a (very narrow) secondary source, the light from which is rendered parallel (just as in Fig. 14-6(b)) by the lens L. The light then passes through the two compartments C_1 and C_2 of the water chamber and the rectangular apertures R_1 and R_2; thence it goes to a mirror M, where the two beams of light are reflected back upon themselves, pass through the water chamber again, and finally, by means of the lens L, are reunited at O, forming a series of interference fringes. These fringes are viewed by the cylindrical ocular E,

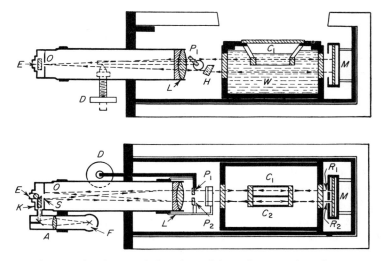

Fig. 14-7. Diagrams in plane and elevation of the Zeiss water interferometer. (Courtesy of Zeiss Instrument Co.)

which gives a magnification of 50 diameters, but in the horizontal direction only.

Besides the two interfering beams of light already considered, another pair proceed from the slit S in a precisely similar way, except that they pass *below* and not through the chamber C, likewise forming at O a second system of interference fringes. This latter fringe system is (practically) fixed in position; its sole purpose is to furnish a set of fiduciary lines which take the place of the crosshairs ordinarily used as reference marks in optical instruments. Accordingly, if the eye is placed at E, one sees two sets of alternate bright and dark bands, the two sets being separated by a narrow line. In each set of fringes only one of the bright bands is pure white; the bands adjacent to it are bordered with blue toward the center and with red on the outside. It is this central achromatic band which constitutes the reference point of each system.

One set of bands can be displaced relative to the other set by tilting the movable inclined plate P_1 (P_2 is fixed); this is effected by turning the micrometer screw with attached drum D. Thus the two achromatic bands can be brought to coincidence, and the corresponding reading on the drum can be observed.

If water is put in one half of the cell and a dilute solution of salt in the other, the number of scale divisions of displacement will be determined by the difference in refractive indices of the solution and the pure solvent. A calibration curve can be obtained by making up solutions of known concentration and comparing them with water. Plotting scale readings against concentration, a line is obtained which is almost straight. The deviation from a straight line is due, not to an inconstant variation of refractive index, but to the fact that a variation of ten scale units at one end of the scale may increase the optical length of the beam more than it would at the other end of the scale. Stated in other words, the thickness of band varies with the scale division because of properties inherent in the lever arm action. The band thickness may vary as much as 10 percent. But since this variation is quite regular, a few points will be sufficient for calibration. The range of the 5-mm chamber is from n_D 1.33320–1.34010 for 3000 divisions, using water as the comparison liquid. This corresponds to a range of 15.0–33.0 on the immersion refractometer. Assuming that the latter can be read to 0.05 division, the precision with this particular chamber is about ten times that of the refractometer. With the 40-mm chamber it would be about 80 times as great, but the range would be one-eighth as great. With this chamber one division corresponds to 1.5–3.0 mg of solute per liter for most aqueous solutions. The greatest differences of concentration which can be directly compared are therefore from 0.45 to 0.90 percent. The range of the measurement with the interferometer can be increased by comparing the solution against solutions having a known amount of solute present. This does not decrease the precision of the measurement. Thus any concentration of solute can be determined if a series of known solutions has been prepared so that each solution of the series differs by no more than 3000 scale divisions from the preceding one.

There are two procedures which one may follow when using the interferometer for analysis. First, it may be used as a direct-reading instrument, as just outlined. A calibration curve is constructed by making up a number of solutions and comparing them with water, preferably the same water as that used in making up the solutions. The readings are plotted against concentration and connected to make a smooth curve. When the unknown is compared with water, its concentration can be read from the curve.

In the other method, the interferometer is used as a zero-reading instrument. In this method, no previous calibration is necessary but an approximate knowledge of the concentration of the unknown solution is required. It is then compared with two solutions, one slightly more and one slightly less concentrated. This method is slightly more laborious for a single determination, but one gains in precision what one loses in convenience. This is so because only a limited portion of the scale is used (the solutions should not differ by more than 200 scale divisions). In addition to not requiring a previous calibration, this method is not subject to the error caused by the apparent shifting of the achromatic band of the interference system. When comparing a solution of a salt with water, it must be remembered that the central band is brought back to its zero position by turning a glass plate. The increase in the refractive index of the liquid is counterbalanced by decreasing the effective thickness of the compensator plate. Since the dispersion power of the solution differs from that of glass, the band system changes its appearance, so that after the concentration of salt has increased sufficiently (usually about 300 scale divisions), there is an apparent shift in the position of the achromatic band which, if not considered, would cause an error of one band width (18 scale divisions). This shows the advantage of working over a very limited portion of the scale.

To secure a precision of ± 0.000001 with the refractometer, the temperature must be regulated to $0.01°$. Since the interferometric method is a differential one, no special regulation of temperature is required in order to determine the difference in n_D of two solutions to 0.0000001. The sensitivity of the instrument, in terms of average parts of solute per million of solvent, is as follows for one scale division:

Refractometer (temperature to 0.01°C) 200–300
Interferometer (simple temperature control) 40-mm chamber 1.5–3.0

The interferometer is not entirely independent of temperature because there is a slight difference between the temperature coefficients of solution and solvent. Thus, a solution of potassium chloride giving a reading of 200 when compared with water at 25° will give a reading of 202 when the two are compared at 20°. With water solutions a variation of $\pm 0.5°$ is permissible even in very accurate work. It is *absolutely necessary*, however, that the *two chambers* should be at exactly the same temperature. With organic liquids accurate control of temperature is required.

Applications

The use of the interferometer in analyzing gases has already been mentioned. It has been used to determine the permeability of balloon fabrics to hydrogen and helium. Many applications are possible in the analysis of gases. Using a 1-meter chamber, 0.02 percent of carbon dioxide or methane in air can be determined.

The interferometer has been used in the investigation of sea water to chart ocean currents and in the analysis of dilute solutions used for freezing-point determinations. It can be used to determine potassium and sodium in a mixture of their sulfates or chlorides with a precision of ± 0.1 mg on a 50-mg sample. The mixture is dissolved in exactly 200 times its weight of water and compared with a standard solution of pure potassium sulfate dissolved in 200 times its weight of water. The reading will range from 430 to 0 as the composition of the mixture ranges from pure sodium sulfate to pure potassium sulfate, and a calibration curve is constructed.

The instrument has been used in water investigations, in measuring adsorption, in investigating colloidal solutions, sewage, fermented liquids, and milk and in biological problems such as measurement of serums, CO_2 in blood, ethyl alcohol in blood, ferment activity, and concentration of heavy water. It has been used to determine the end point in titrations and to follow the velocity of reactions. In acidimetric and precipitation reactions it gives as accurate results as good visual methods. It is necessary to plot the straight lines showing the change in reading with solution added; at the end point a sharp angle occurs. The interferometer is particularly valuable in measuring small changes in the composition of mixtures of two organic liquids as a result of preferential adsorption.

LABORATORY WORK

General Directions for the Abbe Refractometer

1. Be sure that the instrument is clean and in working condition. Make certain that the prisms are clean and dry.

2. Start the temperature-controlling device and adjust to 20°C ± 1°, or better if possible.

3. Turn the milled head to separate the prisms. Introduce a drop of distilled water at the funnel-shaped opening between the prisms, or place it on the lower prism and lock the prisms together. *Special care* must be taken not to touch or scratch the prism.

4. Set the scale near 1.33. Adjust the light source and mirror or tilt the instrument on its bearing until the illumination is as bright as possible.

5. Adjust the dispersion screw on the telescope so that the dividing line between the light and dark halves of the field is as sharp as possible. If the dividing line is not sharp and the two fields are not readily distinguished from each other, place a sheet of white paper over the mirror. This gives a better source of diffused white light.

6. Move the arm carrying the reading telescope until the dividing line cuts the intersection of the cross hairs. Focus the eyepiece so that the cross hairs are clearly seen.

7. Read the index of refraction on the scale, estimating the fourth place. Focus the reading telescope so that the divisions are clearly discernible. The dispersion may be read on the rotating drum.

8. Turn off the *heating element*, if one is being used, and then turn off the water.

9. Open the prisms and clean them with soft tissue moistened with a *little* alcohol. Do not pour or spill alcohol all over the prisms.

10. Close the prisms and replace the cover on the instrument.

11. Do not change any of the adjustments. The instrument has been adjusted to give correct readings.

BE CAREFUL NOT TO SCRATCH THE PRISMS.

Following the foregoing directions determine the refractive index of a liquid supplied by the instructor. Make five settings and take the average. Suitable liquids are sugar solution, alcohol, or an oil. From the refractive index and density of each pure liquid, calculate the specific refractivity and the molar refractivity. Compare your results with theoretical values.

General Directions for the Immersion Refractometer

This experiment consists in determining the percentage by volume or weight of an unknown ethyl alcohol solution and the grams per 100 ml of solute in some salt solution. The only data available for a salt at 25°C are those shown in Fig. 11-12, which is a curve constructed for potassium nitrate from a large number of student results. For other salts Wagner's data at 17.5°C must be used.

For volatile liquids the instrument is provided with a metal container constructed with a glass bottom which fits over the prism and locks with a partial turn. It is advisable to use this instead of a beaker when alcohol solutions are used. It is important that the dot on the attachment correspond to the dot above the prism; otherwise the pins will not fit into the slots properly.

The best way to control the temperature in the water bath (see Fig. 14-3) is to circulate through it, by means of a small centrifugal pump, a stream of water from a large thermostat maintained at the proper temperature. The water bath may be insulated on the side with sheet asbestos or felt to decrease heat exchange.

1. When a constant temperature has been attained, as shown by the protected thermometer in the water bath, place in the holes in the rack provided for this purpose the small beakers of special design containing the solutions to be analyzed, and cover them with crucible covers. Place beside them a beaker of distilled water. The temperature of the latter may be tested with a very small thermometer.

2. When the temperature is constant, place the prism in the beaker of distilled water to attain the proper temperature.

3. Adjust the position of the instrument and of the mirror until the maximum contrast is obtained between the light and dark parts of the field.

4. Adjust the compensator until the dividing line is free from color.

5. Focus by turning the eyepiece until a sharp line is obtained.

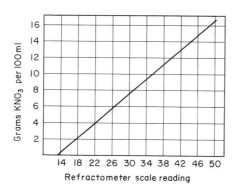

Fig. 14-8. Determination of potassium nitrate by immersion refractometer at 25° C.

6. The reading should be the same as that given in the table on page 401. Fractions of a division are obtained by turning the round vernier until the line just coincides with the lower numerical scale division. Make a series of five settings and take the average. If there is a small correction, it is best to note this and apply it in all measurements. If it is considerable, ask the instructor to reset the instrument.

7. It is desirable to keep the prism in distilled water at the proper temperature when not testing a solution, because then it requires less time to reach the temperature of the solution.

8. Remove the prism from the water, wipe it dry with a soft cloth, and place it in the solution to be analyzed. Make a series of readings and take the average.

9. Refer to the proper table to find the concentration corresponding to the reading.

10. Report the concentration and pertinent data to the instructor.

11. Rinse the prism with distilled water of the same temperature and wipe it dry with a soft cloth. Be very careful not to scratch the prism.

Notes

If a wavy border line is obtained, the temperature of the prism is not uniform.

It is well to take the temperature in the beaker before and after the readings in a given solution. It is recommended to use the volatile liquid container instead of an open beaker for alcohol solutions.

Use either artificial light or daylight, whichever is more convenient.

A change in reading shows that the temperature is changing.

Problems

1. A substance having the analysis C_3H_6O might be either acetone or allyl alcohol. Determine which of these two substances it is from the fact that the molar refraction is 16.97. *Ans.* Allyl alcohol.

2. The refractive index of carbon tetrachloride at 20°C is 1.4573, and the density at 20° is 1.595 g cm^{-3}. Calculate the molar refraction. *Ans.* 26.51.

3. From the atomic refractions, calculate the refractive index at 20°C of nitrobenzene. The density is 1.210 g cm^{-3}. *Ans.* The experimental value is 1.5524.

4. Calculate the specific refraction and the molar refraction for each of these liquids:

Compound	$n_D{}^{20}$	d^{20}
Benzene	1.4979	0.879
Ethanol	1.3590	0.788
Ethyl acetate	1.3701	0.901
Toluene	1.4929	0.866
Water	1.3328	0.998

5. For D_2O, $n_D{}^{20} = 1.32830$, and for water, $n_D{}^{20} = 1.33280$. If the refractive index for a sample is 1.32980, calculate the percent D_2O present.

6. What is the refractive index of a mixture of 10 ml of benzene and 40 ml of nitrobenzene? See Problem 4 for necessary data.

7. A 120-ml sample of wine was distilled to remove all the alcohol; the distillate was diluted to a volume of 100 ml. The reading on the immersion refractometer at 25°C was 26.8. What was the percentage by volume of alcohol in the wine? Necessary tables are in Lange's "Handbook of Chemistry."

Bibliography

Bauer, N., K. Fajans, and S. Z. Lewin, in A. Weissberger (Ed.), *Physical Methods of Organic Chemistry*, 3rd ed., Interscience, New York, 1960. Vol. 1, Part II, Chapter 28.

Tilton, L. W., and J. K. Taylor, in W. C. Berl (Ed.), *Physical Methods in Chemical Analysis*, Academic Press, New York, 1950. Vol. I.

Literature Cited

1. Andrews, L. W., *J. Am. Chem. Soc.*, **30**, 353 (1908).
2. Clemens, C. A., *J. Ind. Eng. Chem.*, **13**, 813 (1921).
3. Leach, A. E., and H. C. Lythgoe, *J. Am. Chem. Soc.*, **27**, 964 (1905).
4. Shippy, B. A., and G. H. Barrows, *J. Am. Chem. Soc.*, **40**, 185 (1918).
5. Wagner, B., *Z. angew. Chemie*, **33**, 262 (1920).

CHAPTER 15

Polarimetry

Polarimetry, the measurement of the change of the direction of vibration of polarized light when it interacts with optically active materials, is one of the oldest of the instrumental procedures. Much of the work on the development of prisms and other devices for the production of polarized light was done in the early part of the nineteenth century. * A small, rough polarimeter seems to be a simple piece of apparatus, but a precision polarimeter is an example of complicated optical equipment.

Polarimetry Theory

Ordinary, natural, unreflected light behaves as though it consisted of a large number of electromagnetic waves vibrating in all possible orientations around the direction of propagation. If, by some means, we sort out from the natural conglomeration only those rays vibrating in one particular plane, we say that we have *plane-polarized light.* Of course, since a light wave consists of an electric and a magnetic component vibrating at right angles to each other, the term "plane" may not be quite descriptive, but the ray can be considered planar if we restrict ourselves to noting the direction of the electrical component. *Circularly polarized light* would represent a wave in which the electrical component (and therefore the magnetic component also) spirals around the direction of propagation of the ray, either clockwise ("right-handed") or counterclockwise ("left-handed").

*See, for example, J. B. Biot, *Mem. prem. classe Inst. France* **13**, 218 (1812); W. Nicol, *Edinburgh New Phil. J.* **6**, 83 (1828).

It is possible, and for many explanations of the interaction of light and matter it is quite enlightening, to represent a plane-polarized ray as the vector sum of two circularly polarized rays, one moving clockwise and one counterclockwise and with the same amplitude of vibration. It is obvious from Fig. 15-1 that at zero time the sum of C_{l_0} and C_{r_0}, the left and right circularly polarized rays, equals P_0, the plane-polarized ray. At the time when C_l is at C_{l_1}, C_r is at C_{r_1}, and the vector sum is P_1, and so on around the circle.

If, following the passage of the plane-polarized ray through some material, one of the circularly polarized components—say, the left circularly polarized ray—has been slowed down, then the resultant would be a plane-polarized ray rotated somewhat to the right from its original position. Figure 15-2 illustrates

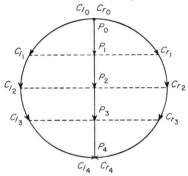

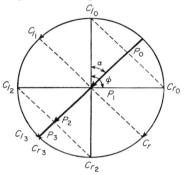

Fig. 15-1. Representation of a plane-polarized ray as the sum of two circularly polarized rays.

Fig. 15-2. Rotation of the plane of polarized light due to slowing down of one of the circular components.

the case where the right-handed ray is 90° ahead of the left-handed ray. The plane-polarized resultant ray is rotated 45°, that is, 90°/2, from the original position. The rotation α is just one-half of the phase difference φ of the two circular components.

The index of refraction n represents the ratio of the velocity of a ray of light in a vacuum c to its velocity in a medium v. That is,

$$n = \frac{c}{v} \tag{15-1}$$

If a substance showed different indices of refraction for the l and r components of a plane-polarized ray, then one beam would be slowed down on passage through the medium, and the plane of polarization of the ray would be rotated. Thus:

$$n_l = \frac{c}{v_l} \quad \text{and} \quad n_r = \frac{c}{v_r} \tag{15-2}$$

$$\frac{v_l}{v_r} = \frac{n_r}{n_l} \tag{15-3}$$

If we let b represent the length of the column of material traversed by the ray; λ_0, the wavelength of the light; ν, the frequency of rotation (or vibration) of the light; and c, the velocity of light in a vacuum; then the difference in degrees, φ, between the two rays is given by Eq. 1.

$$\varphi = \frac{2\pi b\nu}{\nu_r} - \frac{2\pi b\nu}{\nu_l} \tag{15-4}$$

$$= \frac{2\pi b\nu c}{\nu_r c} - \frac{2\pi b\nu c}{\nu_l c} \tag{15-5}$$

$$= \frac{2\pi b n_r}{\lambda_0} - \frac{2\pi b n_l}{\lambda_0} \tag{15-6}$$

$$= \frac{2\pi b}{\lambda_0}(n_r - n_l) \tag{15-7}$$

or

$$\alpha = \frac{\pi b}{\lambda_0}(n_r - n_l) \tag{15-8}$$

and

$$(n_r - n_l) = \frac{\alpha \lambda_0}{\pi b} \tag{15-9}$$

A solution of 3.45 g of sucrose per 100 g of aqueous solution at 18°C shows a rotation α of 99.8° for light of 5000 Å. The tube length b is 10 cm. Using Eq. 15-9, one calculates

$$(n_r - n_l) = \frac{99.8° \times 5000 \times 10^{-8} \text{ cm}}{180° \times 10 \text{ cm}}$$

$$(n_r - n_l) = 2.77 \times 10^{-6}$$

Thus relatively small differences in the index of refraction for right and left circularly polarized light cause appreciable rotation of the plane of polarized light.

Pasteur,[9] van't Hoff,[10] and Le Bel[8] worked out the principles which chemists now recognize as requirements in order that a given molecule possess "optical activity," that is, rotate the plane of polarized light. A compound is optically active in solution if its structure cannot be brought to coincide with that of its mirror image, that is, the compound does not possess a plane or a center of symmetry. If a tetrahedral carbon atom is substituted with four different groups, it is said to be asymmetric and would lead to optical activity unless a second similar asymmetrically substituted carbon atom is contained in the molecule. For example, mesotartaric acid and other meso compounds are not optically active. In the case of many nonplanar compounds, such as spiro compounds, allylenic compounds, and certain substituted biphenyl compounds, dissymmetrical structures with optical activity may result without an asymmetric carbon atom in the molecule. Likewise, optical activity is not limited to carbon compounds but may occur in any dissymmetrical three-dimensional compound.

Cotton[3] discovered an interesting connection between rotatory power and light absorption in optically active compounds. As one approaches certain "optically active" absorption bands in a compound from the long-wavelength side, the rotatory power at first increases strongly, then falls off and changes sign. This effect is known as the *Cotton effect*. Within the absorption band, the specific extinction coefficients for right- and left-hand circularly polarized light are different; that is, $(k_r - k_l) \neq 0$. This effect changes linearly polarized light into elliptically polarized light and is known as *circular dichroism*.

Measurement of Optical Rotation

The rotation exhibited by an optically active substance depends on the thickness of the layer traversed by the light, the wavelength of the light used for the measurement, and the temperature. If the substance measured is a solution, then the concentration of the optically active material is also involved, and the nature of the solvent may also be important. There are certain substances which change their rotation with time. Some are substances that change from one structure to another with a different rotatory power and are said to show *mutarotation*. Mutarotation is common among the sugars. Other substances, owing to enolization within the molecules, may rotate so as to become symmetrical and thus lose their rotatory power. These substances are said to show *racemization*. Mutarotation and racemization are influenced not only by time but by pH, temperature, and other factors. In expressing the results of any polarimetric measurement, it is therefore very important to include all experimental conditions.

The results of polarimetric measurements are reduced to a set of standard conditions. The length employed as standard is 10 cm for liquids and 1 mm for solids. The standard wavelength is that of the green mercury line (5461 Å), although the sodium doublet (5890 Å + 5896 Å) has been widely employed, especially in the older measurements. The standard temperature is 20°C.

Thus, if b is the layer thickness in decimeters, C is the concentration of solute in grams per 100 ml of solution, α is the observed rotation in degrees, and $[\alpha]$ is the specific rotation or rotation under standard conditions, then

$$[\alpha] = \frac{100\alpha}{bC} \tag{15-10}$$

The temperature of the measurement is indicated by a superscript and the wavelength by a subscript written after the brackets.

For a pure liquid, the concentration is unimportant, but temperature changes cause expansion and contraction of the liquid and a consequent change in the number of active molecules in the path of the light. For pure liquids unit density is assumed as standard, and the definition of specific rotation becomes

$$[\alpha] = \frac{\alpha}{b\rho} \qquad (15\text{-}11)$$

where ρ is density.

As mentioned above, the specific rotation $[\alpha]$ changes with wavelength, and the rate of change of specific rotation with wavelength is known as *optical rotatory dispersion*.[4] Drude[6] has shown that the specific rotation may be expressed as a function of wavelength by an equation with several terms.

$$[\alpha] = \frac{k_1}{\lambda^2 - \lambda_1{}^2} + \frac{k_2}{\lambda^2 - \lambda_2{}^2} + \frac{k_3}{\lambda^2 - \lambda_3{}^2} + \cdots \qquad (15\text{-}12)$$

where λ is the wavelength of measurement and $\lambda_1, \lambda_2, \lambda_3, \ldots$ are the constants which can be identified with the wavelengths of maximum absorption of the "optically active" absorption bands.

In a region far removed from an "optically active" absorption band, where the dispersion is normal, the equation of Drude can be simplified to Eq. 15-13.

$$[\alpha] = \frac{k}{\lambda^2 - \lambda_0{}^2} \qquad (15\text{-}13)$$

where λ_0 is a constant representing the wavelength of the nearest optically active absorption band. When $\lambda \gg \lambda_0$, Eq. 15-13 may even be reduced to

$$[\alpha] = \frac{k}{\lambda^2} \qquad (15\text{-}14)$$

Measurements of dispersion are very useful in the identification of mixtures. The dispersion ratio, the ratio of the specific rotation of two different wavelengths, is often used.

Temperature changes have several effects upon the rotation of a solution or liquid. An increase in temperature increases the length of the tube; it also decreases the density, thus reducing the number of molecules involved. It causes changes in the rotatory power of the molecules themselves due to association or dissociation, increased mobility of the atoms, etc. In general, the effect of temperature may be expressed by Eq. 15-15.

$$[\alpha]^t = [\alpha]^{20} + z(t - 20) \qquad (15\text{-}15)$$

where z = temperature coefficient of rotation
t = temperature in degrees centigrade

Substances vary widely in their values of z.

Any liquid or solution, when placed in a magnetic field, rotates the plane of polarized light because of the effect of the magnetic field upon the motion of the electrons in the molecules. This effect was discovered by Faraday[7] and is known as the *Faraday effect*. The rotation χ is positive if in the same direction as the magnetizing current. For most substances χ is positive and is appreciable for many organic substances.

For analytical purposes, the chief interest in polarimetry is to determine the concentration of substances, although abundant correlation between rotation and chemical structure has been found.[5] The relationship between rotation and concentration of a solution is, unfortunately, not strictly linear, so that the specific rotation of a solution is not a constant. The concentration of the measurement should always be stated when $[\alpha]$ is given. The values of the specific rotation extrapolated to infinite dilution may be employed.

The relationship between $[\alpha]$ and concentration may usually be expressed by one of the three equations proposed by Biot.

$$[\alpha] = A + Bq \tag{15-16}$$

$$[\alpha] = A + Bq + Cq^2 \tag{15-17}$$

$$[\alpha] = A + \frac{Bq}{C + q} \tag{15-18}$$

where q = percentage of solvent in the solution

A, B, C = constants

Equation 15-16 represents a straight line, Eq. 15-17 a parabola, and Eq. 15-18 a hyperbola. The constants A, B, and C are determined from several measurements at different concentrations.

Calculations of Polarimetry and Saccharimetry

The equations for the calculation of specific rotation, $[\alpha]$, from measurement of the angle of rotation have already been given (Eq. 15-10 and 15-11). Often it is desired to calculate the molecular rotation M, which is given by the equation

$$M = \frac{[\alpha] \times \text{mol. wt.}}{100} \tag{15-19}$$

The polarimeter is widely used as a saccharimeter in sugar analysis. In the determination of the concentration of sucrose in a substance containing no other optically active material except sucrose, it would be convenient to take 75.2 g of unknown as sample and dissolve it in enough water to make 100 ml of solution. Then, with a 2-dm tube, the rotation in degrees is numerically equal to the concentration of sucrose in percent by weight. This follows from Eq. 15-10, using $[\alpha]_D^{20} = 66.5°$ for sucrose.

This sample, 75.2 g, is rather large, and consequently most modern saccharimeters are not graduated in degrees but in smaller divisions. Several types of graduation have been used. Most modern saccharimeters are graduated in the "International" scheme in which one division equals 0.3462°. It is obvious that one should check the normal weight of any saccharimeter, preferably by calibration with pure sucrose, before any unknowns are run.

Most raw sugar samples contain other optically active substances besides sucrose. When sucrose is heated with acid or with the enzyme invertase, it is "inverted" to form one molecule of fructose and one of glucose. Sucrose has a specific rotation of $+66.5°$, fructose has a specific rotation of $-93°$, and glucose $+52.5°$. Thus the specific rotation changes from $+66.5°$ to $(-93 + 52.5)/2 = -20.2°$ upon inversion. By measuring the change in rotation upon inversion it is possible to determine sucrose in the presence of other optically active substances. The formula used for the determination of sucrose is known as the *Clerget formula*, Eq. 15-20.

$$\text{Percent sucrose} = \frac{100(a - h)}{144 - \dfrac{t}{2}} \times \frac{W}{w} \tag{15-20}$$

where a = rotation in Ventzke degrees of sucrose solution before inversion
h = rotation in Ventzke degrees after hydrolysis
t = temperature in degrees centigrade
W = normal weight for saccharimeter employed
w = weight of sample taken per 100 ml of solution

The Clerget factor, 144 in Eq. 15-20, varies slightly with concentration and with the details of the method of hydrolysis employed. The factor is derived considering the experimentally determined Ventzke readings for inverted sugar, the dilution introduced by the addition of hydrochloric acid (10 ml per 100 ml of solution) necessary for the hydrolysis, and the fact that one molecule of water is used up for each molecule of sucrose hydrolyzed. (See Brown and Zerban[1] for a more complete discussion of this formula and of sugar analysis in general.)

The Polarimeter

The polarimeter consists of the following basic parts:

1. A light source.
2. A polarizer.
3. An analyzer.
4. A graduated circle to measure the amount of rotation.
5. Sample tubes.

Except in the simplest instruments a half-shade device is also included. Some polarimeters may be equipped with photocells or other devices for measuring the intensity of light emerging from the instrument, although most polarimeters are designed for visual observation.

The most common light sources for polarimetry are sodium vapor lamps and mercury vapor lamps. The sodium lamp emits light of wavelengths 5890 Å and 5896 Å plus a little continuous background which can be largely eliminated with a filter of 7 percent potassium dichromate used in a 6-cm-thick layer. The mercury lamp emits light of several wavelengths, the prominent visual lines being at 4358, 4916, 5461, 5770, and 5791 Å. Each line can be isolated with the proper choice of filters (Fig. 13-6). If a continuous light source can be employed, then ordinary sunlight or light from a tungsten filament lamp can be used.

The polarizer (and the analyzer) may be of several different types. One type consists of a crystal, usually calcite or quartz, cut diagonally at such an angle that one component of the light is totally reflected. The second component passes through the second half of the crystal and thus emerges, going in the same direction as the original beams (Fig. 15-3). The two halves of the prism are cemented together with a cement having an index of refraction as near as possible to 1.4865, which is the value of n_e, the extraordinary index of refraction for calcite. The index of refraction for calcite at right angles to the above ray is $n_0 = 1.6584$.

Several different varieties of polarizing (and analyzing) prisms are known. They vary in the angles of the faces of the prism and of the cut diagonally through the prism. The Glan-Thompson prism (Fig. 15-3) and the Nicol prism (Fig. 15-4) are the most common. The Nicol prism requires smaller pieces of calcite and is cheaper but is not as good as the Glan-Thompson prism.

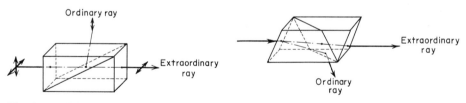

Fig. 15-3.   The Glan-Thompson prism.   Fig. 15-4.   The Nicol prism.

The light emerging from a true Nicol prism is displaced from the original beam and will revolve in a circle as the prism is rotated. Again, two Nicols used together will not produce total extinction at any point for the whole field and thus will introduce uncertainty in the balance point. With either a Nicol or Glan-Thompson prism the entering light must be essentially parallel; otherwise some unpolarized light will be transmitted. Light must not, therefore, be concentrated on the prism by using a converging beam.

Light can also be polarized by reflection from a mirror at the proper angle— Brewster's angle. If light strikes a mirror at such an angle i that

$$\tan i = n \qquad\qquad (15\text{-}21)$$

(where n = refractive index of the mirror material), then only the component vibrating perpendicular to the plane of incidence (parallel to the mirror surface) will be reflected. Reflection is not used in modern polarimeters to produce polarized light. It is interesting to note, however, that light emerging from a monochromator is partially polarized, with the greatest intensity perpendicular to the exit slit. Thus if a monochromator precedes a polarimeter, the slit should be perpendicular to the direction of transmission of the polarizing prism.

A third method of producing polarized light is by the use of Polaroid filters. Polaroid filters are composed of strongly dichroitic crystals oriented in a plastic material. These crystals strongly absorb light vibrating in one direction and only weakly absorb light vibrating in the perpendicular direction. Polaroids can never give 100 percent polarization; also, the light must lie in the region from about 5000 Å to 6800 Å. Polaroids are used, therefore, only on less expensive instruments.

When two prisms, a polarizer and an analyzer, are used together, the intensity of light transmitted through the combination is given by the law of Malus:

$$I = KI_0 \cos^2 \theta \qquad (15\text{-}22)$$

where I = emerging intensity from analyzer
I_0 = incident intensity on analyzer
θ = angle between the directions of transmission of the two prisms
K = factor taking into account reflection and absorption losses in the analyzing prism; K is approximately equal to 1

The graduated circle is fitted with a vernier for more precise measurement of the angle through which the analyzing prism has been rotated. Special reading devices employing a pair of parallel index lines are used on the most precise instruments. A tangent screw with graduated drum allows the borders of an etched line on the main scale to be made to coincide with the two hairlines. With such a device readings can be made to 0.002°.

The polarimeter tubes must have plane and parallel glass discs at the ends. The glass must be free from strain; otherwise the discs will produce a partial circular polarization of the light, and complete extinction of light will be impossible. Each tube should be tested by filling it with water, placing it between crossed prisms, and noting whether the dark field remains dark. The length of polarimeter tubes may be determined by measuring the rotation of a known, strongly rotating liquid or solution—for example, nicotine in ethyl alcohol—at a definite temperature.

In cheaper instruments one measures the position of the analyzer required to give a minimum intensity without the sample in the tubes, and again with the sample in the tubes. The difference in the two readings is the rotation caused by the introduction of the sample. The human eye, however, is much better at *matching* light intensities than is the human mind at *remembering* intensities, as it must if the minimum intensity is to be determined. Consequently, the more precise polarimeters make use of so-called half-shade devices which result in matching two half-fields for a balance point.

Many different half-shade devices are available. Each has its own advantages and disadvantages. The Jellett-Cornu prism (Fig. 15-5) is constructed by sawing a Glan-Thompson prism in two lengthwise, grinding one face down a little, and cementing the parts back together. When light passes through this polarizing prism, the two halves will produce polarized light beams tilted slightly with respect to each other. Rotation of the analyzer prism in front of such a polarizing prism would result in complete extinction, first of one-half of the field and then of the other half. At some intermediate position the two halves of the field would appear of equal brightness. This point is taken as the balance point. The Jellett-Cornu device does not allow variation of the half-shade angle, the angle between the two prisms. Variation of this angle is desirable, since large angles are necessary for precise balancing with weak light sources and small angles give more precise balancing with strong light sources.

The Lippich prism (Fig. 15-6) is a popular half-shade device. A small

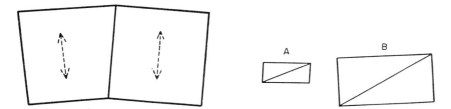

Fig. 15-5.   The Jellett-Cornu prism, end view.   Fig. 15-6.   The Lippich prism, side view.

polarizing prism *A* precedes the large polarizing prism *B*. With such an arrangement one-half of the field can be rotated slightly with respect to the other half. The analyzer must be at some intermediate position in order to achieve equal illumination of both halves of the field. Sometimes two Lippich prisms are used, dividing the field into three parts which match at the balance point. The half-shade angle of any Lippich arrangement is variable by rotating the Lippich prism.

A popular, inexpensive half-shade device is the Laurent half-wave plate. A thin plate of quartz cut parallel to its optic axis is placed over one-half of the field of the polarizer. The quartz plate is cut just thick enough that for a given wavelength of light (usually sodium D lines) the slow ray lags exactly one-half wavelength behind the fast ray. This results in a slight rotation of the light passing through the part of the polarizer covered by the plate. The amount of rotation can be varied by rotating the quartz plate with respect to the polarizing prism, and thus the half-shade angle is variable. The quartz plate is suitable, however, only for the wavelength for which it was constructed. At other wave-lengths it becomes more difficult to find the balance point due to lack of con-trast in the fields as the analyzer is rotated.

The optical arrangement of a precision polarimeter is shown in Fig. 15-7,

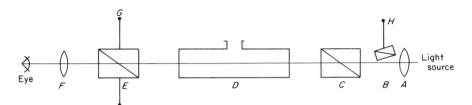

Fig. 15-7. Optical arrangement of a polarimeter with a Lippich half-shade device: *A*, collimating lens; *B*, Lippich half-shade prism; *C*, polarizing prism; *D*, tube; *E*, analyzing prism; *F*, eyepiece; *G*, scale; *H*, lever to adjust half-shade angle.

and an example of a commercial instrument is shown in Fig. 15-8. The Rudolph instrument has a Lippich double field polarizer.

In the instruments of the type described above, the rotation is measured by rotating the analyzer with respect to the polarizer. It is also possible to meas-ure rotatory power by leaving the analyzer permanently crossed with respect to

Fig. 15-8. Rudolph polarimeter. (Courtesy of O. C. Rudolph & Sons.)

the polarizer and compensating any rotation caused by the sample with a piece of quartz which rotates light in the opposite direction to that of the sample. The design of such an instrument is shown in Fig. 15-9. Wedges I and II are made of levorotatory quartz and are ground to the same angle. Wedge I is stationary, but II is movable. Moving wedge II thus varies the thickness of the

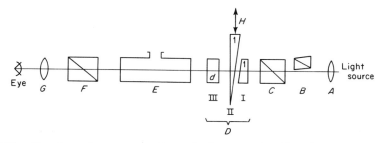

Fig. 15-9. Quartz-wedge compensating polarimeter: *A*, collimating lens; *B*, Lippich half-shade prism; *C*, polarizing prism; *D*, quartz-wedge compensator; *E*, tube; *F*, analyzer prism (position fixed); *G*, eyepiece; *H*, scale and movement device for compensator.

block of levorotatory quartz. Block III is made of dextrorotatory quartz and is of thickness equal to that of wedges I and II when II is in an intermediate position. Thus both positive and negative rotations of the sample can be compensated by moving the wedge in or out from its intermediate position. Compensating polarimeters of the type described above are used largely for sugar analyses and are known as saccharimeters. Fortunately, the rotatory dispersion of quartz and of sucrose and a few other sugar solutions is very nearly the same. Thus if white light were used as a source, the quartz could compensate the rotation of the sugar solution at all wavelengths. If the dispersions were not the same, only light of one wavelength would be compensated completely, and the field would appear colored rather than dark.

Precise saccharimeters using white-light sources are constructed with Glan-Thompson prisms for analyzer and polarizer and with Lippich or Jellett-Cornu half-shade devices. The Laurent half-wave plate is not suitable since it will be a half-wave plate only for one wavelength. A typical saccharimeter made by the Bausch & Lomb Optical Company is shown in Fig. 15-10.

Automatic Recording Polarimeters

Automatic recording polarimeters may be placed broadly in two classes: (1) instruments in which the null-point method is used, and (2) instruments in which a ratio method is used. At present all commercially available instruments fall into the first class. They differ among themselves in the manner in which the null point is achieved. Two will be described in some detail.

The Rudolph spectropolarimeter works on the null-point principle, the null point being ascertained by means of an imposed mechanical oscillation ($\pm\epsilon$) of the analyzer, whose mean angular position is orthogonal with respect to the plane of polarization of the entering light beam (Fig. 15-11). At this point, angular changes of $+\epsilon$ and $-\epsilon$ produce the same current in the phototransducer system. The optical rotation α produced by the introduction of a sample between the polarizer and the analyzer is measured by the angular rotation ($-\alpha$)

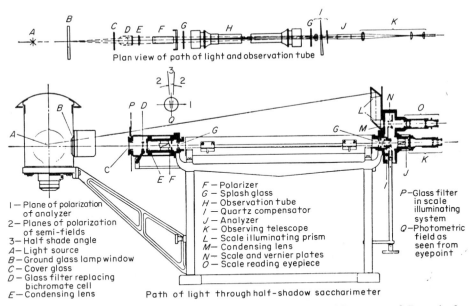

F — Polarizer
G — Splash glass
H — Observation tube
I — Quartz compensator
J — Analyzer
K — Observing telescope
L — Scale illuminating prism
M — Condensing lens
N — Scale and vernier plates
O — Scale reading eyepiece

P — Glass filter
in scale
illuminating
system
Q — Photometric
field as
seen from
eyepoint

1 — Plane of polarization
of analyzer
2 — Planes of polarization
of semi-fields
3 — Half shade angle
A — Light source
B — Ground glass lamp window
C — Cover glass
D — Glass filter replacing
bichromate cell
E — Condensing lens

Path of light through half-shadow saccharimeter

Fig. 15-10. Bausch & Lomb half-shadow saccharimeter. (Courtesy of Bausch & Lomb Optical Co.)

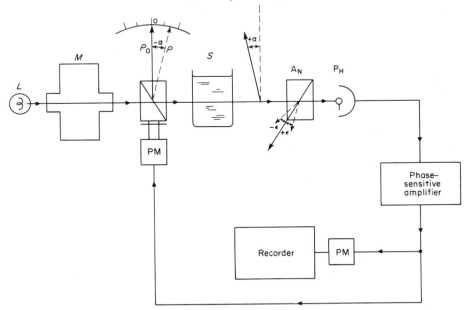

Fig. 15-11. Schematic diagram of the Rudolph spectropolarimeter. The polarizer is rotated through an angle $(-\alpha)$ which is equal and opposite to the angle of rotation of the sample. The angle of scan, $\pm \epsilon$, is induced by a mechanical oscillator. L, light source; M, monochromator; P_0, initial position of polarizer axis; P, final position of polarizer axis; S, sampler; ϵ, angle of scan. (Courtesy of O. C. Rudolph & Sons.)

of the polarizer which is required to restore the balance of the signal output. The analyzer prism is mechanically oscillated to produce a 20-cps modulation of the light beam striking the photomultiplier tube. A portion of its signal is separated, by means of a chopper, into two signals, corresponding to the right and left oscillations of the analyzer. The difference between these two signals is fed into a null-point-seeking servo system, which drives the polarizer to a position which compensates for the rotation of the sample. The recording of the optical activity is obtained by means of a linkage between the angular position of the polarizer and an *X-Y* recording system.

The Cary spectropolarimeter is similar in principle to the Rudolph instrument, except that in the Cary instrument the mechanical oscillation of the analyzer is replaced by an oscillation brought on by a magneto-optical effect. To achieve this, a Faraday cell is placed ahead of the analyzer (Fig. 15-12). The Faraday cell consists of a silica cylinder surrounded by a coil. An alternating current (60 cps) passes through the coil, thus cyclically displacing the plane of

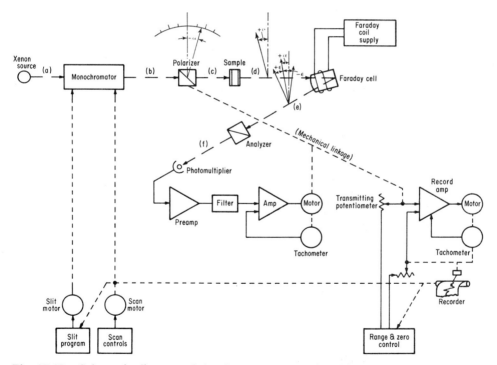

Fig. 15-12. Schematic diagram of the Cary spectropolarimeter. The angle of scan, $\pm\epsilon$, is induced by a Faraday cell. (a) Undispersed, nonpolarized beam; (b) monochromatic nonpolarized beam; (c) monochromatic polarized beam; (d) beam "c" rotated by sample; (e) beam "d" cyclically displaced by Faraday cell; (f) component transmitted by analyzer. (Courtesy of Applied Physics Corp.)

polarization of the beam. A motor energized by the amplified current from the photomultiplier moves the polarizer by means of a mechanical linkage.

LABORATORY WORK

EXPERIMENT 15-1   DETERMINATION OF THE SPECIFIC ROTATION OF A SUBSTANCE

Weigh out from 10 to 20 g of the optically active substance assigned by the instructor. Dissolve in water and dilute to the mark in a 50-ml volumetric flask.

Determine the zero reading of the polarimeter with a tube filled with distilled water. Average several readings for precision.

Fill a 200-mm tube with the solution under investigation. Note the temperature of the solution and determine the rotation. Average several readings for precision. Calculate the specific rotation from the data, using Eq. 15-10.

Dilute 10.00 ml of solution to 25 ml in a volumetric flask. Repeat the determination of $[\alpha]$ on this solution. Repeat the dilution and determination of $[\alpha]$ once again. Plot specific rotation $[\alpha]$ against concentration.

EXPERIMENT 15-2   DETERMINATION OF CONCENTRATION OF SUCROSE SOLUTIONS

This is a simplified experiment designed to illustrate the use of the polarimeter for sucrose analysis, employing inversion of the sucrose. For procedures employed in actual determinations of sucrose in commercial products, see the books by Browne and Zerban, the A.O.A.C., and Bates.[2]

PROCEDURE

A solution of sucrose in water will be furnished as the unknown. Measure the rotation α at room temperature t in a 200-mm tube.

To 50 ml of solution in a flask, add exactly 5 ml of concentrated hydrochloric acid. Insert a thermometer and place the flask in a water bath. Heat the bath slowly at such a rate that the temperature of the sugar solution reaches 68°C in 15 min. Cool the flask quickly. Read the rotation in a 200-mm tube when the temperature has returned to its original value t. Multiply the polarimeter reading on the invert sugar by $\frac{11}{10}$ to allow for the dilution by the acid. This rotation value equals α' in the formula below. Calculate grams of sucrose per 100 ml of solution C by means of the formula

$$C = \frac{\alpha - \alpha'}{1.9175 - 0.0066\,t}$$

Problems

1. One gram of an organic substance was dissolved in 50.00 ml of water. This solution, in a 20 cm tube, read $+2.676°$ in a polarimeter, while distilled water in the same tube read $+0.016°$. Calculate the specific rotation of the substance.

2. Exactly 10 g of raw sugar was dissolved in water and made up to a volume of 100 ml. In a 20 cm tube this solution read 12.648°. After inversion, according to the directions of Experiment 15-2, the solution read $-3.922°$. Calculate the percentage of sucrose in the raw sugar.

3. Calculate Brewster's angle for borosilicate glass of index of refraction, $n_D = 1.47$. Devise an experiment to check this result.

4. Approximately what fraction of light would be removed from a beam of light passing through two polaroids set at 45° with respect to each other?

Bibliography

Carroll, B., and I. Blei, *Science*, **142**, 200 (1963).
Heller, W., and D. D. Fitto in *Physical Methods of Organic Chemistry*, A. Weissberger (Ed.), 3rd ed., Interscience, New York, 1960, Vol. I, Part II, Chapter 33.

Literature Cited

1. Browne, C. A., and F. W. Zerban, *Physical and Chemical Methods of Sugar Analysis*, Wiley, New York, 1941.
2. Browne, C. A., and F. W. Zerban, *Official and Tentative Methods of Analysis*, Association of Official Agricultural Chemists, Washington, D.C., 1945; F. J. Bates, *Polarimetry, Saccharimetry, and the Sugars*, Govt. Printing Office, Washington, D.C., 1942.
3. Cotton, A., *Compt. rend.*, **120**, 989, 1044 (1895); *Ann. chim. phys.*, **8**, 347 (1896).
4. Djerassi, C., *Optical Rotatory Dispersion*, McGraw-Hill, New York, 1960.
5. Djerassi, C., *Science*, **134**, 649 (1961).
6. Drude, P., *The Theory of Optics*, Longmans, New York, 1929.
7. Faraday, M., *Phil. Mag.*, **28**, 294 (1846).
8. Le Bel, J. A., *Bull. soc. chim.*, **22**, 337 (1874).
9. Pasteur, L., *Ann. chim. phys.*, **24**, 442 (1848).
10. van't Hoff, J. H., *La chimie dans l'espace*, Rotterdam, 1874.

Mass Spectrometry

The first mass spectrometer dates back to the work in England of J. J. Thompson in 1912 and of F. W. Aston in 1919, but the instrument which served as a model for more recent ones was constructed in 1932. The mass spectrometer produces charged ions consisting of the parent ion and ionic fragments of the original molecule, and sorts these ions according to their mass/charge ratio. The mass spectrum is a record of the numbers of different kinds of ions—the relative numbers of each are characteristic for every compound, including isomers. A few tenths of a milligram, or less, of sample suffices as long as the material is able to exist in the gaseous state at the temperature and pressure existing in the ion source.

From the mass spectrum a wealth of information can be obtained concerning the composition of mixtures of organic compounds and the elemental analysis of solid state samples. A detailed interpretation of the mass spectrum frequently makes it possible to place functional groups into certain areas of the molecule and to see how they are connected with each other. The molecular weight can be determined directly, even to fractions of a mass unit on more sophisticated spectrometers. In addition, mass spectrometry is an essential adjunct to the use of stable isotopes in investigating reaction mechanisms and in tracer work.

Mass Spectrometer Components

Several distinct methods of producing mass spectra have been devised. Common to most instruments, however, are four units: (1) the inlet system; (2) the ion source; (3) the electrostatic accelerating system; and (4) the ion collector, amplifier, and readout system. The principal difference between the various types of spectrometers lies in the means for separating the ions according to their mass/charge ratio. There must be provision for maintenance of a high vacuum throughout the spectrometer from the entrance to the ion source to the collector electrode. Close control of temperature in the room in which the instrument is housed is important in terms of alignment of the components, in particular the several slits. In the following sections each of these units of a mass spectrometer is discussed in some detail before the several types of spectrometers are considered.

Inlet Sample System

To handle all types of material, different sample systems are required (Fig. 16-1). Introduction of gases involves merely transfer of the sample from

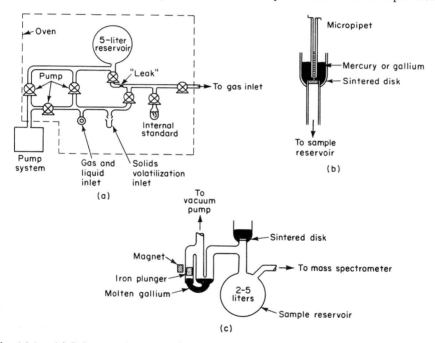

Fig. 16-1. (a) Inlet sample system for mass spectrometer. (b) Introduction of liquids through a sintered disk. (c) Magnetically actuated, gallium cutoff valve.

a gas bulb into the metering volume. The latter is a small glass manifold of known volume (about 3 ml), coupled to a mercury manometer and attached by a port to the inlet manifold. A sample is metered in the standard volume and then expanded into a reservoir volume (perhaps 3 liters) immediately ahead of the sample "leak." The meter pressure ranges from 30 to 50 mm of Hg (1 mm of Hg $\equiv$ 1 torr); after expansion the pressure is 50–100μ.

Liquids are introduced in various ways—by break-off devices (see Fig. 16-2), by touching a micropipet to a sintered glass disk under mercury or gallium (Fig. 16-1), or by hypodermic needle and injection through a silicone rubber dam. The low pressure in the reservoir draws in the liquid and vaporizes it instantly.

Heated inlet systems extend the usefulness of mass spectrometry to polar materials, which are prone to be adsorbed on the walls of the chambers at room temperature, and to less volatile compounds insofar as they possess a vapor pressure of the order of 20 μ at the temperature of the sample reservoir, usually 200°C. The temperature is limited by the materials of construction and by thermal degradation. Above 200°C most compounds containing oxygen or nitrogen are thermally decomposed. Solids melting below the reservoir temperature can be introduced directly. Oftentimes a small amount of chemistry suffices to convert a compound, itself not volatile, into a derivative which still retains all the important structural features but has now sufficient vapor pressure. Magnetically actuated gallium cutoffs are employed as valves (Fig. 16-1).

From the sample reservoir the gases diffuse through a molecular leak into the ion source. Frequently the leak is a pinhole in a metal foil. The preferred type of flow into the ion source depends on the purpose for which the instrument is intended. For analytical work, conditions for molecular flow are usually employed in which collisions between molecules and the walls are much more frequent than collisions between molecules. However, this type of leak is less desirable in instruments designed primarily for isotope ratio work, since repeated measurements are made of the relative concentrations of two members of a mixture. Viscous flow is preferred in which a gas molecule is more likely to collide with other gas molecules than with the surfaces of the container—thus there is no tendency for various components to flow differently from the others.

In continuous-monitoring inlet systems the sample must be admitted to the instrument at or near atmospheric pressure. Consequently, it is necessary to drop the pressure by a viscous flow system to a range in which molecular flow can be achieved by the use of leak perforations of reasonable size. In one system a pair of viscous leaks is arranged through which gas is drawn by an auxiliary mechanical pump; the leaks are so proportioned that the pressure intermediate between them is about 1 mm of Hg. The sample is admitted to the mass spectrometer through a perforated foil from the region of intermediate pressure between the two leaks.

Analysis of high-melting solids is frequently accomplished by use of a radio-frequency spark (1 Mc/sec) of high intensity. Instantaneous discharges with a power output up to 100 kW produce gaseous ions of all constituents at an equal rate without regard to their vapor pressure, thereby avoiding preferential vaporization. Solid samples can also be painted on a thin filament and heated.

The filament is placed just under and parallel to the electron beam in the ion source.

Ion Source

Once past the leak, the neutral molecules find themselves in the ion source, a chamber which is maintained at a pressure of 5 μ and at a temperature of 200°C (within $\pm 1/4$°C of a fixed standard value) (Fig. 16-2, upper diagram). Lo-

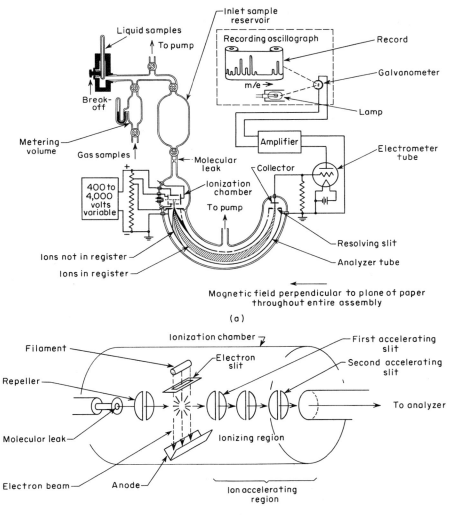

(a)

(b)

Fig. 16-2. (a) Schematic diagram of a 180° magnetic-deflection mass spectrometer and (b) ionization chamber shown in detail. (Courtesy of Consolidated Electrodynamics Corp.)

cated perpendicular to the incoming gas stream is an electron gun. Electrons emitted from a glowing carbonized tungsten filament are drawn off by a pair of positively charged slits through which they pass into the body of the chamber. An electric field maintained between these slits accelerates the electrons. Subsequent collisions with molecules in the passing gas stream produce ionization and fragmentation.

The electric field can be varied from 6 to 100 V. A range from 6 to 14 V is employed in molecular weight determinations, whereas the field is kept in the range from 50 to 70 V to obtain a mass spectrum. In the latter voltage range sufficient energy is available for rupture of any bond in a molecule. At the same time, the voltage lies on the plateau of the ionization efficiency curves of compounds and, therefore, small variations in the electric field have a minimum effect on peak intensity.

After passage through the ion source, the electron beam is collected on an anode. The current to this trap is used to control the electron-beam intensity, so that the rate of formation of ions will be as nearly constant as possible. It is customary to collimate the beam of ionizing electrons by a small magnetic field (of the order of 100 gauss) which is confined to the ionization region.

Accelerating System

The positive ions formed in the ionization chamber are drawn out by a small electrostatic field between the large repeller plate (charged positive) behind them—the original entrance to the ion source which did not affect the molecules while they were yet unionized—and the first accelerating slit (charged negative) (see Fig. 16-2, upper diagram). A strong electrostatic field between the first and second accelerating slit of 400–4000 V accelerates the ions of masses m_1, m_2, m_3 etc., to their final velocities of up to 150,000 meters/sec. The ions emerge from the final accelerating slit (0.076 mm in width) as a collimated ribbon of ions with velocities and kinetic energies given by

$$eV = \tfrac{1}{2}mv_1^2 = \tfrac{1}{2}mv_2^2 = \tfrac{1}{2}mv_3^2 = \cdots \qquad (16\text{-}1)$$

At the start of each spectrum scan, the second of the two accelerating slits is charged to an initial potential of perhaps 4000 V. This charge is then allowed to leak off to ground at a controlled rate over a period of perhaps 20 min. The electrostatic voltages must be stabilized better than 0.01 percent, with a field uniformity of better than 0.1 percent.

Ion-Collection System

The current carried by the ion beam leaving the exit slit of the analyzer tube is small (1×10^{-14} amp) and has to be amplified before recording. In one system ions are collected in a cylinder (Faraday cage) which is connected to the grid of an electrometer tube and to ground through a resistance. The electrometer tube may be replaced by a vibrating reed electrometer, thus converting the output to an a-c signal. Alternatively, the potential of the repeller plate in the ionization chamber may be modulated or the electron output of the filament of the electron gun may be varied synchronously. After amplification, the signal is fed to a strip chart recorder or an oscillograph.

The electron multiplier tube is used in pulse counting mode for fast scans, for high-resolution work, and in vacuum ultraviolet spectrometry. Basically, the multiplier consists of two separate structures—a removable interior electron multiplication unit and an exterior magnet assembly (Fig. 16-3). The electron

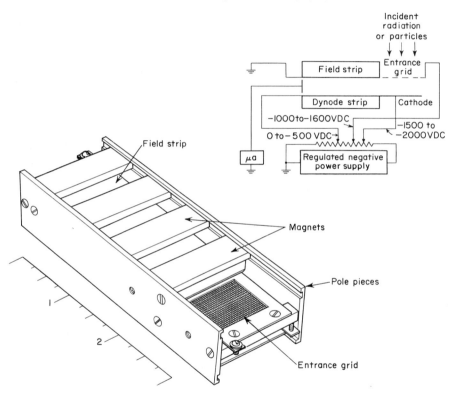

Fig. 16-3. Electron multiplier tube and typical electrical circuit for operating the tube. (Courtesy of Bendix Corporation.)

multiplication unit is comprised of a 90-percent-transparent metallic grid, an easily removed tungsten cathode, one coated glass dynode strip, one coated glass field strip, and a stainless steel anode. Kel-F spacers provide mechanical support and electrical insulation. The exterior structure consists of nine evenly spaced Alnico V permanent magnets bonded to pole pieces, which provides a uniform magnetic field, essentially perpendicular to the electric field, of approximately 400 gauss. A high-resistance coating is applied to a glass substrate to make the field and dynode strips. To operate the multiplier, appropriate potentials are applied to the dynode and field strips by a circuit such as il-lustrated in Fig. 16-3. The multiplier functions on the principle that an electron starting at rest in a crossed electric and magnetic field will describe a simple cycloidal motion perpendicular to the magnetic field, where the dips in the cycloid are directed along the equipotential lines of the multiplier. However, the equipotential lines in the multiplier are directed forward and slightly down-ward so that an electron strikes the dynode surface before it can complete a full cycle (note Fig. 16-8). Since it has a certain amount of kinetic energy (repre-sented by the difference in potential between the point of origin and impact), secondary electrons will be generated in accordance with the principles of secondary emission. Each secondary electron repeats the same type of motion and a cascading action results. The gain is about 10^7 electrons per ion. It is possible to count single ions arriving at the detector.

The recorder must include provision for automatically recording peaks of widely varying amplitude. By the use of five separate galvanometers (a record-ing oscillograph) with relative sensitivities of 1, 3, 10, 30, and 100, spectrum peaks varying in height from 0.2 to 10,000 arbitrary divisions may be signifi-cantly read on 8-in. photographic paper (Fig. 16-2(a), upper right). This en-ables the height of any peak to be recorded within better than 1 percent accuracy over a range of magnitude of 1 to nearly 1000. Peak heights are determined by the difference between the normal trace and the top of the peak.

Anomalous peaks may be formed from metastable ions. These are particles which break up after they have been accelerated in the ion source. The re-sultant light ion has a velocity equal to the velocity of the original particle. Since it has a lighter mass, however, it acts differently in the analyzer section, and comes to a focus at an apparent mass different from its actual mass. An energy selector electrode, placed between the resolving slit (at exit of analyzer section) and the detector and charged to a suitable potential, eliminates the metastable peaks since ions formed from a metastable transition have less energy than normal ions reaching the detector at the same time.

Vacuum System

The mass spectrometer requires a good vacuum system to prevent undue scattering by collision of ions with residual gas molecules. Usually separate mercury or oil diffusion pumps are used in the source and analyzing regions of the spectrometer, backed by a single roughing pump. For high-resolution work the best vacuum attainable within practical considerations of complexity and cost is required; a practical compromise is 10^{-7} torr. The pumps are operated continuously, 24 hr a day.

Mass spectrometers are subject to ills attributable to surface conditions in all regions of the evacuated system. Surface deposits may result in lengthy pump-down periods. Extreme cleanliness must be observed; no volatile lubricants may be employed nor may the hands touch any interior surface. The main body of the instrument is heated to minimize adsorption of polar materials on the walls and consequent lengthy pumpdown periods between samples to avoid background contamination.

Resolution

The resolution of a mass spectrometer is defined as the mass divided by the difference in mass number between two distinguishable neighboring lines of equal height in the mass spectrum. For example, to distinguish oxygen of mass 31.9898 from sulfur of mass 31.9721, a resolution of 1800 is necessary. Similarly, to resolve the CH_4—O doublet at mass 100 fragment, $M/\Delta M \geq 2748$. On the other hand, a resolution of 1 part in 200 adequately distinguishes between mass 200 and mass 201. Resolution is strongly influenced by the pressure in the spectrometer tube and is a function of slit widths, deflection radius, and homogeneity of the ion source. Very high resolution is achieved only with double-focusing spectrometers.

Commercial Mass Spectrometers

Magnetic-Deflection Mass Spectrometer

In the magnetic-deflection mass spectrometer the ions are accelerated by application of an electrostatic field and then are deflected, by application of a magnetic field, through an angle of 60°, 90°, 120°, or 180°.

Ions of mass m and charge e, on passage through an accelerating electric field, attain a velocity v which can be expressed in terms of the accelerating voltage V and the kinetic energy of the ion as it leaves the electric field,

$$\tfrac{1}{2}mv^2 = eV \qquad (16\text{-}2)$$

or, solving for the velocity term,

$$v = (2eV/m)^{1/2} \qquad (16\text{-}3)$$

The ions next enter a uniform magnetic field of constant intensity H that is imposed at right angles to their direction of motion and diverts the fast-moving ions into circular orbits. Equating the centripetal and the centrifugal forces,

$$mv^2/r = Hev \qquad (16\text{-}4)$$

The trajectory is a circle whose radius of curvature r is given by

$$r = mv/eH \qquad (16\text{-}5)$$

and, in view of Eq. 16-3, is a function of the mass/charge ratio of the particles,

$$r = \left(\frac{2V}{H^2} \cdot \frac{m}{e}\right)^{1/2} \qquad (16\text{-}6)$$

Only those ions which follow the path which coincides with the arc of the analyzer tube in the magnetic field will be brought to a focus on the slit of the detector. Ions of different mass/charge ratio will strike the analyzer tube (which is grounded) at some point, be neutralized, and be pumped out of the system along with all other unionized molecules and uncharged fragments.

The magnetic field thus classifies and segregates the ions into beams, each of a different m/e. The ion species which will be collected under a specified set of operating conditions is given by the expression

$$\frac{m}{e} = \frac{H^2 r^2}{2V} \tag{16-7}$$

To obtain a mass spectrum, either the accelerating voltage or the magnetic field strength is varied continuously at a constant rate. Usually the voltage is varied in a fixed magnetic field and each specific m/e from light to heavy is successively brought to a focus on the detector. Quite naturally the magnetic field must be uniform over a large area and possess a current stability (if an electromagnet) even better than the voltage stability of the electrostatic section.

In the Dempster design,[8] shown in Fig. 16-2, the ion beam travels along a 180° trajectory through the magnetic field, which is fixed. A large electromagnet is required. These are expensive to construct and require several kilowatts of power. Thus large power supplies with electronic regulators are required.

The rather bulky magnet required in the Dempster design prompted the development of sector instruments in which the ion source, the collector (resolving) slit, and the apex of the sector-shaped magnetic field lie along a straight line, as shown in Fig. 16-4 for a Nier 60° sector instrument. A sector

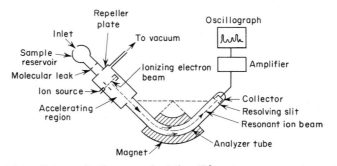

Fig. 16-4. Schematic diagram of a Nier 60° sector mass spectrometer.

angle of 90° has also been employed. Since the magnetic field does not envelop the ion source, a separate source magnet is required. The ion-transit time from the accelerator slits to the magnetic field is significantly longer in the sector-type instrument and, consequently, any peaks resulting from metastable transition products are several times as large as the corresponding peaks in a 180°-type spectrometer.

With either the 180°- or a sector-type spectrometer, a mass resolution of about 1 in 200 mass units can be obtained. Narrower slits, stricter alignment of components, and additional signal amplification enables mass peaks in the range from 200 to 600 to be resolved—the ultimate limit for instruments of this class.

Instruments designed for process control use a permanent Alnico magnet with a field of 4000–6000 gauss. The overall range is restricted. For example, one commercial instrument has a range from 2 to 80 mass units and adequate resolution for separation of adjacent peaks up to about 35. Small, portable spectrometers with a radius of curvature of 5 cm can withstand temperatures of 450°C and operate in the ultrahigh vacuum range (10^{-15} torr).

Example 16-1

For a field strength of 2400 gauss, what voltage range suffices for scanning from mass 18 to mass 200? The radius of curvature of the 180° analyzer tube is 12.7 cm.

From Eq. 16-7 rearranged,

$$V = \frac{H^2 r^2}{2} \cdot \frac{e}{m}$$

$$V = \frac{(2400)^2 (12.7 \text{ cm})^2 (4.8 \times 10^{-10} \text{ esu}) \ (300 \ V/\text{erg/esu})}{(2)(3 \times 10^{10} \text{ esu/emu})^2 (18 \text{ amu}/6.023 \times 10^{23})}$$

$$V = 2478 \text{ V to focus mass 18 on detector}$$

Now, since the mass/charge ratio registering is proportional to the reciprocal of the accelerating voltage,

$$\frac{(m/e)_1}{(m/e)_2} = \frac{V_2}{V_1}$$

$$\frac{18}{200} = \frac{V_2}{2478}$$

$$V_2 = 223 \text{ V to focus mass 200}$$

Isotope-Ratio Spectrometer

A less expensive adaptation of the usual mass spectrometer, the isotope-ratio mass spectrometer, has been made available for work in these fields. In the modified instrument the ion currents from two ion beams—for example, the ion beams from $C^{12}O_2$ and $C^{13}O_2$—are collected simultaneously by means of a double exit slit and are amplified simultaneously by two separate amplifiers. The larger of the two amplified currents is then attenuated by the operator, with a set of decade resistors, until it will exactly balance the smaller current from the other amplifier. The ratio of the two currents is determined from the resistance required. This is a null method and practically eliminates the effect of other variables in the system. A tracer material can be detected even after great dilution.

Double-Focusing Spectrometer

A Mattauch-Herzog spectrometer employs a double-focusing principle—the instrument focuses for both energy (direction) and velocity. An electrostatic analyzer is placed between the ion accelerating slits and the magnetic field. Following the usual acceleration of the ion beams in an electrostatic field, the ions are deflected through a tandem arrangement of an electrostatic analyzer (an energy selector) and then a magnetic analyzer, as shown in Fig. 16-5. The

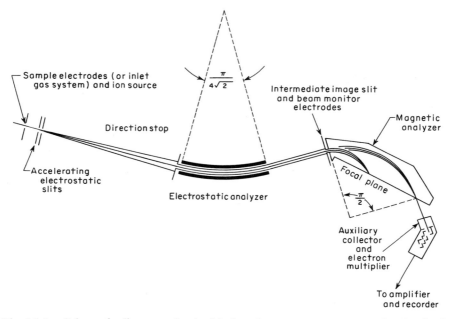

Fig. 16-5. Schematic diagram of a double-focusing mass spectrometer showing basic Mattauch-Herzog geometry. The mass spectrum may be photographed in one exposure. Alternatively, the mass spectrum may be scanned with an electron multiplier.

geometry and parameters are so specified as to focus ions having the same mass/charge ratio but different initial velocities and directions. The improved focus enables entrance and exit slits to be narrowed with a corresponding increase in resolving power up to 20,000 or more. Instruments of this type include the Associated Electrical Industries MS 9, the Consolidated Electrodynamics model 21-110, and one from Nuclide Analysis Associates.

In usage, a preliminary scan is made at low resolution and then selected portions of the mass spectrum are rescanned at high resolution. This shortens the total time for analysis. Several types of detector systems are available for gas analysis, including a single-slit ion collector or a multiplier tube. To analyze metals, semiconductors, and other solids, an rf-spark ion source is required to vaporize part of the sample while keeping most of the sample relatively cool and in its original shape. A photographic plate is used to collect all masses simultaneously and to integrate them over an extended period of time. The plate records a wide mass range of 36:1, which allows all elements in the periodic table, from lithium ($Z = 7$) through uranium ($Z = 238$), to be analyzed in a single exposure. Except for oxygen, carbon, and nitrogen, the detection limit for all elements is about 10 parts per billion at an exposure of around 30 min.

Cycloidal-Focusing Spectrometer[7]

In this instrument a uniform electrostatic field is added perpendicular to the magnetic field and parallel to the direction of ion acceleration (Fig. 16-6).

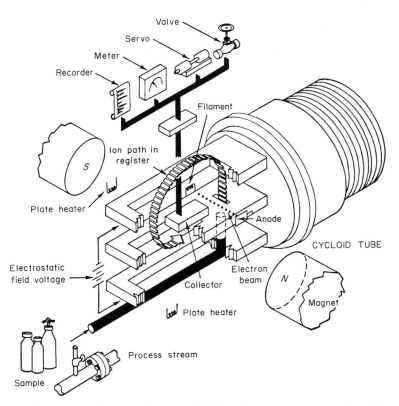

Fig. 16-6. Schematic diagram of a cycloidal-focusing mass spectrometer. (Courtesy of Consolidated Electrodynamics Corp.)

After initial acceleration, the ion beam enters the crossed field region, which causes all ions to travel prolate cycloidal paths instead of circular paths. As either of the two crossed fields is varied, ions of identical mass/charge ratio focus on the fixed collector slit even though not equivalent in energy. This method eliminates the effect of angular and energy aberrations. Analyses up to mass 150 are possible.

Radio-Frequency Spectrometer

The rf spectrometer,[4] sometimes called the Bennett tube,[1] is shown in Fig. 16-7. The charged particles emerging from the ion source are all ac-

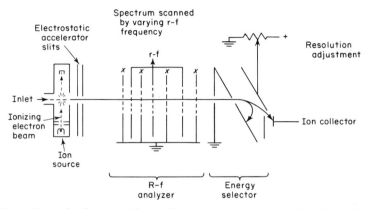

Fig. 16-7.   Schematic diagram of an r-f mass spectrometer. All grids marked x are at the same d-c potential. (Courtesy of Beckman Instruments, Inc.)

celerated to the same energy in an electrostatic field (Eq. 16-1), then they enter one or more rf stages. Each stage is a series of three equally spaced, parallel grids. The central grid is charged with an alternating rf voltage applied with respect to the outer grids which are at ground potential. For any given frequency, only ions of a given mass/charge ratio will travel from grid to grid in time to benefit from another acceleration each time the voltage alternates between positive and negative. Heavier ions fail to reach the grid at the right time and lighter ions pass through the grid too soon. Out of phase ions lose energy, whereas a beam of ions in "tune" with the rf field will accelerate and emerge with maximum energy and speed. A potential energy selector is placed in front of the collector. A retarding potential on a plate (or a grid) deflects (or repels) all ions receiving less than the maximum energy. Only the group of ions with the maximum energy reaches the detector.

Ions in phase with the radio-frequency field will attain a velocity v equal to the product of the frequency f of the rf field in megacycles per second and the spacing between adjacent grids, s, in centimeters, namely,

$$v = sf \qquad (16-8)$$

The mass spectrum is scanned by varying the frequency of the alternating voltage. From Eqs. 16-1 and 16-8, the mass/charge ratio of the ion beam reaching the detector, when reduced to practical *cgs* units, is given by

$$\frac{m}{e} = \frac{0.266V}{s^2 f^2}$$ (16-9)

For negative ion analyses the potential on each grid is reversed.

The rf spectrometer is lightweight, simple in construction, and does not require a magnet. Its range is from 2 to 100 mass units. However, the resolution is only one part in 15, although it can be increased by placing more than one set of rf grids in the analyzer section. The instrument requires a fair amount of circuitry and tends to produce ghost signals, which can be confusing.

Time-of-Flight Spectrometer

In a time-of-flight spectrometer ions of different mass/charge ratio are separated by the difference in the time they require to travel over an identical path from the ion source to the detector electrode, which are situated at opposite ends of an evacuated tube[9] (Fig. 16-8). In the ion source the electron

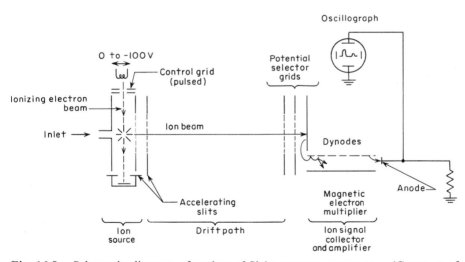

Fig. 16-8. Schematic diagram of a time-of-flight mass spectrometer. (Courtesy of Bendix Corp.)

beam is energized for 0.25 μsec every 100 μsec. The pulses of ions formed by electron bombardment are ejected through a grid from the ion source and are accelerated into a field-free drift space by a high voltage on the ion energy grid. The ions, as a result of the accelerating field, attain a velocity that is a function of their mass/charge ratio. Their drift time down a field-free, straight, 100-cm, evacuated tube is noted. The lightest ions reach the detector first followed by ions of heavier mass. The transit time t (in microseconds) of ions through a distance L (in centimeters), is described by Eq. 16-10:

$$t = L\left(\frac{m}{e} \cdot \frac{1}{2V}\right)^{1/2} \quad \text{or} \quad \frac{m}{e} = \frac{2Vt^2}{L^2} \tag{16-10}$$

The current produced by the ions arriving at the detector—a magnetic electron multiplier which operates in crossed electric and magnetic fields, is displayed on an oscilloscope whose time base is synchronized with, and triggered by, the production of the original ion pulses. An important advantage is the speed in analysis. A complete mass spectrum is scanned in a few microseconds by photographing the oscilloscope traces.

Additional electrodes are usually placed in the drift tube to apply transverse fields which center the ion beam on the path and focus it on the detector. Insertion of a potential selector grid before the detector limits ions reaching the detector to only a selected mass. The polarities of the pulses and accelerating potentials can be adjusted to analyze either positive or negative ions. The instrument is excellent for kinetic studies of fast reactions producing small molecules or radicals and for direct analysis of effluent peaks from a gas chromatograph. Resolution is about 1 part in 200.

Omegatron

In the omegatron (basically a small, compact cyclotron) a cylindrical beam of electrons is ejected through a small opening parallel to a magnetic field and perpendicular to an rf electric field. A line source of ions is formed in the ionizing chamber. Now, in a given magnetic field H, ions with charge e and mass m have a unique cyclotron frequency ω_c, defined as

$$\omega_c = \frac{eH}{m} \tag{16-11}$$

When the frequency of the applied electric field is equal to the cyclotron frequency for ions of a given mass/charge ratio, those ions gain energy and spiral outwards to a collector, as shown in Fig. 16-9. Ions with other mass/charge ratios are forced into smaller circular paths near the axis of the electron beam. Either the magnetic field or the electric field is varied for scanning the mass spectrum.

The resolution of the omegatron varies linearly with the number of revolutions a resonant ion can make before being collected. It can be improved by increasing the magnetic field or by increasing the physical dimensions of the instrument. In an instrument 2 cm on a side operating at 2100 gauss, with accelerating voltage of 90 V and an rf voltage of 2 V, resolution is 1 part in 40. The omegatron is a popular device for analyzing residual gas composition in ultrahigh vacuum systems. It detects partial pressures to 10^{-9} torr. The major advantage of the omegatron is its very compact and simple construction and relatively high sensitivity. Since there are no limiting apertures, virtually all

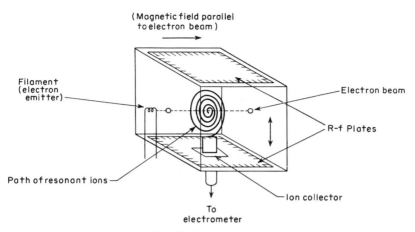

(Magnetic field parallel to electron beam)

Filament (electron emitter)

Electron beam

R-f Plates

Path of resonant ions

Ion collector

To electrometer

Fig. 16-9.   Simplified diagram of an omegatron.

ions produced are collected. Unfortunately, the construction does not lend itself to use with a multiplier collector and therefore has limited ultimate sensitivity. The usable mass range cannot be extended much higher than mass 40.

Correlation of Mass Spectra with Molecular Structure

Arrangement of atoms in molecular structures and strength of the bonds between these atoms direct the manner in which fragments are formed when the molecules are bombarded by high-speed electrons. A molecule may simply lose an electron or it may fragment into ions. The fragment ions may, in turn, break down further. A molecular or *parent ion* is generally observed in considerable strength when the gaseous molecules are bombarded with electrons of energy just sufficient to cause ionization—about 8–14 V for most organic molecules. As the electron energy is increased, the probability of ionization increases, and the parent ion can be formed with excess energy in its electronic and vibrational degrees of freedom. Because redistribution of energy between the bonds takes place rapidly, all the bonds are weakened simultaneously. As soon as the excess energy possessed by the parent ion over its ground state energy becomes equal to the dissociation energy of some bond, the appropriate fragment ion can then be formed. At energies of the order of 50–70 eV, the bombarding electron can remove several electrons from a molecule and fragment ions appear in abundance, both charged and uncharged.

Mass Spectra

The mass spectrum of a compound contains the masses of the ion fragments and the relative abundance of these ions plus the parent ion. The uniqueness of the molecular fragmentation aids in identification. As sufficient molecules are present and dissociated for the probability law to hold, the dissociation fragments will always occur in the same relative abundance for a particular compound. The mass spectrum becomes a sort of "fingerprint" for each compound, as no two molecules will be fragmented and ionized in exactly the same manner on electron bombardment. There are sufficient differences in these molecular fingerprints to permit identification of different molecules in complex mixtures. To a considerable extent the breakdown pattern can be predicted. Conversely, the size and structure of the molecule can often be reconstructed from the fragment ions in the spectrum of a pure compound. For example, Table 16-1 indicates the relative abundance of the significant frag-

Table 16-1 | *Mass Spectral Pattern of Trimethylpentanes*

	RELATIVE ABUNDANCES IN PERCENT		
Mass/charge ratio	2,2,3-Trimethylpentane $$\begin{array}{cc} C & C \\ \mathbf{+} & \mid \\ C-C*C+C-C \\ \mid \\ C \end{array}$$	2,2,4-Trimethylpentane $$\begin{array}{cc} C & C \\ \mathbf{+} & \mid \\ C-C*C-C-C \\ \mid \\ C \end{array}$$	2,3,4-Trimethylpentane $$\begin{array}{cc} C & C \\ \mid & \mid \\ C-C*C*C-C \\ \mid \\ C \end{array}$$
114	0.1	0.02	0.3
99	3	5	0.1
71	1	1	40
57	70	80	9
43	15	20	50

[From H. W. Washburn, H. F. Wiley, S. M. Rock and C. E. Berry, *Ind. Eng. Chem., Anal. Ed.*, **17**, 75 (1945).]

ments produced from three isomeric octanes. In the structural formulas the asterisk indicates the bond which is broken in the most probable process of ionization, and the plus sign indicates the next most probable process. Favored sites for bond rupture in the molecule parallel chemical bond lability. The mass 114 corresponds to the parent ion formed by the loss of a single electron from the parent compound; mass 99 corresponds to the loss of a methyl group plus an electron; mass 71, to the loss of a propyl group plus an electron; mass 57, to the loss of a butyl group; and mass 43, to the loss of an amyl group.

It is usual practice in reporting mass spectra to normalize the data by assigning the most intense mass peak (the so-called *base peak*) a value 100; other peaks are reported as percentages of the base peak.

When working from a mass spectrum it is advisable to tabulate the prominent ion peaks, starting with the highest mass, and also to record the group lost to give these ion peaks. All possible molecular structures are listed, employing a file of common fragment ions encountered in mass spectra.[6] Finally, one attempts to predict the mass spectral features from available correlation data and to check these features against the actual spectrum. For example, the peak at mass 43 is always large for linear paraffins larger than C_4. Mass 30 is always large for primary amines; masses 31, 45, and 59 indicate the presence of oxygen as alcohol or ether; mass 19 indicates fluorine; mass 33 a thiol; mass 60 a monobasic carboxylic acid; mass 77 the presence of a benzene ring; mass 91 the presence of a tolyl group, etc. The mass spectrum and elucidation of the structure of omega-butenyl benzoate is presented in Table 16-2.[2] In structure

| Table 16-2 | *Mass Spectral Data for omega-Butenyl Benzoate* |

m/e	% OF BASE PEAK	STRUCTURAL SIGNIFICANCE[6]
78	40	Phenyl group; ⬡— ; mass 105 minus CO(28)
105	*100*	C_7H_5O; mass 122 minus O or OH; ⬡—C(=O)—
122	2	$C_7H_6O_2$; mass 135 minus CH (or CH_2)
135	2	$C_8H_7O_2$; loses mass 41 from parent (not 15 or 17 which could be CH_3 or OH) suggesting terminal group to be double bonded
176p	3	Fairly strong parent peak; suggests ring
177	0.36	

ISOTOPE ABUNDANCES:

m/e	% OF P
176P	100
177 (P_{M+1})	12.2
178 (P_{M+2})	1.08

EMPIRICAL FORMULA:

$C_{11}H_{12}O_2$ Suggests unsaturation; $1/2(22 + 2 - 12) = 6$ double bonds and/or rings.

All the major peaks can be accounted for by a single chain fragmentation process, thus:

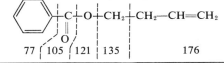

assignments one must always be aware of the frequent occurrence of rearrangement ions. These are fragments which are the result of intramolecular rearrangement at the moment of fragmentation.

Some general features of the mass spectra of compounds can be predicted from general rules for fragmentation patterns:

1. Cleavage is favored at branched carbon atoms: tertiary > secondary > primary, with the positive charge tending to stay with the branched carbon.

2. Double bonds favor cleavage beta to the bond.

3. A substance having a strong parent peak often contains a ring and the stronger the ring the stronger the parent peak.

4. Ring compounds usually contain peaks at mass numbers characteristic of the ring.

5. Saturated rings lose side chains at the alpha-carbon. The peak corresponding to the loss of two ring atoms is much larger than for the loss of one ring atom.

6. In alkyl substituted ring compounds, cleavage is most probable at the bond beta to the ring if the ring has a double bond next to the side-chain.

7. A hetero-atom will induce cleavage at the bond beta to it.

8. Compounds containing a $>C\!=\!O$ group tend to break at this group, with the positive charge remaining with the carbonyl portion.

The presence of atoms in addition to C, H, N and O (for example, Cl, Br, S, and Si) is easy to deduce from the unusual isotopic abundance patterns of these elements. These and other elements, such as P, F, and I, are also detectable from the unusual mass differences which they produce between some fragment ions in the spectrum.

Molecular Identification

In identification of a compound the most important single item of information is the molecular weight. The mass spectrometer is unique among analytical methods in being able to provide this information very accurately. At ionizing voltages ranging from 9 to 14 V it can be assumed that no ions heavier than the molecular (parent) ion will be formed and, therefore, the mass of the heaviest ion, exclusive of heavy-isotope contributions, gives the nominal molecular weight. In a mixture the nominal molecular weights can often be determined from the general appearance of the fragmentation patterns. If mixture components differ in their appearance potentials, proper selection of ionization voltage will eliminate some of the constituents from the mass spectrum. For example, in a mixture of hydrocarbons it is possible to make a clean separation of the saturates (ionization potentials range from 10.2 to 11.2 eV for *n*-paraffins) and the unsaturates (ionization potentials are 9.5–9.7 eV for olefins, and 9.5 eV or slightly less for aromatics).

Further restriction on the number of possible molecular formulas can be achieved by study of the relative abundance of natural isotopes for different elements (Table 16-3) at masses 1 and 2 or more units larger than the parent ion. Observed values are compared with those calculated for all possible com-

Table 16-3 | *Principal Stable Isotopes and Relative Abundances*

H^1	99.985	N^{15}	0.37	S^{34}	4.4
H^2	0.015	O^{16}	99.76	Cl^{35}	75.8
C^{12}	98.89	O^{17}	0.037	Cl^{37}	24.2
C^{13}	1.11	O^{18}	0.20	Br^{79}	50.52
N^{14}	99.63	S^{33}	0.78	Br^{81}	49.48

binations of the naturally occurring heavy isotopes of the elements. A simple formula allows one to calculate the percent of the heavy isotopic contributions from a monoisotopic peak (P_M) to the P_{M+1} peak:

$$100\frac{P_{M+1}}{P_M} = 0.015x + 1.11w + 0.37y + 0.037z$$

and to the P_{M+2} peak:

$$100\frac{P_{M+2}}{P_M} \cong 0.20z + 0.006w(w - 1) + 0.004wy + 0.0002wx$$

for a compound $C_wH_xO_zN_y$. Tables of abundance factors have been calculated by Beynon[3] for all combinations of C, H, O and N up to mass 250.

Table 16-4 illustrates the spectral peak contributions at nominal masses 135

Table 16-4 | *Heavy-Isotope Contributions to Parent Peak of Mass 134*

EMPIRICAL FORMULA	P_{M+1} PEAK	P_{M+2} PEAK
$C_5H_{10}O_4$	5.72	0.94
$C_5H_{14}N_2O_2$	6.47	0.58
$C_6H_{14}O_3$	6.83	0.80
$C_8H_6O_2$	8.82	0.74
$C_9H_{10}O$	9.93	0.64
$C_9H_{12}N$	10.30	0.48
$C_{10}H_{14}$	11.03	0.55

and 136 for a few of the compounds having a parent peak (or possibly a fragment peak) of mass 134. Once the empirical formula is established with reasonable assurance, hypothetical molecular formulas are written. All valency requirements must be satisfied; if not, it is an indication that one is dealing with a molecular fragment other than a parent ion. It is advisable to verify the existence of molecular species by checking against the entries in the formula indices of Beilstein. Although absence from these indices is not definite evidence, it is a strong indication that such a compound may not exist. Compounds containing chlorine, bromine, or sulfur are usually apparent from the prominent peaks at masses P_{M+2}, P_{M+4}, etc. Two general rules aid in writing formulas. If the molecular weight of a C, H, O, and N compound is even, so is the number of hydrogen atoms it contains; if the molecular weight is divisible by four, the number of hydrogen atoms is also divisible by this number. When nitrogen is known to be present, all compounds of C, H, O, S, Si, P, As, and the halogens having an odd molecular weight must contain an odd number of nitrogen atoms.

Once the exact molecular formula has been decided, the sum total of the number of rings and double bonds is also determined by the formula

$$R = \tfrac{1}{2}(2w - x + y + 2)$$

when covalent bonds make up the molecular structure. The number of rings will be that given by Patterson and Capell in their index of ring systems.

If the mass of a parent ion is measured with a high-resolution mass spectrometer, the number of possible empirical formulas can be still further restricted. Since the masses of the elements are not exactly integral multiples of a unit mass, a sufficiently accurate mass measurement alone enables the elemental composition of the ion to be determined. Between nonane and naphthalene, each of nominal mass 128, the difference between the two exact masses is 0.0939 amu, the exact difference between one carbon atom and 12 hydrogen atoms. A resolving power of 1360 would differentiate between these compounds.

For identification work, and using direct evaporation techniques, the normal sample size is 1 μg, but for quantitative work it is usual to use about 100 μg of sample, which is held in a reservoir and used up at the rate of 0.3 percent per minute. Precise mass measurement follows the system employed in isotope-ratio work. The two peaks whose masses are to be compared are displayed alternatively on an oscilloscope. Decade controls are adjusted until the two peaks coincide; the mass ratio is read directly from the decades. Usually a reference mass within 10 percent of the unknown is chosen and, when within this range, the accuracy of mass measurement is always within 5 ppm of the true value. Figure 16-10 shows an actual recording of a five-

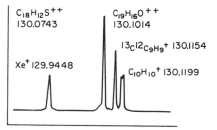

Mass numbers

Fig. 16-10. Mass 130 multiplet from a four-component mixture to which xenon was admitted as a reference mass. Resolution is 12,000. (Courtesy of Associated Electrical Industries, Ltd.)

component multiplet at m/e 130 with the resolving power set for 12,000 at a fractional overlap of 5 percent. The xenon peak was admitted as a reference. Note that the C^{13}-$C^{12}H$ doublet on the extreme right is clearly distinguishable as a doublet although the separation is only 1 part in 29,000. Scanning speed for such selected regions is at the rate of 0.5 min each mass number, or 3 min for a 10 percent change in mass.

Other Applications

Quantitative Analysis of Mixtures

The system employed in quantitative analysis by mass spectrometry is basically the same as that employed in infrared or ultraviolet absorption spectrometry. Spectra are recorded for each component. Consequently, samples of each compound must be available in a fairly pure state. From inspection of the individual mass spectra, known or suspected to be present in a mixture, analysis peaks are selected on the basis of both intensity and freedom from interference by the presence of another component. If possible, mono-component peaks (perhaps parent-ion peaks) are selected. The sensitivity is usually given in terms of the height of the analysis peak per unit pressure—obtained by dividing the peak height for the analysis peak by the pressure of the pure compound in the sample reservoir.

Calculation of sample compositions is simplified if the components of the mixture give spectra with at least one peak whose height is due entirely to the presence of one component. The height of the monocomponent peak is measured and divided by the appropriate sensitivity factor to give its partial pressure. Division then by the total pressure in the sample reservoir at the time of analysis yields the mole percent of the particular component.

If the mixture has no monocomponent peaks, simultaneous linear equations are then set up from the coefficients (percent of base peak) at each analysis peak, one equation for each compound in the mixture with n terms (unless one or more terms are zero) when n components are in the mixture. For the analysis of a butanol mixture,[5] the equations at four masses are set up from coefficients listed in Table 16-5 for the particular instrument:

$$90.58x_1 + 1.47x_2 + 1.02x_3 + 2.46x_4 = M_{56} = 126.7$$
$$0.26x_1 + 100.00x_2 + 17.78x_3 + 4.98x_4 = M_{59} = 301.5$$
$$6.59x_1 + 0.59x_2 + 100.00x_3 + 5.03x_4 = M_{45} = 322.6$$
$$0.79x_1 + 0 + 0.29x_3 + 9.06x_4 = M_{74} = 14.8$$

To achieve greater speed in computation, the matrix of coefficients is inverted, yielding a set of equations in terms of each unknown and the analytic masses:

$$x_1 = 110.70M_{56} - 1.625M_{59} - 0.7442M_{45} - 28.77M_{74} \quad (n\text{-butyl})$$
$$x_2 = 1.39M_{56} + 100.08\ M_{59} - 17.67\ M_{45} - 45.53M_{74} \quad (t\text{-butyl})$$
$$x_3 = -6.83M_{56} - 0.489M_{59} + 100.31\ M_{45} - 53.56M_{74} \quad (sec\text{-butyl})$$
$$x_4 = -9.39M_{56} + 0.157M_{59} - 3.17\ M_{45} + 1108.0\ M_{74} \quad (isobutyl)$$

| Table 16-5 | | Mass Spectral Data (Relative Intensities) for the Butyl Alcohols | | |

| m/e | Percent of base peak (italic) | | | |
	n-BUTYL	sec-BUTYL	t-BUTYL	ISOBUTYL
15	8.39	6.80	13.30	7.47
18	2.18	0.23	0.49	2.05
27	50.89	15.87	9.87	42.20
28	16.19	2.98	1.67	5.94
29	29.90	13.94	12.65	21.17
31	*100.00*	20.31	35.53	63.10
33	8.50	—	—	53.40
39	15.63	3.36	7.70	19.03
41	61.57	10.13	20.82	55.68
42	32.36	1.64	3.32	60.46
43	61.36	9.83	14.45	*100.00*
45	6.59	*100.00*	0.59	5.03
55	12.29	2.06	1.55	4.35
56	90.58	1.02	1.47	2.46
57	6.68	2.74	9.02	3.89
59	0.26	17.78	*100.00*	4.98
60	—	0.64	3.26	0.57
74	0.79	0.29	—	9.06

[From A. P. Gifford, S. M. Rock and D. J. Comaford, *Anal. Chem.*, **21**, 1026 (1949).]

Peaks from the mixture spectrum are substituted into the inverse matrix equations, yielding the number of divisions of base peak due to each component. Division by the appropriate sensitivity factor (Table 16-6) yields the partial

| Table 16-6 | | Analysis of a Mixture of Butyl Alcohols† | | |

COMPONENT	VALUE OF x	SENSITIVITY, DIVISIONS PER MICRON	PARTIAL PRESSURES, MICRONS	MOLE, %
n-Butyl	$x_1 = 12{,}871$	1151	11.18	24.4
t-Butyl	$x_2 = 23{,}976$	2093	11.46	25.0
sec-Butyl	$x_3 = 30{,}555$	2698	11.33	24.8
Isobutyl	$x_4 = 14{,}234$	1205	11.81	25.8

†Mass peaks used: 45, 56, 59, and 74.
[From A. P. Gifford, S. M. Rock, and D. J. Comaford, *Anal. Chem.*, **21**, 1026 (1949).]

pressure of each component. Each partial pressure is divided by the total computed pressure, yielding mole percent. The sum of the partial pressures determined in this way should equal the total sample pressure. A discrepancy would indicate an unsuspected component or a change in operating sensitivity.

An outstanding feature of mass spectrometric analysis is the large number of components that can be handled without need for fractionation or concentration. Mixtures containing up to as many as 30 components can be analyzed, and quantities of material as low as 0.001 mole percent can be detected in hydrocarbon mixtures. Calculations are usually carried out on high-speed automatic computors. More complex mixtures, covering a wide boiling range, may require a rough or simple distillation before analysis. Precision normally falls within the range of ± 0.05 to ± 1.0 mole percent.

Solid State Analyses

Solid state mass spectroscopy, in contrast with optical emission, has a very simple spectrum. The mass spectrum of each element consists of a principal line repeated at fractional mass values, but at reduced intensities, due to ions with multiple charges. The intensity of lines of any element at the same atomic concentration is roughly equal (within a factor of two) for most compounds, greatly facilitating semiquantitative analysis. Signal/noise ratios of 10^6 to 1 are available with double-focusing spectrometers, so that not only can trace impurities be detected, but sample sizes in the submicrogram range are feasible. Surface contaminants can be distinguished from bulk impurities, since the vacuum spark initially samples the surface of a solid. Techniques are available for handling insulators, and even the solid residue remaining from an evaporated liquid drop can be analyzed. Sensitivity is about 10 parts per billion, and is limited chiefly by the scattering of the ions enroute through the instrument by residual gas atoms.

Use of Stable Isotopes

Stable isotopes can be used to "tag" compounds and thus serve as tracers to determine the ultimate fate of the compound in chemical or biological reactions. The mass spectrum displays amounts of the added isotope in the fragment ions as well as in the parent ion. Thus, the position of the tracer isotope in the molecule can often be determined without laborious chemical degradation techniques.

A number of stable isotopes in sufficiently concentrated form are available, including practically all of the isotopes of the lighter elements: H, B, C, N, O, S, and Cl. These isotopes complement the relatively larger number of radioactive isotopes.

The isotope-dilution method, described in Chapter 9 for radioactive isotopes, can be employed equally well with stable isotopes to determine the amount of substance present in a complex mixture. It is only necessary to know the ratio of isotopes present in the added sample of the substance, the ratio present in the final sample isolated from the mixture, and the weight of the added sample. It is not necessary that the analyte be separated quantitatively from the mixture; only a few milligrams of pure substance are necessary.

Leak Detection

Cheap, compact, portable mass spectrometers, designed especially for detecting leaks in systems, are capable of detecting as little as 1 part of helium in 400,000 parts of air. In use, the system under test is evacuated and a continuous sample of gas from it is pumped through a throttle valve into the leak detector. A small jet of helium is directed at the area suspected of leaking. When helium from the probe jet passes through a leak into the system, the increased ion current, or an audible signal device, permits location of the leak to within 0.1 cm.

Ultra-High-Vacuum Measurements

Following the development of ultra-high vacuum systems, it became apparent that it was necessary to know not only the total pressure but also the partial pressures of the specific gas components and their identity. It is particularly important in surface physics and surface chemistry to know the type of gases absorbed and desorbed from surfaces.

Two specific characteristics of mass spectrometers which are of prime importance are resolution and sensitivity. Resolution is seldom a problem. One rarely encounters gaseous components with mass number greater than about 44. Interest is usually centered about such components as hydrogen, helium, methane, water vapor, neon, oxygen, nitrogen, carbon monoxide, carbon dioxide, and possibly lithium, sodium, potassium, fluorine and chlorine. Sensitivity involves both the absolute sensitivity of the instrument at normal operating conditions and also the limit of sensitivity, which is the lowest partial pressure which practically can be detected. Pressures will generally be less than 10^{-8} torr, and minor components should be identifiable even though their pressures may be as low as 10^{-16} torr (this value corresponds to approximately 1 molecule/cm^3).

The mass spectrometer must be compatible with the vacuum system and experimental setup with which it is being used. In general the complete instrument must be capable of bakeout and must be constructed of components which would enable the maintenance of pressures well below 10^{-8} torr. This requirement eliminates the use of organics and plastics or any other materials having high vapor pressure in any portion of the construction.

Problems

1. With an electromagnetic-focusing mass spectrometer, having a range of values from 3000 to 500 V, and $r = 12.00$ cm, what must be the value of the fixed magnetic field in order to focus successively on the detector a range of masses from $m/e = 15$ to $m/e = 60$?

2. To resolve a blend of 2-(n-hexyl) dibenzothiophene, 2-(n-decyl)naphthalene, and n-$C_{19}H_{40}$, what resolution is required for the parent peaks? *Ans.* 1 part in 2170.

3. What resolving power is needed to separate (a) the C_2H_8—S doublet at mass 200; (b) the N_2—CO doublet at mass 150; and (c) the CH_2—N doublet at mass 200? *Ans.* (a) 1 part in 9090.

4. The hydroxyl radical was produced by an electrical discharge in water vapor. An energy-scale shift of 2.59 eV is required to match the ionization curve for OH with the ionization curve for argon, used as an internal standard with a known ionization potential of 15.76 eV. The appearance potential of the OH^+ ion from water was also measured and found to be 18.19 eV. From these values compute (a) the ionization potential of the OH radical and (b) the dissociation energy of the H—OH bond. *Ans.* (a) 13.17 eV.

5. For a drift length of 100 cm, what is the difference in arrival time between ions of $m/e = 44$ and $m/e = 43$ when the accelerating voltage is 2800 V?

6. What is the theoretical mass range for a time-of-flight instrument if the beam is energized for 0.25 μsec every 100 μsec? Comment on the actual resolution of the instrument (1 part in 200 mass units) and suggest reasons (including decay time of a signal) for failure to attain the theoretical value. *Ans.* 5600 mass units.

7. Indicate the points of bond rupture in the molecule which would lead to each major mass fragment: (a) 2-methyl-2-butanol which has peaks of appreciable intensity at $m/e = 73$, 59, and 55: (b) 7-n-propyltridecane with peaks at $m/e = 183$, 141, and 85; (c) diisopropyl ether with peaks at $m/e = 87$, 59, 45, and 43; (d) acetophenone with peaks at $m/e = 120$, 105, and 77; (e) tert-butylacetate with peaks at $m/e = 101$, 59, 57, and 43.

8. Which mass spectral pattern arises from furfuryl acetate and which from ethyl furoate? Structure I gives peaks at $m/e = 140$, 112, and 95, whereas structure II has peaks at $m/e = 140$, 98, and 81.

9. What is the probable structure of the compound $C_{16}H_{34}$, which exhibits two fragment peaks, at 169 ($C_{12}H_{25}$) and 85 (C_6H_{13}) and weak peak at P-15?

10. Two hydroxy isomers have these patterns. Identify them. In each case the parent peak at 89 is absent. In one $m/e = 74$, 58 (very strong), 43, and 31; and in the other, $m/e = 74$, 59, 43, and 30 (strong).

11. The mass spectral data for a pure liquid (b.p. = 139°C; sp. grav. = 0.976) for significant masses is

m/e	28	43	85	100	101
% of base peak	12.5	100	45	35p	2.5

The empirical formula is $C_5H_8O_2$. Identify the compound; confirm the identification from the isotopic abundance information. *Ans.* acetylacetone.

12. What is the probable composition of a molecule of mass 142 whose $P + 1$ peak is 1.1 percent of the parent peak? *Ans.* CH_3I since only one carbon is indicated plus a heavy monoisotopic element.

13. From the isotopic abundance information, what can be deduced concerning the empirical formula of each of these compounds?

m/e	% OF BASE PEAK	m/e	% OF BASE PEAK	m/e	% OF BASE PEAK	m/e	% OF BASE PEAK
90(P)	100	89(P)	17.12	206(P)	25.90	230(P)	1.10
91	5.61	90	0.58	207	3.24	232	2.12
92	4.69	91	5.36	208	2.48	234	1.06
		92	0.17				

Ans. Mass 206 contains two sulfur atoms. The $P + 2$ peak is too small for chlorine or bromine and too large for one sulfur.

14. The abundance of heavy isotopes is treated in terms of the binomial expansion: $(a + b)^n$ where a is the relative abundance of light isotopes, b is the relative abundance of heavy isotopes, and n is the number of atoms of the particular element present in the molecule. (a) For a molecule containing three chlorine atoms, what would be the intensity ratios of the peaks at mass x, $x + 2$, $x + 4$, and $x + 6$? (b) Same for two bromine atoms. (c) Same for three bromine atoms. *Ans.* (a) Ratios will be 27:27:9:1

15. Deduce the number and type of halogen atoms present in a molecule from the abundance of heavy isotopes and the intensity ratios:

	x	$x + 2$	$x + 4$	$x + 6$	$x + 8$
Compound A	30	29	10	1	—
Compound B	13	30	19	6	1
Compound C	5	20	30	19	5
Compound D	23	30	7	—	—
Compound E	18	30	14	2	—

Ans. Compound A, note the answer to Problem 14(a).

16. Deduce the intensity ratios for ions containing (a) two chlorine atoms and one bromine atom and (b) two bromine atoms and one chlorine atom. *Ans.* (a) Note compound E in Problem 15.

17. Deduce the structural formula for each of these compounds from the mass spectral data:

$C_4H_8O_2$		$C_4H_6O_2$		$C_6H_{12}O_2$	
m/e	% OF BASE PEAK	m/e	% OF BASE PEAK	m/e	% OF BASE PEAK
27	39.3	15	27.7	27	38.2
29	19.8	26	22.4	29	54.5
39	14.8	27	68.1	41	14.5
41	23.7	29	13.0	43	21.2
42	24.7	42	11.8	57	100
43	22.3	55	100	75	27.6
45	19.1	58	8.4	87	5.4
60	100	59	5.2	101	2.4
73	27.1	85	12.3	116(P)	0.04
88(P)	1.6	86(P)	2.1		

Ans. Compound $C_4H_6O_2$ is methyl acrylate.

18. The mass spectral data for two pure compounds are tabulated:

	A		B
m/e	% OF BASE PEAK	m/e	% OF BASE PEAK
39	8	29	18
41	7	39	23
65	8	51	29
77	8	65	18
91	20	78	50
105	4	91	*100*
119	*100*	105	41
134(*P*)	21.53	134(*P*)	57.4
135	2.58	135	5.80
136	0.16	136	0.41

Identify each compound from the fragmentation pattern and the isotopic abundance information. *Ans.* Compound A is *p*-isopropyl toluene (the exact substitution pattern could not be ascertained from mass spectral data alone)

19. The significant portion of the mass spectral data is given for the individual alcohols. Select appropriate analytical masses and write a series of four equations in terms of divisions of base peak due to each of the four alcohols.

	PERCENT OF BASE PEAK				UNKNOWN MIXTURES		
m/e	Methyl	Ethyl	*n*-Propyl	Isopropyl	A	B	C
15	35.48	9.44	3.77	10.70			
19	0.29	3.13	0.90	6.51			
27	—	21.62	15.20	15.50			
29	58.80	21.24	14.14	9.49			
31	*100*	*100*	*100*	5.75			
32	68.03(*P*)	1.14	2.25	—	600	600	2350
33	0.98	—	—	—			
39		—	4.00	5.52	4800	3000	3000
43		7.45	3.18	16.76			
45		37.33	4.39	*100*			
46		16.23(*P*)	—	—	1000	1100	698
59		9.61	3.58		4000	2300	5000
60			6.36(*P*)	0.44(*P*)			
Sensitivity, divisions per micron	8.76	17.98	26.51	23.47			

20. The mixture peaks for three unknown mixtures of alcohols are shown in Problem 19. For each mixture compute the mole percent of each alcohol. *Ans.* Compound B contains 2.5 percent methanol, 13.5 percent ethanol, 6.9 percent *n*-propanol, and 77.0 percent isopropanol.

Bibliography

Beynon, J. H., *Mass Spectrometry and Its Application to Organic Chemistry*, Elsevier, Amsterdam, 1960.

Biemann, K., *Mass Spectrometry: Applications to Organic Chemistry*, McGraw-Hill, New York, 1962.

Budzikiewicz, H., C. Djerassi, and D. H. Williams, *Interpretation of Mass Spectra of Organic Compounds*, Holden-Day, San Francisco, 1964.

McLafferty, F. W., "Mass Spectrometry," in F. C. Nachod and W. D. Phillips (Ed.), *Determination of Organic Structure by Physical Methods*, Vol. II, Academic Press, New York, 1962.

Silverstein, R. M., and G. C. Bassler, *Spectrometric Identification of Organic Compounds*, Wiley, New York, 1963.

Stewart, D. W., "Mass Spectrometry," in A. Weissberger (Ed.), *Technique of Organic Chemistry*, 3rd ed., Vol. 1, Part IV, Interscience, New York, 1960.

Literature Cited

1. Bennett, W. H., *J. Appl. Phys.*, **21**, 143 (1950).
2. Beynon, J. H., *Mikrochim. Acta*, 437 (1956).
3. Beynon, J. H., *Mass Spectrometry and Its Application to Organic Chemistry*, Elsevier, Amsterdam, 1960.
4. Donner, W., *Appl. Spectroscopy*, **8**, 157 (1954); *ISA J.*, **3**, 89 (1956).
5. Gifford, A. P., S. M. Rock, and D. J. Comaford, *Anal. Chem.*, **21**, 1062 (1949).
6. McLafferty, F. W., "Mass Spectral Correlations," *Advan. Chem. Ser.*, **40**, American Chemical Society, Washington, 1963.
7. Robinson, C. F., and G. Hall, *Rev. Sci. Inst.*, **27**, 504 (1956).
8. Washburn, H. W., H. F. Wiley, and S. M. Rock, *Ind. Eng. Chem., Anal. Ed.*, **15**, 541 (1943).
9. Wiley, W. C., and I. H. McLaren, *Rev. Sci. Inst.*, **26**, 1150 (1955).

CHAPTER 17

Thermoanalytical Methods

Thermoanalytical methods involve techniques such as thermogravimetric analysis (TGA), differential thermal analysis (DTA), and thermometric titrations. Data are obtained as continuously recorded curves which may be considered as thermal spectra. These thermograms characterize a system, single or multicomponent, in terms of the temperature dependencies of its thermodynamic properties and physicochemical reaction kinetics.

Thermogravimetric analysis involves changes in weight of a system under investigation as the temperature is increased at a predetermined rate. Differential thermal analysis consists of measuring changes in heat content, as a function of the difference in temperature between the sample under investigation and a thermally inert reference compound, as the two materials are heated to elevated temperatures (or cooled to subnormal temperatures) at predetermined rates. In this manner enthalpic changes, such as melting, vaporization, crystallographic phase transition, or chemical changes, are detected from the endo- and exothermal bands and peaks that appear on the thermograms. The corresponding weight changes are detected by thermogravimetric analysis. Complete thermoanalytical data are obtained only by utilizing both methods of analysis. The information obtained, coupled with X-ray diffraction, optical and chemical analysis of the residues, and any evolved gases, provides a quantitative estimation of solid-state reactions.

Thermometric titrations involve changes in solution temperature which are plotted against volume of titrant. Thermovolumetry provides a means of following a gas-absorbing or gas-producing reaction by continuously recording the change in the volume of gas consumed or evolved as the material is heated to elevated temperatures at a constant rate.

Thermogravimetric Analysis

Interest in thermogravimetry has increased in recent years because of the commercial availability of automatic, continuously recording thermo-balances which are rugged, reliable, and accurate. In dynamic thermogravimetry a sample is subjected to conditions of continuous increase in temperature, usually linear with time, whereas in isothermal or static thermogravimetry the sample is maintained at a constant temperature for a period of time during which any changes in weight are noted.

Apparatus

The basic instrumental requirements for thermogravimetric analysis are (a) a precision balance, (b) a furnace programmed for a linear rise of temperature with time, and (c) a recorder. It is desirable to have a reaction chamber within the furnace which permits work to be carried out under a wide variety of conditions (e.g., inert, oxidizing, or reducing atmospheres or under vacuum), thus making possible the analysis of any gaseous product.

Balances are either the null-point or the deflection types of instruments. The former incorporates a suitable sensing element that detects any deviation of the balance beam and provides the application of a restoring force, proportional to the change in weight, to return the beam to its original null point. This restoring force is then recorded either directly or through a transducer. Deflection instruments—based on a conventional analytical balance, a helical spring, a cantilever beam, a strain gauge, or a torsion balance—involve the conversion of deviations into a record of the weight change. The recording system should be able to record both temperature and weight continuously and to make a periodic record of the time. A continuous record of weight and temperature ensures that no features of the thermograms are overlooked.

Furnace design and control must be designed to provide a suitable smooth input so that it can maintain either a linear heating program ($10°-600°C/hr$) or a fixed temperature. Control is generally achieved via a thermocouple situated as close to the furnace winding as possible. Some form of stepless control of power supply to the furnace avoids thermal pulsing effects and the consequent ragged weight record. Nichrome winding permits a maximum temperature of around $1100°C$; platinum-rhodium, up to $1450°C$. Higher temperatures can be achieved by using a graphite tube furnace, but the control and measurement of temperatures introduce problems.

Methodology

Plateaus on the decomposition curve, indicative of constant weight, represent stable phases over the particular temperature interval. An inflection may imply the formation of an intermediate compound, or the adsorption of a volatile product on (or in) the new solid phase. The thermogram for calcium oxalate monohydrate is shown in Fig. 17-1. Successive plateaus correspond to the anhydrous salt, calcium carbonate, and calcium oxide.

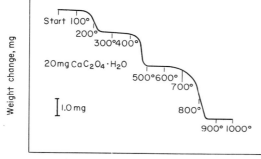

Fig. 17-1. Thermogravimetric evaluation of calcium oxalate monohydrate; heating rate 6°C/min.

In interpreting thermogravimetric curves, one must always be cognizant that the decomposition temperature is a function of method, apparatus, and procedure. There is often little correlation between results from isothermal runs and nonisothermal runs. The discrepancies arise from the dynamic nature of the method.

Correction must be applied for the apparent weight change of the empty sample pan to arrive at the actual weight change occurring in the specimen. This procedure is considered to be more satisfactory than the use of a tare container in a separate furnace, in view of the possible nonuniformity of the hot zones in the two furnaces. This apparent weight change is caused by the interplay of a complex combination of several factors, such as air buoyancy, convection effects within the furnace, container geometry, radiation effects, the atmosphere in the furnace, and the fact that the specimen support is subject to a temperature gradient within the furnace.

The shape of the corrected thermogravimetric curve is influenced for a particular compound by (a) the heating rate, (b) the sample, (c) the crucible, and (d) the atmosphere. At any given temperature, the extent of decomposition is greater at a slow rate of heating than for a similar sample heated at a faster rate. The heat of reaction will affect the difference between sample temperature and furnace temperature, causing the sample temperature to lead or lag the furnace temperature, depending on whether the reaction is exothermic or endothermic. When successive reactions are involved, the rate of heating may well determine whether or not these reactions will be separated. The use of a small, finely divided sample is to be preferred. Equilibrium between sample and product gas and with the furnace temperature will be governed somewhat by the bulk of the material in the crucible. The environmental atmosphere immediately surrounding the reacting particles influences the curve. Even small changes in the composition of this atmosphere can affect the thermogram, as shown in Fig. 17-2. In humidified air at low heating rates, good plateaus are

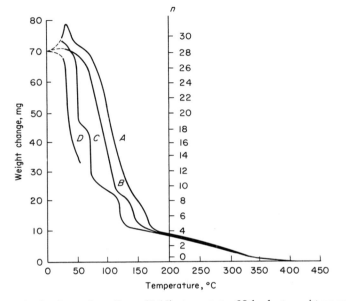

Fig. 17-2. Dehydration of sodium (5:12) tungstate 28-hydrate. Atmosphere and heating rates: *A*, Humidified air, 300°C/hr; *B*, Humidified air, 150°C/hr; *C*, Humidified air, 10°C/hr; *D*, Room air, 10°C/hr; n = moles water per $5Na_2O \cdot 12WO_3$; sample weight 0.5000 g. After A. E. Newkirk, *Anal. Chem.*, **32**, 1560 (1960). (Courtesy of *Analytical Chemistry*.)

obtained. Restriction of effluence to the immediate vicinity of the sample, permitting escape of gas but preventing exchange between the sample cavity and the ambient atmosphere, affords better definition of weight losses. A simple piston in the sample holder is adequate.

Applications

Application of thermogravimetric analysis includes the investigation of analytical procedures, the elucidation of suitable weighing forms for many elements, testing materials that are actual or potential analytical standards, and the direct application of the technique to analytical determinations.

Thermogravimetry is regularly used for determining the drying ranges of precipitates. However, the dynamic nature of the technique must be considered when interpreting the best drying temperature. The most reliable information will be gained by using several different heating rates or a slow rate of heating, possibly with preliminary air drying. Plateaus for hydrates sometimes depend on the initial water content.

The apparent pattern of thermal decomposition of pure compounds may suggest reaction schemes to account for the degradation. The breakdown of organic polymers has received much attention. The sample is heated in an inert atmosphere or under vacuum. Thermogravimetric data can be used to evaluate kinetic parameters of weight changes in reactions. Graphical methods for the determination of the order of reaction x and the activation energy, E_A, can be obtained from the equation

$$-\frac{E_A/(2.303)R\,\Delta T^{-1}}{\Delta \log W_r} = -x + \frac{\Delta \log (\partial w/\partial t)}{\Delta \log W_r} \tag{17-1}$$

where R is the gas constant, T the absolute temperature, and $W_r = (W_c - W)$, where W is the weight loss at time t and W_c is the weight loss at completion of the reaction. Either by plotting a graph of

$$\frac{\Delta \log (\partial w/\partial t)}{\Delta \log W_r} \text{ vs } \frac{\Delta T^{-1}}{\Delta \log W_r}$$

or other suitable arrangement, it is possible to derive values for both E_A and x.

Differential Thermal Analysis

In differential thermal analysis the temperature difference between the specimen and a thermally inert reference substance is continuously recorded as a function of furnace temperature. Actually, thermogravimetry and differential thermal analysis are complementary techniques in that the information obtained by the application of one approach is often enhanced by the application of the other method. The range of phenomena measurable in the course of a DTA run is much larger than in a TGA determination. Thus, during TGA, pure fusion reactions, crystalline transitions, glass transitions and crystallization, and solid state reactions with no volatile products would not be indicated because they engendered no change in weight of the specimen. However, the use of TGA frequently allows one to describe with some exactness the stoichiometry involved in chemical changes which are indicated during DTA by an exothermal or endothermal departure from the base line.

Apparatus

A differential thermal analyzer includes five basic components: (1) sample holder with thermocouple assembly inside, (2) a furnace assembly, (3) flow control system, (4) a preamplifier and recorder, and (5) a furnace power programmer and controller. The schematic diagram of Fig. 17-3 illustrates a typical commercial instrument. Dual thermocouples measure the difference in temperature between a sample S and an essentially inert reference substance R as both are heated in a metal or ceramic block by a furnace operated by a temperature programmer and controller. The differential thermocouple output, after suitable amplification in a high-gain, low-noise preamplifier, is fed

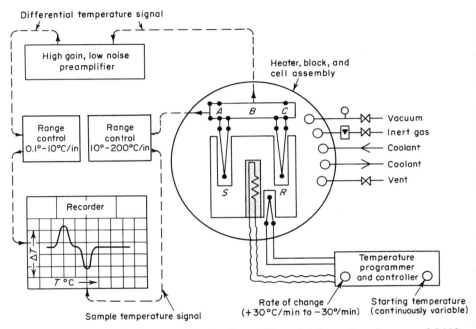

Fig. 17-3. Schematic diagram of the Du Pont differential thermal analyzer, model 900. (Courtesy of E. I. Du Pont de Nemours, Inc.)

to the recorder, one axis of which is driven by the block temperature signal and which is measured by a third thermocouple. Thermocouples are usually platinum vs platinum/10% rhodium, unsheathed.

Versatility is achieved with a high-temperature, pressure-vacuum electric furnace. A motor-driven variable autotransformer provides a nearly constant heating rate. Heating rates (or cooling rates) can be adjusted continuously from $0°–30°C/min$ on some instruments, whereas others provide the user with a choice of several commonly used heating rates: $2°$, $4°$, $8°$, and $16°C/min$. Sample temperatures up to $500°C$ are usual; maximum temperatures employed are about $1000°C$. Relatively small sample volumes make evacuation easy and minimize thermal gradients.

Methodology

To operate a differential thermal analyzer, one merely inserts a very thin thermocouple into a disposable sample tube—the latter perhaps 2 mm in diameter and containing 0.1–10 mg of sample. A duplicate tube contains a reference material, such as alumina, alundum powder, or quartz sand, or it may be empty. The two tubes are inserted into the sample block, side-by-side, and heated (or cooled) at a uniform programmed rate. Since differential thermal analysis is a dynamic method, it is essential that all aspects of technique be standardized in order to obtain reproducible results. These include pre-treatment of the specimen, particle size and packing of the specimen, dilution of the specimen, and nature of the inert diluent. Crystalline materials should be ground to pass through a 100-mesh sieve. For colloidal particles, such as clays, micelle size is the critical feature. For some types of samples the atmosphere must be controlled, either to suppress an undesirable reaction such as oxidation or to learn the nature of a reaction, as, for example, by varying the pressure of a gaseous reaction product.

The plot of ΔT as a function of T is an indication of the energy gains or losses in the specimen under investigation. When an endothermic change occurs, the specimen temperature lags behind the reference temperature because of the heat required to carry out the transition. When the transition is complete, thermal diffusion brings the sample back to equilibrium quickly. The thermal trace would show a sharp depression followed by a return to nearly a zero value for ΔT.

The two curves shown in Fig. 17-4 illustrate a differential thermal analysis trace and the complementary relationship of differential thermal analysis and thermogravimetric analysis. The endothermal dehydration of calcium acetate monohydrate to the anhydrous salt is the first reaction that occurs and is manifested by an endothermal band on the DTA curve between 200° and 250°C, and a weight loss plateau on the thermogravimetric curve at a comparable temperature region. The anhydrous salt is stable up to temperatures of approximately 350°–400°C, at which point endothermal decomposition reactions occur that are sensitive to the presence of oxygen in the environment. It is apparent from the thermogravimetric curves that the highly exothermal oxidative degradation that occurs in an oxygen atmosphere is completely different from the endothermal reaction occurring in argon. Calcium carbonate is a product of the reaction in all cases. In the presence of carbon dioxide, the decomposition reaction appears to be similar to that occurring in argon, namely, decomposition of the salt to acetone, a volatile degradation product and a residue of calcium carbonate. The final stage is the decomposition of calcium carbonate to calcium oxide, which is a function of the partial pressure of the CO_2 in contact with the sample. The endothermal band for the carbonate decomposition is sharply peaked over a narrower temperature range in the CO_2 atmosphere.

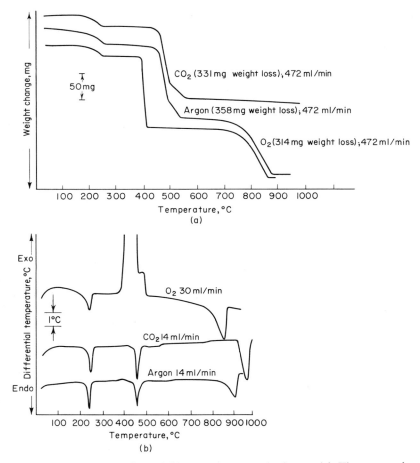

Fig. 17-4. Thermograms for calcium acetate monohydrate. (a) Thermogravimetric evaluation, 6°C/min. (b) Differential thermal analysis investigation, 12°C/min. Particular atmosphere above the solid phase is indicated for each thermogram. After Bulletin 2380, American Instrument Co., Inc.

Differential Scanning Calorimeter

The differential scanning calorimeter, available from Perkin-Elmer Corporation, records the difference in electric power required to keep a test sample and a reference material at equal temperatures as they are heated or cooled at rates up to 80°C/min. The power difference shows up during physical or chemical transitions in the sample and is equivalent to the thermal energy absorbed or released during the transition.

Two sample pans—one each for test and reference materials—are mounted on separate heating coils. A resistance thermometer is attached to each pan. A control unit regulates the power supplied to each coil. It keeps sample and reference temperatures equal to each other, and it raises or lowers these temperatures at a preset, uniform rate. Samples are sealed in metal foil packets before use. Often an empty foil sample holder can be used as the reference.

Power changes are recorded on a strip chart recorder as peaks superimposed on a straight line. The area of a peak corresponds to the amount of energy absorbed or emitted. Its position on the chart indicates the temperature of transition.

To distinguish between physical transitions and sample decomposition, analyses may be carried out in an inert gas atmosphere. If sampled by a thermal conductivity cell, products of decomposition show up on an auxiliary recorder coincident with peaks due to thermal changes on the differential scanning calorimeter chart.

Applications

The most voluminous literature on DTA deals with minerals, ceramics, and clays. Compositions of mixed clays can be quickly identified. The major application in inorganic studies has been in checking the thermal stabilities of compounds. Other applications have been to check the identities of compounds and to ensure that in a specific reaction a new compound is formed and that the product is not simply unreacted original material. The technique presents an elegant method for investigating solid-phase reactions, phase transformations and inversions in single compounds, and for investigating reaction kinetics and phenomena associated with polymerization, thermal and oxidative degradation, solvent retention, curing or drying properties of a product.

Thermograms of typical explosives and propellants provide a wealth of information useful in the manufacture, storage, and application of these high-energy materials. For example, in Fig. 17-5 the endotherms, marked A in the traces, indicate either crystalline phase transitions or melting. The exothermic departure from the base line, marked B, is caused by the onset of thermal decomposition (the limit for safe handling). The temperature of runaway decomposition, marked C, is the upper limit of stability. The temperature and shape of the endotherms associated with first-order transitions reflect the purity of the materials. Lowering of decomposition temperatures warns of potential hazards that may have developed because of the presence of sensitizing impurities. The onset of exothermic decomposition indicates a temperature range to be avoided when quantities of the material larger than the sample are processed, because limited heat transfer in massive sections may permit self-heating to a temperature high enough to cause runaway decomposition.

Thermometric Titrations

In thermometric titrations one utilizes heats of reaction to obtain titration curves. Solution temperature is plotted against volume of titrant. Titrant is delivered from a thermostated buret into a solution contained within a thermal-

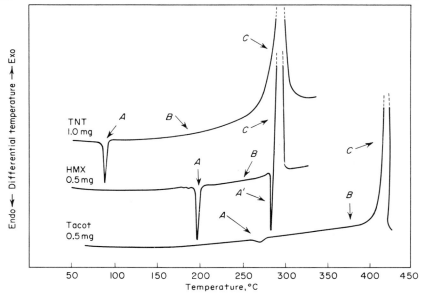

Fig. 17-5. Thermograms of several explosives. *A*, crystalline phase transition or melting; *B*, onset of thermal decomposition; *C*, runaway decomposition. Tacot is Dupont's trademark for its temperature-resistant high explosive. (Courtesy of E. I. Du Pont de Nemours, Inc.)

ly insulated vessel, and the temperature change of the solution—either upon continuous addition of titrant or after each successive incremental addition—is recorded. A sharp break in the curve marks the end point. Thermometric titrations have been applied to neutralization, complexation, redox, and precipitation reactions. Since thermometric titrations are not affected by the solvent's dielectric constant, they can be used in nonaqueous media. They can also be used to titrate liquid solutions with gaseous reagents and, in some cases, to titrate gases with other gases in the absence of a liquid phase.

Apparatus

The titration apparatus is shown in Fig. 17-6. It consists essentially of (a) a motor-driven buret, (b) an adiabatic titration chamber, (c) a thermistor bridge assembly, and (d) a recorder. In order to minimize heat transfer between the solution and its surroundings, the titrations are performed in an insulated beaker closed with a stopper provided with holes for the buret tip, a glass stirrer, and a temperature-monitoring device. The titrant is delivered from a buret that is contained within a thermostated water jacket to hold the temperature of the titrant within $\pm 0.05°C$. To obviate volume corrections and to minimize temperature variations between the titrant and the solution, the concentration of the titrant is as a rule 10–100 times larger than that of the reactant. Conditions are chosen so that a volume of titrant not exceeding 1–

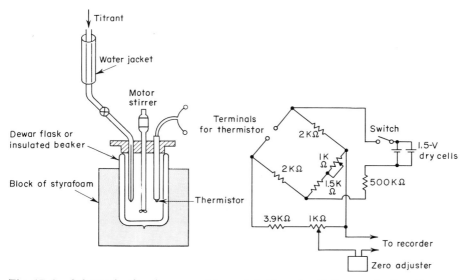

Fig. 17-6. Schematic titration assembly and bridge circuit for conducting thermo-metric titrations. After H. W. Linde, L. B. Rogers, and D. N. Hume, *Anal. Chem.*, **25**, 494 (1953). (Courtesy of *Analytical Chemistry.*)

3 ml is required in each titration. Use of an automatic device that delivers reagent at a constant rate (e.g., 600 μl/minute) permits recording.

The solution is mixed uniformly with a stirrer driven by a constant-speed motor at 600 rpm.

Temperature changes are measured conveniently by a sensitive thermistor-sensing element with fast response, which is sealed entirely in glass and im-mersed in the solution.[3] A Beckmann-type thermometer and thermocouples have also been employed. These latter temperature-sensing devices are not as sensitive as thermistors but may be used satisfactorily when the reactants are relatively concentrated (about 0.5 M).

During operation, the beaker thermistor is connected to one arm of the Wheatstone bridge shown in Fig. 17-6. The values of the circuit components listed are for a thermistor having an approximate resistance of 2000 Ω and a sensitivity of $-0.04\ \Omega/\Omega/°C$ in the 25°C temperature range.* A change of 1°C corresponds to an unbalance potential of 15.7 mV. To obtain optimum results, temperatures of the titrant and sample solutions should be within 0.2°C of each other before a titration is begun. As titrant is added to the beaker, and heat of reaction is generated or absorbed, the bridge is unbalanced due to cor-responding changes in the resistance (temperature) of the beaker thermistor. The bridge unbalance potential is plotted by the recorder.

*Western Electric Company, Type 14B.

A small heating element, located inside the titration vessel, can be used to warm the sample solution to the temperature of the titrant and as a calibrating device in estimating heats of reaction (q.v.).

A differential thermal apparatus overcomes some of the problems encountered in thermometric titrations. Temperature-sensing elements are placed in both the sample and blank solutions. Sensitivity is improved and extraneous heat effects, such as stirring and heats of dilution, are greatly minimized. The electrical circuit is modified as shown in Fig. 17-7.

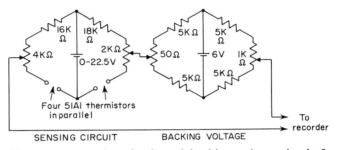

Fig. 17-7. Temperature-sensing circuit and bucking voltage circuit for differential thermometric titrations and reaction enthalpies. After B. C. Tyson, Jr., W. H. McCurdy, Jr., and C. E. Bricker, *Anal. Chem.*, **33**, 1641 (1961). (Courtesy of *Analytical Chemistry*.)

Methodology

In conventional types of titrations, e.g., potentiometric, conductometric, etc., determination of end points depends on free energy effects. Thermometric titration curves, however, represent a measure of the entire enthalpy change, which includes the entropy as well as the free energy involved. Titrant is added at a constant rate to the titrand so that the voltage output of the thermistor temperature transducer varies linearly with time up to the equivalence point. The method avoids obscuration of end points from color of solution or poisoning of electrodes.

Idealized titration curves are shown in Fig. 17-8. Point *A* is where the temperature readings were begun, and line *AB* is a trace of the temperature of the solution before the addition of titrant. If the line *AB* shows a marked slope, it is an indication of excessive heat transfer between the solution and its surroundings. At point *B* the addition of titrant was begun; line *BC* shows the gradual evolution of the heat of reaction; and point *C* is the end point. Line *CD* may slope downward or upward. The straight-line portions of the curve are extrapolated to give the initial and equivalence points, and the distance between them is measured along the time axis of the chart to ascertain the volume of titrant consumed in the reaction.

For dilute solutions the heat evolved is small. When 1 ml of $1M$ NaOH is added to 30 ml of 0.033 M HCl, the temperature rise is about 0.4°C. Similarly,

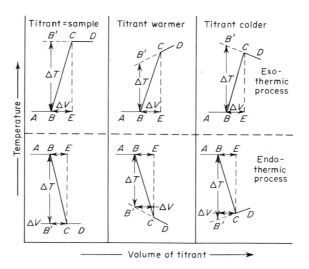

Fig. 17-8. Idealized thermometric titration curves. *AB*, blank run (no titrant added); *B*, start of titration; *C*, end point; *CD*, excess reagent line; *CB'*, extrapolated excess reagent line for ΔT; *B'B* (ΔT), temperature difference used to evaluate enthalpies; *BE* (ΔV), stoichiometric volume to end point.

when $1M$ Na₂EDTA and $0.033\ M$ MgCl₂ are employed, the temperature falls by about 0.08°C. Thermometric titrations are feasible with systems giving rates of temperature change greater than 0.01°C/sec. Precautions must be taken to avoid transfer of heat between the titration vessel and its surroundings. Random temperature fluctuations should not exceed 0.001°C during a titration.

The lower limit of concentrations that can be successfully titrated in the more favorable cases is about 0.002 *M*. The accuracy to be expected is ±1 to 2 percent.

Acid-Base Titrations

Thermometric titrations permit analysts to carry out, accurately and rapidly, many quantitative determinations not previously possible. In acid-base titrations, the point is clearly demonstrated by the curves in Fig. 17-9, which are characterized by well-defined end points for both HCl and the much weaker boric acid. The enthalpy change of neutralization is not very different for either acid. The actual value may be estimated from the relation

$$\Delta H = T\Delta S - RT \ln K \qquad (17\text{-}2)$$

where K is the acid (or base) dissociation constant. Fast, clear end points are obtainable for other weak acids and bases even in emulsions and thick slurries. A mixture of sodium hydroxide and sodium carbonate can be determined with good accuracy, as can acids in the presence of hydrolyzable cations, because of the large difference between the enthalpy changes for the respective reactions.

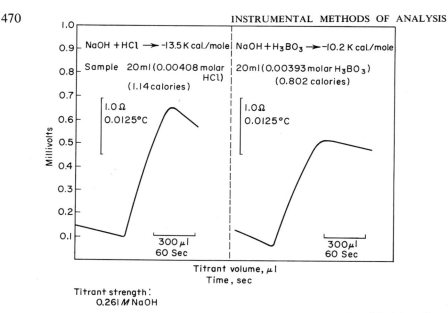

Fig. 17-9. Thermometric titration of hydrochloric acid and of boric acid with sodium hydroxide (0.2610 M).

The method is very useful in titrating acetic anhydride in acetic acid-sulfuric acid acetylating baths, aniline in aniline salts by acetylation, water in concentrated acids by titration with fuming acids, and free anhydrides in fuming acids. In fact, methods based on heats of reaction offer one of the few approaches to the analysis of concentrated solutions of these materials.

Nonaqueous systems are well suited for enthalpy titrations. Attention must be paid to the heat of mixing of solvents and dilution, whose effects are sometimes quite appreciable. The lower specific heats of many organic solvents introduce a favorable sensitivity factor.

Other Applications

Good results can be obtained in precipitation and ion-combination reactions such as those of chloride with silver and divalent cations with EDTA. Phase relations have been studied in precipitation reactions.

Aromatic sulfonic acid amides are converted by sodium hypochlorite to monochloramines in neutral or alkaline solutions.

Benzene has been determined rapidly and with good precision in the presence of cyclohexane by measuring the heat of nitration. A standard nitrating acid mixture is added to the mixture of benzene and cyclohexane; the temperature rise is a direct function of the benzene present.

The temperature rise occurring during the exothermic reaction of water and acetic anhydride in glacial acetic acid solution, catalyzed by a trace of perchloric acid, has been employed to determine the concentration of either of these reactants in the presence of an excess of the other. The temperature rise which takes place is a direct measure of the component being determined. By an alternate procedure, either water or the anhydride is titrated in glacial acetic acid solution with a standard solution of the other until no further temperature rise occurs.

The heat of reaction can be estimated with a heater immersed in the titration beaker. The operator must carefully measure the resistance of the heating element, the voltage applied to the heater, and the period of time that heat is applied to a carefully weighed solution. Electrical caloric input equals the product of watts and seconds divided by 4.185. By varying the time the heater is energized, a series of caloric values vs recorder output can be obtained, and a calibration curve of calories vs millivolts (recorder divisions) constructed. Thereafter, heats generated by thermometric reactions can be compared with the calibration curve to determine heats of reaction. This approach has been used to estimate the heats of successive steps in the formation of metal-ammine complexes,[4] the heats of chelation,[1] and heats of reaction in fused salts under virtually isothermal conditions.[2] For the effective enthalpy changes to approximate $\Delta H°$, the concentration of the species titrated must be in the millimolal or centimolal concentration range, yielding temperature changes of the order of $0.1°$–$1°C$ during the titration.

LABORATORY WORK

General Procedure for Thermometric Titrations

Motor-driven burets, 5 ml in capacity, with delivery rate of about 0.01 ml/sec, are suitable. However, other size burets and different delivery rates can be employed. Efficient stirring permits a titrant addition rate up to 10 ml/min.

The solution of the sample (and blank or solvent in differential work) is placed in suitable-size Dewar flasks or polyethylene cups mounted in Styrofoam plastic and suspended in a rigid metal framework.

With the sample container in position, each should enclose a temperature-sensing element, a capillary buret tip, and the glass rod of a motor-driven stirrer, all of which are installed in holes drilled through the cover of the container. The cover should fit snugly into the container.

Suitable thermistors will have characteristics similar to these specifications: cold resistance at 25°C, 2000–4000 Ω; temperature coefficient at 25°C, $-4.0°/°C$; thermal time constant in still water, about 1 sec. Several thermistors connected in parallel enable one to utilize a lower input impedance recorder and still have the advantage of the high temperature coefficient of high resistance thermistors.

EXPERIMENT 17-1   DETERMINATION OF QUANTITY OF REACTANT PRESENT

Place a 50- to 75-ml portion of a sample solution in the container and place the container in its insulated compartment. Insert the titration assembly, buret, thermistor, and stirring rod. Adjust the bucking voltage (zero adjust) until a suitable base line is obtained on the recorder. Start the chart drive and the buret about 10 sec later. About 10 sec after the titration is complete, as indicated by a change in slope of the chart recording, stop the buret. Suggested systems include 0.01 to 0.1 N solutions of any acid or base titrated with an appropriate titrant whose concentration is about 10- to 100-fold greater.

EXPERIMENT 17-2 ΔH DETERMINATION

The procedure, up to this point, is similar to that above. With the bucking circuit, readjust the base line to a suitable level on the recorder. Turn on a heating coil immersed in the solution. After a temperature change similar to that observed in the titration has occurred, turn off the heating coil. Adjust the base line again and make another recording of the heating rate. During the recording of each heating curve, the voltages across the heating coil and a standard resistor are measured with a potentiometer.

The product of the two measured voltages, when divided by the resistance of the standard resistor, gives the heating rate of the coil in joules per second. From the slopes of all heating curves and of the titration curve, the heat of the reaction can be calculated from the equation,

$$\Delta H = \frac{E_1 E_2 S_1}{(4.185)R\ NFS_2} = \text{calories per milliequivalent}$$

where E_1 and E_2 are the voltages across the heating coil and standard resistor, respectively, R is the resistance of the standard resistor, N is the normality of titrant whose flow rate F is in milliliters per second, and S_1, S_2 are slopes of titration heating curves.

EXPERIMENT 17-3   BENZENE IN CYCLOHEXANE BY HEAT OF REACTION

Assemble the titration apparatus and electrical circuit described in Experiment 17-1. Omit the buret. Secure a stopwatch or timer.

Prepare the nitrating acid by mixing 2 volumes of 70 percent nitric acid ($d = 1.41$) with 1 volume of 95 percent sulfuric acid ($d = 1.82$).

1. Weigh 50 g of sample into a 4-oz Bakelite screw-cap bottle. Place the bottle containing the sample and a bottle containing the nitrating acid in a thermostat at about 20°C until the contents have attained an equilibrium temperature.

2. Transfer 50 ml of nitrating acid to the Dewar flask and insert the motor stirrer. Wait 3 min and then start the motor stirrer. After 1 min, record the initial temperature.

3. Stop the motor. Pour the sample into the flask and start the stirrer. Take readings of the temperature after an elapsed time of 1, 2, 3, and 5 min.

4. Construct a calibration curve of temperature rise in a 3-min interval vs percent benzene in cyclohexane. Run pure cyclohexane and standards containing 0.5–5.0 percent benzene by weight.

Note. A thermometer graduated to 0.1°C is adequate for temperature measurements of the range of benzene contents suggested. Lower limits could be achieved through the use of the thermistor circuit.

Problems

1. A differential thermal analysis trace contains an endothermal band. It is unaltered by increasing the partial pressure of oxygen in the furnace atmosphere, but is shifted to a higher temperature in a carbon dioxide atmosphere. What conclusions can be drawn? *Ans.* The sample is a carbonate.

2. On the cooling cycle the exothermal band coincides with the endothermal band on the heating cycle. Comment on the reversibility of the process.

3. Deduce the transitions involved in the thermal decomposition of the mineral hydromagnesite, $3MgCO_3 \cdot Mg(OH)_2 \cdot 3H_2O$, when heated in an atmosphere of carbon dioxide. Problem 17-4 shows the differential thermal analysis curve. *Ans.* Between 25° and 300°C the compound evolves 3 moles of water of hydration, and 1 mole of water from $Mg(OH)_2$, leaving an intermediate compound with a 3:1 mole ratio of $MgCO_3$ to MgO. This is followed by formation of 2:1 mole ratio of carbonate to oxide, and finally, the release of the last 2 moles of CO_2. The exotherm corresponds to a crystal lattice transition, amorphous MgO to the cubic form.

4. Compare the thermogravimetric trace for $CaC_2O_4 \cdot H_2O$ (in Fig. 17-1) with the differential thermal analysis trace shown below. (a) Deduce the products at each enthalpic change and the transition involved. (b) Explain the exotherm observed only in an oxygen atmosphere at 500°C. (c) Recommend temperatures

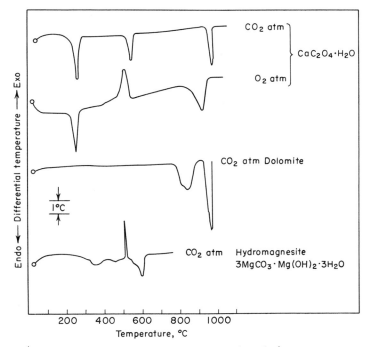

Problem 17-4. Differential thermal analysis curves.

suitable for the gravimetric determination of calcium when the final weighing form is $CaCO_3$ and when it is CaO.

5. The decomposition curve for dolomite ($MgCO_3 \cdot CaCO_3$), shown on page 473, differs markedly from a similar curve for $MgCO_3$ alone (note the trace for hydromagnesite, the final endotherm). Can you suggest an explanation. *Ans.* Dolomite is believed to exist as a calcium salt of a carbonato-magnesium anion, $Ca[Mg(CO_3)_2]$.

6. Below are indicated the curves for the thermal decomposition of calcium sulfate dihydrate. (a) Identify the nature of each transition. (b) Devise a method for determining the dihydrate in hemihydrate mixtures by DTA and by TGA

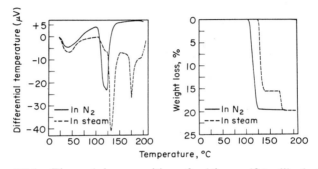

Problem 17-6.   Thermal decomposition of calcium sulfate dihydrate.

methods. *Ans.* (b) See R. A. Kuntze, *Mat. Res. Std.*, **2**, 646 (1962), and H. G. McAdie, *Anal. Chem.*, **35**, 1844 (1963).

7. The thermal decomposition of copper sulfate pentahydrate is represented below. (a) Identify each phase. (b) Below what temperature should the crystals

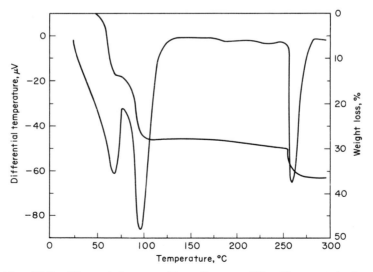

Problem 17-7.   Thermal decomposition of copper (II) sulfate pentahydrate.

be maintained to ensure presence of the pentahydrate (assuming, of course, the partial pressure of water vapor is also controlled)? (c) Above what temperature would the anhydrous salt be an equilibrium product?

8. The thermal decomposition of cobalt(II) oxalate precipitate is pictured below, as carried out in a chamber that is open to the air. (a) What hydrate predom-

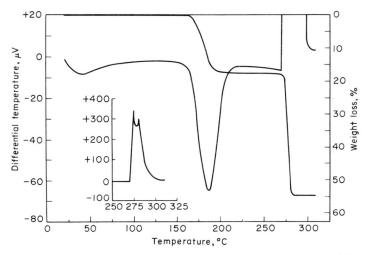

Problem 17-8. Thermal decomposition of cobalt (II) oxalate precipitate.

inates? (b) Postulate the composition of the residue obtained at 300°C. *Ans.* (a) The dihydrate. (b) Apparently a mixture of Co_2O_3 and Co_3O_4 (actual X-ray data indicated only the latter)

9. The thermal decomposition of ammonium nitrate in an atmosphere of dry nitrogen shows no weight loss up to 140°C, then a small weight loss at higher temperatures. Three endotherms (at 55°, 130° and 172°C) appear on the DTA trace. What transition is probably associated with each endotherm?

10. The thermograms of the urea-*n*-dodecane inclusion compound, obtained in an atmosphere of nitrogen, are shown on page 476. (a) Identify the phase transition that occurs at the 90°C-endotherm and the cause of the weight loss of 22.45 percent. (b) What type of transition is probably associated with the sharp endotherm at 135°C? Note that the weight loss commences immediately following the endotherm. (c) What reaction is causing the weight loss above 140°C?

11. The thermal decomposition of a sample of $MnCO_3$ contains only an endotherm at 660°C in an atmosphere of CO_2. In an atmosphere of oxygen, the endotherm appears at 660° and is followed by a rather sharp exotherm at 740°C. What are the reactions involved in each particular atmosphere?

12. The thermogravimetric analysis of lead carbonate in a closed chamber is shown on page 476. Complementary DTA curves show an endotherm for each TGA plateau. Deduce the products at each thermal halt (but ignore the small loss at 230°C).

13. The DTA curve for potassium sulfate exhibits an endotherm centered about 586°C. A complementary TGA curve shows no weight change. What type of transition is suggested?

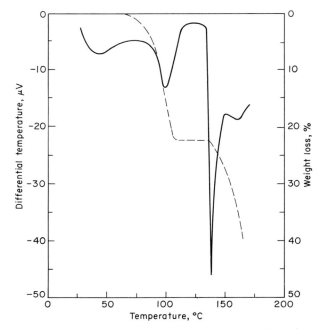

Problem 17-10. Thermal decomposition of urea-*n*-dodecane inclusion compound.

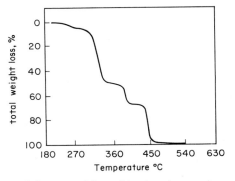

Problem 17-12. Thermal decomposition of lead carbonate in a closed chamber.

14. A solid-state reaction between 240 mg of Na_2CO_3 and 1260 mg of WO_3 in an atmosphere of CO_2 resulted in a weight loss of 0.995 g at 624°C. When heated alone, Na_2CO_3 showed no weight change up to 1000°C; nor did WO_3 up to its volatilization temperature. Increasing separately the weight of carbonate did not affect the weight loss, whereas a series of experiments indicated that each 100 mg of WO_3 increased the weight loss by 7.8 mg when excess of carbonate was present. Deduce the solid-state reaction and product.

15. An unstable inorganic compound, $CH_8O_3N_2$, suffers a weight loss of 67 mg at 70° and a further loss of 14 mg of a clear liquid at 100°C. No residue remains. What is the original salt? *Ans.* Ammonium carbonate.

Bibliography

Wendlandt, W. W., *Thermal Methods of Analysis*, Interscience, New York, 1964.

DTA AND TGA METHODS

Coates, A. W., and J. P. Redfern, "Thermogravimetric Analysis—A Review," *Analyst*, **88**, 906 (1963).

Duval, C., *Inorganic Thermogravimetric Analysis*, 2nd ed., Am. Elsevier, New York, 1963.

Garn, P. D., "Thermal Analysis—A Critique," *Anal. Chem.*, **33**, 1247 (1961).

Gordon, S., and C. Campbell, *Anal. Chem.*, **32**, 271R (1960).

Symposium on Thermal Methods of Analysis, *Anal. Chem.*, **32**, 1558–1588 (1960); **35**, 1834–1852 (1963).

THERMOMETRIC TITRATIONS

Jordan, J., *Record of Chemical Progress*, Hooker-Kresge Library, **19**, 193 (1958).

Keily, H. J., and D. N. Hume, *Anal. Chem.*, **28**, 1294 (1956).

Linde, H. W., L. B. Rogers, and D. N. Hume, *Anal. Chem.*, **25**, 494 (1953).

Literature Cited

1. Jordan, J., and T. G. Alleman, *Anal. Chem.*, **29**, 9 (1957).
2. Jordan, J., et al., *Anal. Chem.*, **32**, 651 (1960).
3. Linde, H. W., L. B. Rogers, and D. N. Hume, *Anal. Chem.*, **25**, 404 (1953).
4. Poulsen, I., and J. Bjerrum, *Acta Chem. Scand.*, **9**, 1407 (1955).

Methods for the Analysis of Gases

Five methods for the analysis of gases are grouped in this chapter. These are only a selection of the possibilities. Many of the methods discussed in other chapters can also be used for the determination of gaseous constituents: visual and ultraviolet spectrophotometry, infrared spectrophotometry, interferometry, X-ray absorption, polarography, and mass spectrometry are examples.

Thermal Conductivity

All gases possess the ability to conduct heat, but in varying degrees. This difference can be used to determine quantitatively the composition of binary gaseous mixtures or more complex mixtures if all the components of the mixture have about the same thermal conductivity except for the one component being measured.

The thermal conductivity of a gas is defined as the quantity of heat (in calories) transferred in unit time (seconds) in a gas between two surfaces 1 cm^2 in area, and 1 cm apart when the temperature difference between the surfaces is 1°C. Absolute values of the thermal conductivity are seldom needed for analytical purposes, but a number of values are gathered in Table 18-1.

Hot-Wire Cells

A thermal conductivity detector consists of heat-sensing elements, each situated in a separate cavity in a brass or stainless steel block which serves as a heat sink. The heat-sensing elements are either thermistors or resistance

Table 18-1	*Thermal Conductivities of Gases and Vapors*

GAS	$\lambda \times 10^5$ (0°C)	$\lambda/\lambda_{\text{AIR}}$ (100°C)	APPROXIMATE BRIDGE OUTPUT IN MILLIVOLTS RELATIVE TO AIR†		
			4-W	4-W-2	2-GBT
Acetone	2.37	0.557	−3.4	−10.2	−12.0
Air	5.83	1.000	—	—	—
Ammonia	5.22	1.04	2.5	7.5	8.8
Argon	—	0.696	−2.0	−6.0	−7.0
Carbon dioxide	3.52	0.700	−3.0	−9.0	−10.5
Carbon monoxide	—	0.960	−0.4	−1.2	−1.4
Chlorine	—	0.323	−10	−30	−35
Ether	—	0.747	−3.6	−10.8	—
Helium	34.80	5.53	17.2	51.6	60
Hydrogen	41.60	7.10	28	84.0	98
Methane	7.21	1.45	3.5	10.5	12.2
Nitrogen	5.81	0.996	−0.25	−0.75	−0.9
Oxygen	—	1.014	0.45	1.35	1.6
Sulfur dioxide	—	0.350	−37.5	−37.5	−44

†4-W filaments are helical bare tungsten wires, four cells in parallel; 4-W-2 filaments consist of two helical wires in series in each cell; 2-GBT are two nominal 8,000-Ω glass bead thermistors on platinum support. (Courtesy of Gow-Mac Instrument Company.)

wires. In the hot-wire cell, filaments are straight or helical bare wires which are stretched along the axis of a metal cavity, as shown in Fig. 18-1. The wire is

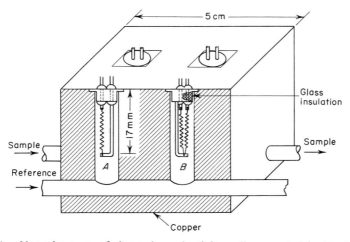

Fig. 18-1. Hot-wire type of thermal conductivity cells mounted in blocks. Shown in detail are (*A*) a single-filament unit and (*B*) a double-filament unit. (Courtesy of Gow-Mac Instrument Co.)

kept under tension by platinum-iridium springs—essential because the length changes with temperature. Filaments are fabricated from some metal or alloy with a high temperature-coefficient of resistance, such as platinum, Kovar (alloy of Co, Ni, and Fe), or tungsten.

What is measured is the difference in thermal conductivity between the reference (carrier) gas and the reference gas diluted with sample. Usually four thermal conductivity cells, mounted in a cell block, are connected to form the arms of a Wheatstone bridge. The electrical circuitry is shown in Fig. 18-2. One lead from a low-voltage, d-c power supply is connected to the

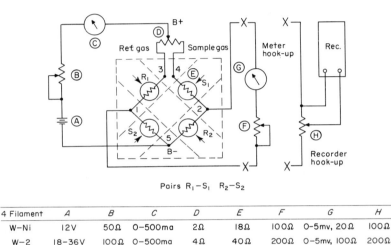

Pairs R_1-S_1 R_2-S_2

4 Filament	A	B	C	D	E	F	G	H
W–Ni	12V	50Ω	0–500ma	2Ω	18Ω	100Ω	0–5mv, 20Ω	100Ω
W–2	18–36V	100Ω	0–500ma	4Ω	40Ω	200Ω	0–5mv, 100Ω	200Ω

Fig. 18-2.   Circuitry for four-filament, hot-wire, thermal conductivity cell. (Courtesy of Gow-Mac Instrument Co.)

Wheatstone bridge through a resistance for adjusting the heating current, which is read off the indicating milliammeter. The other lead goes to the contactor of a 2-Ω potentiometer which serves for a precise balancing of the bridge when reference gas is flowing through all cells. A parallel arrangement of four cells gives better compensation for temperature and power supply variations and permits axial wires to be slightly different in length and diameter. Two filaments in opposite arms of the bridge are surrounded by the reference gas, which conducts away heat generated by the current. The temperature of the filaments will rise until the rate of heat flow away from the filament to the metal block matches the heat generated by the current in the hot-wire resistance element. Similarly, the other two filaments are surrounded by the sample gas. The temperature gradient depends upon the thermal conductivity of the gas surrounding the hot wire and the temperature of the wire. As the wire is cooled by the gas stream it assumes a definite resistance: the higher the thermal conductivity of the gas, the lower the resistance of the wire, and vice versa. The greater the difference in thermal conductivities of the reference and sample gas, the greater the unbalance of the Wheatstone bridge. The extent of the unbalance may be measured by a galvanometer or a high-impedance potentiometer-type recorder. It is possible to make the thermal conductivity method either continuously recording, or controlling, or both.

The internal design of the cell varies with the intended use. For fast response, as in gas chromatography, the filaments should be placed directly in the gas stream. This, however, results in an undesirable sensitivity to flow and pressure changes, so a compromise is effected by bypassing only a fraction of the gas stream directly through the cell (see Fig. 18-3), whereas in the design

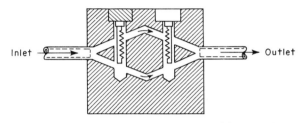

Fig. 18-3. Bypass design of hot-wire thermal conductivity cell for rapid response. (Courtesy of Gow-Mac Instrument Co.)

shown in Fig. 18-1, the gas reaches the measuring filament by diffusion. Equilibrium is attained in 30–60 sec. This cell design is independent of pressure when the pressure is high enough to make the mean free paths of the molecules very small fractions of the distance between the confining walls.

The sensitivity of the detector may be raised by fabricating two helical wires in series or increasing the temperature of the heated wires. However, a temperature limit is imposed by the glowing point of the heated wire and also by the sensitivity to decomposition of the gaseous components.

Thermistor Cells

The hot wires may be replaced with thermistors. These are electronic semiconductors of fused metal oxides whose electrical resistance varies with temperature and lies between that of conductors and insulators. Thermistors are extremely sensitive to relatively minute temperature changes because they possess a large negative temperature coefficient. A thermistor in bead form encapsulated in glass may replace the hot wire in thermal conductivity cells.

The electrical circuit for use with thermistor cells is shown in Fig. 18-4; it differs only in recognizing the larger resistance of a thermistor as compared with a resistance wire. The sensitivities of a 4-W-2 hot wire assembly (see Table 18-1, footnotes) and a thermistor cell are comparable when the cell block

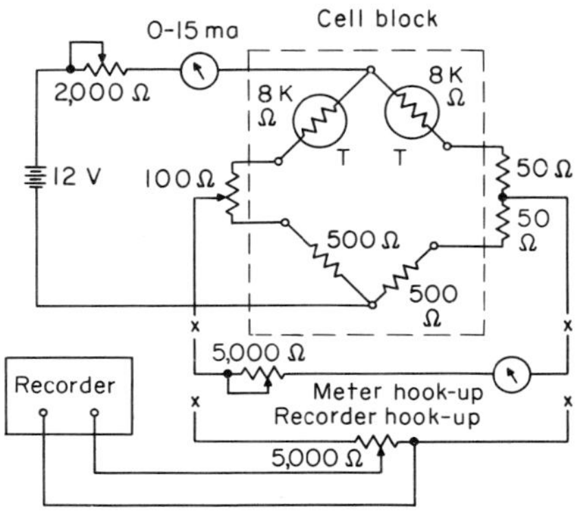

Fig. 18-4. Circuitry for thermal conductivity bridge with thermistors as sensing cells. (Courtesy of Gow-Mac Instrument Co.)

is near room temperature. The thermistor has the advantage of smaller cell volume, but this is offset by the thermal inertia of the thermistor cell and decreased sensitivity when the cell block is maintained at elevated temperatures.

Applications

In most applications of thermal conductivity, the instrument has to be engineered for the particular application. To aid in evaluating the method and developing sampling systems, the Gow-Mac Instrument Company offers a series of compact, self-contained units.

The thermal conductivity method is easily applied to the determination of the composition of a binary mixture, provided that the two gases have different thermal conductivities. An example is oxygen in electrolytic hydrogen or nitrogen in helium in the latter stages of separation from natural gas. A multicomponent mixture can be treated as a binary mixture if all components but one remain constant, as, for example, the determination of hydrogen in uncarburated water gas from which carbon dioxide and steam have been removed leaving only nitrogen and carbon monoxide. Similarly, if all components of the mixture other than the one being measured vary in the same ratio to each other, an analysis is possible. Helium, methane, or carbon dioxide in air are examples. However, temperature coefficients are important in some mixtures because the difference between certain pairs of gases may reverse its sign as the temperature changes—for example, ammonia with air or nitrogen, water with air, and butane with air. Sometimes the proportion of constituents other than the test substance are related to an equilibrium. An example is the relationship among hydrogen, carbon dioxide, carbon monoxide and air in exhaust gases of combustion engines which permits the air/fuel ratio to be determined.

Example 18-1

The feasibility of the thermal conductivity method for a particular system can be estimated from the information in Table 18-1, columns 4–6, and by reference to Fig. 18-5. In many cases a small segment of the curve, such as 0–1 percent H_2 in O_2, is virtually linear.

The approximate bridge output (for four tungsten, W-2, filaments which consist of two helical bare wires in series in each cell) is 1.35 mV for pure oxygen and 84.0 mV for pure hydrogen. Assuming for the moment that over the 0–100 percent range the response is linear, contrary to information in Fig. 18-5, the bridge output will vary from 1.35 mV to

$$(0.01)(84.0) + (0.99)(1.35) = 2.16 \text{ mV}$$

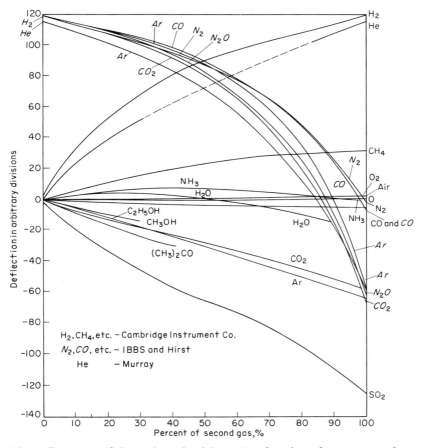

Fig. 18-5. Response of thermal conductivity cell as function of percentage of second gas in air or in hydrogen or helium. (Courtesy of Gow-Mac Instrument Co.)

for 1% H_2 in O_2, a span of 0.81 mV. On a 2-mV potentiometric recorder, with zero suppression to place the reading for pure oxygen at zero, the sensitivity would be $\pm 0.012\%$ H_2 per 1 percent full-scale deflection, equivalent to a sensitivity of ± 120 ppm. Actually, the slope of the hydrogen response curve from 0–10 percent is approximately 10-fold greater, which would make the sensitivity $\pm 0.0012\%$ H_2 (± 12 ppm) per 1 percent full scale deflection. A slight improvement would result from the use of a thermistor bridge.

In the foregoing examples, the reference gas is often sealed in the reference arms of the Wheatstone bridge. Usually only a limited range over which linearity can be assumed is needed for the particular process control.

Frequently a constituent may be removed by some chemical means and the thermal conductivity of the unaltered gas sample is compared with the conductivity of the treated gas sample. The unaltered gas sample is passed through the sample cells, through a chemical reagent or adsorbent, and then through the reference arms of the bridge. The procedure can be continued with another pair of thermal conductivity cells, ad infinitum, until all the components are determined. For example, the use of copper oxide at elevated temperatures removes carbon monoxide and hydrogen, whereas passage over Hopcalite catalyst* removes only carbon monoxide. Methane can be burned to carbon dioxide and water, and the products removed by adsorption.

Gas Density

At constant temperature and pressure one mole of any pure, ideal gas will occupy the same volume as one mole of any other ideal gas. Consequently, the density of an ideal gas is a direct linear function of the molecular weight of that gas. Although this is strictly true only for ideal gases, nearly all real gases behave as ideal gases at temperatures near room temperature and pressures near atmospheric. Two designs of the gas-density detector are in commercial use: the original Martin[2] design and the recent Nerheim[3] design. Both function on the same basic operational principles but differ in sensing elements, configuration, and simplicity.

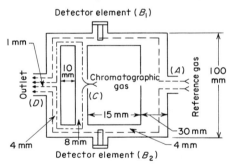

Fig. 18-6. Nerheim gas-density balance. Schematic view as mounted in a vertical plane. (Courtesy of Gow-Mac Instrument Co.)

Detector Elements

The Nerheim configuration, Fig. 18-6, illustrates the principle of operation. With the conduit network mounted vertically, the reference (carrier) gas enters at A, splits into two streams, and exits at D. Two flowmeters, B_1, B_2, are installed, one in each stream, and are wired in a Wheatstone bridge. When the flow is balanced, the detector elements, which are a matched pair, are equally cooled and the bridge is balanced, thus giving a base-line (zero) trace. The detector elements may be either hot wires or thermistors, depending upon the desired operating temperature. These are connected via an electrical bridge to a recording potentiometer (Fig. 18-7). The sample gas (or effluent from a chromatographic column) enters at C, splits into two streams, mixes with the reference gas in the horizontal conduits, and exits at D. The sample gas never comes into contact with the detector elements, thus avoiding problems caused by corrosion or carbonization.

*A mixture of Ag_2O, Co_3O_4, and MnO_2.

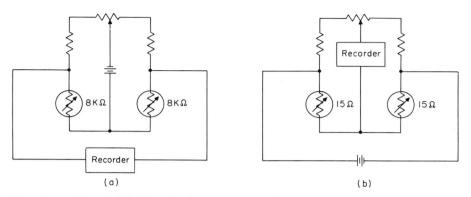

Fig. 18-7. Electrical bridges for flowmeter in gas-density balance. (a) Parallel bridge for thermistors and (b) series bridge for filaments. After A. G. Nerheim, *Anal. Chem.*, **35**, 1640 (1963). (Courtesy of *Analytical Chemistry*.)

If the sample gas is of the same density as the reference, there will be no unbalance of reference streams or of the detector elements. When the sample gas carries transient trace impurities which are heavier than the reference gas, the density of the heavier molecules will cause a net downward flow, partially obstructing the flow $A–B_2–D$, with a temperature rise of element B_2, and permitting a corresponding increase in the flow $A–B_1–D$, with a temperature decrease of element B_1. In a similar manner, lighter molecules will cause a net upward flow and the reverse will be true, namely, a temperature rise of element B_1 and decrease of element B_2 with a signal of opposite polarity from the first case. Bridge unbalance is linear over a broad range and directly related to the gas density difference. Calibration for individual components is eliminated because the response depends on a predictable relationship—the difference in molecular weight of component and reference gas:

$$\Delta\rho = k\frac{n_s(M_s - M_r)P}{RT} \tag{18-1}$$

where k is a constant whose value depends on cell geometry, viscosity, the flow measuring system, and the thermal conductivity of the gases; M_s and M_r are the molecular weights of the sample and reference gases; and n_s is the mole fraction of component in the sample.

The sensitivity of the gas density detector with thermistor sensor is comparable to that of a thermistor type of thermal-conductivity cell, and requires no amplification at room temperature. The hot-wire sensor, which is one-sixth the sensitivity of thermistors at 25°, may require low-level amplification at 100°C. The low noise level of the detectors permits effective use to 300°C, although the sensitivity decreases rapidly with increasing temperature for thermistors, being at 250° one-fifth that at 50°C. The Nerheim design has an effective sample volume of approximately 5 ml, making it suitable for all applications except operations in gas chromatography with a Golay column and efficient high-speed packed columns. Commercial units of the gas-density detector have been licensed to the Gow-Mac Instrument Co., Inc. These units have interchangeable flowmeters and may be operated to 300°C.

The Ranarex specific-gravity indicator operates on an interesting principle. The gas is given a rotating motion by means of an impeller fan. This fan drives the gas against the blades of an impulse wheel, producing a torque. The greater the density of the gas, the greater the coupling between the two wheels and the greater the torque produced on the second wheel. In order to eliminate changes in fan speed, temperature, humidity, and atmospheric pressure, a comparing set of wheels is used with air as the reference gas. The two fan wheels are run by the same motor but in opposite directions. The two torque wheels are mechanically coupled to each other, and the difference in torque is registered on a dial. The dials may be calibrated directly in percentage of constituent sought or in specific gravity units. Automatic recording and control can be provided for, if desired. The principle and design of this device are further illustrated in Fig. 18-8.

Heat of Combustion

The heat of reaction evolved by a gas when it burns at a filament or in the presence of a catalyst can be used to determine combustible gases in a mixture. One device used for the detection of explosive gas mixtures is quite similar in construction to the thermal-conductivity apparatus. The gas is passed through a cell containing a heated filament. The combustion of the gas raises the temperature and the resistance of the filament as compared to that of a reference filament. The reference and active filaments form two arms of a Wheatstone bridge circuit. The degree of unbalance of the bridge furnishes a measure of the concentration of combustible gas. The scales can be calibrated directly in percentage of alcohol, ether, methane, carbon monoxide, or other combustible gas.

Another type of instrument measures the increase in temperature as the combustible gas is burned in contact with a catalyst. The gas is drawn in by a motor through a flowmeter to insure a constant rate of flow. The sample passes through a dehydrating agent to remove water vapor and finally through a bed of "Hopcalite" catalyst, which promotes the oxidation of the carbon monoxide to carbon dioxide. The heat liberated by this oxidation is proportional to the concentration of carbon monoxide. Two thermocouples—one in the incoming gas stream and one imbedded in the catalyst—are used to measure the heat evolved. Such instruments are very sensitive. The range for carbon monoxide is 0–0.15 percent. The recorder scale can be calibrated to 0.005 percent and can be estimated to 0.001 percent.

Follow the 5 points for explanation of principle

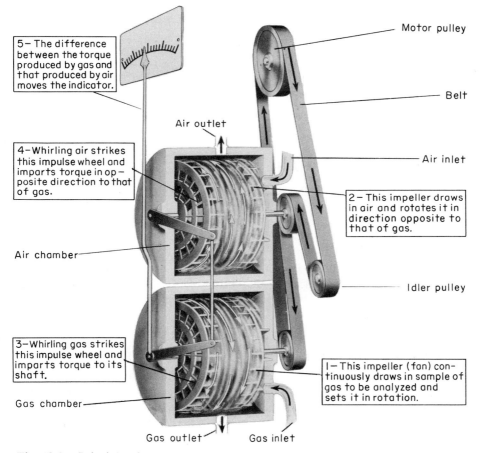

5− The difference between the torque produced by gas and that produced by air moves the indicator.

Motor pulley

Belt

Air outlet

Air inlet

4−Whirling air strikes this impulse wheel and imparts torque in op− posite direction to that of gas.

2− This impeller draws in air and rotates it in direction opposite to that of gas.

Air chamber

Idler pulley

3−Whirling gas strikes this impulse wheel and imparts torque to its shaft.

1− This impeller (fan) con− tinuously draws in sample of gas to be analyzed and sets it in rotation.

Gas chamber

Gas outlet   Gas inlet

Fig. 18-8. Principle of the Ranarex specific gravity indicator. (Courtesy of Permutit Co.)

Velocity of Sound in Gases

The velocity of sound in a gas is given by the following equation:

$$v = \sqrt{\frac{\gamma P}{\rho}} \tag{18-2}$$

where v is velocity, P is pressure, ρ is density, and $\gamma = C_p/C_v$, the ratio of the specific heats at constant pressure and constant volume. The ratio of the specific heats, γ, depends somewhat on the nature of the gas, being 1.67 for a monatomic gas, 1.40 for diatomic gases, 1.33 for triatomic gases, and approaches 1.0 for polyatomic gases. This is not a great variation, and for most gases or gas mixture γ can be assumed to be essentially a constant. If we substitute in Eq. 18-2

$$\frac{nM}{V} = \rho \qquad (18\text{-}3)$$

where n is number of moles, M is molecular weight, and V is volume, we obtain the following relationships:

$$v = \sqrt{\frac{\gamma PV}{nM}} \qquad (18\text{-}4)$$

or since

$$PV = nRT = nK$$

where $K = $ a constant, if T remains constant,

$$v = \sqrt{\frac{\gamma K}{M}} \qquad (18\text{-}5)$$

Thus the velocity of sound in a gas is practically proportional, at constant temperature, to the reciprocal of the square root of the molecular weight. The molecular weight must be interpreted as the average molecular weight for a gaseous mixture.

Magnetic Susceptibility

Oxygen, nitric oxide, and nitrogen dioxide are unique among the ordinary gases in that they are paramagnetic; that is, they are attracted into a magnetic field. Most gases are slightly diamagnetic—repelled out of a magnetic field. Oxygen is several times more paramagnetic than nitric oxide or nitrogen dioxide. The values of the volume susceptibilities are 146.6, 65.2, and 4.3×10^{-9}, respectively. Advantage is taken of this property of oxygen in gaseous oxygen analyzers.

Gaseous oxygen is measured on the basis of change in magnetic force acting on a test body suspended in a nonuniform magnetic field when the test body is surrounded by the gas sample. The Beckman paramagnetic oxygen analyzer (Fig. 18-9) incorporates a small glass dumbbell suspended on a taut quartz fiber in a nonuniform magnetic field. When no oxygen is present, the magnetic forces exactly balance the torque of the fiber. However, when a sample containing oxygen is drawn into the chamber surrounding the dumbbell, the magnetic force is altered causing the dumbbell spheres to rotate away from the region of maximum magnetic flux density. The degree of rotation is proportional to the partial pressure of oxygen in the sample. A small mirror attached to, and rotating with, the dumbbell throws a beam of light on a translucent scale of the instrument. The scale is calibrated in concentration of oxygen present. Instruments are capable of sampling static or flowing gas samples, free of solids or liquids.

Areas of application include oxygen absorption studies on plants and tissues, respiratory studies, anesthesiology, air pollution studies, food processing, and flue gas analysis. Instruments are calibrated for the span and range desired, with the reference gas specified. With a span of 5 percent oxygen full scale, an accuracy of ±0.05 percent oxygen can be achieved. Standard cell volume is

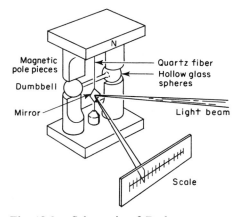

Fig. 18-9. Schematic of Beckman paramagnetic oxygen analyzer. (Courtesy of Beckman Instruments, Inc.)

8–10 ml, although for static samples a 3-ml cell volume is possible. Response time is about 10 sec.

The instrument marketed by the Hays Corporation, and shown in Fig. 18-10 utilizes the magnetic properties of oxygen along with thermal conductivity for the measurement of oxygen in a gas. The gas sample is passed across the bottom of a gas cell containing an electrically heated hot wire.

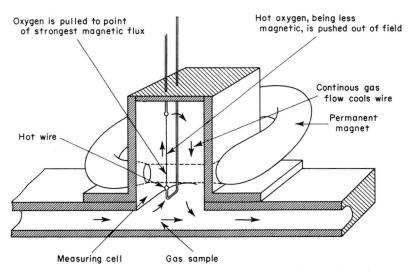

Fig. 18-10. Schematic of Hays Magno-Therm oxygen recorder: schematic operation of analyzing cell. (Courtesy of Hays Corporation)

A strong magnetic flux from a permanent magnet is directed across the wire. The oxygen is pulled into the region around the hot wire by the magnetic flux and is heated by the wire. Oxygen loses its magnetic susceptibility in inverse proportion to the square of the absolute temperature, and therefore the heated, relatively demagnetized gas is continually displaced by the cooler, more magnetic oxygen moving in from below. A flow of gas proportional to the amount of oxygen present is set up around the hot wire. The hot wire is cooled, and its resistance is thereby decreased. The resistance of the wire in the analysis cell is compared with the resistance of a similar wire in a comparison cell by means of a Wheatstone bridge circuit. The comparison cell contains the same sample of gas as the measuring cell but does not have a magnetic flux around the wire. Thus all variables except the cooling due to the oxygen present are canceled. The zero setting of the instrument is checked by swinging the magnet away from the measuring cell without interrupting the gas flow. The overall accuracy of the instrument is claimed to be ± 0.25 percent oxygen up to 20 percent and ± 2.5 percent of range up to 100 percent.

LABORATORY WORK

E X P E R I M E N T   1 8 - 1   DETERMINATION OF CARBON DIOXIDE IN AIR BY THE THERMAL-CONDUCTIVITY METHOD

A determination of the percentage of carbon dioxide in air will be used as an example of the thermal-conductivity method. Dry air is used as the reference standard, although wet air could be used equally well. Carbon dioxide has a lower thermal conductivity than air. Since the composition of the air remains constant, the carbon dioxide–air mixture will be treated as a binary mixture.

Gas-handling system. A convenient and simple gas-handling system can be constructed from a gas buret and a large, round-bottomed flask (for example, 1-liter capacity). Place a two-hole stopper in the flask and fit one hole with a capillary stopcock reaching to the bottom of the flask. Fit the second hole with a capillary stopcock reaching just below the stopper. Measure the volume of the flask up to the stopper by filling with water and pouring into a graduated cylinder.

A gas sample is prepared by first flushing the flask with carbon dioxide–free air, evacuating the flask slightly with a water pump, and admitting from the gas buret a measured volume of carbon dioxide through the short stopcock. The stopcock is opened momentarily to the air through a soda-lime tube to equalize the pressure. The gas sample is forced through the analysis cells by admitting through the long stopcock a retaining liquid such as mercury or a saturated salt solution containing a few drops of hydrochloric acid per liter.

PROCEDURE
1. Connect the parts as indicated in Fig. 18-2 or 18-4.
2. Fill the capped tube for the reference cells with a drying agent, such as magnesium perchlorate, silica gel, or Drierite (do not use calcium chloride). Insert a small plug of glass wool and screw the free end into the reference cell outlet. Close the other end of the reference cell outlet with the plug provided with the unit.
3. Adjust the current to the recommended value for the unit employed by adjusting the variable resistances. Maintain this current throughout the experiment.

4. A drying tube containing the same desiccant as was sealed into the reference cells should be placed before the analysis cells.

5. Pass dry air slowly through the analysis cells and adjust the resistor at the end of the Wheatstone bridge (the $2-4-\Omega$ resistor) until a balance is obtained. Balance is indicated by a zero potential reading on the potentiometer.

6. Synthesize a sample containing about 1 percent carbon dioxide by volume and pass it slowly through the analysis cells. If only a small sample is available, the sample may be trapped in a balloon or in a gas-absorption pipet and returned through the cells. Measure the off-balance potential on the potentiometer when equilibrium is reached.

7. Synthesize several other carbon dioxide–air mixtures containing up to about 10 percent of carbon dioxide, and measure the corresponding potentials on the potentiometer.

8. Plot the potential against concentration of carbon dioxide.

9. Obtain an unknown sample and measure the potential of the bridge when the unknown is passed through the analysis cells. Determine the percentage of carbon dioxide from the calibration curve for the instrument.

EXPERIMENT 18-2   ANALYSIS OF A BINARY LIQUID MIXTURE BY THE
                    THERMAL-CONDUCTIVITY METHOD

Linde and Rogers[1] have described a method of analyzing gaseous mixtures resulting from the passage of an inert "carrier" gas through a volatile liquid or liquid mixtures. Binary liquid mixtures of different compositions are easily prepared for use in making calibration curves and as unknowns.

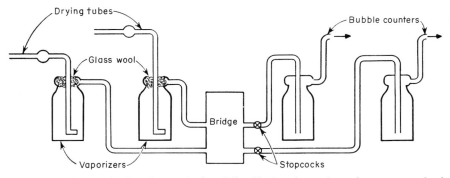

Fig. 18-11. Gas train for the analysis of liquids by thermal-conductance method.

Gas-handling system. Figure 18-11 shows a simple gas-handling train, which consists of two drying tubes on the gas-train inlets, four 125-ml (or larger) gas-washing bottles (two preferably fitted with fritted dispersion disks), the thermal conductance bridge whose wiring diagram appears in Fig. 18-2, and two glass stopcocks to control the flow rates. The vaporization gas-washing bottles have glass wool in their necks to catch any liquid droplets. The latter two bubble counters are for gauging the rate of flow. To prevent supercooling of the liquid undergoing vaporization it is well to immerse the two vaporizer washing bottles in a large container filled with water. The source of the carrier gas can be a compressed-air line, a nitrogen or oxygen tank, a helium tank, or room air drawn through the system by means of a vacuum line or an aspirator. Some arrangement should be made to vent the fumes from the gas outlets.

Table 18-2 lists the unbalance produced by vapors obtained from pure liquids at about 25°C. with a hot-wire thermal-conductance unit. The reference gas was either dried air or nitrogen. The algebraic difference between any two of these liquids will serve as an indication of the order of magnitude of the sensitivity which could be expected if the two were used to prepare a series of binary mixtures. Water-acetone mixtures or methyl alcohol paired with either acetone or benzene produce satisfactory binary mixtures.

Table 18-2	*Relative Unbalance Produced by Vapors Obtained from Pure Liquids at About 25°C*

COMPOUND	UNBALANCE, MILLIVOLTS	CARRIER GAS
Water	16.4	Dried air
	15.0	Nitrogen
Methanol	3.5	Nitrogen
Acetone	-60	Nitrogen
Benzene	-57	Dried air
n-Butanol	-1.6	Dried air

PROCEDURE

1. Assemble the gas-handling train, Fig. 18-11, and the thermal-conductance bridge, Fig. 18-2 or 18-4.

2. Place one of the two liquids assigned as your binary system into both vaporizer washing bottles. Adjust the carrier-gas flow rate at about 3–6 bubbles per second and a head of water of about 2 in. in the bubble counters.

3. Turn on the current to the bridge and adjust the current through the circuit to the recommended value for the unit employed. Maintain this current throughout the experiment.

4. After the bridge is allowed to warm up for 15 min, it is brought to an approximate balance by adjusting the 2-Ω radio-type potentiometer. The balance of the bridge is checked at approximately 5-min intervals. After about 15 min or when the changes in balance have become less than 0.5 mV/min (or 1 μa/min) the bridge is assumed to have reached equilibrium.

5. Prepare a series of standard mixtures containing 10, 20, 30, and 40 volume percent of one component. Large 100-ml burets are convenient measuring instruments for the two liquids.

6. Remove the pure liquid from one of the vaporizer bottles, rinse with the 10 percent v/v mixture, and add the 10 percent mixture until its height equals the liquid in the other vaporizer, now chosen to be the pure base component of the binary mixtures. Readings are taken until a constant value is reached. A period of about 10–15 min is usually required, depending upon the volatility of the components.

7. Repeat the preceding step with each of the remaining standard samples, and then with the unknown mixture. Plot the results in the form of a graph, interpolate to find the unknown concentration, and report the result.

8. To determine the maximum sensitivity of the thermal-conductance method, prepare a second series of standards which lie within one of the preceding 10 percent

intervals—e.g., a series of solutions containing now 10, 12, 14, 16, 18, and 20 volume percent of the variable component. Repeat steps 6 and 7.

Notes. Methyl alcohol-acetone mixtures do not have quite as high a sensitivity as water-acetone mixtures, but equilibrium is attained more rapidly. It matters little which component is considered the base material, although the discrimination is better for smaller volume percentages of the component with the higher molecular weight (acetone or benzene) in mixtures.

Problems

1. Design a thermal conductance circuit for handling these product gases:
   (a) Automobile carburetors—10%–15% CO_2 in air (plus CO.)
   (b) Ammonia synthesis; 70%–80% H_2 in N_2 plus NH_3.
   (c) Electrolytic H_2 with O_2 plus N_2 impurities (0%–0.4%).
   (d) Carbon dioxide (0%–10%) in air.
   (e) Hydrogen (0%–0.2%) impurity in electrolytic oxygen.
   (f) Methane (0%–5%) in air.

2. For each mixture in Problem 1, compute the bridge output when using four tungsten filaments and a 2-mV recorder. Estimate the sensitivity per 1 percent full-chart deflection.

3. Design a system for the continuous analysis of CO_2 and H_2 in a stream consisting of 34% CO_2, 15% CO, 40% H_2, 10% CH_4, and 1% N_2.

4. Calculate the ratio of the velocity of sound in air to that in helium at STP.

5. Compare the gas analysis methods described in this chapter, and also methods described in other chapters, as to sensitivity, selectivity, time required for analysis, applicability to continuous analysis in process streams, and level of operator's skill.

Bibliography

Daynes, H. A., *Gas Analysis by Measurement of Thermal Conductance*, Cambridge U. P., New York, 1933.

Weaver, E. R., in W. G. Berl (Ed.), *Physical Methods in Chemical Analysis*, Vol. II, pp. 387–437, Academic Press, New York, 1951.

Literature Cited

1. Linde, H. W., and L. B. Rogers, *J. Chem. Educ.*, **28**, 576–577 (1951).
2. Martin, A. J. P., and A. T. Jones, *Biochem. J.*, **63**, 138 (1956).
3. Nerheim, A. G., *Anal. Chem.*, **35**, 1640 (1963).

C H A P T E R | 19

Gas Chromatography

Chromatography is a physical method for separating components in a mixture. The basis of the method lies within the separation column, which normally is a small-diameter tubing packed with a stationary bed of large surface area. A mobile phase percolates through the stationary bed. The name "gas chromatography" denotes that the moving phase is a gas. "Gas-solid chromatography" is the specific term applied to the process when the stationary phase is an active solid adsorbent. "Gas-liquid partition chromatography" has, as a stationary phase, a liquid distributed over the surface of a solid support.

The basic processes responsible for separations by gas-solid and gas-liquid chromatography are adsorption and partition, respectively. The latter is more popular. Although separations may be performed by elution, frontal, and displacement analyses, in practice, the elution technique is the most common and the only one considered henceforth.

In the elution method of gas chromatography, a stream of carrier gas flows through the column. A sample is injected into the carrier gas as a "plug" of vapor which is swept into the head of the packed chromatographic column. Separation of components that comprise the sample results from a difference in the multiple forces by which the column materials tend to retain each of the components. Whether the nature of retention is adsorption, solubility, chemical bonding, polarity, or molecular filtration, the column retains some components longer than others. When in the gas phase the components are moved toward the column outlet, but they are selectively retarded by the stationary phase. Consequently, all components pass through the column at varying speeds and emerge in the inverse order of their retention by the column materials. The process is outlined schematically in Fig. 19-1.

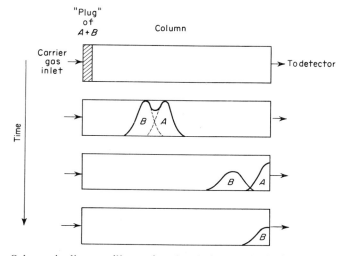

Fig. 19-1. Schematic diagram illustrating the elution method of gas chromatography.

Upon emerging from the column, the gaseous phase immediately enters a detector attached to the column. Here the individual components register a series of signals which appear as a succession of peaks above a base line on the recorded curve, or chromatogram. A typical chromatogram is shown in Fig. 19-2. The area under the peak is a quantitative indication of the component; the time lapse between injection and emergence of the peak serves to

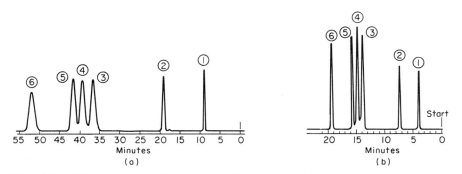

Fig. 19-2. Chromatogram of a mixture of aromatics: (a) Four-meter ($\frac{1}{4}$-in.) packed column with 20% 7, 8-benzoquinoline as stationary phase. Temperature 100°C. (b) 30-meter (0.25 mm) Golay column coated with 7, 8-benzoquinoline. Temperature 86°C. Sample components: 1 benzene, 2 toluene, 3 ethyl benzene, 4 *para*-, 5 *meta*-, and 6 *ortho*-xylene. (Courtesy of Perkin-Elmer Corp.)

identify it. A significant advantage of the elution technique is the self-purging feature in which the column is returned usually to its original condition at the end of each analysis.

Gas Chromatographs

Basically, all laboratory gas chromatographs consist of six parts: (1) the pressure regulator and flow meter for the carrier gas supply, (2) a sample injection system, (3) the separation column, (4) the thermal compartment, (5) the detection system, and (6) strip-chart recorder or other device for indicating the output of the detector. For some purposes, a carrier-gas purifier and collection system for effluent gas are included. The components

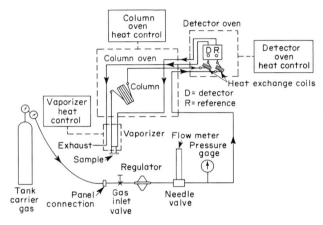

Fig. 19-3. Schematic of a gas chromatograph.

are shown schematically in Fig. 19-3. In the following sections each of these parts is discussed in some detail.

Pressure Regulator and Flow Meter

Operating efficiency of a chromatograph is directly dependent on the maintenance of a highly constant carrier gas flow rate. Carrier gas from the tank passes through a toggle valve, a flowmeter, a few feet of metal capillary restrictors, and 0–4 atm pressure gauge. The flowmeter, with a range of 0–200 ml/min, indicates flow rate in the reference side of the thermal conductivity cell. Flow rate is adjustable at this point by means of a needle valve mounted on the base of the flowmeter and is controlled by the capillary restrictors. On the downstream side of the pressure regulator, a tee may split the flow and direct it to the sample and the reference sides of the detector.

Contaminants in the carrier gas may affect column performance and detector response when ionization detectors are used. Inclusion of a trap containing a molecular sieve 5A is usually sufficient for removal of hydrocarbon gases and water vapor; for measurements requiring extreme sensitivity a trap at $-180°C$ in a bath of liquid nitrogen may be used. Ultrapure H_2 for use in flame ionization devices can be generated by the Serfass apparatus, commercially available.

One can minimize contamination by desorption of gases from surfaces of the apparatus, or by diffusion through walls of connecting tubing, by using shortest possible connecting tubing, taking scrupulous care to avoid leaks, and whenever possible using polytetrafluoroethylene.

Sample Injection System

The most exacting problem in gas chromatography is presented by the sample injection system. This deceptively simple little device must introduce the sample in a reproducible manner and, if a liquid, vaporize it instantaneously. Tremendous amounts of heats are required—yet the sample must not be decomposed nor pressure surges created. A precise amount of sample has to be metered and transferred to the column without fractionation, condensation, or adsorption of components.

Liquid samples are injected by hypodermic syringes through a self-sealing, silicon rubber septum (compressed by means of a threaded nut) into a heated metal block—flash evaporator. A typical arrangement is shown in Fig. 19-4. The metal block which encloses the capillary is heated by a controlled resistance heater. Here the sample is vaporized as a "plug" and carried into the column by the carrier gas. Every effort should be made to get the needle tip close to the packing or well down into the heated block ahead of the column. The manipulation of the syringe is virtually an art developed with practice. Insertion, injection, and removal of the needle should be performed quickly. For maximum efficiency one should use the smallest possible sample consistent with detector sensitivity—$1-10 \mu l$.

Solids are dissolved in volatile liquids, or temporarily liquefied by exposure to infrared heat. Pyrolysis offers a technique for certain types of materials.

Gas samples are injected by a gas-tight syringe or gas-sampling valve, called a *stream splitter*. In the simplest form this is merely a glass system of three stopcocks, between two of which there is a standard volume in which gas is trapped. Gas from this bypass capillary loop is introduced into the column by sliding or rotating a valve to connect the loop with the stream of carrier gas. A stream splitter serves also to obtain minute ($<0.01 \mu l$) liquid samples for capillary columns and small-bore packed columns. The liquid sample is introduced by standard techniques, vaporized, and mixed with the carrier gas, and then the gas flow is divided before entering the column. The stream splitter must be highly nondiscriminatory and separate each component of the sample mixture in exactly the same ratio.

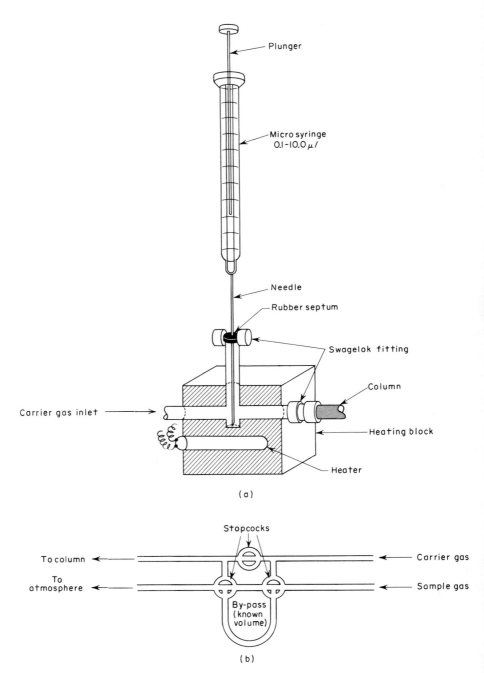

Fig. 19-4.   Sample inlet systems. (a) Hypodermic needle syringe and heater block for liquids;   (b) gas sample introduction.

Chromatographic Column

The heart of the chromatograph is the column—packed or capillary—in which the separation is effected. The packed column is commonly 4-mm (i.d.) tubing of stainless steel, copper, cupronickel, or glass, either bent in a U-shape or coiled. Lengths run anywhere from 120 cm to 150 m. Connections are made with Swagelok fittings, making it easy to install the proper column for each separation desired.

Among the variety of solid supports available, those derived from diatomaceous earth are most popular. The latter is prepared from a calcined diatomaceous earth which has been mixed with a clay binder, baked, crushed, and screened. Trade names include GC-22 Super Support, Sil-O-Cell C-22 Firebrick, and Chromosorb P and W.* Adsorbents such as silica gel, molecular sieves, alumina, and activated charcoal are used as the stationary phase in gas-solid chromatography. The range of particle size should be kept to a minimum, perhaps 60/80, 80/100, or even 100/120 mesh material. If one is attempting to prepare his own column, detailed procedures should be consulted. Columns covering a wide variety of support material and liquid phases are available commercially (Table 19-1). The general requirements of a liquid

Table 19-1 | *Typical Liquid Phases*

SOLVENT	SUITABLE FOR SOLUTE TYPE	UPPER TEMPERATURE LIMIT, °C
Paraffin oil (Nujol)	Paraffin, olefin, halide	150
Squalane	Paraffin, olefin	140
Silicone oils	Paraffin, olefin, ester, ether	200 (M.W. dependent)
Silicone greases	Paraffin, olefin, ester, ether	350
Polyglycols (Carbowaxes, Ucon)	Amine, nitrile, ketone, ester, alcohol, ether, aromatics	100 to 200 (M.W. dependent)
Dinonyl phthalate, diisodecyl phthalate	General for polar types	130 150
β,β'-Oxydipropionitrile	General for polar types and aromatics	<100
Apiezon L grease	General for polar types	300

[In part from S. Dal Nogare and R. S. Juvet, Jr., *Gas-Liquid Chromatography*, Interscience, New York, 1962, page 43.]

phase are (1) good solvent properties for components, (2) differential partitioning of sample components, (3) high thermal stability, and (4) a low vapor pressure at the column temperature. The solvent has been varied from

*Chromosorb W (white) is prepared by calcination with sodium carbonate as a fluxing agent; Chromosorb P (pink, also called R) is calcined without a flux.

about 2 to 30 percent by weight of the stationary phase. Conditioning the column prior to use is necessary to remove any materials which may tend to come off when the packing is first heated for several hours at the maximum temperature of subsequent use.

Although the support material is commonly thought of as being inert and nonactive in the separation process, this is definitely not true. Interaction between the solute and support material becomes increasingly evident as the solutes become more polar, as the weight of liquid phase is decreased, and as the sample size is decreased. Some workers recommend treating the support with a disilazane prior to adding the solvent phase.

Capillary or Golay columns are open tabular columns with inside diameters of 0.25–0.50 mm. Lengths run anywhere from 30 to 300 m. They are coated on the inside with a retentive liquid phase. Columns of this type possess higher efficiency in contrast to standard packed columns. As a result, better separations are obtainable and can be achieved at lower temperatures and in a shorter time. This is an advantage in analyses involving components of widely varying volatilities.

Carrier gas is either nitrogen, helium, hydrogen, or argon. Availability, purity, and the type of detector employed determine the choice. Table 18-1 may be a useful guide in the selection of a carrier gas for a particular analysis when thermal conductivity cells are employed for detection. Helium is preferred for thermal conductivity detectors because of its high thermal conductivity relative to that of most organic vapors, but it is expensive and not readily obtainable in some countries. Argon is used with one type of cross-section ionization detector.

Thermal Compartment

Precise control of the column temperature is a requisite, whether it is intended to maintain an invariant temperature or to provide a programmed temperature. Temperature of the column oven should be controlled by a system which is sensitive to changes of 0.01°C and which maintains control to 0.1°C. Usually an air bath chamber surrounds the column and air is circulated by a blower through the thermal compartment. Separate temperature controls are desirable for the vaporizer block and detector oven.

Programs are available which feature linear and nonlinear temperature programming of sample and reference columns. A matched set of sample and reference columns is installed in the thermal compartment. The control system operates by continuously varying the wattage supplied to a proportional heater. Often the program is taped or inked on special Mylar format sheets. Curved rates of temperature rise, linear sections, and isothermal operation can be plotted as required. The format sheet is installed on a rotating drum and the program line is followed by an optical scanner linked to a servo system. The compartment temperature can be raised at various rates up to a maximum of 60°C/min in the lower temperature ranges and about 35°C/min at higher temperatures. Column temperatures, at the completion of a run, must be dropped from about 300° to less than 100°C in a few minutes if the column is to be readied for the next run.

A pyrolyzer accessory (optional on instruments) consists of a flash heater and separate control unit attached to the vaporizer block. Temperatures vary from a few degrees above ambient to 1100°C. Samples are placed directly on, or around, the heating element.

Detectors

The type of column is to some extent a determining factor in the choice of detectors. For packed columns, this will be a hot wire (or thermistor) thermal conductivity cell, gas-density cell, or cross section detector. For capillary columns, it will be an ionization gauge—flame, beta ray, electron capture, or radio frequency. The latter group can also be used for packed columns, if suitably attenuated.

A comparison of detectors is rendered difficult since no one function describes their performance equally. Applicability—discrimination—response time—linear dynamic range—sensitivity—background signal—all these factors must be considered. With exception of the cross-section method, detectors do not respond faithfully to high gas or vapor concentration. Between 0.01 and 1 percent by volume is usually their upper limit of linear dynamic range.

The standard method of detection is accomplished with a thermal conductivity cell (see Chapter 18).[5] Filaments within the cell form a Wheatstone bridge that detects the difference in thermal conductivity between the stream of carrier gas that contains the sample components and reference stream of pure carrier gas before the injection point. This difference in thermal conductivity generates a signal that is amplified to drive a recorder pen to a proportional height on a strip-chart recorder. Large and small components are kept on scale by using a precise attenuator with a multirange selector switch.

The gas-density detector, discussed in Chapter 18, with an effective volume of 5 ml, is suitable for use with packed columns. It is an absolute detector whose quantitative response is predictable from the molecular properties of the gas—true also of the cross-section ionization detector, discussed later in this section.

The fundamental physical process underlying the operation of all ionization detectors is the conduction of electricity by gases. At normal temperatures and pressures a gas behaves as a perfect insulator; if, however, electrically charged atoms, molecules, or free electrons are present, their free motion in the direction of an electrical field renders the gas conducting. In the absence of conduction by the gas molecules themselves, the increased conductivity due to the presence of very few charged molecules can be observed, and this explains the great sensitivity of ionization methods for gas analysis.

The flame ionization detector[4] consists of a stainless steel burner assembly installed in the detector compartment and an electrometer system in a separate unit adjacent to the gas chromatograph. Often it is installed in tandem with the thermal conductivity cell. A schematic view of the detector is shown in Fig. 19-5. The column effluent enters the burner base through millipore

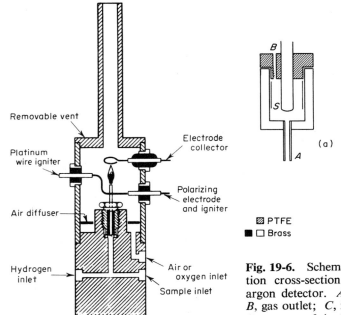

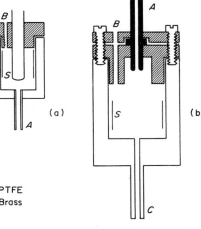

Fig. 19-6. Schematics of (a) an ionization cross-section detector and (b) an argon detector. A, inlet for carrier gas; B, gas outlet; C, inlet for scavenger gas; S, source of ionizing radiation. After J. E. Lovelock, *Anal. Chem.*, **33**, 162 (1961). (Courtesy of *Analytical Chemistry*.)

Fig. 19-5. Schematic diagram of a flame ionization detector. (Courtesy of Beckman Instruments, Inc.)

filters which remove contaminating particles. Hydrogen is mixed with the gas stream at the bottom of the jet and air or oxygen is supplied axially around the jet. The hydrogen flame burns at the tip, perhaps a 20-gauge capillary, which also functions as the cathode and is insulated from the body by a ceramic seal. The collector electrode, located about 6 mm above the burner tip, consists of a loop of platinum. In series with the flame gases is a selection of resistors ranging from 10^7 to 10^{10} Ω. A vibrating reed electrometer is often used as impedance converter to provide sensitivities up to 5×10^{-13} amp. Basically the flame ionization detector is a carbon counting device which produces a current proportional to the number of ions or electrons formed in the flame gases between the burner jet and the collector. It responds to all organic compounds except formic acid. Response is greatest with hydrocarbons and diminishes with increasing substitution of other elements. Apart from vapors of elements in groups I and II of the periodic classification, these being elements ionized in flames (see Chapter 11), it does not respond to inorganic compounds. The linear dynamic range is 10^7. Sensitivity is high because of an inherently low noise level, 10^{-12} amp. Insensitivity to water, the permanent gases, and most inorganic compounds is advantageous as it simplifies the resolution of components in analysis of aqueous extracts and in air pollution studies.

Cross-section ionization detectors accomplish practically all of their ionization by the collision of particles emitted by a disintegrating radioisotope with molecules of gas in the cell. The passage of energetic radiation from a beta emitter, such as Sr^{90}, through a gas in an ionization chamber produces a steady concentration of ion pairs. A potential of 300–1000 V ensures collection of the electrons. In general, the denser polyatomic gases and vapors are more strongly absorbing than a light carrier gas such as hydrogen or helium. When either of these is the carrier gas, other gases and vapors when also present provide an increased current in proportion to their concentration. Other carrier gases can be used but at the expense of some loss of sensitivity compared with hydrogen or helium. A detector is shown in Fig. 19-6, with materials of construction and dimensions indicated. Chamber volume is 0.5–5.0 ml. Cross-section ionization detectors offer the only method capable of measuring gas concentrations up to 100 percent within the detector. Response to any substance can be calculated from the values of the atomic cross sections of its constituent atoms. A disadvantage is its low sensitivity (10^{-7} g/sec).

The argon ionization detector[2] is basically the same in construction as the cross-section ionization detector. However, argon is used as carrier gas. Two reactions are involved in this detector: (1) Electrons are produced by bombardment of argon atoms with beta particles emanating from a foil containing a strontium-90 source. These are accelerated across a potential of about 1000 V and, upon collision with other argon atoms, raise them to the metastable electronic level (11.6 eV). (2) As vapors of molecules emerge from the column and enter the detector through the anode, which is a hollow tube (Fig. 19-6), collisions with the metastable argon atoms usually result in the transfer of energy. Dissociation and ionization will take place since the dissociation and ionization energy of most molecules and atoms is less than 11.6 eV. The body of the ionization chamber is swept with a stream of clean, dry argon. Sensitivity is about 0.08 μg/ml; the linear dynamic range is 10^5. The argon detector does not respond to water vapor, methane, oxygen, carbon dioxide, nitrogen, carbon monoxide, ethane, acetonitrile, or fluorocarbons. It is an ideal detector for quantitative measurements at extreme sensitivity where a rapid response is desired. Performance is seriously impaired by the presence of air or water vapor in the carrier gas.

The electron capture detector,[3] unlike other ionization detectors, measures the loss of signal due to recombination phenomena rather than measuring a positively produced electrical current. As the carrier gas (nitrogen) flows through the detector, beta particles from a tritium source ionize the nitrogen molecules and form "slow" electrons. These slow electrons migrate to the anode under a fixed voltage which can be varied from 10 to 100 V. Collected, these electrons produce a steady (baseline) current. The introduction of an electron-capturing gas or vapor causes a decrease in current flow, the decrease being related to the logarithm of the concentration of the capturer (cf. Beer's law in absorption spectrophotometry). The stream of carrier gas flows in opposition to the motion of the negative ion carriers, thus increasing chances for encountering positive ions and improving the overall detector sensitivity (without impeding the collection of free electrons). The loss of current is a measure of the amount and electron affinity of the components in the carrier gas. The electron capture detector is extremely sensitive to certain molecules, such as organic and inorganic halogen-containing compounds, anhydrides, peroxides, 1,2-diketones, nitrates, ozone, oxygen, and organometallic compounds. Electron affinity is difficult to predict, but it appears to be related to the ease of dissociation of a heteroelement from the compound. Carbon and hydrogen have virtually no affinity for free electrons. Detector discrimination can be regulated through the potential applied to the collector electrode—the response of weakly capturing compounds can be abolished in turn by increasing the applied potential since response for different classes ceases at well-defined applied potentials. Sensitivity is 3×10^{-14} amp; background current is 3×10^{-9} amp. Linear dynamic range is only 10^3, however. An elegant area of application for this detector is analysis of insecticides.

The last type of detector to be discussed involves a corona discharge which is excited at radio frequencies—the r-f detector. The detector consists of a cylindrical metal chamber, about 2.5 cm in length and 3.5 mm in diameter, containing within it a fine wire supported coaxially. Radio frequency energy, derived from a 40-Mc crystal oscillator and power amplifier, is applied to the central wire through a capacitor. The direct-current potential developed across a 500-Ω resistor between this wire and the surrounding metal cylinder is fed directly to a millivolt recorder. The detector operates with helium or neon as carrier gas. The exact basis of operation has not been explained; the rectification, however, of an r-f corona discharge in helium at atmospheric pressure is affected by the presence of other gases in the helium. Sensitivity is less than with the flame or argon ionization detectors, and response is critically sensitive to changes in temperature, requiring care in temperature regulation of the detector housing. Ancilliary equipment is another drawback. The r-f detector would seem to be useful where a general detector of the ionization category is desired and the use of radioactive sources or of hydrogen and flames is thought to be undesirable or hazardous.

Recording of Signal Current

In the area of readout, the choice of recorder determines the ultimate accuracy of the chromatogram. Speed of response should be under one second. All ionization detectors generate some signal in the presence of pure carrier gas. This background current ranges from 10^{-8} to 10^{-11} amp. The maximum signal in the presence of vapor consistent with a linear response is in the range 10^{-6} to 10^{-8} amp. The apparatus for measuring current must be capable of responding faithfully to all currents in the range 10^{-6} to 10^{-13} amp and must have some provision for offsetting the background current of the detector in use. In practice these needs are met by a series of good quality resistances connected across the input of a potentiometric recorder. The background current is offset by a variable potential applied to the base of the resistances.

Where a response time longer than one second is sufficient, vibrating capacitor electrometers are recommended. For rapid measurements in the range of 10^{-3} to 1 sec, a vacuum-tube electrometer is needed. Separate integrators, which can sum the total charge of ions liberated by the presence of the test substance, are useful.

In dual-channel instruments the effluent stream, at column end, is divided by a stream splitter to feed two detectors. The signals from these two detectors are amplified by individual amplifiers which, in turn, drive separate recorders.

Gas Chromatography Theory

Gas chromatography theory cannot be discussed in detail, nor can the complex interactions of all the variables be considered. For details the literature should be consulted. On the other hand, a brief treatment of basic parameters should help in understanding the technique.

Retention Behavior

On a chromatogram the distance from point of sample injection on the time axis to the peak of an eluted component emerging from the column is called the uncorrected retention time, t_R, for the particular component. It is a function of column temperature, T_c, carrier flow rate, F_c, the affinity between sample component and liquid phase comprising the stationary phase, and the weight of the liquid phase. The uncorrected, experimental retention volume, V_R, given by

$$V_R = t_R F_c \qquad (19\text{-}1)$$

is independent of volume flow rate of carrier gas as measured at some point beyond the column at ambient pressure and temperature. Gas flow rate must be converted for subsequent computations to column temperature and outlet pressure. With wet flowmeters allowance must be made for the vapor pressure of water, and with capillary meters for the pressure drop across the capillary.

The air spike, shown in Fig. 19-7, measures the transit time for a nonretained substance such as nitrogen, hydrogen, air, or the rare gases. Converted to

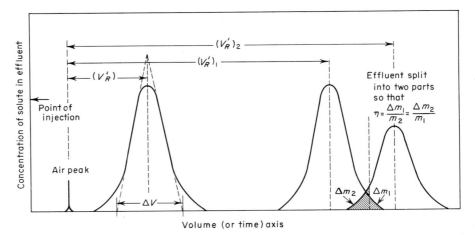

Fig. 19-7. Idealized elution peaks showing notation and method of handling over-lapping bands.

volume, V_{air}, it represents the interstitial volume of gaseous phase in the column, V_M, plus any dead volume in the injection port and detector. Retention volumes measured from the air peak provide an adjusted retention volume, V'_R,

$$V'_R = t_R F_c - t_{air} F_c = V_R - V_{air} \qquad (19\text{-}2)$$

The retention volumes change with amount of sample; consequently, the significant retention volume is one obtained by extrapolation to zero sample size.

The mobile phase is compressible. Since it moves more slowly near the inlet than at the exit of the column, a pressure gradient correction factor j must be applied to the adjusted retention volume to give the net retention volume V_N, namely,

$$V_N = jV'_R \qquad (19\text{-}3)$$

The same correction applied to the experimental retention volume provides the corrected retention volume, V_R^0

$$V^0_R = jV_R \qquad (19\text{-}4)$$

The correction factor is given by the expression

$$j = \frac{3}{2} \frac{[(P_i/P_o)^2 - 1]}{[(P_i/P_o)^3 - 1]} \qquad (19\text{-}5)$$

where P_i is the carrier gas pressure at the inlet to the column, and P_o that at the outlet. This factor stresses the importance of a small pressure drop across the column—achieved by operating the column under high inlet and outlet pressures.

Columns that have high liquid phase loadings will exhibit large retention values. In order to take into account the weight of liquid phase in a column, the specific retention volume, V_g, is defined as

$$V_g = (273/T_c)(V_N/W_L) \qquad (19\text{-}6)$$

where W_L is weight of liquid phase. It corresponds to the volume of carrier gas required to remove half of the solute from a hypothetical column at a specified temperature ($0°C$ unless otherwise specifically stated) which contains one gram of a liquid phase and which has no pressure drop or apparatus dead space.

When the solute enters the column it immediately equilibrates between the solvent phase and the mobile gaseous phase. The concentration (or weight) in each phase is given by the partition coefficient

$$K = C_L/C_M \qquad (19\text{-}7)$$

where C_L, C_M are the concentrations of solute in the solvent phase and gas phase, respectively. For example, when $K = 1$, the solute will distribute itself evenly between the two phases and thus will spend half the time in the gas phase and half the time in the liquid phase, emerging at a retention time equal to twice the retention time of the air peak. If the partition isotherm is linear, the partition coefficient will be a constant independent of the solute concentration. Generally this is true at the low concentration prevailing in gas-liquid chromatography; however, nonideal behavior relative to the mass transfer of solute between the liquid and gaseous phases leads to broadening of the peak and, sometimes, to skewing.

At the appearance of a peak maximum at the column exit, one-half of the solute has eluted in the retention volume V_R, and half remains in the volume of the gaseous phase V_M, plus the volume of the solvent phase V_L at the column temperature. Thus,

$$V_R C_M = V_M C_M + V_L C_L \qquad (19\text{-}8)$$

Rearranging and inserting the partition coefficient, we get

$$V_R = V_M + K V_L \qquad \text{or} \qquad V_R - V_M = V_N = K V_L \qquad (19\text{-}9)$$

provided the compressibility factor j is applied. Retention volumes will be determined by the term $K V_L = K(W_L/\rho_L)$, where W_L is the weight of the liquid phase and ρ_L its density at the temperature of the column. Since the coefficient of cubical expansion of most organic liquids lies between 0.5×10^{-3} and 1.5×10^{-3}, it will usually be adequate to obtain ρ_L by measurement of the density at room temperature and estimation with a coefficient of $10^{-3}/°C$. Now from Eqs. 19-6 and 19-9,

$$K = V_g \rho_L (T_c/273) \qquad (19\text{-}10)$$

A common method of reporting retention information is in the form of relative retention ratio, some solute being chosen as the standard and the retention volumes (or times) of other solutes being given as a ratio of this:

$$\alpha = K_2/K_1 = V_g/(V_g)_s = V'_R/(V'_R)_s \qquad (19\text{-}11)$$

Relative retentions are unaffected by carrier flow rate, pressure gradient, or weight of solvent phase, and for accurate work need be corrected only for dead space, possible effect of variation in the injection temperature, and extrapolation to zero sample load. The procedure is to analyze the sample, the standard component, and also a nonadsorbed gas, under exactly the same experimental conditions. The emergence time, as read from the chart records, of the air peak is subtracted from the emergence time of each of the others. The ratio of the adjusted retention times is then equal to the ratio of the corresponding values of K or V_g, one of which is usually known or can be calculated.

Example 19-1

From experimental observations on a packed column of Celite 545 (65/100 mesh) containing 0.6 ml (1.4 g) of the ethyl ester of Kel-F acid 8114 per gram of Celite, these data were obtained:

> Column length: 1 m, containing 7 g of solvent on 12 g of support.
> Column temperature: 80°C.
> Carrier (nitrogen) gas flow: 72 cc/min at 760 mm and 30°C.
> Interstitial column volume: 21 cc at 760 mm and 30°C.
> Inlet pressure: 1345 mm of mercury.
> Outlet pressure: 760 mm of mercury.
> Dead volume: 3 cc.
> Retention time for $C_8F_{16}O$: 6.59 min.

The carrier flow rate is corrected to column temperature and outlet pressure by the gas law.

$$F_c = 72(353/303) = 83.9 \text{ cc/min}$$

The experimental retention volume is

$$V_R = (6.59)(83.9) = 552 \text{ cc}$$

Correcting for the interstitial volume and the dead volume, the adjusted retention volume is

$$V'_R = (552) - (3) - 21(353/303) = 524 \text{ cc}$$

From Eq. 19-5, the pressure gradient correction factor is calculated from the experimental ratio, $P_i/P_o = 1.77$. The net retention volume is

$$V_N = (0.71)(524) = 372 \text{ cc}$$

and the corrected retention volume is

$$V^0_R = (0.71)(552 - 3) = 392 \text{ cc}$$

To obtain the partition coefficient, the net retention volume is divided by the volume of the column liquid,

$$K = 372/3 = 124$$

and to obtain the specific retention volume, the net retention volume is divided by the weight of the column liquid and multiplied by $273/T_c$

$$V_g = (372/7)(273/353) = 41.1 \text{ cc/g}$$

The partition coefficient is related to the column temperature by the relation

$$K = ae^{\Delta H_s/RT_c} \qquad (19\text{-}12)$$

where ΔH_s is the partial molar heat of solution of solute in the liquid phase. Because ΔH_s is likely to vary in a similar way for closely related compounds, it may be expected that the logarithm of the partition coefficient (or relative retentions) will be approximately a linear function of $1/T_c$ as shown in Fig. 19-8. It is evident that the elution times of individual components can be

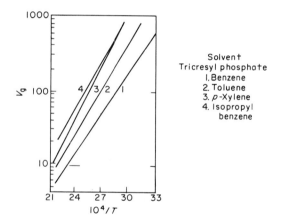

Solvent
Tricresyl phosphate
1. Benzene
2. Toluene
3. *p*-Xylene
4. Isopropyl benzene

Fig. 19-8. Temperature dependence of aromatic compounds. Solvent: tricresyl phosphate; 1. benzene, 2. toluene, 3. *p*-xylene, 4. isopropyl benzene. After D. Ambrose, A. I. M. Keulemans, and J. H. Purnell, *Anal. Chem.*, **30,** 1582 (1958). (Courtesy of *Analytical Chemistry*.)

altered by adjusting the column temperature. Lower column temperatures often lead to increased retention but not necessarily improved separation of components. Only data such as given in Fig. 19-8 can establish the facts.

Example 19-2

The results for separation of *p*-xylene and *iso*-propylbenzene on a column of tricresyl phosphate are illustrated in Fig. 19-8. The degree of separation varies considerably with temperature. At about 190°C ($10^4/T = 21.6$) *p*-xylene is eluted first and the relative retention is about 1.3, whereas at 120°C it has decreased to about 1.2. Extrapolation of the plot for isopropylbenzene shows that it intersects that for *p*-xylene at 70°C. If further extrapolation is justified, the order of elution below 70°C would be reversed, while at 70°C separation could never be effected in a column of this liquid phase.

Thus a knowledge of ΔH_s and V_k immediately makes it possible to draw the inverse temperature plot since the former quantity enables calculation of the slope of the line while the latter gives an intercept at one temperature.

Resolution

The separation of two solutes depends on their retention behavior. The degree to which two chromatographic peaks are separated can be characterized as a function of the particular packed column, irrespective of other factors influencing overall column efficiency. Doubling the length of a column, while holding the carrier flow rate constant, will double the retention volume of a compound.

Relative peak sharpness Q can be defined as the ratio of retention volume to the volume width of the peak

$$Q = V_R'/\Delta V \qquad (19\text{-}13)$$

where ΔV is the volume corresponding to the intercept of the front and rear tangents to the inflection point on the base of the elution curve (see Fig. 19-7). ΔV is also equivalent to four standard deviations (4σ).

The number of theoretical plates in a column, and also the separation factor S, is related to the peak sharpness by

$$N = 16Q^2 = (V_R'/\sigma)^2 \qquad (19\text{-}14)$$

The apparent number of theoretical plates, N, usually varies with the particular component, in particular when V_R' does not differ greatly from V_{air}. Many peaks are unsymmetrical, and V_R' may vary with the amount of solute eluted. However, the retention volume of the rear of the elution curve, V_{rear}, often remains constant. Consequently, Eq. 19-14 may be rewritten

$$N = \left(\frac{4V_{rear}}{\Delta V} - 2\right)^2 \qquad (19\text{-}15)$$

Exact separation between peaks occurs when back and front of adjacent peaks reach the base line at the same point. Because a chromatographic peak approaches in shape a Gaussian distribution, a complete physical separation of adjacent components can never be attained. The cross contamination between adjacent peaks depends on (1) the separation between the peak maxima, $(V_{R,2} - V_{R,1})$, and (2) the shape and width of each peak ΔV. The resolution of a column can be defined by

$$R = \frac{2(V_{R,2} - V_{R,1})}{\Delta V_1 + \Delta V_2} \qquad (19\text{-}16)$$

If not greatly different in concentration from each other, two adjacent components will be separated within 98% when their peak maxima are separated by six standard deviations, that is, when $R = 1.5$. Values of R less than 1.5 imply incomplete separation.

Relative retention is usually known, or can be estimated from the chromatogram, and from this ratio one can predict the number of theoretical plates necessary for a specific column and pair of components

$$N = 16\left(\frac{\alpha}{\alpha - 1}\right)^2\left[\left(\frac{\beta}{K_2}\right) + 1\right]^2 \tag{19-17}$$

where β is the ratio V_M/V_L and K_2 is the partition coefficient for the second component eluted. In practical chromatography, only enough plates are required to reduce the degree of cross contamination in the peaks to a desired experimental level η. Glueckauf[1] has published curves relating the cross contamination of two peaks as a function of the number of theoretical plates for various values of the relative retention ratio, as given in Eq. 19-11. The Glueckauf plot is shown in Fig. 19-9.

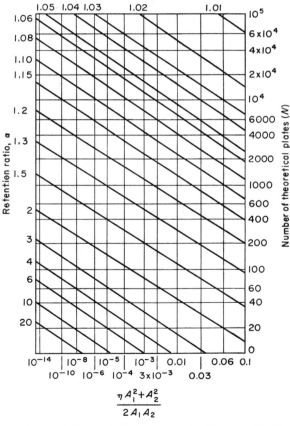

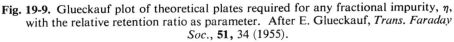

Fig. 19-9. Glueckauf plot of theoretical plates required for any fractional impurity, η, with the relative retention ratio as parameter. After E. Glueckauf, *Trans. Faraday Soc.*, **51**, 34 (1955).

The extent of cross contamination is estimated from the experimental elution curves. It might be calculated on the assumption that the effluent from the column is divided into two portions to give products of equal purity, i.e., $\eta_1 = \Delta m_2/m_1$, $\eta_2 = \Delta m_1/m_2$ and $\eta_1 = \eta_2$. When the products are unequal in purity, the fractional impurity η must be multiplied by the factor: $(A_1^2 + A_2^2)/2A_1A_2$, where A_1, A_2 are the areas of the elution curves. In theory, the purity of each product increases as the ratio m_1 to m_2 (the area of each solute elution curve—proportional to mass of each solute) deviates from unity; under these conditions the division of the effluent should be made not half-way between the peaks, but nearer the peak involving the least solute (see Fig. 19-7).

Example 19-3

From Fig. 19-7, assume that the normalized areas are $A_1 = 0.6$ and $A_2 = 0.4$. The S.F. $= 60/33 = 1.8$. To resolve these peaks with a fractional impurity content $\eta = 0.01$ (1%), first calculate the product:

$$\eta(A_1^2 + A_2^2)/2A_1A_2 = 0.01(0.36 + 0.16)/0.48 = 0.0108$$

The number of theoretical plates is derived from the Glueckauf plot (Fig. 19-9) by extending a vertical line from this value on the abscissa to the corresponding diagonal line for S.F. $= 1.8$. The ordinate corresponding to this intersection is approximately 60 plates.

If the height equivalent to a theoretical plate (HETP) is 0.25 cm, the required column length L is given by

$$L = N(\text{HETP}) = (60)(0.25) = 15 \text{ cm}$$

Efficiency

The number of theoretical plates in a separation column is obtained from peak dimensions (Eq. 19-14 and 19-15). The HETP is that length of column from which the gaseous phase leaving the exit end (of the plate) is in equilibrium with stationary phase at the entrance end. It is obtained from N and the length L of the column:

$$\text{HETP} = L/N \qquad (19\text{-}18)$$

HETP is basically a measure of the extent of band broadening during the transit time of the solute.

The dependence of HETP on average carrier gas velocity v is expressed by the van Deemter equation:

$$\text{HETP} = A + B/v + Cv \qquad (19\text{-}19)$$

The A term, equal to $2\lambda d_p$ and attributed to eddy diffusion, represents the multiple path effect of gas flow through a packed column. It incorporates the packing density λ and the average particle diameter d_p of the stationary support. For capillary columns this term is zero, of course. The B term, $2\gamma D_g$, expresses the tortuosity γ of the channels in the packed column and the molecular diffusion coefficient D_L of the solute in the gas phase. The C term is given by $(8/\pi^2)[k/(1 + k)^2](2 d_f^2/D_L)$. It reflects the resistance to mass transfer between the gaseous and liquid phase, and within the liquid phase. The $k/(1 + k)^2$ portion, where k is the fraction of solute in the liquid and gaseous phases $[K = k\beta = k(V_M/V_L)]$, states the rate at which a solute band passes through the column. Other significant quantities are the effective thickness of the film of liquid phase d_f and the reciprocal of the diffusion coefficient D_L of solute in the liquid phase.

The van Deemter equation provides a great deal of practical information for construction of efficient columns. The plot of the equation (Fig. 19-10) yields

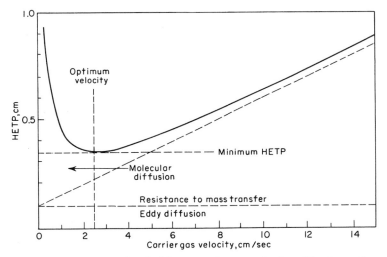

Fig. 19-10. Plot of average plate height vs carrier gas velocity with schematic presentation of terms in the van Deemter equation.

a hyperbola with a minimum $A + 2(BC)^{1/2}$ at $v = (B/C)^{1/2}$. Conditions should be adjusted so that terms B and C are balanced; all terms are kept as small as possible to provide a minimum HETP for the solute most difficult to separate in a mixture. Small particle diameter of stationary phase and small ranges of particle sizes aid in reducing HETP. A heavier carrier gas causes less diffusion in direction of flow and thus gives sharper peaks, but this factor has to be balanced against viscosity of the gas and its relation to the pressure drop in the column, also the effect of the nature of the gas on the sensitivity of the detector. A solvent should be selected in which the solute has moderate (but not large) solubility. A decrease in column temperature increases the solubility of vapors in the liquid phase, but it will increase the viscosity of the stationary liquid and hence decrease the diffusivity of solutes in the liquid. Some liquids solidify at lower temperatures. A very thin film of liquid phase leads to greater efficiency so long as this is accomplished without reduction of the total amount of solvent in the column, in which event the sample size must also be reduced to avoid overloading. Viscosity of the column liquid affects the diffusion of solute within the liquid phase. Plots of theoretical plate number vs carrier gas flow have a maximum, unlike plots of HETP vs gas velocity, which show a minimum. This means that if the carrier gas flow is higher than the optimum, the efficiency of the column drops. On the other hand, the time of analysis becomes shorter. Since the peak height increases steadily with the flow rate, the column efficiency can be traded for speed or for the attainment of sharper peaks.

Solvent Phase

No single stationary liquid phase will serve for all separation problems or be usable at all column temperatures. Indeed it is rarely possible to separate all components of any complex mixture by use of a single packed column. One approach is to make separate fractionations on columns of distinctly different types of solvents. An alternate is to pass a multicomponent fraction from a first system into a second and different system which will resolve those particular components. The separation of closely boiling compounds of the same general molecular class can be resolved only by employing a large number of theoretical plates and exploiting some small structural differences through the use of a selective solvent phase.

Solvents can be classified by their gas-chromatographic behavior into three groups: (1) nonpolar, comprising high-boiling paraffins, Apiezon oils and grease, and silicones; (2) moderately polar, including esters of high-molecular-weight alcohols, such as dinonyl phthalate, and high-boiling alcohols themselves; and (3) strongly polar, such as the polyglycols and their esters. A number of columns are listed in Table 19-1.

Relative retention values for classes of solutes are given for typical columns in Table 19-2. Only solubility forces are involved with nonpolar solvents. This type of column is useful for effecting separations according to boiling points in a homologous series; it behaves like a high-efficiency distillation column, without complications caused by azeotrope formation. A nonpolar column gives little or no separation of different types of compounds possessing similar boiling points. As the polarity of the solvent phase is increased, aromatic hydrocarbons are retarded relative to aliphatics—to such an extent that on a polyethylene glycol column all the aliphatic hydrocarbons boiling below 200°C are eluted before the aromatics appear. On columns of solvents, such as polyoxyethylene, solubility forces plus hydrogen bonding are involved. In fact, glycol is capable of forming a network of multiple hydrogen bonds. Ingredients will tend to be eluted in order of polarity.

At times, specific separations require the use of stationary phases that possess a selected interaction with one or more of the components to be separated. For example, silver nitrate dissolved in glycol separates unsaturated hydrocarbons, and 7,8-benzoquinoline has been used for separation of *m*- and *p*-xylene.

Table 19-2	Relative Retentions (n-pentane = 1) of Various Solute Classes at Three Boiling Point Levels for Several Liquid Phases								
LIQUID PHASE COLUMN TEMP, °C	SILICONE OIL (D.C. 703) 100°			Di-2-ETHYLHEXYL SEBACATE 100°			POLYDIETHYLENE GLYCOL SUCCINATE 100°		
B.P. LEVEL, °C	60	100	140	60	100	140	60	100	140
Solute classes									
n-Paraffins	1.7	4.3	13.5	2.2	5.0	13	1.5	2.9	5.6
2-Methylalkanes	1.6	4.2	—	1.8	5.0	13	1.0	1.9	—
1-Olefins	1.9	5.2	15.4	2.2	5.4	16	1.7	3.4	—
2-Olefins	1.9	5.2	15.4	2.5	5.4	16	2.0	4.4	—
Alkynes	2.2	6.4	19	2.3	6.3	19	. . .	. . .	. . .
Alkylbenzenes	—	7.9	23.0	—	9.3	27	—	18.4	50
n-Alcohols	0.76	2.6	—	1.1	3.7	—	33	54	140
2-Alcohols	—	3.0	—	2.0†	5.0	—	30	46.8	145
t-Alcohols	—	3.6	—	2.3†	6.0	—	24	45.6	160
Aldehydes	2.1	6.2	—	1.8	7.0	—	14.3	30	61
Ketones	1.9	6.0	19.7	1.4	6.5	—	20.5	37	80
Acetate esters	2.3	6.9	25	1.7	6.4	20	16	30	61
Ethers	2.1	6.4	18	1.9	6.2	20	9.2	56	—

†At 80°C.

The lower limit of temperature for any column packing is its melting point, which is above room temperature for some of the greases and waxes. The upper limit of usefulness depends on the vapor pressure of the solvent phase— the effect of the solvent bleeding upon the base-line stability of the recorded chromatogram and, of course, the life of the column. The upper temperature limit is usually about 70°C below the high-vacuum boiling point (at a pressure of 0.1 mm of mercury) of the solvent.

Application of Gas Chromatography

Programmed Temperature Chromatography

The separation of constituents in samples composed of compounds with a wide range of boiling points can be accelerated by raising the temperature of the entire column at a uniform rate—usually a linear temperature program— during the analysis. The sample is placed directly on a relatively cool column in the normal manner. During the initial part of the warmup period, the components have time to reshuffle and arrange themselves in the order in which they will ultimately emerge. Each band is further resolved as it moves down the column. Earlier peaks, representing low-boiling constituents, emerge essentially as they would from an isothermal column operated at a relatively low temperature. However, the higher-boiling materials which on a low-temperature isothermal column would emerge as flat peaks—often undetected—will be kept bunched by the rapidly increasing temperature. Consequently, an extremely wide boiling range of components may be separated in less time, and the peaks on the chromatogram are sharper and more uniform in shape (Fig. 19-11) and hence are more amenable to quantitative interpretation.

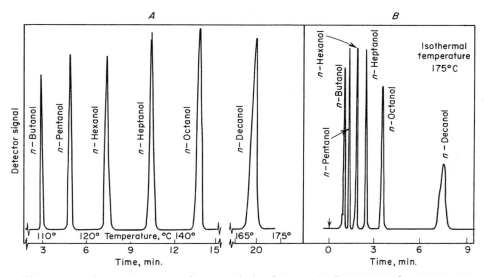

Fig. 19-11. Chromatograms of an alcohol mixture. A. Programmed temperature from 100° to 175 °C. B. Isothermal operation at 175 °C. (Courtesy of American Instrument Co.)

A major problem is to find partitioning agents that are stable over a wide temperature range and still specific enough to give good separation of samples with varied chemical characteristics. Carrier gas must be maintained at a constant flow rate even though resistance to flow in the column changes. The pressure on the detector (and reference) is kept constant by expelling the gaseous phase to the atmosphere. A heat exchanger may be needed between the column exit and detector to avoid drift due to changing carrier-gas temperature for detectors where drift is inadmissible. Often separate heaters are used for detector and injection port housings so that these functions will be unaffected by column temperature changes. Extremely efficient heat transfer must be available for fast heating and fast cooling of the column— achieved usually by means of an air bath circulated at high velocity and changed once or twice a second. Column bleeding near the upper temperature limit affects the base-line stability. The most satisfactory remedy is by use of dual columns—carrier gas from one column passing through the reference detector, and carrier gas from the other passing through the sample detector.

Under a linear programmed temperature the temperature is uniform over the length of column but rises at a rate of $r°/\min$. For each component eluted the significant temperatures are (1) the temperature of the column when the sample was injected and (2) the retention temperature T_R, the temperature of the column when the peak emerges. For any given column this retention temperature depends on the ratio of heating rate to carrier gas flow rate F (rather than on either one alone).

$$\int_{T_0}^{T_R} \left(\frac{1}{V_T} \right) \partial T = \frac{r}{F} \qquad (19\text{-}20)$$

An analytic evaluation of the integral is difficult and a graphical method is preferable. The isothermal retention volumes for the solutes of interest are summarized as plots of $\log (V_R - V_{\text{dead}})_T$ against $1/T$. From such a family of lines and from the values of $V_{\text{dead space}}$, determined for the particular ap-

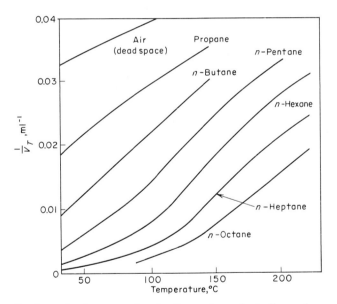

Fig. 19-12. Reciprocal of corrected retention volume including column dead space as a function of column temperature. After H. W. Habgood and W. E. Harris, *Anal. Chem.* **32**, 451 (1960). (Courtesy of *Analytical Chemistry*.)

paratus, plots of $(1/V)_T$ against temperature are constructed as in Fig. 19-12. The required integrals are the areas under these curves from an arbitrary initial temperature to higher temperatures, as plotted in Fig. 19-13 against the upper temperature limit.

The necessary isothermal retention volumes may be obtained by direct

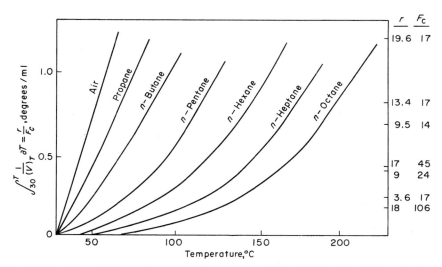

Fig. 19-13. Plot of integral—areas under curves of Fig. 19-12. On right ordinate are various programs whose r and F_c values are given. After H. W. Habgood and W. E. Harris, *Anal. Chem.*, **32**, 451 (1960). (Courtesy of *Analytical Chemistry*.)

measurement or from the literature. Published values are usually the volumes of carrier gas at column temperature and mean pressure. They must therefore be corrected to some chosen standard temperature, since the flow rate is constant only when expressed at constant temperature.

The number of theoretical plates for programmed temperature gas chromatography is given by the expression

$$N = 16\left[\frac{(V_T)_R}{\Delta V}\right]^2 \qquad (19\text{-}21)$$

where ΔV is the volume equivalent to the base-line intercept of the peak. A column used for programmed temperature chromatography has essentially the same number of plates as it does in isothermal chromatography.

In a practical analysis it is desirable to operate a column for high efficiency, minimum time of analysis, maximum sensitivity, and peak shapes most amenable to quantitative interpretation. In the choice of values for r and F some compromise is necessary, and the best values for one solute may not be best for others. In general, the higher r is, the sooner peaks emerge, but because they emerge at higher temperatures the column efficiency is decreased. The emergence temperature may be decreased by increasing F, but this will eventually also lead to a decrease in efficiency and, with most detectors, a decrease in sensitivity.

Gas-Solid Chromatography

The gas chromatographic separation of the permanent gases, rare gases, and certain light hydrocarbon gases is achieved with gas-solid chromatography and temperature programming. Using a silica gel column, carbon dioxide is separated (also acetylene, and from each other) but the other gases emerge as a single composite peak. Molecular sieves provide adequate separation. Molecular sieves are zeolites which have been prepared under conditions conducive to production of rather uniform pore sizes: 4A, 5A and 13X are commercial varieties. Using linear programmed temperature gas chromatography, hydrogen, oxygen, nitrogen, methane, ethane, carbon dioxide, and ethylene separate, as shown in Fig. 19-14, on a four-foot molecular sieve 5A

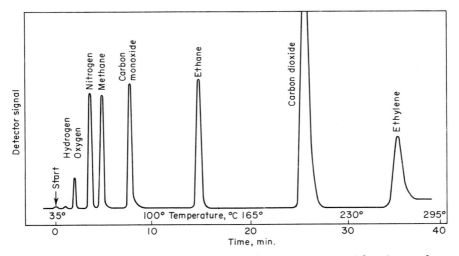

Fig. 19-14. Linear programmed temperature chromatogram on 4-ft column of molecular sieve 5A. Temperature programmed at 6.4°C/min from 35° to 291°C. After J. M. Schlater, L. Mikkelsen, and M. G. Beck, in "Lectures on Gas Chromatography 1962," edited by H. A. Szymanski, page 121, Plenum Press, New York, 1963.

column. The temperature was programmed from 35°–291°C in 40 min. The programming technique also separates nitric oxide and nitrous oxide in the presence of other gases and light hydrocarbon gases.

Qualitative Identification

The relative retention volume of an unknown substance provides a strong clue to its identity. For unequivocal identification at least two columns are required containing stationary phases with different characteristics. One should be polar and the other nonpolar. A standard reference substance is also chromatographed under identical operating conditions, and the relative retention volume of each peak obtained from the sample is calculated. Graphs of logarithm of relative retention volume versus the number of carbon atoms in the molecule for the members of a homologous series are useful. Tables of relative retention volumes for various solvent phases, operating at various temperatures, are helpful. Certain detectors discriminate against specific compounds.

Scope is extended by isolating separated components in traps, cooled in liquid air, which are inserted immediately after the detector. The isolated fractions can then be further examined by suitable chemical and instrumental methods, such as infrared absorption, nuclear magnetic resonance, or mass spectrometry.

Quantitative Results

The chromatographic peak is the only source of quantitative analytical data. Ordinarily the chromatogram is made by a strip chart recorder connected to the detector. Two conditions must prevail: (1) The output of the detector-recorder system must be linear with concentration. The linear dynamic range expresses this range and, coupled with sensitivity, the limits. (2) The flow rate must be constant so that the time abscissa may be converted to volume of carrier gas. Under these conditions, peak area can be used as a function of component present. It can be measured by triangulation, disc integrator, or planimeter. Volume of sample injector and detector, and changes in retention volume, due to a changed column efficiency do not affect peak area, nor does temperature unless it changes the sensitivity of the detector. Peak height can also be related to weight of component for a given apparatus by calibration; any variable, however, that affects retention volume or peak shape will alter the peak height and must not be changed after calibration. A plot of relative peak heights will not be linear because of the broadening of the elution peak as sample size is increased.

Pyrolysis

Nonoxidative thermal fission (pyrolysis) extends the applicability of gas chromatography to substances which are nonvolatile. The method consists of applying a small amount of a material, either as solid or solution, to a platinum coil which is then placed in the carrier gas stream and heated electrically within 15–20 sec from ambient temperature to 1100°–1300°C. Materials, such as rubber, plastics, alkaloids, paint, films, fiber, and tars, will give characteristic volatile breakdown products. Even though the products may be unknown, the chromatographic pattern aids in characterizing the parent substance. For example, polystyrene and glycerol break down to yield a simple trace and easily identified fission products (Fig. 19-15). Most materials, however, produce complex traces with many diverse peaks representing literally dozens of fission products. These traces, although not amenable to chemical interpretation, are nevertheless characteristic and are useful for comparative purposes, much as a fingerprint.

Preparative-Scale Chromatography

The isolation of macro amounts of materials involves more than simply scaling up columns in size. In fact, the use of large-diameter columns with a

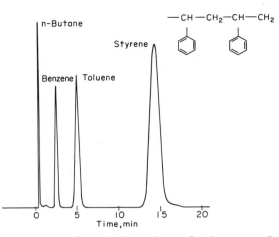

Fig. 19-15. Chromatogram of pyrolysis products of polystyrene. Sample size, 22 μg. Temperature of column, 100°C. (Courtesy of Wilkens Instrument & Research, Inc.)

single injection of a large sample introduces a number of difficulties—such as the need for instantaneous evaporation of the large sample and possibility of channeling and excessive band spreading in the wider columns. Repetitive automatic injections of small samples on a narrow column prove more efficient. A high percent of solvent phase is necessary to accommodate the sample without overloading. Temperature programming ensures better separation of component peaks.

In one commercial instrument (Wilkens Aerograph Autoprep A-700), columns are coiled 1-cm aluminum tubes, 30–60 m long and packed with a 30 percent liquid phase. At the beginning of a run the oven turns on, and the sample (0.1–2.0 ml) is automatically injected. As the pen on the recorder starts to move upward on the first peak, it produces a signal which causes the collector table to rotate and accurately index the first sample bottle under the heated collector orifice. When the recorder pen completes its trace of the first peak and nears the base line again, another signal rotates the table to the waste position, where it remains until the second peak emerges. As many as eight component peaks may be collected. After the final peak, the table indexes back to the precollection (waste) position, and the oven is cooled to the initial temperature by compressed air. At the end of this period, another sample is automatically injected, to repeat the cycle.

Continual Analysis

One of the major disadvantages of gas chromatography for process control— namely, the cyclic nature of analyses—is largely overcome by employing high-speed units which perform analyses so fast that operation is essentially continuous. Analytical cycles of 1 min or less are possible in closed-loop control of chemical processes. With digital systems it is possible to program the sequence of operation of several chromatographic units and transmit the results in any desired sequence.

LABORATORY WORK

Numerous commercial gas chromatographs are available. A simple but very useful gas chromatograph in kit form is available from Gow-Mac Instrument Co., Madison, N.J. A manual, "Experimental Gas Chromatography," by J. M. Miller has been written to illustrate the principles and technique through a series of tested experiments. Suggested experiments, largely from this manual, are outlined below.

Directions for Use of Gas Chromatograph

Close the needle valve on the gas cylinder. Turn on the gas by opening the main cylinder valve. Adjust the diaphragm valve so that the pressure on the second gauge reads about 14 psig. Slowly open the needle valve. Check the flow with flow meter. Adjust the flow to the desired value with the needle valve; 60–80 ml/min is good for many columns. Increase the pressure if necessary. Purge at least five minutes.

Rotate the "current adjust" knob to its counterclockwise limit for thermal conductivity units. Turn the filaments "ON". Adjust the current to the desired value (200 ma in helium; 100 ma in air) with the "current adjust." Turn on the recorder. Use the "zero control" to adjust the pen to about 5% to 10% of full scale deflection. NEVER OPERATE THE FILAMENTS UNLESS GAS IS FLOWING.

Turn on the injection heater. Turn on the oven, if desired, and adjust to the desired temperature. Use as low a temperature as possible to get optimum separation.

Wait until the base line is stabilized. Inject sample and record chromatogram. AVOID SAMPLES CONTAINING WATER.

Turning off the instrument. Turn off the oven, the injection heater, the recorder, and the filament current. Close the needle valve, open the diaphragm valve, and then close the main valve on the gas cylinder. Open the needle valve to bleed off the pressure on the gauge.

Use of Syringes in Injecting Samples

In filling a microliter syringe with liquid it is usually desirable to exclude all air initially. This can be accomplished by repeatedly drawing liquid into the syringe and rapidly expelling it into the liquid. Viscous liquids must be drawn into the syringe slowly; very fast expulsion of a viscous liquid could split the syringe. Draw up about twice as much liquid into the syringe as you plan to inject.

The following procedure should be used to adjust the volume of a liquid in the syringe. Hold the syringe vertically with the needle pointing up. Push the plunger until it reads the desired value. Wipe off the needle with tissue. Draw some air into the syringe now that the exact volume of liquid has been measured. This will serve two purposes: first, the air will give a peak on the chromatogram which will be used to calculate "adjusted" retention volumes; second, the air prevents any liquid from being expelled if the plunger is accidentally pushed.

Injection Procedure

Hold the syringe in two hands. Use one (normally the left) to guide the needle into the septum, and the other to provide force to pierce the septum and to prevent the plunger from being forced out by the pressure in the gas chromatograph.

Insert the needle in the septum, depress the plunger, and withdraw the needle (keeping the plunger depressed) as rapidly as possible. Insert the needle until it touches the back of the injection block, but do not force it hard enough to dull or bend the needle.

This technique is necessary in order to insure that the sample is injected into the flowing gas stream, rather than into the "dead volume" in the injection block.

When high-boiling liquids are being used, the syringe should be washed out with a volatile solvent like acetone. This can be done by repeatedly pulling the wash liquid into the syringe. Then remove the plunger and dry the syringe by pulling air through it. Attach the barrel of the syringe to a water aspirator. This way air is pulled in through the needle and dust cannot get into the barrel to clog it. Wipe the plunger with a tissue and reinsert. Observe all of the directions on the sheet supplied with the syringe by the manufacturer.

EXPERIMENT 19-1 EFFECTS OF CHANGES IN CARRIER GAS FLOW

Inject 1 μl of some pure compound (and including some air) into the column. Operate the column at some convenient temperature. Adjust the flow of carrier gas to about 140 ml/min for the run.

When the peak has eluted, lower the flow rate to 120 ml/min, inject a fresh sample, and record the elution curve. Repeat the experiment at flow rates of 100, 80, 60, and 40 ml/min.

Calculate the number of theoretical plates for your compound at each of the flow rates. From the column length, calculate the HETP at each flow rate. Plot the values of HETP versus carrier gas flow rate. Estimate the terms in the van Deemter equation. What is the optimum linear gas velocity and corresponding HETP?

EXPERIMENT 19-2 EFFECT OF TEMPERATURE ON RETENTION TIMES

Stabilize the column at 150°C (if compatible with liquid phase packing). Adjust the carrier gas flow to the optimum value, and inject a sample containing two adjacent members of a homologous family, or members separated by two methylene groups for higher molecular weights.

Repeat the experiment at different column temperatures: 120°, 100°, 80° and 50°C.

Tabulate the retention time for the components at each column temperature. Graph the logarithm of the retention time vs the carbon number.

If sufficient information is available, calculate the partition coefficient of each component. Graph the logarithm of the partition coefficient vs the reciprocal of the absolute temperature. From the slope of the graph, calculate the heat of solution for each component.

EXPERIMENT 19-3 RESOLUTION OF MIXTURES

Stabilize the column temperature at 100°C and adjust the carrier gas flow to the optimum value. Inject a mixture known to give overlapping peaks under the particular operating conditions. This data may be available from the preceding experiment.

Repeat the experiment using unequal amounts of the overlapping components in the mixture.

By triangulation, determine the relative peak sharpness and the number of theoretical plates in the column. Calculate the resolution between the two peaks. From the relative retention and the theoretical number of plates, estimate the fractional impurity for each peak.

EXPERIMENT 19-4   QUANTITATIVE ANALYSIS OF MEMBERS OF A HOMOLOGOUS SERIES

Prepare a mixture of n-alkanes, or n-alcohols, or other suitable homologous series by mixing a known number of drops of each component in a small vial. Inject a 1 μl sample of each component separately into the column, and then a 2 μl sample of the mixture.

Graph the adjusted retention time (logarithmic coordinates) vs the carbon number on one graph, and vs the boiling point for each component on another graph.

Determine the respective areas of each component in the mixture. Calculate the percent of each component and compare your results with the known composition of the mixture.

More precise results could be obtained by preparing a series of calibration curves for each component by plotting the area of the respective peak vs percent (by weight or by volume) of the component in the mixture.

EXPERIMENT 19-5   QUALITATIVE ANALYSIS

Stabilize the column temperature and adjust the carrier gas flow. Inject a 5 μl sample of some commercial fluid (e.g., lighter fluid) or an organic liquid which is supposedly fairly pure (e.g., cyclohexane).

Also run chromatograms of 1-μl samples of appropriate known compounds. For lighter fluid, these compounds should be run: benzene, toluene, and at least two normal paraffins.

Establish the identity of each peak in the chromatogram of the unknown sample by reference to runs of known materials and by comparison with tabulated relative retentions. To use the tabulated retention values, it may be advisable to adjust the column temperature and carrier flow rate to conform with the tabulated conditions.

Problems

1. Compute the relative retention when $V_R = 100$, $(V_R)_s = 50$, and $V_{air} = 20$. *Ans.* $\alpha = 2.7$.

2. Adjusted retention times (in minutes) for straight-chain saturated paraffins on 60/80 mesh Chromosorb containing 20 percent by weight of silicone oil (DC 200) are tabulated at 50°C (carrier flow = 100 ml min^{-1}) and at 100°C ($F = 82$ ml min^{-1}):

Temp.	C_1	C_2	C_3	C_4	C_5	C_6	C_7	C_8
50°	0.00	0.30	0.90	2.30	6.50	16.0	38.7	92.6
100°	0.00	0.10	0.50	1.20	2.40	4.90	9.70	19.0

(a) Calculate the adjusted retention volumes of each component. (b) At each column temperature, calculate the retention ratio relative to n-pentane. (c) Plot log V'_R (or t'_R) vs the carbon number.

3. Under a particular set of operating conditions, with helium as carrier gas, the terms in the van Deemter equation were $A = 0.1$ cm, $B = 0.30$ cm^2/sec, $C = 0.05$ sec. (a) Graph the equation and sketch the contribution of each of the terms. (b) Calculate the minimum HETP and the optimum carrier flow. *Ans.* HETP = 0.345 cm at $v = 2.45$ cm/sec (see also Fig. 19-10).

4. A gas-liquid packed column with nitrogen as carrier gas has $A = 0.1$ cm, $B = 0.075$ cm²/sec, $C = 0.01$ sec. (a) Graph the van Deemter equation and sketch the limiting regions of each term. (b) Calculate the minimum HETP and the optimum carrier flow.

5. On a Sterchamol column, containing 30 percent by weight of hexadecane, these values of HETP for specific linear velocity of nitrogen carrier gas were obtained for n-butane at 30°C:

| HTEP (cm): | 0.189 | 0.125 | 0.139 | 0.187 |
| v (cm/sec): | 0.71 | 1.38 | 2.72 | 6.12 |

(a) Graph the results and estimate the terms in the van Deemter equation. (b) What is the optimum linear gas velocity and corresponding HETP?

6. On a 30 percent liquid paraffin-Celite packed column, operated at 42°C, these values for HETP and hydrogen gas velocity were obtained using n-hexane:

| HETP (cm): | 0.465 | 0.423 | 0.635 | 0.510 | 0.552 | 0.631 | 0.692 | 0.749 |
| v (cm/sec): | 4.2 | 3.0 | 0.91 | 1.51 | 5.55 | 7.0 | 8.0 | 9.0 |

(a) Graph the data and calculate the terms in the van Deemter equation. (b) What is the optimum linear gas velocity and corresponding minimum HETP? *Ans.* $A = 0.045$ cm, $B = 0.475$ cm²/sec, $C = 0.073$ sec; HETP = 0.415 cm at $v = 2.55$ cm/sec.

7. For the column in Problem 5, the retention volume (in millimeters of chart travel) was 153.6 mm for propane and 415.4 mm for n-butane. The base line widths were 13.6 and 33.9 mm, respectively. Chart speed was 305 mm/hr. Column length was 360 cm. Inlet pressure = 783 mm of Hg, and outlet pressure = 757 mm of Hg. Calculate the number of theoretical plates and the HETP. *Ans.* $N = 2040$ and HETP = 0.18 cm for propane; $N = 2380$ and HETP = 0.15 cm for n-butane.

8. The column in Problem 7 had these values: $V_L = 15.34$ cm³ and free gas volume, $V_M = 68.58$ cm³. Calculate the partition coefficient for propane and n-butane. The linear velocity at average column pressure was 0.71 cm/sec. The free gas cross section of the column was 0.191 cm². *Ans.* $K = 11.4$ for propane and 38.9 for n-butane.

9. The following data were obtained on a 25 percent dinonylphthalate-80/100 mesh Chromosorb column, 91.5 cm in length, operated at 53°C, which contained 2.50 g of dinonylphthalate (density = 0.9712 g/cm³ at 20°C) and 7.50 g of oven-dried Chromosorb. Recorder speed was 2.54 cm/min.

Compound	F_c (ml/min)	t'_R (cm)	P_0 (cm)	P_i (cm)
Benzene	48.0	52.0	75.8	122.2
Cyclohexene	51.7	42.1	75.2	123.9
Cyclohexane	52.6	31.0	75.2	124.4

For each compound, calculate (a) the adjusted retention volume, (b) the net retention volume, (c) the specific retention volume, and (d) the partition coefficient. *Ans.* For cyclohexane, $V_g = 159$, $V'_R = 642$ ml, $V_N = 475$.

10. These data were obtained on a 4-ft column of 30 percent dinonylphthalate-Celite 535, operated at 100°C, with a gas flow of 18 ml/min (at atmospheric pressure): $P_0 = 210$ mm of Hg, $P_i = 890$ mm of Hg, $t'_R = 6.0$ min for isopropyl nitrate, and $t'_R = 9.0$ min for toluene. Calculate (a) the adjusted retention volume, (b) the net retention volume, and (c) estimate the specific retention volume assuming the packing contained 4.0 g of liquid phase.

11. On a column of 20 percent dinonylphthalate-Chromosorb W, operated at 100°C, inlet pressure 25 lbs/in², outlet pressure at atmospheric, and 70 ml/min flow rate, the adjusted retention times were 12.9, 29.9, and 58.4 min for benzene,

toluene, and ethylbenzene, respectively. Estimate the retention times of these components on the column described in Problem 10.

12. Derive an expression to show that relative retention is increased by reducing the column temperature. *Ans.* $\alpha = (a_2/a_1) \exp [(\Delta H_2 - \Delta H_1)/RT]$.

13. A chromatogram of fatty acid methyl esters is shown in Fig. 19-16. (a) Record the retention times of each component peak. (b) Calculate the adjusted retention volumes. (c) The column contained 6.67 g of diethylene glycol succinate. Calculate the specific retention volumes. Assume $j = 0.8$. (d) Assigning the palmitate ester a retention value equal to 1.00, calculate the retention ratio of the other esters.

14. A series of methyl esters of the fatty acids were chromatographed. Time (in minutes) at peak maximum for known saturated esters were: $C_{12} = 2.65$, $C_{14} = 4.6$, and $C_{20} = 27.0$. On a sample, run under identical conditions, peaks were observed at 2.55, 8.3, 15.2, 26.9 and 48 min. Which esters were present in the sample?

15. Setting $\alpha = 1.10$, $\beta = 100$ (which corresponds to about 2 percent liquid phase), and $K_2 = 100$, calculate the number of theoretical plates required for the separation. *Ans.* $N = 3870$.

16. Repeat Problem 15 for $\alpha = 1.05$.

17. Repeat Problem 15 for $\beta = 8$ (which corresponds to about 15 percent liquid phase).

18. Repeat Problem 15 for $K_2 = 25$.

19. Assuming $\Delta H_s = 5.0$ kcal/mole and $K = 100$ at 400°K, estimate the value of the partition coefficient at 300°K. *Ans.* 796.

20. Using the information in Problem 2, calculate the theoretical number of plates required for a separation of equal amounts of the n-alkanes from each other when the fractional impurity is not to exceed (a) 0.5 percent; (b) 0.1 percent.

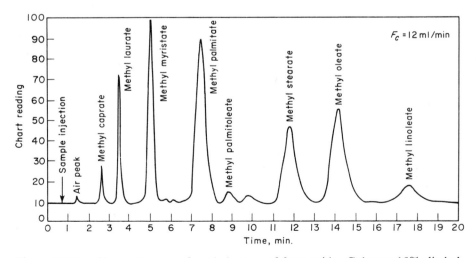

Figure 19-16. Chromatogram of methyl esters of fatty acids. Column: 15% diethylene glycol succinate on 40/60 mesh firebrick operated at 220°C with helium as carrier gas. Inlet pressure: 1520 mm of Hg; outlet pressure: 740 mm of Hg.

21. Calculate the theoretical number of plates required for the separation of *n*-propyl acetate from *n*-propanol (less than 0.1 percent cross contamination in the chromatogram) when the latter occurs as an impurity equal to about 2 percent. On a polyethylene glycol column the partition coefficients are 66.2 and 114, respectively.

22. If the ester and alcohol in Problem 21 had been separated on a polypropylene glycol column, the partition coefficients for which are 110 and 124, respectively, would the separation have required more or fewer theoretical plates?

23. The information in Table 19-3 represents the data obtained when butandiol succinate liquid phase at 195°C was used for the analysis of a coconut oil methyl ester sample. The electronic integrator printed the time (in minutes and seconds) at the start and the maximum of each peak and the peak area in counts. (a) Calculate the percent of each component present in the chromatogram. (b) By reference to Fig. 19-16, identify as many peaks as possible. *Ans.* Peak number 9 is methyl laurate; 38.45 percent is present.

Table 19-3 | *Results for Methyl Esters of Fatty Acids in Coconut Oil*

PEAK NO.	TIME min/sec	AREA COUNTS	PEAK NO.	TIME min/sec	AREA COUNTS
1	02/32 02/34	142	10	04/34 04/37	94
2	02/39 02/41	61	11	04/51 04/54	75
3	02/41 02/43	513	12	05/48 05/59	11398
4	02/50 02/51	64	13	07/19 07/23	49
5	02/53 02/55	5159	14	09/21 09/32	12263
6	03/14 03/16	44	15	16/35 16/54	2295
7	03/17 03/25	4313	16	17/49 18/17	5983
8	03/38 03/41	39	17	20/51 21/05	501
9	04/03 04/13	26856			

24. From the information in Table 19-3, estimate the number of theoretical plates in the column for several of the major constituents. Assume the peaks are symmetrical. *Ans.* Peaks 7 and 9 indicate $N = 2590$.

25. Assuming that the number of theoretical plates equals 2000 in the column used for the separation of the methyl esters of the fatty acids in Problem 23, calculate

the separation factor and the fractional impurity anticipated for each major component. *Ans.* Peaks 7 and 6 have a separation factor of 1.045 and fractional impurity of about 0.6 percent (peak 7).

26. A series of saturated aliphatic aldehydes (total amount = 3.0 mg) were chromatographed on a column consisting of 33 percent silastomer DC 156, operated at 180°C. Adjusted retention times, base widths, and peak heights were

Component	C_5	C_6	C_7	C_8	C_9	C_{10}
t'_R, min	10.1	13.25	18.75	24.3	32.75	45.0
Δt, min	3.0	4.5	4.5	5.7	8.5	13
Height, mm	16	17	16.5	17	14.5	12.5

(a) Calculate the amount of each aldehyde in the sample. (b) For each peak estimate the theoretical number of plates in the column. (c) Peaks for C_5 and C_6 aldehydes are incompletely separated at the column temperature employed. How many theoretical plates would be required to reduce the impurity in each peak to 1 percent? *Ans.* (a) C_7 = 12.8 percent; (c) N should be about 300.

27. Tabulated are elution data obtained on a liquid paraffin column:

Solute	ΔH_s	V_g	Solute	ΔH_s	V_g
n-Pentane	5.99	8.2	1-Hexene	7.45	18.2
n-Hexane	6.80	17.8	1-Heptene	8.78	39.5
n-Heptane	7.32	40.0	1-Octene	10.00	82.1
2-Pentene	6.43	8.1			
2-Hexene	7.60	26.0			
2-Heptene	8.52	55.0			

(a) Graph the inverse temperature plot for each solute. (b) the more difficult separations involve the pairs n-pentane plus 2-pentene and n-hexane plus 1-hexene. At which column temperature could each pair be resolved within 98 percent from each other if the column contains 800 theoretical plates? (c) Could the separations be accomplished at room temperature with a longer column? *Ans.* (b) At 60°C for pentane-pentene pair, assuming equal amounts of each; retention ratio is 1.17.

28. Specific retention volumes at the specified column temperatures for some chlorinated hydrocarbons on Apiezon L column are listed:

Temperature, °C	CH_2Cl_2	$CHCl_2CH_3$	$CHCl_3$	CCl_3CH_3	CCl_4	$CCl_2=CCl_2$	ϕCl
50	29.5	52.8	83.8	115	153	—	—
74	14.8	26.0	40.4	53.5	72.1	301	374
97	8.08	14.0	21.0	29.5	37.1	142	176
125	4.58	7.65	10.9	14.4	17.9	55.5	68.2

The density of the liquid phase at 74°/4°C is 0.859 g/cm³. Column contained 4.58 g of liquid on approximately 13.3 g of 30/60 mesh Chromosorb.
(a) Graph the data and compute the heat of solution for each solute. (b) Calculate the partition coefficient at each temperature for each solute. *Ans.* ΔH_s = 7.33 kcal/mole for CCl_4; K = 131 for CCl_4 at 50°C.

29. Column operating conditions for the separation of methylnaphthalenes on Silicone oil 710 were as follows:

Column	1	2	3
Weight of liquid phase, g	5.55	1.44	0.40
Temperature, °C	182	142	100
Gas flow, ml/min	208	192	415
Pressure ratio, P_i/P_0	3.76	3.26	4.33
Volume gas phase, ml	15	18	22

Retention volume, ml			
1-methyl	1020	870	1350
2-methyl	910	780	1200
Base width, ml			
1-methyl	92	72	127
2-methyl	77	64	115

(a) Estimate the resolution of the two peaks for each column. (b) Calculate the number of theoretical plates as measured from the individual peaks. (c) Predict the number of theoretical plates required for a resolution of 98 percent. *Ans.* (c) N_{req} = 3220 for all columns.

30. Restricting oneself to the information contained in Table 19-2, which column would you recommend for the separation of these materials:

    (a) *n*-Propanol and *n*-propyl acetate.
    (b) Acetone and acetaldehyde.
    (c) Elution of alcohols ahead of ethers, and the reverse.
    (d) Separation of minor amounts of oxygenated compounds from hydrocarbons in a mixture of boiling range 90°–110°C.
    (e) Aromatics from saturated compounds.
    (f) Paraffins from olefins over boiling range 40°–80°C.
    (g) *n*-Alcohols from each other.
    (h) Acetate esters from each other.
Ans. (a) Silicone oil 703. (See *Anal. Chem.* **30**, 2 (1958).)

31. Assuming that HETP = 0.1 cm, what column lengths would be required for each separation in Problem 30, assuming 1 percent fractional impurity?

32. A pure sample of $CHCl_2CHCl_2$, when put through an Apiezon L column at 97°C, a pressure of 937 mm of Hg, and a flow rate of 75 ml/min, possessed a retention time of 19.5 min measured from the air peak. Two days later a sample, believed to be identical, was injected into the same column operated at 97°C but at an inlet pressure of 833 mm of Hg and at a flow rate of 54 ml/min. The observed retention time, measured from the air peak, was 24.8 min. On both days the pressure at the column outlet was 630 mm of Hg. What are your conclusions? *Ans.* V'_R = 1152 and 1150, respectively.

Bibliography

Brenner, N., J. E. Callen, and M. D. Weiss (Ed.), *Gas Chromatography*, Academic Press, New York, 1962.

Dal Nogare, S., and R. S. Juvet, Jr., *Gas-Liquid Chromatography*, Interscience, New York, 1962.

Desty, D. H. (Ed.), *Vapour Phase Chromatography*, Academic Press, New York, 1957.

Keulemans, A. I. M., *Gas Chromatography*, 2nd ed., Reinhold, New York, 1959.

Noebels, H. J., R. F. Wahls, and N. Brenner, (Ed.), *Gas Chromatography*, Academic Press, New York, 1961.

Pecsok, R. L. (Ed.), *Principles and Practice of Gas Chromatography*, Wiley, New York, 1959.

Phillips, C. S. G., *Gas Chromatography*, Academic Press, New York, 1956.
Purnell, H., *Gas Chromatography*, Wiley, New York, 1962.
Scott, R. P. W. (Ed.), *Gas Chromatography*, Butterworths, Washington, D.C., 1960.
Szymanski, H. A. (Ed.), *Lectures on Gas Chromatography*, Plenum Press, New York, 1963.

Literature Cited

1. Glueckauf, E., *Trans. Faraday Soc.*, **51,** 34 (1955).
2. Lovelock, J. E., *Anal. Chem.*, **33,** 162 (1961).
3. Lovelock, J. E., and S. R. Lipsky, *J. Am. Chem. Soc.*, **82,** 431 (1960).
4. McWilliam, I. G., and R. A. Dewar, *Gas Chromatography* (D. H. Desty, Ed.), Vol. 2, p. 142, Butterworths, London, 1958.
5. Schmauch, L. J., and R. A. Dinerstein, *Anal. Chem.*, **32,** 343 (1960).

CHAPTER 20

Introduction to
Electrometric Methods of Analysis

The field of electroanalytical chemistry encompasses a wide variety of techniques based upon the various phenomena occurring within an electrochemical cell. The amount or concentration of a component is sensed in terms of (1) the effect of that component upon an impressed voltage, (2) the effect of passage of current through the sample in changing the chemical state of the component, or (3) the effect of the component upon an electrode inserted in the sample. Table 20-1 contains a brief summary of the chief kinds of electrometric methods, classified according to the quantity measured.

Table 20-1 | *A Summary of Electrometric Methods of Analysis*

QUANTITY MEASURED	NAME OR DESCRIPTION OF THE METHOD

Electromotive force vs concentration of component of interest	(1) At zero current drawn from the electrodes
	    (a) Potentiometric titration
	    (b) Measurement of ionic activities or concentrations; e.g., pH
	(2) At small constant current
	    (a) Potentiometry at constant current

Electromotive force vs time (at constant current)	(b) Chronopotentiometry

Table 20-1 (cont.) | *A Summary of Electrometric Methods Of Analysis*

QUANTITY MEASURED	NAME OR DESCRIPTION OF THE METHOD
Resistance (conductance)	(1) Conductometric titration
	(2) Concentrations measured by resistance after calibration with known mixtures
Current-voltage	Polarography
Current vs concentration of component of interest	(1) Amperometric titration
	(2) Amperometry at small constant applied potential
Coulombs (current × time)	(1) Coulometry at constant electrode potential
	(2) Coulometric titration
Weight of separated phase	Electrogravimetry

The general relationships between current, potential, and composition of an electroactive system are depicted in the three-dimensional representation of Fig. 20-1. The various types of two-dimensional variations observed in the diverse techniques can be visualized from the intersection with the solid surface of a plane perpendicular to a particular axis. For example, at any particular concentration a polarographic curve may be obtained by changing the voltage and observing the current. Amperometric titration curves are obtained by observing the current at a constant voltage. A plane corresponding to zero current intersects the surface to yield the usual potentiometric titration curve.

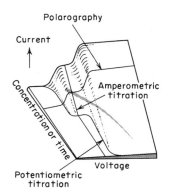

Fig. 20-1. Three-dimensional representation of the relationship between current, potential, and composition of a system. After C. N. Reilley, W. D. Cooke, and N. H. Furman, *Anal. Chem.*, **23**, 1226 (1951). (Courtesy of *Analytical Chemistry.*)

Types of Electrochemical Cells

There are two types of electrochemical cells: galvanic (or voltaic) and electrolytic. A galvanic cell consists of two electrodes and one or more solutions (i.e., two half-cells) and is capable of spontaneously converting chemical energy more or less completely into electrical energy and supplying this energy to an external source. In these cells, a chemical reaction involving an oxidation at one electrode and a reduction at the other electrode occurs. The electrons evolved in the oxidation step are transferred at the electrode surface, pass through the external circuit, then return to the other electrode where reduction takes place. When one of the chemical components responsible for these reactions is depleted, the cell is no longer capable of supplying electrical energy to an external source and the cell is "dead."

If electrical energy is supplied from an external source, the cell through which the current is forced to flow is called an *electrolytic cell*. Electrochemical changes are produced at the electrode/solution interfaces, and concentration changes are produced in the bulk of the system. Actually, a galvanic cell is built up from the products of the electrolytic cell that accumulate at the electrodes. If the external current is turned off, the products tend to produce current in the opposite direction.

At the exact point where the galvanic emf is opposed by an equal applied emf, no current flows through the cell in either direction. In this condition of null balance, the potential generated at the interface of an indicator electrode will reflect the composition of the solution phase, provided that the indicator electrode is selected so that its potential is sensitive to the desired component in the solution phase. However, it is not possible to measure the potential of a single electrode, because any electrical contact between the bulk of the solution and an external circuit is itself another electrode/solution interface. It is only possible to measure the potential of one electrode relative to another —the reference electrode. Before we proceed, the matter of electrode potentials requires clarification.

Electrode Potentials

There are two major factors that determine the electrode potential relative to another electrode. First is the electrolytic solution pressure of the element, which is the tendency of an active element to send its ions into solution. At a given temperature and pressure this is a characteristic constant for a stable form of an element, but it varies if the electrode is strained mechanically or if a metastable crystalline form of the metal is present. Second is the activity of the dissolved ions of the element, which in turn varies with their concentration at constant temperature. Depending on the nature of the element and the concentration of its ions in solution, the potential of the electrode may be positive, zero, or negative relative to the solution.

Following the convention adopted by the International Union of Pure and Applied Chemistry at Stockholm in 1953,* electrode potentials are regarded as the emf of cells formed by the combination of an individual half-cell with a standard hydrogen electrode, any liquid junction potential which arises being

---

*A complete account of the several sign conventions and the IUPAC recommendations can be found in a paper by T. S. Licht and A. J. deBéthune in *J. Chem. Educ.*, **34**, 433 (1957).

set at zero. Thus, when the emf of each half-cell is mentioned, what is actually implied is the emf of the cell:

$$\text{Pt, } H_2(1 \text{ atm}) \mid H^+(m = 1.228) \parallel M^{+n}(a = 1), M^0$$

Standard hydrogen electrode   Individual half-cell
Liquid junction

The emf is divided into two contributory electrode potentials, $E^0{}_{H^+,H_2}$ and $E^0{}_{M^{+n},M^0}$, the cell emf being their difference. If all the substances participating in the reversible operation of the cell at a particular temperature are in their standard states, the free energy change of the cell reaction

$$(n/2) H_2 + M^{+n} = nH^+ + M^0 \tag{20-1}$$

will have its standard value $\Delta\mathcal{F}^0$, and the emf of the cell will be the standard cell emf, $E^0{}_{cell}$. These are related by the expression

$$\Delta\mathcal{F}^0 = -nFE^0{}_{cell} \tag{20-2}$$

in which F is the value of the faraday. When the cell reaction is a spontaneous one, $\Delta\mathcal{F}$ is negative; this requires the cell emf to be positive. The convention universally adopted is that the standard potential of the hydrogen electrode shall be taken as zero at all temperatures, thus setting up the normal hydrogen electrode (NHE) scale of electrode potentials. Returning to the expression for the emf of the cell, the electrode potential of the metal half-cell is equal in sign and magnitude to the electrical potential of the metallic conducting lead on the right when that of the similar lead on the left is taken as zero. The expression implies further that a reaction, as shown in Eq. 20-1, occurs when positive electricity flows through the cell from left to right. If this is the direction of the current when the cell is short-circuited, the emf of the half cell (a reduction) will be positive, the reaction will proceed spontaneously (a galvanic cell), and the free-energy change will be negative. Standard electrode potentials for a number of selected half-cell reactions are given in Appendix A.

The individual half-cell on the right is written to represent a metal/metal ion electrode reaction. It could equally well have been written to represent another gas/ion system or ion/ion system; each of these reactions take place at an inert metal electrode, such as gold or platinum.

When the electromotive forces of the half cells

$$Zn \mid Zn^{+2}$$

$$Ag, AgCl \mid Cl^-$$

$$Pt \mid Fe^{+2}, Fe^{+3}$$

are intended, these being oxidation reactions, the reactions implied are

$$Zn \mid Zn^{+2} \parallel H^+ \mid H_2, Pt \qquad Zn^0 + 2H^+ \rightarrow Zn^{+2} + H_2 \tag{20-3}$$

$$Ag, AgCl \mid Cl^- \parallel H^+ \mid H_2, Pt \qquad Ag^0 + Cl^- + H^+ \rightarrow AgCl + 1/2H_2 \tag{20-4}$$

$$Pt \mid Fe^{+2}, Fe^{+3} \parallel H^+ \mid H_2, Pt \qquad Fe^{+2} + H^+ \rightarrow Fe^{+3} + 1/2H_2 \tag{20-5}$$

These electromotive forces should not be called electrode potentials, although they may be denoted oxidation potentials.

To lessen the confusion that has arisen over the years concerning the two terms—electrode potential, an observed, invariant physical quantity, and the emf of a half-reaction, which may be defined as a reduction reaction or as an oxidation reaction—it should be remembered that the two terms are distinctly different. The sign of the emf of a half-reaction depends on the direction in which the reaction is written. Only when written as a reduction reaction will the sign of the emf of the half-reaction correspond to the sign of the electrode potential.

If direct electrical measurements prove impractical, the position of a couple in the standard electromotive series may be determined by thermochemical measurements, from equilibrium studies, or from kinetic experiments that show whether the half-cell is oxidizing or reducing relative to couples of known potentials.

Effect of Concentration on Electrode Potentials

The potential E of any electrode is given by the generalized form of the Nernst equation

$$E = E^0 + \frac{RT}{nF} \ln \frac{a_{ox}}{a_{red}} \tag{20-6}$$

Where E^0 is the standard electrode potential, R is the molar gas constant (8.316 VQ/degree), T is the absolute temperature, n is the number of electrons transferred in the electrode reaction, F is the faraday, and a_{ox} and a_{red} are the activities of the oxidized and reduced forms, respectively, of the electrode action. If concentrations are substituted for activities, common logarithms for natural logarithms, and numerical values inserted for the constants, assuming the temperature to be 25°C, the Nernst equation becomes

$$E = E^0 + \frac{0.0591}{n} \log \frac{[ox]}{[red]} \tag{20-7}$$

A change of one unit in the logarithmic term changes the value of E by $59.15/n$ mV. For many analytical purposes, a system is considered quantitatively converted when 0.1 percent or less of the original electroactive species remains. For a metallic ion-metal system, such as the Ag^+/Ag^0 system,

$$E = E^0 + 0.0591 \log [Ag^+] \tag{20-8}$$

the value of the electrode need shift by only $3 \times 0.0591 = 0.177$ V, or in general, by $3 \times 0.0591/n$ volt for a quantitative conversion. On the other hand, for an ion-ion system, such as Fe^{+3}/Fe^{+2},

$$E = E^0 + 0.0591 \log \frac{[Fe^{+3}]}{[Fe^{+2}]} \tag{20-9}$$

the shift would depend on the original concentration of both ions.

Effect of Complex Formation on Electrode Potentials

The effect of reagents that can react with one or both participants of an electrode process will be examined next. The simplest case involves a single ionic species formed over a range of concentrations of complexing agent. A typical example is the silver ion/silver metal couple in the presence of aqueous ammonia, where the $Ag(NH_3)_2^+$ complex ion constitutes the major ionic species in the solution phase.

The formation of the silver diammine complex is represented by the equilibrium

$$Ag^+ + 2NH_3 \rightleftharpoons Ag(NH_3)_2^+ \tag{20-10}$$

for which the formation constant is written as

$$K_f = \frac{[Ag(NH_3)_2^+]}{[Ag^+][NH_3]^2} = 6 \times 10^8 \tag{20-11}$$

For the half-reaction involving the silver ion/silver couple,

$$Ag^+ + e^- = Ag^0 \tag{20-12}$$

the Nernst equation is expressed by Eq. 20-8. Combining Eq. 20-11 with Eq. 20-8 yields the potential of a silver electrode in aqueous ammonia systems,

$$E = E^0 + 0.0591 \log \frac{1}{K_f[NH_3]^2} + 0.0591 \log [Ag(NH_3)_2^+] \tag{20-13}$$

The shift in electrode potential caused by the complexing agent is contained in the second term of Eq. 20-13.

For a couple involving two oxidation states of a metal in solution, such as the aquo-cobalt species,

$$Co^{+3} + e^- = Co^{+2}; \qquad E^0 = 1.84 \text{ V} \tag{20-14}$$

in the presence of aqueous ammonia, both the cobalt(II) hexammine and the cobalt(III) hexammine species predominate. The respective formation constants are

$$\frac{[Co(NH_3)_6^{+2}]}{[Co^{+2}][NH_3]^6} = K'_f = 10^5 \qquad \frac{[Co(NH_3)_6^{+3}]}{[Co^{+3}][NH_3]^6} = K''_f = 10^{34} \tag{20-15}$$

Substitution of these values into the Nernst equation for the cobalt system gives

$$E = E^0 + 0.0591 \log \frac{K'_f}{K''_f} + 0.0591 \log \frac{[Co(NH_3)_6^{+3}]}{[Co(NH_3)_6^{+2}]} \tag{20-16}$$

Here the shift in potential is a function of the ratio of the formation constants for each electroactive species. Generally, the higher oxidation state will form the more stable complex and, if it does, the shift in electrode potential will be in the negative direction.

The application of electrode potential data to systems is complicated by the occurrence of unsuspected reactions involving hydrolysis, dissociation, and association. Often the equilibrium constants required to correct for these effects are not known. For example, the ferricyanide-ferrocyanide couple is markedly affected by pH. Instead of the tabulated value of $+0.36$ V, solutions containing equal concentrations of the two species yield potentials of $+0.71$ V, $+0.56$ V, and $+0.48$ V when measurements are made in 1.0 M, 0.1 M, and 0.01 M hydrochloric acid media. Both the ferrocyanide and ferricyanide ions are known to associate with hydrogen ions; however, the $H_4Fe(CN)_6$ is a weaker acid, and the third and fourth steps of ionization ($pK_3 = 3$; $pK_4 = 4.3$) indicate significant formation of $H_2Fe(CN)_6^{-2}$ in solution.

Reference Electrodes

Before one can measure the emf of a cell that contains an indicator electrode, it is necessary to have also a reference electrode whose behavior is reproducible and constant. The reference electrode should be relatively easy to assemble from materials and chemicals ordinarily available and, once prepared, should be stable and possess an invariant potential over an extended period of time, even during passage of the small currents necessary in obtaining measurements. The potentials of several reference electrodes are given in Table 20-2.

Table 20-2	Electrode Potentials of Reference Electrodes in Volts as a Function of Temperature			
TEMPERATURE, °C	0.1 M CALOMEL	1.0 M CALOMEL	SATURATED CALOMEL	1.0 M Ag/AgCl
0	0.3357	0.2883	—	0.2365
10	.3362	.2868	0.2528	.2314
15	.3360	—	.2508	.2286
20	.3358	.2844	.2476	.2256
25	.3356	.2830	.2444	.2223
30	.3353	.2815	.2417	.2190
38	.3352	—	.2375	—
40	.3345	.2782	.2379	.2121
50	.3315	.2745	.2308	.2045
60	.3248	.2702	.2235	.1965
80	—	—	.2083	.1787
95	—	—	—	.1651

The ultimate reference electrode is a normal hydrogen electrode (NHE), a platinized platinum electrode immersed in a solution of 1.228 N hydrochloric acid (unit activity), and the hydrogen gas at 760 mm pressure. The properties of this electrode are described more fully on page 587. For convenience, the hydrogen gas electrode is usually replaced by a secondary reference electrode, most often a mercury/mercurous chloride or a silver/silver chloride electrode. Each is an electrode of the second kind (q.v.).

Calomel Electrodes

Calomel electrodes comprise a nonattackable element, such as platinum, in contact with mercury, mercurous chloride (calomel), and a neutral solution of potassium chloride of known concentration and saturated with calomel. The half-cell may be represented by

$$\text{Hg} \mid \text{Hg}_2\text{Cl}_{2\text{ saturated}}, \quad \text{KCl } (x M)$$

where x represents the molar concentration of potassium chloride in the solution. The saturated calomel electrode (SCE), in which the solution is saturated with potassium chloride (4.2 M), is commonly used because it is easy to prepare and maintain. For accurate work the 0.1 M or 1.0 M electrodes are preferred, because they reach their equilibrium potentials more quickly and their potential depends less on temperature than does the saturated type.

Construction of some commercial versions of calomel electrodes is illustrated in Fig. 20-2. A typical one consists of a tube 5–15 cm in length and 0.5–1.0 cm in diameter. The mercury-mercurous chloride paste is contained in an inner tube connected to the saturated potassium chloride solution in the outer tube by means of an asbestos fiber or ground glass seal in the end of the outer tubing. An electrode such as this has a relatively high resistance

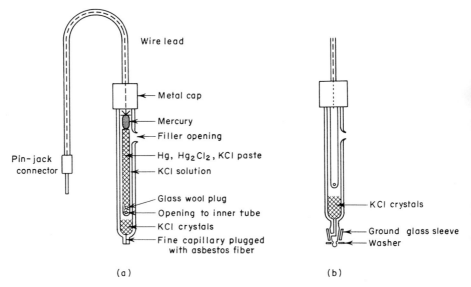

Fig. 20-2.   Calomel electrodes: (a) fiber type and (b) sleeve type.

(2000–3000 Ω) and very limited current-carrying capacity before exhibiting severe polarization.

The saturated calomel electrode exhibits a perceptible hysteresis following temperature changes, due in part to the time required for solubility equilibrium to be established. Those designed for measurements at elevated temperatures have a large reservoir for potassium chloride crystals. Calomel electrodes become unstable at temperatures above 80°C and should be replaced with silver/silver chloride electrodes.

In measurements in which any chloride ion contamination must be avoided, the mercurous sulfate and potassium sulfate electrode may be used.

Silver/Silver Chloride Electrodes

The silver/silver chloride electrode consists of metallic silver (wire, rod, or gauze) coated with a layer of silver chloride and immersed in a chloride solution of known concentration that is also saturated with silver chloride. The cell formed is

$$\text{Ag} \mid \text{AgCl}_{saturated}, \quad \text{KCl}(xM)$$

It is a small compact electrode and can be used in any orientation. Electrode potentials are known[1] up to 275°C.

Preparation of the silver chloride coating can be more difficult than fabrication of a calomel electrode. Silver chloride is appreciably soluble in concentrated chloride solution, necessitating the addition of solid silver chloride to assure saturation in the bridge solution, yet entailing the risk that silver chloride may precipitate at the liquid junction when it is in contact with a solution of low chloride-ion content.

In nonaqueous titration studies this electrode occupied a preeminent position for many years, although the calomel electrode can and has been employed in virtually all types of solvent systems. Reproducibility of results vary from ±10 to ±20 mV in the more aqueous solvent mixtures, to ±50 mV in the nearly anhydrous media. Special salt bridges are often necessary.

Salt Bridges and Liquid Junctions

Connection between a separate reference and indicator electrode (or anode and cathode in electrolytic cells) is usually by a junction which allows the passage of ions but does not permit the solutions to mix. Various styles of electrolyte junction have been designed: a ground glass plug or tapered sleeve, a wick of asbestos fiber sealed into glass, an agar bridge rendered conductive by an electrolyte, a porous glass plug, a dual-junction glass rivet, and a flowing junction involving a palladium annulus or capillary drip. No single type can be used in all situations.

At the boundary between two dissimilar solutions (or solids), there is always a fairly high resistance, which involves an appreciable ohmic drop. A junction potential is always set up. It results from the fact that the mobilities of positive and negative ions diffusing across the boundary are unequal. Because of this difference, one side of the boundary accumulates an excess of positive ions. The junction potential adds to or subtracts from the potential of the reference electrode, depending on which side of the boundary becomes positive. The junction potential is less when the ions of the electrolyte have nearly the same mobilities. Potassium chloride (or NH_4NO_3) is a preferred solution in a salt bridge because the mobilities of potassium and chloride ions are nearly equal and are practically unaffected by temperature. When a saturated solution comprises one side of a boundary, the junction potential amounts to 1 or 2 mV under many aqueous solution conditions unless the second solution is strongly acidic or alkaline, since the hydrogen and hydroxyl ion mobilities are much greater than other ions. Approximate liquid-junction potentials are given by Milazzo[2] for a number of boundary systems.

The leakage rate of the bridge solution should be low, but satisfactory performance depends upon continuous, unimpeded, positive flow of the filling solution through the junction. The asbestos fiber and palladium annulus junction provide a small electrolyte flow, only 0.1–0.01 ml per day. Day-to-day stability of the junction potential is 2 mV for the asbestos fiber junction, 0.2 mV for the palladium annulus, and 0.06 mV for the ground glass sleeve. The asbestos fiber junction is good for general use, although it tends to clog in some media, especially colloids and suspensions. The palladium annulus is recommended for microtitrations and pH measurements for clinical solutions and applications under high pressure or vacuum. The ground glass sleeve is better for precipitation titrations, titrations in nonaqueous solvent systems, and the handling of colloids and suspensions. Double junction, sleeve type salt bridges overcome problems with leakage of undesirable ions into the sample solution or compatibility of filling and sample solutions (e.g., nonaqueous systems).

Bibliography

Clark, W. M., *Oxidation-Reduction Potentials of Organic Systems*, Williams and Wilkins, Baltimore, 1960.

Latimer, W. M., *Oxidation Potentials*, 2nd ed., Prentice-Hall, Englewood Cliffs, N. J., 1952.

Lingane, J. J., *Electroanalytical Chemistry*, 2nd ed., Interscience, New York, 1958.

Ives, D. J. G., and G. J. Janz, *Reference Electrodes*, Academic Press, New York, 1961.

Literature Cited

1. Greeley, R. S., W. T. Smith, Jr., M. H. Lietzke, and R. W. Stoughton, *J. Phys. Chem.*, **64**, 652, 1445 (1960).
2. Milazzo, G., *Elecktrochemie* (translated by W. Schwabl), p. 98, Springer-verlag, Vienna, 1952.

Potentiometric Methods

Potentiometric methods embrace two major types of analyses: the direct measurement of an electrode potential from which the concentration of an active ion may be derived, and the changes in the electromotive force of an electrolytic cell brought about through the addition of a titrant.

Electrode Systems

Potentiometric methods are based upon the quantitative relationship between the emf of a cell as given by the distribution of potential:

$$E_{cell} = E_{reference} + E_{indicator} + E_{junction} \qquad (21\text{-}1)$$

and the concentration of a component of interest, as expressed by the Nernst equation for the indicator electrode, which is sensitive to the desired component. Reference electrodes are expected to assume a potential which is independent of the composition of the solution. Hopefully, the junction potential is assumed to remain more or less constant. When these conditions obtain, the indicator electrode can supply information about the concentration or nature of substances capable of exchanging electrons.

Reference electrodes and liquid-junction potentials have been discussed in Chapter 20. Now we need to consider the indicator electrode. In physical shape it may be in the form of a wire, a billet, or a button set in plastic or glass. It may respond directly to a given ion activity in the solution, indirectly through one or more equilibria involving a precipitate or complex species, or to the ratio of an ion-ion system.

Inert Electrodes

The potential of an inert electrode, usually gold or platinum, immersed in a solution containing both the oxidized and reduced states of a homogeneous and reversible oxidation-reduction system, should reflect the ratio of the two oxidation states. The only role of this type of electrode is to provide or accept electrons. An example is platinum in contact with a solution of ferric and ferrous ions. For the half-reaction

$$Fe^{+3} + e^- = Fe^{+2}; \qquad E^0 = 0.76 \text{ V} \qquad (21\text{-}2)$$

the Nernst expression is

$$E = 0.76 + 0.0591 \log \frac{[Fe^{+3}]}{[Fe^{+2}]} \qquad (21\text{-}3)$$

Platinum electrodes are unsuitable for work with solutions containing powerful reducing agents, such as chromous, titanous, and vanadous ions, because platinum catalyzes the reduction of hydrogen ion by these reductants at the platinum surface. Consequently, the interfacial electrode potential will not reflect the changes in the composition of the solution. In these cases a small pool of mercury will serve because of the high overpotential associated with the deposition of hydrogen gas on a mercury surface.

In many redox titrations, the inert electrode is not reversible for one of the half-reactions, as in the case for thiosulfate in iodometric titrations. However, if the nonreversible system attains chemical equilibrium quickly with a reversible system (e.g., with I_2, I^-), the latter will serve as the potential-determining half-reaction. When chemical equilibrium is attained more slowly, mixed potentials may be involved; these bear no simple relationship to the activities of the reacting species although a stable equilibrium potential is rapidly attained. Sometimes the inert electrode behaves more or less like an oxygen electrode toward dissolved oxygen. If properly preconditioned, it may exhibit a memory for particular systems.

Electrodes of the First Kind

Electrodes of this class are reversible with respect to the ions of the metal phase. They consist of a metal in contact with a solution of its own ions, e.g., silver dipping into a silver nitrate solution. For the half-reaction

$$Ag^+ + e^- = Ag^0; \qquad E^0 = 0.80 \text{ V} \qquad (21\text{-}4)$$

the Nernst expression is

$$E = 0.80 + 0.0591 \log [Ag^+] \qquad (21\text{-}5)$$

By convention, the activity of the pure massive metal (or any solid phase) is taken as unity.

Electrodes of metals more negative than hydrogen are usually irreversible, and the irreversibility becomes especially noticeable when the corresponding metal ion concentration becomes very small, as it will in the vicinity of an end point in a potentiometric titration. As a result, electrodes of this type are limited to silver, copper, and mercury.

Simple amalgam electrodes also belong among electrodes of this class. For zinc, the reaction at the electrode is

$$Zn^{+2} + Hg^0 + 2e^- = Zn(Hg) \tag{21-6}$$

and the electrode potential is

$$E = E^0 + 0.029 \log \frac{[Zn^{+2}]}{[Zn(Hg)]} \tag{21-7}$$

where the term in the denominator is the activity of the zinc in the amalgam. Because the activity of zinc in the amalgam is constant, the expression reduces to an equation whose potential is directly dependent upon the zinc ion concentration (cf. Chapter 25 on polarography).

Electrodes of the Second Kind

A metal coated with a layer of one of its sparingly soluble salts comprises an electrode of the second kind. Consider a silver wire coated with a thin deposit of silver chloride. At the silver/silver chloride solution interface the electrochemical equilibrium is

$$AgCl(s) + e^- = Ag^0 + Cl^- \tag{21-8}$$

In addition, there is a chemical equilibrium

$$AgCl(s) = Ag^+ + Cl^-; \qquad K_{sp} = 1 \times 10^{-10} \tag{21-9}$$

Combining Eqs. 21-5 and 21-9, we arrive at the Nernst expression for Eq. 21-8

$$E = 0.80 + 0.0591 \log K_{sp} - 0.0591 \log [Cl^-] \tag{21-10}$$

This reduces to

$$E = 0.22 - 0.0591 \log [Cl^-] \tag{21-11}$$

Experiment has shown that a silver wire without any visible coating will give the same effect when dipped into a solution of chloride, perhaps because the wire is covered by a minute layer of silver chloride through oxidation by the air. The sparingly soluble substance need only saturate the solution near the electrode.

Electrodes of this kind can be used for the direct determination of the activity of either the metal ion or the anion in the coating; also as an indicator electrode to follow titrations involving either. Several oxide electrodes are responsive to hydrogen ions; included among them is the antimony/antimonous oxide electrode (page 589). The calomel and silver/silver chloride reference electrodes belong to this class.

Electrodes of the Third Kind

As an example of an electrode of the third kind, consider the situation upon adding an equilibrated paste of a mercurous salt mixed with a second insoluble salt, each containing the same anion, to a pool of mercury. For an oxalate system, the electrolytic cell would be represented by

Hg, $Hg_2C_2O_4$, CaC_2O_4 | Ca^{+2} || KNO_3 salt bridge || Reference electrode

The electrode responds to the concentration of calcium ions.

A restriction involves the relative solubilities of the metal salts involved—in the example, the mercurous salt must be less soluble (or less dissociated) than the calcium salt. If solubility equilibrium is attained slowly, such electrodes will be rather sluggish. Favorable conditions have been studied.[11]

A version of this type of electrode is often used in chelometric titrations. A small mercury electrode (Fig. 21-1) in contact with a solution containing metal ions to be titrated and a small added quantity of mercury(II)-chelonate, HgY^{2-n}, exhibits a potential corresponding to the following half-cell:

$$Hg, HgY^{2-n}, MeY^{2-n}, Me^{+2}$$

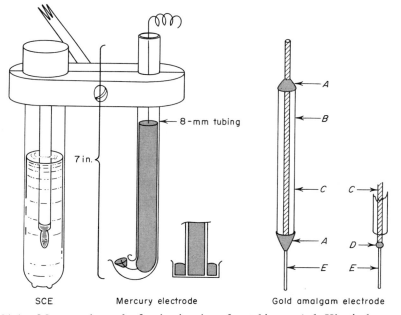

SCE   Mercury electrode   Gold amalgam electrode

Fig. 21-1. Mercury electrodes for the titration of metal ions. *A*, de Khotinsky cement; *B*, glass tubing; *C*, brass rod; *D*, solder; *E*, gold wire. After C. N. Reilley, R. W. Schmid, and D. W. Lamson, *Anal. Chem.*, **30,** 953 (1958). (Courtesy of *Analytical Chemistry*.)

The potential for this indicator electrode may be found by combining the Nernst expression for a mercury electrode with the equations for the stability constants of the 1:1 mercury(II)-chelonate and the 1:1 metal chelonate (assumed here to be a divalent metal). This yields the expression

$$E = E^0_{Hg^{+2},Hg} + 0.0296 \log \frac{[Me^{+2}][HgY^{2-n}]K_{MeY}}{[MeY^{2-n}]K_{HgY}} \qquad (21\text{-}12)$$

Because the slight solubility of mercury(II)-chelonate assures saturation of the solution (at least in the vicinity of the electrode), the potential of the electrode bears a linear relationship with log $[Me^{+2}]$, and consequently, the electrode serves as a pM indicator electrode in the titration of a large number of metal ions with EDTA and related chelons. The mercury electrode can take the form of a pool or be an amalgamated platinum electrode or a gold amalgam electrode.[19]

Measurement of Cell emf

The act of measuring the emf of a cell must not cause a significant departure from equilibrium conditions. However, all instruments for measuring emf, or for indicating that a measuring circuit is off balance, require a transfer of electricity in order to operate. Although this quantity of electricity may be vanishingly small, it follows in principle that the electrodes of a cell must be "working electrodes," that is, electrodes which are not subject to serious polarization when a small current flows across the electrode-solution interface. The choice of instrument is restricted to a potentiometer or a vacuum-tube voltmeter (VTVM). Commercial pH meters are VTVM whose scales are usually calibrated in voltage units as well as pH units. These meters are discussed in Chapter 22.

The Potentiometer

The potentiometric method of measurement is a comparison technique (i.e., a null-balance method) in which the unknown cell emf to be measured is compared with a known emf source. The instrument with which this comparison is made is called a *potentiometer*.

The circuit diagram of a simple potentiometer is shown in Fig. 21-2. A working battery, a 1.5-V or 3.0-V dry cell, is connected across a rheostat

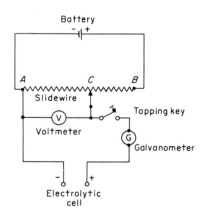

Fig. 21-2. A simple, functional potentiometer. Voltmeter, 0–3 V (10,000 Ω resistance); galvanometer, 10^{-6} amp/mm; slidewire, 100 Ω resistance; battery, 1.5-V or 3.0-V dry cell.

or slidewire *AB* which need not be uniform in resistance or scaled. Proper polarities observed, a set of working electrodes is connected at point *A* and to a contactor *C*, through the null-point galvanometer and a tapping key. The voltmeter *V* is connected so the current that actuates it does not flow through the cell or galvanometer. By trial, a position of the contactor is sought such that the flow of current through the galvanometer is minimized when the tapping key is momentarily depressed. In this condition the potentiometer is balanced or "nulled." The emf of the pair of working electrodes is read directly on the voltmeter. Precision is limited by the precision of the voltmeter reading.

A more elegant potentiometer is shown in Fig. 21-3. The slidewire may be

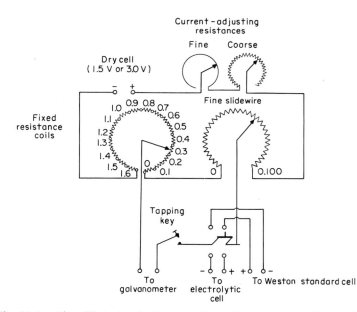

Fig. 21-3. Simplified circuit diagram of a typical commercial potentiometer.

merely a straight wire of resistance metal stretched tightly along a meter scale, a spiral wire wound on a drum of insulating material, or a set of coils, each of fixed resistance, in series with an extended slidewire, also of the same resistance. The latter arrangement permits interpolation between the coil settings. In the typical student potentiometer, there may be 15 fixed 10-Ω resistors, each of which corresponds to an increment of 0.1 V, and a 10-Ω slidewire graduated into 100 divisions which permits direct reading to 1 mV. Connections are made with heavy-gauge copper wire and soldered contact points. Sliding contact is made with metal leaves brushing over large-area surfaces. The potentiometer scale is calibrated by setting the contactors, C (and C'), at a point which corresponds to the emf of a standard voltage source, for example, a Weston cell. By trial, the voltage drop across the slide-wire is varied by changing the current with a current-adjusting resistance until the flow of current through the galvanometer is minimized. In subsequent use the voltage drop between A and any setting of C (plus C') will be directly proportional to the position of the contactor, that is,

$$E_{cell} = (R_{ACx}/R_{ACs})E_{\text{Weston cell}} \qquad (21\text{-}13)$$

Since the setting $(R_{AC})_s$ was deliberately made equal to $E_{\text{Weston cell}}$,

$$E_{cell} = (R_{AC})_x \qquad (21\text{-}14)$$

in volts.

The sensitivity of a measurement depends ultimately upon the sensitivity of the galvanometer relative to the resistance of the circuit; that is, the current which must be drawn in order to detect a deviation from the null position of the galvanometer. For general purposes, a moving-coil galvanometer whose sensitivity is approximately 10^{-7} amp/mm is suitable. Precise work demands suitably damped multiple-reflection light-spot galvanometers whose sensitivities range up to 10^{-10} amp/mm. When the internal resistance of an electrolytic cell exceeds 1.0 MΩ, the D'Arsonval type of galvanometer is no longer suitable as the null-balance detector. A high-impedance VTVM must be employed.

Example 21-1

Suppose that the true potential between an indicator and a reference electrode in a given solution is 1.0 V, and the internal resistance of the cell is 100 MΩ. If the voltage measuring device has a resistance of 10^9 Ω, the current that will flow in the circuit is

$$i = \frac{E}{R} = \frac{1.0}{10^8 + 10^9} = 9.0 \times 10^{-10} \text{ amp}$$

This current, flowing through the cell resistance, generates a voltage difference across it equal to

$$iR_{cell} = (9 \times 10^{-10})(1 \times 10^8) = 0.09 \text{ V}$$

The voltage is opposite in polarity to the cell emf; hence, the net voltage apparent to the voltmeter is only 0.91 V. The measured voltage is thus 9 percent in error due to the current that flowed during the measurement. In order to reduce the error to the order of 0.1 percent, the resistance of the voltmeter would have to be at least as great as 10^{12} Ω, so that the current being drawn from the electrode is not greater than 10^{-12} amp.

Standard Weston Cells

The accurate measurement of a cell emf requires the use of a standard cell whose emf is precisely known. For this purpose, the Weston cell is almost universally used. A diagram of this cell is shown in Fig. 21-4. It may be represented as follows:

$$\text{Cd(Hg)} \mid \text{CdSO}_4.8/3\text{H}_2\text{O}_{\text{saturated}}, \text{Hg}_2\text{SO}_4 \text{ saturated} \mid \text{Hg}$$

At 25°C the Weston cell has a value of 1.0183 V for the saturated cell and 1.019 V for the unsaturated cell. The latter is obtained by using a slightly undersaturated solution of cadmium sulfate and incorporating no solid cadmium sulfate in the cell itself. Since in the saturated cell the activities of the cadmium and mercurous ions in the solution are invariant at any given temperature, the cell maintains a constant voltage for long periods of time. The cell has a temperature coefficient of about -0.4 mV/°C for the saturated type, and about one-fourth this magnitude for the unsaturated type.

Direct Measurement of Single Ion Concentrations

The direct potentiometric measurement of ion activities is based upon the fact that definite energy level differences exist between two different states of the same matter, and that these differences are proportional to the relative populations of the atoms or ions concerned. In the case of electrolytic solutions, these energy level differences can be measured as an electrode potential, if a suitable indicator electrode is available. The important topic of the measurement of pH is treated separately in Chapter 22.

Metal-Ion-Sensitive Glass Electrodes

When oxides of aluminum and boron replace part of the silica in the glass structure, a glass electrode develops a response to univalent cations other than

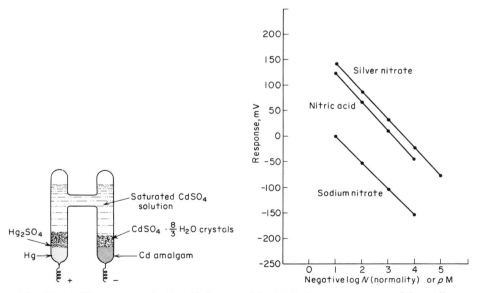

Fig. 21-4. Weston standard cell (saturated type).

Fig. 21-5. Response curves of the sodium-ion electrode to various monovalent cations. (Courtesy of Beckman Instruments, Inc.)

hydrogen ion, but not to polyvalent cations. One type electrode is particularly sensitive for sodium (and silver) ions, as indicated by the calibration curves in Fig. 21-5, and reflects ion concentrations over the range of $1.0–10^{-4}\ M$. Because it responds selectively to silver in the presence of sodium, the electrode is useful in argentometric titrations. The pH response is not entirely nullified; hence cation determinations are usually made on solutions whose pH lie between 7 and 10 (for sodium determinations), and 4 and 8 (for silver determinations). In general, the pH must be adjusted to at least 3 units greater than the highest pAg and 4 units greater than the highest pNa to be measured. When the potassium ion activity exceeds that of sodium by a factor of ten, or lithium and aluminum exceed sodium by a factor of two, the electrode response departs from the theoretical Nernst slope for sodium ion.

The cationic glass electrode has a sensitive tip that is highly specific, in varying degrees of sensitivity, to the monovalent cation: potassium, lithium, silver, hydrogen, ammonium, and sodium. The fundamental factor governing the selectivity of glasses towards ions in solution is thought to ·be the coulombic association, and the free energy change thereof, of metal ions with oxygen ions in the glass lattice.[4]

Cation-sensitive electrodes can be used with most pH meters, especially those equipped with a scale expansion circuit.[7] Their d-c impedance is about 10 MΩ.

Chloride-Ion Concentration

A silver/silver chloride billet electrode, formed from a blended powder of silver and silver chloride molded together under high pressure, is useful for measurement of chloride-ion concentrations either continuously or intermittently. Temperature range of the electrode is $-5°$ to $100°C$. When employed with conventional instruments calibrated in pH or millivolt units, a calibration curve is prepared on semilog paper of millivolts vs chloride-ion concentration. Chloride concentrations in the range from 0.1 to 50,000 $\mu g/ml$ may be sensed; concentrations less than 10 $\mu g/ml$, however, require special precautions. It is advisable to maintain constant temperature during measurement, for the solubility relationship of silver chloride varies markedly with temperature at low concentrations.

For measurements on an intermittent basis, sufficient time should be allowed for the electrode to reach equilibrium with the sample solution. The electrode will exhibit a certain response delay if an attempt is made to measure solutions of grossly different chloride-ion concentrations.

Since the chloride-ion measurement is a type of oxidation-reduction measurement (Eq. 21-11), the electrode cannot be used in solutions containing strong oxidizing or reducing agents. Nor can the electrode be used in solutions which contain ions that form compounds with silver less soluble than silver chloride—e.g., sulfide and bromide. Substances such as ammonia or cyanide which form stable ion complexes with silver must be avoided also.

Null-Point Potentiometry

The method is based on concentration cell measurements. The reference solution in one side of a concentration cell is diluted or made more concentrated by addition of standard reagent, until the concentration of unknown in the unknown half-cell equals that of the concentration in the reference half-cell, as evidenced by zero cell emf.[16] As compared with classical concentration cell measurements,[6] the dependence upon an absolute measurement of cell emf is eliminated. Constant ionic strength is maintained by "swamping" both half-cells with an inert salt or acid.

With silver indicator electrodes, chloride-ion concentrations from 10^{-1} to 10^{-6} M, and iodide-ion concentrations as low as 10^{-8} M are determinable. The response of an inert electrode immersed in a cerium(IV)/(III) system or an iron(III)/(II) system reflects the complexation of cerium(IV) or iron(III) with fluoride ion.

Potentiometric Titration Methods

When a potentiometric titration is being performed, interest is focused upon changes in the emf of an electrolytic cell as a titrant of precisely known concentration is added to a solution of the analyte. The method can be applied to all titrimetric reactions provided that the activity of at least one of the substances involved can be followed by means of a suitable indicator electrode. Usable is any electrode system out of which a change of potential may be derived which follows the Nernst equation. Reproducible equilibrium cell emf is of no concern here. Requirements for reference electrodes are greatly relaxed, and it is only necessary that the response of one of the two electrodes of a pair be substantially greater or faster than that of the other. The cell emf can be measured at zero current (null balance) or with a constant electrolysis current flowing through the cell.

Chief advantages of the potentiometric method are applicability to turbid, fluorescent, opaque, or colored solutions, or when suitable visual indicators are unavailable or inapplicable. The method presents the possibility of a succession of end points in the titration of a mixture. Titrations in nonaqueous media are often dependent upon the method. As compared with color indicators, the end point can be located precisely, even with dilute solutions.

Equipment needed to carry out a classical potentiometric titration is illustrated in Fig. 21-6. In certain instances simplifications in equipment are possible.

Location of the End Point

The critical problem in a titration is to recognize the point at which the quantities of reacting species are present in equivalent amounts—the equivalence point. The titration curve can be followed point by point, plotting as ordinate successive values of the cell emf vs the corresponding volume (or

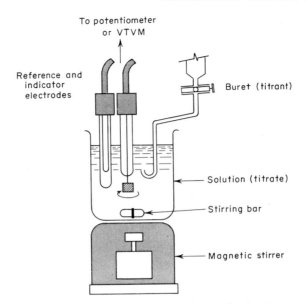

Fig. 21-6. Equipment for potentiometric titrations.

Table 21-1	*Potentiometric Titration Data in Vicinity of an End Point*†		
VOLUME OF TITRANT, ml	CELL EMF, pH UNITS	$\Delta p H/\Delta V$	$\Delta^2 p H/\Delta V^2$
19.50	6.46		
		1.30	
19.60	6.59		+1.00
		1.40	
19.70	6.73		+2.00
		1.60	
19.80	6.89		+9.35
		3.00	
19.85	7.04		+52.0
		5.60	
19.90	7.32		+124
		11.80	
19.95	7.91		−136
		5.00	
20.00	8.16		−24.0
		3.80	
20.05	8.35		−5.00
		3.40	
20.10	8.52		
		1.60	
20.20	8.68		

†Volume at end point = $19.90_0 + 0.050\,[124/(124 + 136)] = 19.92_4$ ml.
pH at end point   = $7.32 + 0.59\,[124/(124 + 136)] = 7.60$.

milliequivalents) of titrant added. Additions of titrant should be the smallest accurately measured increments that provide an adequate density of points across the pH (or emf) range. Typical data are gathered in Table 21-1. Over most of the titration range the cell emf varies gradually, but near the end point the cell emf changes very abruptly as the logarithm of the concentration(s) undergoes a rapid variation. The resulting titration curve will resemble Fig. 21-7. The problem in general is to detect this sharp change in cell emf that occurs in the vicinity of the equivalence point. The equivalence point may be calculated, as will be outlined later. Usually the analyst must be content with finding a reproducible point, as close as possible to the equivalence point, at which the titration can be considered complete—the end point. By inspection the end point can be located from the inflection point of the titration curve: the point which corresponds to the maximum rate of change of cell emf per unit volume of titrant added. Distinctness of the end point increases as the reaction involved becomes more nearly quantitative. Once the cell emf has been established for a given titration, it can be used to indicate subsequent end points for the same chemical reaction.

In the immediate vicinity of the equivalence point the concentration of the original reactant becomes very small, and it usually becomes impossible for the ion or ions to control the electrode potential. The cell emf will become unstable and indefinite because the indicating electrode is no

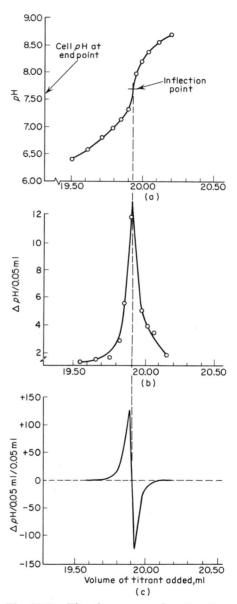

Fig. 21-7. Titration curves for data in Table 21-2. (a) Experimental titration curve, (b) first derivative curve, and (c) second derivative curve.

longer poised—i.e., it is not bathed with sufficient quantities of each electro-active species of the desired redox couple. If the electroactive species are not too dilute, a drop or two of titrant will suffice to carry the titration through the equivalence point and into the region stabilized by the electroactive species of the titrant. However, solutions more dilute than 10^{-3} M generally do not give satisfactory titration end points unless special procedures are employed.

An end point may be located more precisely by plotting successive values of the rate of change of cell emf vs each increment of titrant in the vicinity of the inflection point. Increments need not be equal but should not be too large or too small. The position of the maximum on the first derivative curve, Fig. 21-7, corresponds to the inflection point on the normal titration curve. Once the end point volume is known, the corresponding cell emf at the end point can be obtained from the original titration curve. The end point can be even more precisely located from the second derivative curve, which is obtained by plotting the cell emf-volume acceleration vs the volume of titrant added. At the end point the second derivative becomes numerically equal to zero as the value of the ordinate rapidly changes from a positive to a negative number. Although either of these methods of selecting the end point is too laborious to do manually for each titration, they become feasible with appropriate electronic circuits (Fig. 21-15).

Oftentimes, tabulation of titration data will suffice to locate the end point by interpolation without the necessity of constructing derivative curves. In Table 21-1, the first two columns are original data. The third and fourth columns are the calculated values which would be used to plot the first and second derivative titration curves, respectively. A simple mathematical method for arriving at the pH (or emf) and volume of titrant at the end point is also outlined.

Particularly in acid-base titrations, a titration of a solution prepared like the sample solution, omitting only the sample itself (i.e., a blank), should also be run. In Fig. 21-8, curve B is a conventional titration curve with volume of titrant plotted against pH. Only the inflection at pH 8.0 is immediately apparent. The titration of the blank, curve C, is shown below. When the blank curve is subtracted volume-wise from the sample curve, the resulting curve A shows clearly the presence of two more inflections at pH values of 2.0 and 10.5. The preparation of blank curves is also desirable when handling relatively dilute solutions, when a minor constiutent is suspected in the sample, or when impurities are present in the solvent.

Use of Two Indicating Electrodes

Variation of the difference in electrode potential of two indicating electrodes can be followed sometimes during a titration. Generally only changes in the cell emf, but not the actual value, will be provided. Of course this is sufficient for many titration purposes. Elimination of the usual reference electrode

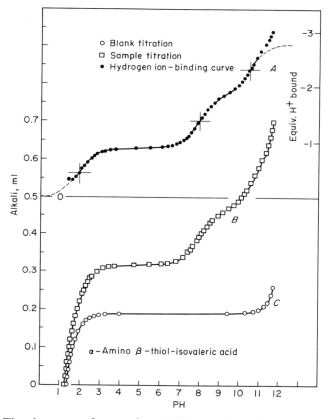

Fig. 21-8. Titration curves for α-amino-β-thioisovaleric acid. After T. V. Parke and W. W. Davis, *Anal. Chem.*, **26**, 642 (1954). (Courtesy of *Analytical Chemistry.*)

and its attendant salt bridge eliminates leakage of the bridge electrolyte and minimizes the liquid junction potential which is desirable when solutions possessing high resistance (true for many nonaqueous systems) are involved.

A simple indicating electrode for reference purposes consists of a platinum (or other type) electrode inserted into the delivery tip from the buret—the buret electrode[21]—or inside a capillary tube which contains a small portion of the original solution—the shielded electrode.[17] These electrodes, pictured in Fig. 21-9, assume a definite though not predictable potential and, since each is in contact with a solution of unchanging composition, maintain a constant potential throughout the titration which may be used for reference. Paired with a second indicating electrode dipping into the main solution, the usual S-shape titration curve is obtained. A platinum electrode serves as reference for most types of titrations. An antimony electrode in the buret paired with an

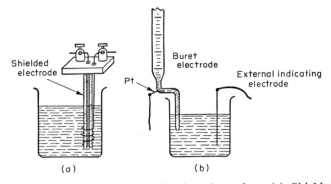

Fig. 21-9. Systems consisting of two-indicating electrodes. (a) Shielded capillary reference electrode and (b) buret electrode.

antimony indicating electrode is useful for a strongly basic titrant such as sodium aminoethoxide in basic nonaqueous solvents.

The glass electrode may be employed as an electrode of reference in a medium of fixed, or buffered, pH or rather high hydrogen-ion concentration. Paired with a silver electrode, the combination finds use in argentometric titrations because leakage from the salt-filling solution of a reference electrode is eliminated. In redox titrations, the glass electrode can be paired with platinum.

A graphite or tungsten electrode placed in the main solution serves well as a reference electrode, although these elements tend to reduce the amplitude of the change of cell emf by reason of their own response curves. This is insignificant in the case of a graphite/platinum electrode pair in neutralization reactions, and the tungsten/platinum pair in many redox systems. With two fast chemical half-reactions, a differential-shaped titration curve is obtained, but when one reaction is slow in establishing its equilibrium at the graphite or tungsten surface, a distorted S-shaped curve is obtained. An informative study of the tungsten electrode is available.[10]

An interesting system is provided by the pair: platinum and platinum/10% rhodium electrodes. Each acts as an indicating electrode of the second kind in neutralization reactions, presumably because of a thin layer of platinum oxide on each surface which renders each electrode responsive to hydrogen ions, in addition to the usual response to redox systems exhibited by an "inert" electrode. Whereas the platinum electrode responds rapidly to changes in solution composition, the platinum/10% rhodium electrode lags ever so slightly. Consequently, if the titrant is added rapidly and uniformly, the pair will exhibit a maximum difference in response at the equivalence point when the logarithmic term in the Nernst expression is changing most rapidly. A first derivative curve is obtained. This pair of electrodes proves useful with automatic differential titrators (q.v.).

Titrations at Constant Electrolysis Current (Polarized Titrations)

Differential electrolytic potentiometry involves the observation of potentials across two indicator electrodes in a stirred solution during the passage of a minute, highly stabilized current. The apparatus required is a pair of wire electrodes, a resistor, a battery, and a meter (Fig. 21-10). Flexible arrange-

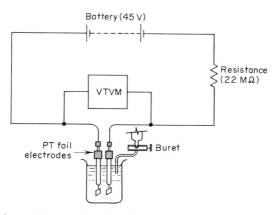

Fig. 21-10. Equipment for conducting titrations at constant electrolysis current (approximately 2 μa with values of voltage and resistance indicated).

ments permit variation of the resistance from 10^6 to 10^{13} Ω and of voltage from 1 to 1200 V with facilities for measuring currents down to 10^{-6} amp. An extra indicator electrode may be added for comparative simultaneous zero-current potentiometric titrations, and a reference indicator electrode may be included so that individual electrode potentials may be monitored.

The electrode chosen must be appropriate to the reaction involved. Glass electrodes are not suitable. The electrode area should be kept small, 0.5 cm² or less, and should be of equal area for reversible reactions. For irreversible reactions there is some advantage in making the inactive electrode smaller. The current density required for optimum differentiation depends on the equilibrium constant of the reaction and especially on the concentration of the titrant. For a 0.1 N titrant it is about 1 μamp cm⁻², and it decreases with decreasing titrant concentration. Good stabilization of the current is required. The ballast load, the product of the ballast resistance in ohms and the source voltage in volts, should exceed 10^9 and preferably 10^{10}. At low values, potentials become unsteady and erratic, and current fluctuations also occur. At very high values, response times increase and the Johnson noise in the ballast resistor increases.

The shape of the titration curve can be predicted from current-voltage curves.[8] For example, consider the titration of copper(II) with EDTA:

$$Cu^{+2} + H_2Y^{-2} = CuY^{-2} + 2H^+ \qquad (21\text{-}15)$$

wherein the indicator electrodes are polarized with the small current indicated by the horizontal dashed line in Fig. 21-11, which contains the pertinent current-voltage curves. The initial potentials adopted by the cathode and anode will be the values at the intersections of the horizontal current line with the current-voltage curves; namely, E and F, respectively. The cell emf

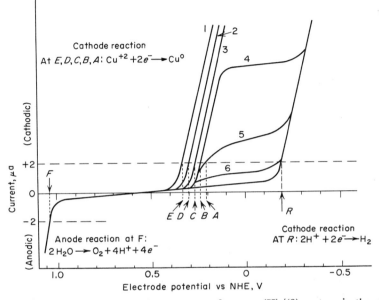

Fig. 21-11. Schematic current-voltage curves of copper (II)/(0) system in the presence of hydrogen ions. The potential scale is approximately real; the current scale is arbitrary.

is then the difference, $F - E$. Curves 1 through 3 represent the Cu^{+2}/Cu^0 system at the beginning of the titration, when the titration is 91 percent complete, and when it is 99 percent complete. The difference in potential between each succeeding curve (from E to D, and from D to C) is 29.6 mV, as would be expected from the Nernst expression. The place where each curve intersects the zero-current axis (points E, D, and C) is the "null potential," as measured by the usual zero-current technique. However, in the vicinity of the equivalence point the mass transfer characteristics of the cupric ions up to the cathode surface must be considered. A concentration gradient is established and the current carried through the cell by the cupric ions becomes limited (curves 4 through 6). As soon as the current-carrying ability (the limiting current plateau) of the copper system falls below the electrolysis current being forced through the circuit, the potential of the cathode shifts quickly from point A to a value set by any other redox system which is able to poise the electrode, as, for example, the reduction of hydrogen ions at point R. All this time the other indicating electrode has maintained a constant potential because the anode reaction at its surface is the oxidation of water (EDTA is not electroactive). The appearance of the titration curve is shown by curve 1 in Fig. 21-12.

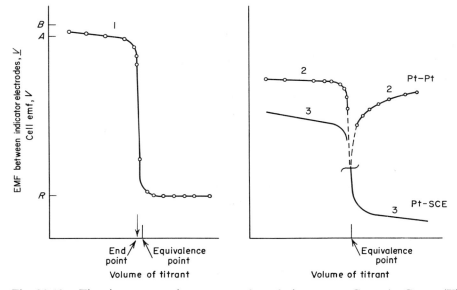

Fig. 21-12. Titration curves using constant electrolysis current. Curve 1: Copper(II) titrated with EDTA (data from Fig. 21-11); Curve 2: Iron(II) titrated with cerium(IV) at finite current flow; and Curve 3: Iron (II) titrated with cerium(IV) under zero-current condition.

When the titrant also possesses a set of current-voltage curves which lie within the boundary conditions imposed by the solvent and supporting electrolyte, the titration curve resembles curve 2 in Fig. 21-12. Such a titration would be iron(II) with cerium(IV). Prior to the equivalence point the cathode potential is established by the Fe^{+3}/Fe^{+2} system. After the equivalance point the cathode potential becomes stabilized and the anode becomes the indicating electrode for the Ce^{+4}/Ce^{+3} system. Titration curves take the form of the first derivative of the zero-current indicator electrode curve. The anode curve is displaced along the volume axis so that its potential rise occurs before that of the zero-current electrode, while the cathode curve is displaced in the opposite direction.

The vertical displacement of anode from cathode—the differential potential —then traces a sharp peak. The magnitudes of the anode lead and cathode lag are proportional to the differentiating current density. With electrodes of equal area, reversible reactions and equal diffusion coefficients, the lead and lag are equal and a symmetrical differential curve is obtained. However, the end point and equivalence point usually do not coincide, because of imperfection in reversibility of the electrode processes. Also electrolysis is occurring continuously at both electrodes; often the products are removed from the solution—for example, the copper(II) ions in the first example would be reduced to metallic copper at the cathode. The titration error will be a function of the electrolysis current and the time taken for the titration. Furthermore, the end point will be premature by an amount that is a function of the magnitude of the electrolysis current in comparison with the concentration of unreacted analyte, which gives rise to the limiting current of identical value. The titration error can be minimized by setting the electrolysis current at as small a value as possible and providing rapid stirring to improve the rate of mass transfer to (and away from) the electrode surfaces.

A major advantage of titrations at constant current is that only one electroactive system needs to be present, either the titrant or the analyte. In fact, no advantage accrues in use of the method for two electroactive systems which establish steady potentials rapidly. For the latter case the largest potential change occurs prematurely with polarized electrodes, whereas it occurs exactly at 100 percent of the equivalence-point volume when no electrolysis current is flowing.

Automatic Titrators

When performed manually so as to give a detailed titration curve or merely to locate precisely an end point, a potentiometric titration is a tedious and time-consuming operation. For routine analyses the method does not have the speed and simplicity of comparable procedures employing visual indicators. Automatic equipment for performing, and if desired, recording, the titration curve in its entirety provides a logical solution to the problem, albeit at some capital outlay. An automatic titrator enables an operator to perform other tasks while the instrument delivers the requisite titrant and stops the delivery at a preset end point or, perhaps, continues beyond the end point when the entire curve is traced. Maximum benefit may be obtained from the equipment, particularly with slow reactions. The addition of the next increment will be delayed until the measured electrode potential falls below the value selected for the end point. The instrument will continue to repeat the final stages of the titration until a stable end point is obtained.

The basic features of commercial automatic titrators are alike. In the delivery unit, with no current passing through the solenoids, a short length of flexible tubing is squeezed shut in some manner. With the instrument set up and the buret level read, a switch is pressed to start the titration. The solenoid is energized, the pressure on the tubing is released, and titrant is allowed to flow through the delivery tip. The titration proceeds at a fast rate until a predetermined distance from the end point, when the anticipation control automatically slows the delivery of titrant. At the end point the delivery is stopped.

The anticipation control is the key to highly precise automatic operation. It is set to anticipate the end point (preset on some instruments) by a chosen number of pH units or millivolts. The decreased rate of delivery precludes overstepping the preset end point while permitting a rapid delivery of titrant during the initial stages of the titration.

A schematic circuit diagram of an automatic titrator is shown in Fig. 21-13.

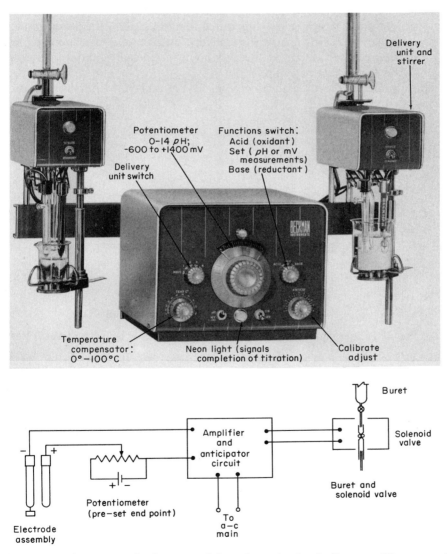

Fig. 21-13. An automatic titrator and its schematic circuit diagram. (Courtesy of Beckman Instruments, Inc.)

The control unit includes a calibrated potentiometer, a null-sensing amplifier, and an anticipator circuit. To operate, the potentiometer is set at the pH or potential expected at the end point, the electrode assembly is immersed in the sample solution, and the operating switch is depressed. The difference signal arising between the cell emf and the preset voltage on the potentiometer is amplified, and the output from the amplifier energizes the solenoid valve, or relay, in the delivery unit. As the end point is approached, the difference signal diminishes. When the two signals are matched, the delivery of titrant is stopped. If, upon additional mixing, the cell emf falls below the preset voltage, the controller relay will cause the delivery unit to dispense more titrant. This cycling repeats until a stable end point is reached without ever overshooting the end point.

An automatic recording titrator (Fig. 21-14) plots the complete titration

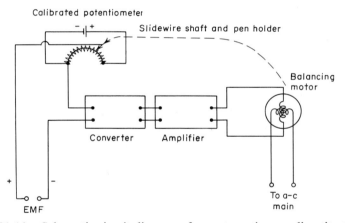

Fig. 21-14. Schematic circuit diagram of an automatic recording titrator.

curve. It is started and stopped manually. In this type of titrator the difference signal arises between the cell emf and an adjustable voltage from a calibrated potentiometer whose slidewire contact is positioned by the same motor that drives the recorder pen. The difference signal (always very small) is converted to alternating current by a converter and then amplified. The output of the amplifier energizes one winding of the two-phase motor; the other winding is permanently connected to the 110-V main. Thus, the servosystem involves actuating the motor which drives the contactor on the slidewire of the potentiometer in a direction to match the cell emf and to preserve the null-balance. The pen traces the change in balancing voltage (and the corresponding cell emf) on the chart to provide a permanent record. No previous knowledge of the end point is required, and reevaluations can be made at a later date. This feature is a distinct advantage where completely unknown systems are run and where there may be successive inflection points. The chart-drive motor and syringe-delivery or constant buret-delivery unit must be synchronized to ensure a constant delivery rate throughout the entire operation.

In place of conventional burets, the delivery units can be designed around various types of syringes. These are operated by a motor-driven micrometer screw which actuates the plunger. Syringe-delivery units offer protection to the titrant from atmospheric oxidation, contamination, and loss of volatile solvent. To ensure rapid signal response, the delivery tip is placed close to the indicating electrode and in front, with respect to the direction of stirring, so that the indicating electrode is bathed by solution at a more advanced stage of titration.

A fully automatic commercial unit (Fisher Scientific Co.) will accept serially samples placed in a turntable. After each titration the turntable rotates, indexes the next sample solution beneath the electrode holder, lowers the electrode assembly, delivery tip, and stirring rod into the beaker, and actuates the titration switch to perform the next titration. Each time, the syringe is refilled with titrant and a printer prints out the amount of titrant delivered. This type of automatic instrument is ideal for performing multiple analyses in which the fundamental analytical procedure remains fixed over a period of time, as in a quality control situation.

The equivalent of plotting a second derivative curve is accomplished automatically in another type of autotitrator,[15] whose schematic diagram is shown in Fig. 21-15. The cell emf is fed directly to the control grid of a conventional amplifier. The amplified voltage is differentiated by a resistance-capacitance differentiator, R_1C_1, and the output is closely proportional to the first derivative

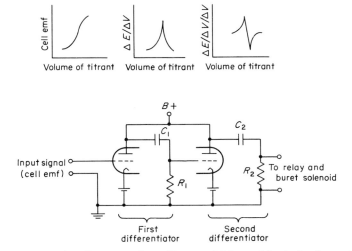

Fig. 21-15. Schematic diagram of a (Sargent-Malmstadt) derivative-autotitrator. (Courtesy of E. H. Sargent & Co.)

curve. Repeating the operation once again produces an output proportional to the second derivative of the titration curve, and a voltage ideally suited to trigger a relay system which closes the buret delivery unit (or terminates an external electrolysis signal) at the inflection point of the titration curve. All types of reactions are applicable if they possess a suitable reaction rate and the concentrations lie within 0.1–0.01 N. The derivative-autotitrator is definitely not applicable to titrations based on very slow reactions, whether these are the electrode reactions themselves, the fundamental chemical reaction, or intermediate secondary reactions. The method is invalidated when acceleration of cell emf becomes a function of some rate of change other than that of the rate of delivery of titrant, which is 1–6 ml/min. Too slow a delivery rate means too small a second derivative signal, which may not actuate the thyratron relay. The relay must be set to reject spurious fluctuations to prevent a premature cutoff of the delivery unit; consequently, the actuating signal at the true end point must exceed any operating fluctuations.

Sensitivity

The sensitivity of a potentiometric titration is limited by the accuracy of the measurement of electrode potentials at low concentrations. Below 10^{-5} N, the residual current interferes with zero-current potentiometry. Similarly, the current in polarized titrations cannot be fixed at less than the residual current which is the order of the limiting current for a 10^{-5} N solution. A 10^{-2} N solution can therefore be titrated with an accuracy of 0.1 percent, but a 10^{-3} N solution can be titrated with an accuracy of only 1 percent. Other titration methods are needed for solutions more dilute than 10^{-3} N, the limiting concentration in potentiometric titration methods.

Classes of Chemical Titrations

The principles governing the major types of potentiometric titrations will be examined briefly as a foundation on which potentiometric methods can be built. For more detailed discussion, the reader is referred to Lingane,[12] Charlot, Badoz-Lambling, and Tremillon,[2] or Kolthoff and Elving.[9]

Oxidation-Reduction Reactions

Oxidation-reduction reactions can be followed by an inert indicator electrode. The electrode assumes a potential proportional to the logarithm of the concentration ratio of the two oxidation states of the reactant or the titrant, whichever is capable of properly poising the electrode. Let us assume that the reactant is the principal system—e.g., the iron(III)/(II) system in the titration with cerium(IV). At the start of the titration the minute amount of one oxidation form (ferric ion) leaves the system without a definite electrode potential. However, as soon as a drop or two of ceric solution has been added, the concentration ratio of ferric/ferrous ions assumes a definite value and, likewise, the electrode potential of the indicator electrode. During the major portion of the titration the electrode potential changes gradually. Only as the equivalence point is approached does the concentration ratio change rapidly again. Past the equivalence point, the indicator electrode ceases to be affected by the ferric/ferrous system and will assume a potential dictated by the ceric/cerous system. For various ratios of ferric/ferrous system, the corresponding electrode potential is

Ratio, Fe^{+3}/Fe^{+2}	10^{-3}	10^{-2}	10^{-1}	1	10	100	1000
Electrode potential,	0.594	0.653	0.712	0.771	0.830	0.889	0.948

At the equivalence point in an oxidation-reduction reaction,

$$a_{ox_1} + b_{red_2} = a_{red_1} + b_{ox_2} \qquad (21\text{-}16)$$

the electrode potential is the weighted mean of the standard electrode potentials of reactant and titrant:

$$E_{equiv.\,pt.} = \frac{bE_1^0 + aE_2^0}{a + b} \qquad (21\text{-}17)$$

When $a = b$, the titration curve is symmetrical around the equivalence point, but when $a \neq b$, the titration curve will be markedly asymmetrical and the point of inflection will not coincide with the equivalence point. The difference will depend upon the ratio a/b. If $a > b$, the inflection point will occur when excess oxidant$_1$ is present in solution, that is, before the equivalence point. The inverse is true when $b > a$.

Chemical reactions (acid-base changes, complexation) can displace the electrode potentials in a way that often lends itself to a quantitative treatment. For example, cobalt salts may be titrated potentiometrically by making use of the reaction with standard potassium ferricyanide solution in the presence of a high concentration of ammonium citrate and of aqueous ammonia.[3] Under these conditions, the aquo-cobaltous ion is converted to the corresponding ammine complex which can be oxidized to the cobalt(III) hexammine complex by the ferricyanide. Although the aquo-cobalt species possess a very high reduction potential,

$$Co^{+3} + e^- = Co^{+2}; \qquad E^0 = 1.84 \text{ V} \qquad (21\text{-}18)$$

as compared with the ferri/ferrocyanide couple,

$$Fe(CN)_6^{-3} + e^- = Fe(CN)_6^{-4}; \qquad E^0 = 0.36 \text{ V} \qquad (21\text{-}19)$$

in the presence of aqueous ammonia, the ammine complexes of cobalt predominate. The formation constants for the cobalt(III) hexammine and cobalt(II) hexammine are

$$\frac{[Co(NH_3)_6^{+3}]}{[Co^{+3}][NH_3]^6} = 10^{34} \qquad \frac{[Co(NH_3)_6^{+2}]}{[Co^{+2}][NH_3]^6} = 10^5$$

Substituting the values for cobaltic and cobaltous ions into the Nernst equation for the cobalt equilibrium gives

$$E = 1.84 + 0.059 \log \frac{[Co(NH_3)_6^{+3}]}{[Co(NH_3)_6^{+2}]} + 0.059 \log \frac{10^5}{10^{34}} \qquad (21\text{-}20)$$

Although the difference between the reduction potential of the titrant and the cobalt system is slightly less than the minimum of 0.36 V, the difference of 0.26 V does permit the reaction to proceed within about 1 percent of completion. Air must be rigorously excluded and the temperature held at 0°–5°C. Usually the standard ferricyanide solution is added in excess and the unused amount is back-titrated with standard aquo-cobaltous solution. Replacement of ammonia by a stronger complexing agent, such as ethylenediammine, results in a greater difference in cell emf and a sharper end point. Unfortunately, additional interferences are introduced, whereas the titration in ammoniacal medium is virtually specific for cobalt.

Complexation, coupled with control of pH, plays an important role in the titration of manganese(II) ion with permanganate ion in pyrophosphate solution:[14]

$$4Mn^{+2} + MnO_4^- + 8H^+ + 15H_2P_2O_7^{-2} = 5Mn(H_2P_2O_7)_3^{-3} + 4H_2O \qquad (21\text{-}21)$$

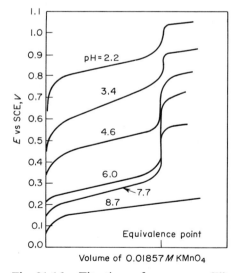

Fig. 21-16. Titration of manganese(II) with permanganate ion in pyrophosphate solution. After J. J. Lingane and R. Karplus, *Ind. Eng. Chem., Anal. Chem.,* **18,** 191 (1946). (Courtesy of *Analytical Chemistry.*)

The change in potential at the equivalence point at a pH between 6 and 7 is large (about 300 mV); the equivalence point potential is 0.47 V vs SCE. The method is subject to few interferences. Vanadium causes difficulties when the amount is equal to or larger than the amount of manganese because of its sluggish reoxidation by permanganate, unless the titration is performed at a pH of 3.5. The titration curves are shown in Fig. 21-16.

In general, the reduction potential of a metal complex, or of a metal ion in equilibrium with a complexing agent, is decreased by complex formation. Three effects are involved:[13] The coordinating effect is the combination of a metal ion with an electron donor. The charge effect is simply the charge on the resulting complex. The electronic effect relates to the degree of stability of the electron configuration in the metal complex. The first two always tend to increase the tendency toward oxidation to a higher valence state; the third effect may work in either direction.

Ion Combination Reactions

Reactions in this category involve the formation of a sparingly soluble compound or a slightly dissociated material. Argentometric titrations are illustrative. For the chloride, and similar precipitation systems, the titration curve can be calculated from Eq. 21-11 or equivalent equations. At the equivalence point,

$$[Ag^+] = [Cl^-] = \sqrt{K_{sp}} \qquad (21\text{-}22)$$

Typical halide titration curves are shown in Fig. 21-17.

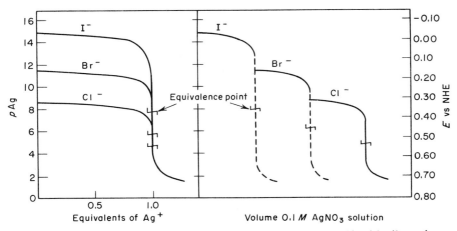

Fig. 21-17. Theoretical titration curves of halide ions (0.1 M each) with silver nitrate solution and a silver indicator electrode. The dashed segments are the separate curves for iodide and bromide ions.

For an ion combination reaction involving a soluble complex, such as

$$Ag^+ + 2CN^- = Ag(CN)_2^- \qquad (21\text{-}23)$$

the electrode potential is given by the expression

$$E = 0.80 + 0.059 \log \frac{1}{K_f [CN^-]^2} + 0.059 \log [Ag(CN)_2^-] \qquad (21\text{-}24)$$

where K_f is the formation constant of the dicyanoargentic ion. At the equivalence point

$$[Ag^+] = \tfrac{1}{2}[CN^-] = \sqrt[3]{\frac{[Ag(CN)_2^-]}{4K_f}} \qquad (21\text{-}25)$$

The magnitude of the inflection point on the titration curve depends upon the degree of insolubility of a precipitate, or the extent of dissociation of a complex. Successive titrations are feasible when one compound is markedly less soluble, or dissociated, than another; that is, $K_1/K_2 \geq 10^6$ and $K_1 > 10^8$, where the constants symbolize solubility product constants or instability constants. Application of potentiometric titration methods to precipitation reactions is limited by factors adversely affecting the character of precipitates, and applicability to this category is restricted by unavailability of indicator electrodes.

To extend the applicability of potentiometric methods in ion-combination reactions, ingenious indicating systems have been devised. These are generally redox systems which are introduced in small quantity, and which, associated with an indicating electrode, enable the activity of certain ions to be followed. For example, in the presence of a small and constant concentration of iodine, an inert platinum electrode will indicate the activity of iodide ions in an argentometric titration. The titration of zinc can be followed with the ferricyanide/ferrocyanide half-reaction. A small amount of ferricyanide ion is added to the sample solution (zinc ferricyanide is fairly soluble) and the titration performed with addition of potassium ferrocyanide solution

$$3Zn^{+2} + 2K^+ + 2Fe(CN)_6^{-4} \rightarrow K_2Zn_3[Fe(CN)_6]_2 \downarrow ; \quad K_{sp} \simeq 10^{-17}$$
$$(21\text{-}26)$$

The electrode potential can be calculated from the Nernst expression for the ferricyanide/ferrocyanide half-reaction

$$E = 0.36 + 0.059 \log \frac{[Fe(CN)_6^{-3}]}{[Fe(CN)_6^{-4}]} \qquad (21\text{-}27)$$

and the individual concentrations of potassium, zinc, and ferrocyanide ions present at each stage of the titration. As the equivalence point is approached, the electrode potential changes rapidly and reflects the change in ferrocyanide concentration.

A versatile indicator electrode for titration of metal ions with EDTA was described on page 545.

Acid-Base Reactions

Titrations of acids and their conjugate bases can be broken down conveniently into several categories, including consideration of nonaqueous solvent systems. Indicating electrodes are discussed in Chapter 22, pages 587–592.

In the titration of a completely dissociated acid (or base), the pH at the equivalence point is that of pure water (in the absence of dissolved CO_2), namely, 7. For a reaction to be complete within 0.1 percent, the initial concentration must not be less than 10^{-4} N.

For an incompletely dissociated acid, the hydrogen-ion concentration at the equivalence point is given by the expression

$$[H^+] = \sqrt{\frac{K_w K_a}{C_{salt}}} \qquad (21\text{-}28)$$

As the acid becomes progressively weaker, the distinctness of the inflection point diminishes, and the pH at the equivalence point shifts to higher values. Feasibility of a particular titration is determined by the product, $K_a[HA]$. For an uncertainty of 0.1 percent or less, and in aqueous solution, the product should exceed 10^{-8}, assuming that the titrant is completely dissociated and 0.1 N in strength.

The accuracy with which two successive equivalence points may be located will depend on the absolute and relative strengths of the two acid groups and their concentrations. Difficulty is encountered in locating the break in the titration curve at a ratio of the first to the second dissociation constant of 100, and the ratio must be greater than 10^5 to 1 to give a sharp inflection point. However, by using transparent masks with theoretical curves, it is possible to estimate pK_a values at the extremes of the pH scale where only a portion of the complete theoretical curve can be distinguished (see Fig. 21-8).[18] Groups whose pK_a values differ by as little as 1 pK unit can be resolved, provided at least half of each hydrogen ion-binding curve is free from overlap and permits matching with the masks. The chart in Fig. 21-18 relates pK_a values with a number of dissociating groups of organic acids. In addition, it is possible to distinguish further between various types of acidic and basic groups by performing the titration at several temperatures or in a nonaqueous solvent. The heat of dissociation for a monocarboxylic acid is usually less than 2 kcal mole^{-1}, and for a phenolic group it is about 6 kcal mole^{-1}, whereas for basic groups it is generally larger than 5 kcal mole^{-1}.

Acid-Base Titrations in Nonaqueous Solvents

Many acids or bases that are too weak for determination in water become susceptible to titration in appropriate nonaqueous solvents. The resolution of mixtures, particularly dibasic acids, may be improved.

The major considerations in the choice of a solvent for acidimetric reactions are its acidity and basicity, its dielectric constant, and the physical solubility of a solute. Acidity is important because it determines to a large extent whether or not a weak acid can be titrated in the presence of a relatively high concentration of solvent molecules. Phenol, for example, cannot be titrated as an acid in aqueous solution because water is too acid and present in too high a concentration to permit the phenolate ion to be formed stoichiometrically by titration with a base. In other words the intrinsic basic strength of the phenolate and hydroxide ions are not sufficiently different for the reaction:

$$\phi\text{—OH} + OH^- \rightleftharpoons \phi\text{—O}^- + H_2O \qquad (21\text{-}29)$$

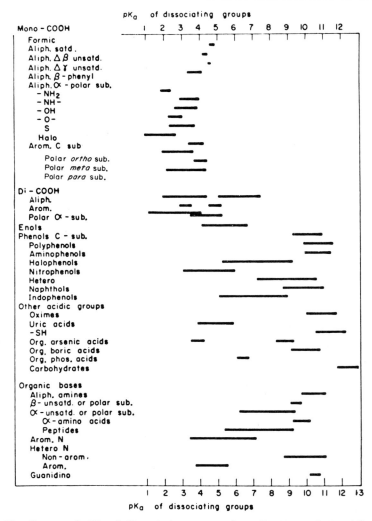

Fig. 21-18. Range of pK_a of dissociating groups from literature data. After T. V. Parke and W. W. Davis, *Anal. Chem.* **26,** 642 (1954). (Courtesy of *Analytical Chemistry.*)

to proceed quantitatively to completion. In less acid solvents, such as dimethylformamide or pyridine, this titration can be carried out readily with a stronger basic titrant, the alkoxide ion:

$$\phi\text{—OH} + \text{RO}^- \rightarrow \phi\text{—O}^- + \text{ROH} \tag{21-30}$$

The solvent must not be strongly basic if resolution of the strong and moderately strong acids is to be achieved, because of the "leveling effect" of a basic solvent on the stronger acids. In ethylenediamine, sulfonic and carboxylic acids are both levelled to the ammonium type ion; thus,

$$\left.\begin{array}{c} RSO_3H \\ RCOOH \end{array}\right\} + H_2N\!-\!C_2H_2\!-\!NH_2 \rightarrow \left.\begin{array}{c} RSO_3^- \\ RCOO^- \end{array}\right\} + H_2N\!-\!C_2H_2\!-\!NH_3^+ \qquad (21\text{-}31)$$

whereas in dimethylformamide only the sulfonic acid is levelled. An ideal solvent for the titration of an acidic mixture should be sufficiently weak in acidity to permit titration of the most weakly acid component and sufficiently weak in basicity to permit resolution of the strongest components.

Most of the acids can be classified as uncharged, positively charged, or negatively charged. The members of any one class may vary in relative strength to a certain extent as the dielectric constant of the solvent is changed, but in general they behave in a similar manner. However, acids of different charge type change greatly in relative strength as the solvent is changed. The positively charged acids, such as the ammonium ion, become stronger relative to an uncharged acid, such as acetic acid, as the dielectric constant is reduced. The protolysis reaction

$$NH_4^+ + SH \rightleftharpoons SH_2^+ + NH_3 \qquad (21\text{-}32)$$

does not result in the formation of new charged species as does the reaction

$$HOAc + SH \rightleftharpoons SH_2^+ + OAc^- \qquad (21\text{-}33)$$

Negatively charged acids, such as the bisuccinate ion, tend to become weaker relative to an uncharged acid.

The apparent strength of an acid in a solvent may be expressed empirically in terms of its midpoint potential or half-neutralization point. The difference in the midpoint potentials of two acids in the same solvent can serve as a measure of the resolution achieved; it should be roughly 200–300 mV, depending on the slope of the plateaus in the titration curves.

Solvents may be divided into several classes. Amphiprotic solvents are those which possess both acidic and basic properties. They undergo self-dissociation, or autoprotolysis, that is,

$$SH + SH \rightleftharpoons SH_2^+ + S^- \qquad (21\text{-}34)$$

to produce a solvonium ion SH_2^+ and a solvate ion S^-. Representative amphiprotic solvents include water, the lower alcohols, and glacial acetic acid. The product of the ion concentrations gives the autoprotolysis constant

$$K_{auto} = [SH_2^+][S^-] \qquad (21\text{-}35)$$

It is 14 in water, varies from 15 to 19 in alcohols, and is about 14 in glacial acetic acid. Aprotic solvents have no acidic or basic properties, and if their dielectric constant is low, they have low ionizing power. These include aromatic and aliphatic hydrocarbons and carbon tetrachloride. Finally, there are a number of solvents with basic properties but essentially no acidic tendencies. These include amines, dimethylformamide, ketones, and ethers.

When a solute is dissolved in an amphiprotic solvent, the position of equilibrium depends on the relative acidic or basic strengths of the solute and solvonium ion (or solvate). The position of the autoprotolysis ranges, relative to the intrinsic strength of index acids, is indicated schematically in Fig. 21-19.

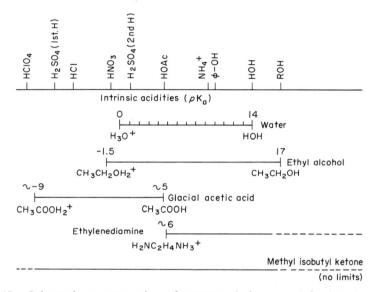

Fig. 21-19. Schematic representation of autoprotolysis ranges of selected solvents, in relation to the intrinsic strength of certain index acids. Influence of dielectric constant is not included.

Although a base must have a dissociation constant greater than about 10^{-8} for successful titration in water, the accurate determination of compounds with basic dissociation constants (in water) of 10^{-12} is possible with a less basic solvent such as glacial acetic acid. Amino acids yield sharp end points, since the carboxylic acid group is swamped, thus removing the zwitterion equilibrium. Commonly, the titrant is a solution of perchloric acid in dioxane or glacial acetic acid which has been standardized with either potassium acid phthalate (phthalic acid is the product) or sodium carbonate. In an analogous fashion, basic solvents enhance the properties of weak acids. Phenols and carboxylic acids produce distinctive end points in butylamine or ethylenediamine, and these plus sulfonic acids can be differentiated from each other in dimethylformamide. The titrant is usually sodium aminoethoxide or a quaternary base.

The effect of the dielectric constant coupled with the decrease in solvent basicity is well illustrated for the titration of oxalic acid, succinic acid, or sulfuric acid singly in isopropyl alcohol. In each instance two well-resolved end points are present, whereas in water a single inflection is obtained for sulfuric and succinic acid and only a poorly defined inflection indicates the existence of the first replaceable hydrogen in oxalic acid. Similarly, solutions containing perchloric and acetic acid exhibit two distinct inflections, and the degree of resolution is comparable with that of the dibasic acids. The reason is the difference in charge type between perchloric and acetic acid (or more correctly the solvonium ion and acetic acid), which makes the change in relative strength so large. Likewise, dibasic acids are a mixture of a positively charged acid (the solvonium ion) or an uncharged acid (succinic acid, first hydrogen) and a negatively charged acid (HSO_4^-, $HC_2O_4^-$, etc.) In addition, the weaker basicity of isopropyl alcohol lessens the extent of "leveling" of the first hydrogen of sulfuric acid and the perchloric acid, which increases the difference between the midpoint potentials of the titration curves.

Aprotic solvents have certain advantages over the other classes of solvents. By not interacting with dissolved solutes, no leveling action is exerted. Except for the influence of the dielectric constant, each solute will exhibit its intrinsic acidic or basic strength. Having no autoprotolysis limits, the range of applicability is limited only by the strength of the acid or base titrant. The former is usually perchloric acid or p-toluene sulfonic acid, the latter a quaternary ammonium base. If suitably spaced, a series of successive end points can be achieved in a solvent such as methyl isobutyl ketone (Fig. 21-20).

The electrode systems vary with the solvent employed. The glass-calomel electrode system is suitable where the solvent is either acetonitrile, an alcohol, or a ketone, or for differentiating titrations in dimethylformamide, provided

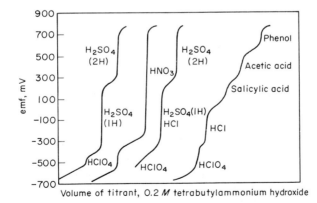

Fig. 21-20. Resolution of acid mixtures in methyl isobutyl ketone. Glass-calomel electrodes. After D. B. Bruss and G. E. A. Wyld, *Anal. Chem.* **29**, 232 (1957). (Courtesy of *Analytical Chemistry.*)

that the titrant consists of either potassium hydroxide or alkoxide or tetra-alkyl-ammonium hydroxide (i.e., no sodium compounds). It is advisable to replace the aqueous salt bridge of the calomel electrode by either a saturated solution of potassium chloride in methanol or N-tetraalkyl ammonium chloride solution. A glass electrode does not function as an indicator electrode in the more strongly basic solvents if the titrant contains sodium compounds. In this situation a pair of antimony electrodes forms a satisfactory combination, one dipping into the titrant and the other into the solution. A platinum electrode sealed into the buret and a glass indicator electrode give stable and reproducible potentials when solutions in methyl isobutyl ketone are titrated with quaternary ammonium hydroxide in benzene-methanol. The chloranil indicator electrode has been used in glacial acetic acid. Solvents with low dielectric constant exhibit such high internal resistance that it is difficult to find electrodes which function satisfactorily. When the dielectric constant is 5 or less, potentiometric methods are unsuitable. A review of potentiometric electrode systems in nonaqueous titrimetry has been published.[20] Brief surveys of titrations in nonaqueous media are available and should be consulted for operational details.[1,5]

Other Nonaqueous titrations

Other types of reactions are also feasible in nonaqueous solvents, particularly when solubility is a strong consideration. In petroleum products, the titration of hydrogen sulfide and mercaptans, either singly or in combination, is done in a 1:1 mixture of methanol-benzene (plus dissolved sodium acetate) with a methanolic solution of silver nitrate. The electrode system consists of a silver indicator electrode coupled with a calomel reference electrode connected to the sample solution by means of an agar bridge containing 3 percent potassium nitrate in the gel.

The Karl Fischer method for the determination of water is an excellent example of a well-known redox reaction conducted in methanol solution. Iron(II) perchlorate is useful as a reductant in glacial acetic acid.

LABORATORY WORK

General Instructions for Potentiometric Titrations

Assemble the titration equipment as shown in Fig. 21-6, or consult the manufacturer's bulletin supplied with a particular commercial instrument. The reference electrode may be a calomel or silver-silver chloride half-cell. The indicator electrode is assigned by the instructor or else is selected from among those discussed in the text for the appropriate class of titration.

Stir the solution in the beaker gently without producing a vortex. Measure or read the potential difference between the electrodes before any titrant is added. Record the reading and the volume of titrant in the buret. Add 2–3 ml of titrant from a 50-ml buret (or appropriate quantities from other size burets or microsyringes), stir for about 30 sec or until the potential difference becomes constant, measure the cell emf, and record the reading of the titrant volume in the buret. Additions of titrant should be of such volume to provide an adequate density of points across the pH or emf range. For example, about 5–10 points per pH unit (or $59/n$ mV) are adequate in the region where a group (pK_a or E^0) is being titrated and in the vicinity of an end point. Continue the additions until the equivalence point has been exceeded by 1–2 pH units (or 50–100 mV).

Plot the cell emf as ordinates vs the volume of titrant added as abscissa. Draw a smooth curve through the points. Locate the equivalence point by calculating the anticipated cell emf. Compare this value with the point on the curve which corresponds to the steepest portion of the titration graph. Also locate the end point by plotting $\Delta E/\Delta ml$ for small increments of titrant in the vicinity of the end point, or by estimating the volume of titrant by the method outlined in Table 21-1.

EXPERIMENT 21-1 ACID-BASE TITRATIONS

A. Aqueous Systems

Each student will be assigned a titration system; the sample size and titrant strength will be specified. Suggested systems are:

1. Acetic acid, 0.1 N, with 0.1 N NaOH.
2. Sodium carbonate, 0.05 M, with 0.1 N HCl.
3. Phosphoric acid, 0.05 M, with 0.1 N NaOH.
4. Boric acid, 0.1 N, in the presence of mannitol (4 g/50 ml volume) with 0.1 N NaOH.

B. Glacial Acetic Acid

Perchloric acid, 0.1 N, is prepared by adding slowly with stirring 8.5 ml of 72 percent perchloric acid to 900 ml of glacial acetic acid (or purified dioxane) followed by 30 ml of acetic anhydride. Allow the mixture to stand for 24 hr before use. Standardize against primary grade potassium hydrogen phthalate.

Suggested basic solutes:

1. Potassium hydrogen phthalate. Dissolve approximately 0.1 g (weighed accurately) in 25 ml of glacial acetic acid with gentle boiling to effect solution. Insert a pair of small glass and calomel electrodes. Stir the solution and titrate with 0.1 M perchloric acid solution, using a 10-ml buret.
2. Sodium carbonate. Dissolve approximately 0.05 g of the anhydrous salt, weighed accurately.
3. Urea. Dissolve about 0.05 g, weighed accurately, in acetic anhydride. A blank titration is recommended.
4. Aniline, or chloroaniline. Dissolve about 0.1 ml, weighed accurately by difference from a small beaker.

C. Methanol or Ethanol

Hydrochloric acid, 0.1 N, is prepared by adding 9.0 ml of reagent grade hydrochloric acid to 1 liter of absolute methanol. It is standardized against sodium carbonate as follows: Dissolve approximately 0.1 g of freshly dried sodium carbonate (weighed accurately) in the smallest possible amount of glacial acetic acid, taking care to avoid loss during the effervescence. Evaporate to dryness and dissolve the residue in 20 ml of methanol. Insert a glass-calomel electrode system. The calomel electrode should be the sleeve-type salt bridge or some type of salt bridge with a relatively large area of solution contact. Titrate with 0.1 N hydrochloric acid.

Potassium hydroxide, 0.1 M, is prepared by dissolving approximately 6 g of pellets in a small volume of methanol in the absence of air. Dilute to 1 liter with additional methanol and protect the solution from absorption of carbon dioxide. Standardize against the 0.1 M hydrochloric acid solution.

Suggested titration systems:

1. Mixture of hydrochloric acid and acetic acid. Place in a 150-ml beaker 10 ml of 0.1 M hydrochloric acid in methanol and 0.1 ml of glacial acetic acid. Dilute to 50 ml with methanol. Titrate with 0.1 M potassium hydroxide in methanol. Repeat the titration with the inclusion of 10 ml of water in the solvent mixture. Note the change in position of the titration curve for hydrochloric acid and the indistinctness of the first inflection point.

2. Oxalic acid. Dissolve 0.2 g (weighed accurately) in 50 ml of isopropyl alcohol and titrate with 0.1 M potassium hydroxide solution. Be sure to titrate both replaceable hydrogen ions.

EXPERIMENT 21-2   OXIDATION-REDUCTION TITRATIONS

A. Determination of Cobalt with Ferricyanide

Into a 250-ml beaker place 10 ml of 0.05 M potassium ferricyanide solution, 10 ml of 5 percent ammonium citrate solution, and 100 ml of 5 N aqueous ammonia solution. Immerse the beaker in crushed ice (or add crushed ice directly) to lower the temperature to 3°–5°C. Insert a smooth platinum foil electrode and a calomel or other reference electrode. Stir the solution and titrate with 0.1 N cobaltous solution (prepared from effluoresced crystals of the reagent grade cobalt sulfate heptahydrate). The cell emf falls from about 300 mV initially to about 100 mV in the vicinity of the end point when the reference electrode is a SCE.

An unknown cobalt solution may be determined by adding an aliquot to an excess of standard potassium ferricyanide solution, and titrating the unused ferricyanide solution with standard cobalt solution. For samples that may be high in iron, use 30% ammonium citrate solution.

B. Determination of Manganese with Permanganate

Place 150 ml of a 0.27 M sodium pyrophosphate solution (freshly prepared) in a 400-ml beaker, and adjust the pH to 6–7 by the addition of concentrated sulfuric acid from a graduated pipet. Add 25 ml of 0.05 M manganese solution and, if necessary, readjust the pH. Insert a bright platinum electrode and a calomel electrode. Stir the solution and titrate with 0.01 M potassium permanganate solution. Remember that the permanganate ion undergoes only a 4-electron change to the $+3$ state. If the vanadium content exceeds the manganese content in a steel sample, adjust the pH to 3.4–4.0.

C. Other Suggested Systems

Titrate a ferrous sulfate solution, 0.05–0.1 M, with either 0.1 M ceric sulfate, 0.02 M potassium permanganate, or 0.0167 M potassium dichromate in a solution that is approximately 1 M in sulfuric acid. Repeat the titration with the addition of 5 ml of 85 percent phosphoric acid to complex the ferric ions as they are produced.

EXPERIMENT 21-3   ARGENTOMETRIC TITRATION OF HALIDES

A. Determination of a Single Halide

Place 25 ml of a 0.1 M sodium chloride solution in a 250-ml beaker and dilute to about 100 ml with water. Insert a bright silver wire plus a reference electrode with a fiber-type connection or with an intermediate salt bridge containing a nonhalide filling solution. Titrate with 0.1 M silver nitrate solution.

Repeat the titration with a 0.1 M potassium iodide or a 0.1 M potassium bromide solution. Note the differences in cell emf at the midpoint of each titration curve; compare with the calculated values.

Repeat the titration with a 0.1 M potassium iodide solution in an aqueous solution that is 1 M in ammonia. Note the difference in the position of the titration curve after the equivalence point.

B. Mixture of Halides

Place 10 ml of a 0.1 M sodium chloride solution and 15 ml of a 0.1 M potassium iodide solution in a 250-ml beaker and dilute to about 100 ml with water. Titrate with 0.1 M silver nitrate solution.

Repeat the titration with this change: titrate the iodide ion in an ammoniacal solution, and after the end point is reached, acidify the solution with nitric acid and titrate the chloride ion.

C. Determination of Iodide with Redox Indicating System

Place 25 ml of a 0.1 M potassium iodide solution in a 250-ml beaker and dilute to about 100 ml with water. Add about 0.5 ml of a saturated solution of iodine in alcohol, freshly prepared. Insert a bright platinum electrode and a calomel reference electrode. Titrate with 0.1 M silver nitrate solution.

EXPERIMENT 21-4   COMPLEXOMETRIC TITRATIONS WITH EDTA

Mercury indicator electrode. Lightly amalgamate a gold wire electrode with mercury, or use a mercury pool emanating from a J-tube or other small cup-like container (Fig. 21-1). Wash the mercury with dilute nitric acid and then rinse thoroughly with distilled water. After each titration, rinse the mercury thoroughly.

PROCEDURE

Place 25 ml of the metal-ion solution (approximately 0.05 M) in a 250-ml beaker, add 25 ml of the appropriate buffer solution (about 0.5 M in each component), and 1 drop of 0.0025 M mercury(II) EDTA solution. Insert the amalgam electrode and a calomel reference electrode. Titrate with 0.05 M disodium dihydrogen ethylenediaminetetraacetate.

Conditions for the titration of selected metal ions are:

At pH 2 in chloroacetic acid system—thorium, mercury, or bismuth.

At pH 4.7 in a sodium acetate-acetic acid buffer—copper, zinc.

At pH 10 in an ammonium chloride-aqueous ammonia buffer—cobalt.

EXPERIMENT 21-5   DETERMINATION OF ZINC WITH FERROCYANIDE

Place 25 ml of 0.1 M zinc chloride solution in a 250-ml beaker. Add approximately 10 g of ammonium chloride and 1 ml of 0.001 M potassium ferricyanide solution. Insert a bright platinum electrode and calomel reference electrode. Titrate with a 0.067 M potassium ferrocyanide solution.

EXPERIMENT 21-6   DETERMINATION OF APPARENT DISSOCIATION CONSTANTS

Dissolve about 10 mg of the base (or acid) in exactly 5 ml of water. Insert a set of micro glass and calomel electrodes. Titrate with a 2 M HCl (or KOH) solution delivered by a microsyringe buret having a total capacity of 0.2 ml and reading to 0.0002 ml. Obtain readings over the interval of pH from the initial point up to pH 12.

Plot the conventional titration curve. Repeat the titration on a blank solution prepared like the sample solution, omitting only the sample itself. Subtract the blank

curve volumewise from the sample curve, and plot the resulting data. Estimate the
pK_a value from each inflection within ± 0.05 pK_a unit. For overlapping inflection
points, or inflection points near the extremities of the pH scale, it is desirable that the
curves be replotted as equivalents of bound hydrogen ion vs pH on a uniform scale—
perhaps 1 in. per equivalent and 0.5 in. per pH unit. Compare with a theoretical curve
calculated from the expression

$$pH = pK_a + \log [a/(1 - a)]$$

where a is the fraction of the sample in the dissociated state for acids or the associated
state for bases.

Make a tentative assignment of structure of the dissociating group from the chart
in Fig. 21-18 if your compound is an organic acid or base.

E X P E R I M E N T   2 1 - 7   TITRATION   WITH   CONSTANT   ELECTROLYSIS CURRENT

Connect one terminal of a 45-V dry cell through a 22-MΩ resistor to a platinum foil
electrode, and connect the other terminal of the dry cell directly to a second platinum
foil electrode. Also connect a high-impedance VTVM across the terminals of the
platinum electrodes. The circuit should resemble Fig. 21-10.

Place 10 ml of a 0.1 M ferrous sulfate solution in a 150-ml beaker. Add 40 ml of
water and 3 ml of concentrated sulfuric acid. Insert the pair of platinum electrodes.
Titrate with 0.1 M ceric sulfate solution.

Repeat the titration with 0.0167 M potassium dichromate solution as the titrant.

If time is available, the titration can be performed with various values of the electrolysis current flowing through the solution other than the $2\mu a$ suggested in the
directions for assembly of the circuit components.

E X P E R I M E N T   2 1 - 8   STUDY   OF   THE   RESPONSE   OF   A   PLATINUM-TUNGSTEN ELECTRODE COMBINATION

Place 25 ml of 0.1 N ferrous ammonium sulfate solution into a 250-ml beaker. Add
5 ml of 36 N sulfuric acid and, if desired, 5 ml of 85 percent phosphoric acid. Dilute
to 100 ml.

Insert into the solution a platinum electrode, a tungsten electrode, and a standard
reference electrode. The tungsten electrode should be polished immediately before
use or else immersed for a few seconds in molten sodium nitrite and then washed
thoroughly with distilled water. The fusion mixture should be barely molten or the
tungsten will quickly dissolve.

Connect the leads from the platinum and tungsten electrodes to the opposite ends
of a single-pole double-throw switch. Connect the lead from the center tap of the
switch and the lead from the reference electrode to a potentiometer or vacuum tube
voltmeter.

Proceed with the titration using 0.1 N potassium dichromate as titrant. After the
addition of each increment of titrant, measure the potential of the platinum and
tungsten electrodes against the reference electrode.

Plot the indicator electrode potential against the volume of titrant for the platinum-
calomel and the tungsten-calomel pair of electrodes separately. Also plot the difference
in potential between the platinum and tungsten electrodes.

In a separate titration, measure the difference in potential between the platinum
and tungsten electrodes now connected directly to the potentiometer or vacuum tube
voltmeter. Connect the tungsten electrode in place of the calomel reference electrode.

Problems

1. Sketch the titration curves you would expect from the titration of each of the following aqueous systems:

   (a) 0.1 M solution of H_3PO_4 titrated with 0.2 M NaOH.

   (b) A solution 0.05 M in Na_3PO_4 and 0.1 M in Na_2HPO_4 titrated with 0.1 M HCl.

   (c) A 0.1 M solution of ammonia titrated with 0.1 M HCl.

2. Construct the complete curve for the titration of 50 ml of 0.1 M titanous chloride ($TiCl_3$), $E^0 = 0.10$ V, with a 0.1 M solution of methylene blue ($E^0 = 0.52$) in 1 M HCl.

3. Construct the titration curve for the titration of the solution resulting from passage of 0.01 M vanadium solution through an amalgamated zinc reductor; titrant is 0.1 M cerium(IV). $E^0 = -0.255$ for V^{+3}/V^{+2}, $E^0 = 0.361$ for VO^{++}/V^{+3}, and $E^0 = 1.000$ for VO_2^+/VO^{++}.

4. Sketch the titration curves you would expect from the titration of each of the following nonaqueous systems. Express the ordinate values in units of 0.059 V.

   (a) A mixture of an alkyl sulfonic acid ($pK_a = -7$) and an alkyl carboxylic acid ($pK = 4$) dissolved in methyl isobutyl ketone and titrated with tetra-n-butylammonium hydroxide.

   (b) A solution of aniline in glacial acetic acid titrated with $HClO_4$.

   (c) A mixture of HCl and acetic acid dissolved in isopropyl alcohol and titrated with sodium isopropoxide.

   (d) A mixture of acetic acid and phenol in n-butylamine titrated with sodium aminoethoxide.

5. Calculate the potential at the equivalence point in the potentiometric titration of each of these systems; assume the reference electrode is saturated calomel: (a) Titration of stannous ions with ceric ions; (b) titration of uranium(IV) with iron(III); (c) titration of VO^{++} with cerium(IV) in 1 M H_2SO_4; (d) titration of arsenic(III) with bromate in 5 M HCl.

6. From the information in Fig. 21-17, estimate the error in the location of the end point, as contrasted with the equivalence point, for (a) iodide and (b) bromide when all three halides are present in mixtures. Disregard any error attributable to mixed salt formation.

7. The following pH readings were obtained for corresponding volumes of 0.100 N NaOH in the potentiometric titration of a weak monobasic acid:

0.00 ml = 2.90	14.00 ml = 6.60	16.00 ml = 10.61
1.00 ml = 4.00	15.00 ml = 7.04	17.00 ml = 11.30
2.00 ml = 4.50	15.50 ml = 7.70	18.00 ml = 11.60
4.00 ml = 5.05	15.60 ml = 8.24	20.00 ml = 11.96
7.00 ml = 5.47	15.70 ml = 9.43	24.00 mi = 12.39
10.00 ml = 5.85	15.80 ml = 10.03	28.00 ml = 12.57
12.00 ml = 6.11		

   (a) Plot the above values of pH against milliliters of NaOH solution. (b) What is the pH value at the equivalence point? (c) What volume of NaOH corresponds to the equivalence point? (d) What is the ionization constant of the acid?

8. In the titration of a 10.0 ml aliquot from a cyanide plating bath, the following voltmeter readings, with SCE as reference, were obtained for corresponding volumes of 0.100 M silver nitrate solution:

8.00 ml = − 530 mV	15.40 ml = − 40 mV	30.00 ml = 100 mV
10.00 ml = − 500 mV	15.50 ml = 0 mV	30.20 ml = 135 mV
12.00 ml = − 450 mV	16.00 ml = +14 mV	30.40 ml = 180 mV

13.00 ml = −420 mV	18.00 ml = 28 mV	30.60 ml = 290 mV
14.00 ml = −405 mV	20.00 ml = 35 mV	30.80 ml = 315 mV
14.50 ml = −350 mV	24.00 ml = 42 mV	31.00 ml = 330 mV
15.00 ml = −320 mV	27.00 ml = 56 mV	31.50 ml = 350 mV
15.10 ml = −270 mV	28.00 ml = 70 mV	32.00 ml = 365 mV
15.20 ml = −210 mV	29.00 ml = 84 mV	34.00 ml = 380 mV
15.30 ml = −130 mV		

(a) Plot the above values against the volume of silver nitrate solution. (b) What is the millivolt reading at each end point? (c) What volume of silver nitrate corresponds to each end point? (d) Estimate the formation constant of $Ag(CN)_2^-$ from the voltmeter reading at the point halfway to the first end point (e) Estimate the solubility product of AgCN from the voltmeter reading at the point halfway to the second end point.

9. In the titration of iron(II) using the differential potentiometric method with a constant electrolysis current, the following readings were obtained for corresponding volumes of 0.1 M cerium(IV):

2.00 ml = 50 mV	9.60 ml = 410 mV	10.75 ml = 400 mV
4.00 ml = 50 mV	9.80 ml = 740 mV	11.00 ml = 365 mV
6.00 ml = 50 mV	10.00 ml = 705 mV	12.00 ml = 300 mV
8.00 ml = 100 mV	10.25 ml = 515 mV	14.00 ml = 250 mV
9.00 ml = 155 mV	10.50 ml = 460 mV	16.00 ml = 205 mV
9.40 ml = 205 mV		

(a) Plot the millivolt readings against the volume of cerium solution. (b) What volume of cerium corresponds to the end point?

10. By reference to Fig. 2J-18 and to the additional information supplied, identify the following materials:
(a) Intensely colored in alkaline form, colorless in acid form; heat of ionization = 5900 cal/mole; pK_a = 4.5.
(b) Monobasic acid, pK_a = 6.15; no aromatic group or hetero atoms.
(c) pK_a = 1; halide test positive; heat of ionization = 1000 cal/mole.
(d) pK_1 = 5.41 and pK_2 = 10.4.
Ans. (b) Acetylacetone is a possibility; (d) *p*-aminophenol.

11. An electrode responsive to sodium ion, upon calibration, yielded these millivolt readings at 20°C: 0.100 N = 0.0; 0.0100 N = 56; 0.001 N = 112; 0.0001 N = 168. (a) What sodium ion normality corresponds to a reading of 80 mV? (b) Comment on the adherence of the electrode response to the theoretical Nernst slope. *Ans.* (a) 0.0035 N; (b) slope is 56 mV per 10-fold change, whereas the ideal response is 58.2 mV at 20°C.

12. Calculate the potential of the indicator electrode after the addition of 10, 50, 90, 99, and 101 percent of the equivalent amount of 0.1 M $K_4Fe(CN)_6$ in the titration of 0.1 M zinc chloride with 0.001 M $K_3Fe(CN)_6$ in the solution. The solubility product of $K_2Zn_3[Fe(CN)_6]_2$ = 10^{-17}. Assume that the volume does not change during the titration.

Bibliography

Charlot, G., J. Badoz-Lambling, and B. Tremillon, *Electrochemical Reactions*, Am. Elsevier, New York, 1962.

Lingane, J. J., *Electroanalytical Chemistry*, 2nd ed., Interscience, New York, 1958.

Literature Cited

1. Beckett, A. H., and E. H. Tinley, *Titrations in Non-aqueous Solvents*, 3rd ed., British Drug Houses, Ltd., Poole, England, 1962.
2. Charlot, G., J. Badoz-Lambling, and B. Tremillon, *Electrochemical Reactions*, Am. Elsevier, New York, 1962.
3. Chirnside, R. C., H. J. Cluley, and P. M. C. Proffitt, *Analyst*, 72, 354 (1947).
4. Eisenman, G., in *Symposium on Membrane Transport and Metabolism*, Czech. Acad. of Science, Academic Press, New York, 1961.
5. Fritz, J. S., *Acid-Base Titrations in Nonaqueous Solvents*, G. Frederick Smith Chemical Co., Columbus, Ohio, 1952.
6. Furman, N. H., and G. W. Low, *J. Am. Chem. Soc.*, 57, 1585 (1935).
7. Keegan, J. J., and G. Matsuyama, *Anal. Chem.* 33, 1292 (1961).
8. Kolthoff, I. M., *Anal. Chem.*, 26, 1685 (1954).
9. Kolthoff, I. M., and P. J. Elving, *Treatise on Analytical Chemistry*, Part I, Vol. 1, Interscience, New York, 1959.
10. Kolthoff, I. M., *Anal. Chem.*, 26, 1685 (1954).
11. LeBlanc, M., and O. Harnapp, *Z. physik. Chem.*, A166, 321 (1931).
12. Lingane, J. J., *Electroanalytical Chemistry*, 2nd ed., Interscience, New York, 1958.
13. Laitinen, H. A., *Chemical Analysis*, McGraw-Hill, New York, 1960.
14. Lingane, J. J., and R. Karplus, *Ind. Eng. Chem., Anal. Ed.*, 18, 191 (1946).
15. Malmstadt, H. V., and E. R. Fett, *Anal. Chem.*, 26, 1348 (1954).
16. Malmstadt, H. V., and J. D. Winefordner, *Anal. Chim. Acta*, 20, 283 (1959).
17. Müller, E., *Z. physik. Chem.*, 135, 102 (1928).
18. Parke, T. V., and W. W. Davis, *Anal. Chem.*, 26, 642 (1954).
19. Reilley, C. N., and R. W. Schmid, *Anal. Chem.*, 28, 947 (1956); *J. Am. Chem. Soc.*, 78, 5513 (1956).
20. Stock, J. T., and W. C. Purdy, *Chem. Revs.*, 57, 1159 (1957).
21. Willard, H. H., and A. W. Boldyreff, *J. Am. Chem. Soc.*, 51, 471 (1929).

The Measurement of pH

The pH scale is a series of numbers which express the degree of acidity (or alkalinity) of a solution, as contrasted with the total quantity of acid or base in some material as found by an alkalimetric (or acidimetric) titration. As defined by Sørensen, who introduced the term,

$$pH = -\log [H^+] \qquad (22\text{-}1)$$

Involved is the negative logarithm of the hydrogen-ion concentration expressed in molarity. However, it is the activity of the hydrogen ion that is formally consistent with the thermodynamics of the pH electromotive cell, and the activity definition is

$$paH = -\log a_{H^+} \qquad (22\text{-}2)$$

Now $[H^+]$ and $f_{\pm}[H^+]$ are often the most useful units for expressing the acidity of aqueous solutions, where $f_{\pm}$ is the mean ionic activity coefficient. Unfortunately, the established experimental pH method cannot furnish either of these quantities. Consequently, the term pH is merely a mathematical symbol of convenience, widely accepted, but devoid of exact thermodynamic validity. For those interested in a detailed treatment of the historical development of the concept of pH, the treatise by Clark[6] and the more recent work by Bates[1] should be consulted. The relationship among $[H^+]$, $[OH^-]$, pH, and OH is given in Table 22-1 for aqueous solutions.

Table 22-1	Relationships Among $[H^+]$, $[OH^-]$, pH, and pOH in Aqueous Solution at 25°C			
$[H^+]$	pH	pOH	$[OH^-]$	
1.0×10^1	-1	15	1.0×10^{-15}	Strongly acid
10^0	0	14	10^{-14}	
10^{-1}	1	13	10^{-13}	
10^{-2}	2	12	10^{-12}	
10^{-3}	3	11	10^{-11}	Weakly acid
10^{-7}	7	7	10^{-7}	Neutral
10^{-11}	11	3	10^{-3}	Weakly alkaline
10^{-12}	12	2	10^{-2}	
10^{-13}	13	1	10^{-1}	
10^{-14}	14	0	10^0	Strongly alkaline

Basic Principles

The acidity of a solution will depend upon several factors: (a) the chemical nature of the acid, as expressed by the degree of dissociation (or association of a base), pK$_a$; (b) the relative concentrations of acid and its conjugate base, and the total ionic strength of the solution; and (c) the temperature of the solution as it affects the dissociation of water and the dissociation of the acid. For acids which are not dissociated completely, the expression for the pH of the solution is

$$pH = pK_a + \log \frac{[A^-] + [H^+]}{[HA] - [H^+]} \qquad (22\text{-}3)$$

Except when the hydrogen-ion concentration is comparable to the concentrations of HA or A$^-$, the expression can be simplified to

$$pH = pK_a + \log \frac{[A^-]}{[HA]} \qquad (22\text{-}4)$$

Buffer Solutions

A buffer may be defined as a solution which maintains a nearly constant pH value despite the addition of substantial quantities of acid or base. Generally it consists of a mixture of an incompletely dissociated acid and its conjugate base. In selecting a particular buffer, three characteristics should be considered: the buffer value β, the dilution value pH$_{1/2}$, and the change of pH with change in temperature, ΔpH$/\Delta T$.

The Van Slyke buffer value β indicates the resistance of a buffer to change in pH upon addition of an acid or base. It is defined as

$$\beta = \Delta B/\Delta pH$$

where B is an increment of completely dissociated base (or acid) in gram equivalents per liter that is required to produce unit change in pH within the solution. In the selection of a buffer system, pK_a should be as close as possible to the desired pH. Under this condition the ratio $[A^-]/[HA]$ in Eq. 22-4 is close to unity, and the buffer value will be large. For high buffering capacity, the concentrations of the buffering components should be high, yet consistent with considerations of ionic strength of the medium and the concomitant effect upon pH measurements.

The pH of the buffer solution should also be relatively insensitive to changes in the total concentration of the buffer components at a fixed ratio of $[A^-]/[HA]$. The dilution value is defined as the change of pH that results from a 1:1 dilution of the solution with pure water.

Solutions of specified composition for many pH values are compiled in the treatises by Clark[6] and Bates.[1] In the Clark and Lubs series which spans the range from pH 1.0 to 10.2, the ingredients are phthalic acid ($pK_1 = 2.90$, $pK_2 = 5.41$), potassium dihydrogen phosphate ($pK_2 = 7.13$), and boric acid ($pK = 9.24$), which are combined in suitable proportions with hydrochloric acid or sodium hydroxide (see Table 22-6). MacIlvaine's standard buffer spans the range from pH 2.2 to 8.0 and involves mixing citric acid ($pK_1 = 3.09$, $pK_2 = 4.75$, $pK_3 = 5.50$) and potassium dihydrogen phosphate solutions in certain proportions. In the last example, combining several acids of varying strength, but whose pK_a values differ by less than two units, with the respective conjugate bases provides a universal buffer solution which covers a wider range of pH values than any single system, yet a solution which exhibits considerable buffering capacity over the entire useful range. Buffer tablets, available from chemical supply houses, eliminate the preparation, storage, and mixing of buffering ingredients, and need only be dissolved in the specified volume of pure water to obtain the pH value specified on the container.

pH Reference Standards

The National Bureau of Standards (U.S.) has assigned "conventional" pH values to five primary reference buffer solutions. In addition, two secondary reference standards have been established, one for the highly acidic range and the other for the highly alkaline range. The compositions and pH values of these reference solutions are given in Table 22-2.

Operational Definition of pH

The "conventional" pH value is defined in an operational manner, as follows

$$pH = pH_s + (E - E_s)/0.000198T \qquad (22\text{-}5)$$

In this definition, T is the temperature in degrees Kelvin, and E and E_s are, respectively, the emf of a pH cell of the usual design

Electrode reversible to hydrogen ions	Unknown or standard buffer solution	Salt bridge	Reference Electrode

Table 22-2 | *National Bureau of Standards Reference Buffer Solutions*

(Numbers given are "conventional" pH values. Properties of these buffer solutions are included at the foot of each column. For preparation of these solutions, consult Table 22-5.)

TEMPERA-TURE, °C	SECONDARY STANDARD, 0.05 M K TETROX-ALATE	KH TARTRATE (SATD. AT 25°C)	0.05 M KH PHTHALATE	0.025 M KH$_2$PO$_4$, 0.025 M Na$_2$HPO$_4$	0.0087 M KH$_2$PO$_4$, 0.0302 M Na$_2$HPO$_4$	0.01 M Na$_2$B$_4$O$_7$	SECONDARY STANDARD, Ca(OH)$_2$ (SATD. AT 25°C)
0	1.67	—	4.01	6.98	7.53	9.46	13.43
10	1.67	—	4.00	6.92	7.47	9.33	13.00
15	1.67	—	4.00	6.90	7.45	9.27	12.81
20	1.68	—	4.00	6.88	7.43	9.23	12.63
25	1.68	3.56	4.01	6.86	7.41	9.18	12.45
30	1.68	3.55	4.02	6.85	7.40	9.14	12.30
38	1.69	3.55	4.03	6.84	7.38	9.08	12.04
40	1.69	3.55	4.04	6.84	7.38	9.07	11.99
50	1.71	3.55	4.06	6.83	7.37	9.01	11.70
60	1.72	3.56	4.09	6.85	—	8.96	11.45
70	1.74	3.58	4.12	6.85	—	8.93	—
80	1.77	3.61	4.16	6.86	—	8.89	—
90	1.79	3.65	4.20	6.88	—	8.85	—
95	1.81	3.67	4.23	6.89	—	8.83	—

Buffer Value, β	0.070	0.027	0.016	0.029	0.016	0.020	0·09
Dilution Value, $\Delta pH_{1/2}$	+0.186	+0.049	+0.052	+0.080	+0.07	+0.01	−0.28
$\Delta pH/\Delta T$ (at 25°C)	+0.001	+0.0014	+0.0012	−0.0028	−0.0028	−0.0082	−0.033

[From R. G. Bates, *J. Research Natl. Bur. Standards* (U. S.), **66A,** 179–183 (1962).]

which contains first the "unknown" solution, and secondly, a standard reference solution of known pH, namely, pH$_s$.

The NBS pH standards were assigned pH$_s$ values from measurements of the emf of cells containing hydrogen gas and silver-silver chloride electrodes (i.e., without a liquid junction):

$$\text{Pt} \mid \text{H}_2(1 \text{ atm}), \text{H}^+ \text{ Cl}^- \text{ (plus K}^+ \text{ Cl}^-\text{), AgCl} \mid \text{Ag}$$

by the equation

$$E = E^0 - 0.000198T \log f_{H^+} f_{Cl^-} m_{H^+} m_{Cl^-} \tag{22-6}$$

where E^0 is the standard potential of the cell.[2,3] Upon rearranging Eq. 22-6 in terms of the acidity function, $p(a_{H^+} f_{Cl^-})$

$$p(a_{H^+} f_{Cl^-}) = -\log f_{H^+} f_{Cl^-} m_{H^+} = (E - E^0)/0.000198T + \log m_{Cl^-} \tag{22-7}$$

The pH_s of the chloride-free buffer solution is computed from the equation

$$pH_s = p(a_{H^+}f_{Cl^-})^0 + \log f^0_{Cl^-} \qquad (22\text{-}8)$$

where $p(a_{H^+}f_{Cl^-})^0$ is the value obtained by evaluation of $p(a_{H^+} f_{Cl^-})$ at several concentrations of chloride, and extrapolation to zero chloride concentration. The activity coefficient of chloride ion is defined by the equation

$$-\log f^0_{Cl^-} = \frac{A\sqrt{\mu}}{1 + 1.5\sqrt{\mu}} \qquad (22\text{-}9)$$

where μ is the ionic strength, which should be maintained equal to, or less than, 0.1, and A is a parameter of the Debye-Huckel theory having a different value at each temperature. The recommended values of pH_s are summarized in Table 22-2. The total uncertainty in pH_s, exclusive of any liquid junction potentials introduced during calibration of pH equipment, is estimated as 0.005 pH unit (0°–60°C) and 0.008 pH unit (60°–95°C). The necessity of estimating the individual activity coefficients of chloride ion in each reference solution deprives the pH_s value of exact fundamental meaning. Nevertheless the operational definition of pH, chosen in part for its reasonableness but largely for its utility, agrees as closely as possible with the mathematical concepts evolved from the present state of solution theory.

Interpretation of Measured pH

The operational definition of pH, given in Eq. 22-5, emphasizes that the determination of pH is essentially a determination of a difference of emf as recorded in a pH cell containing first a reference buffer and then a test solution. The definition demands only that the electrode potential of the reference electrode remains constant while measurements of E and E_s are being made. Unfortunately, the definition makes no allowance for the presence of a liquid junction potential or a change in the value of the junction potential when the reference standard is replaced by an unknown solution. Hopefully, the liquid junction potential is assumed to remain constant from one measurement to another, and its value is combined with the value of the reference electrode. However, at pH values less than 2 or greater than 12, and for ionic strengths greater than 0.1, the reproducibility of the liquid junction potential is seriously impaired and errors as large as several tenths of a pH unit can result. To detect any serious impairment of the response of the measuring device and electrode assembly outside the pH range 2–12, the tetroxalate solution and the calcium hydroxide solution are included among the pH reference buffers but are designated secondary standards.

For pH measurements with an accuracy of 0.01 to 0.1 pH unit, the limiting factor is often the electrochemical system, that is, the characteristics of the electrodes and the solution in which they are immersed. Another source of error is due to temperature, for not only does the proportionality factor between cell emf and *p*H vary with temperature, but dissociation equilibria and junction potentials also have significant temperature coefficients. For accuracy of ±0.01 *p*H unit, the temperature should be known to ±2°C. Ideal solutions are those with compositions that match closely the primary standards of reference. Specifically, they are aqueous solutions of buffers and simple salts, of ionic strengths between 0.01 and 0.1, with only low concentrations of nonelectrolytes. In industrial processes, fortunately, a highly accurate knowledge of the *p*H of a solution is seldom required. Neither is it necessary to know exactly what a particular *p*H value means. It is sufficient to know that at a certain stage in an industrial process a particular *p*H value is maintained.

Electrodes for *p*H Measurements

The characteristics of the hydrogen gas electrode, the quinhydrone electrode, the antimony electrode, and the glass electrode, which commonly form the *p*H-responsive electrode of *p*H cells, are discussed in this section. Handbooks contain standard voltage-*p*H tables for the first three electrode systems covering the entire range of *p*H values.

Hydrogen Gas Electrode

The hydrogen gas electrode consists essentially of a piece of clean platinum foil, coated with a thin layer of finely divided platinum to hasten establishment of the electrical potential, which is capable of making the reaction

$$H^+ + e^- = \tfrac{1}{2}H_2(g) \qquad (22\text{-}10)$$

at the platinum-solution interface proceed reversibly. The electrode is immersed in the solution under investigation and electrolytic hydrogen gas (99.8 percent purity adequate) at 1 atm pressure is bubbled through the solution and over the electrode in such a way that the electrode surface and the adjacent solution will be saturated with the gas at all times. Electrode life is 7–20 days before its response becomes sluggish.[11] One form of construction is illustrated in Fig. 22-1.

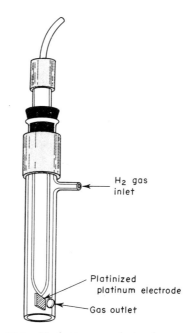

H₂ gas inlet

Platinized platinum electrode

Gas outlet

Fig. 22-1. Hydrogen-gas electrode assembly.

The essential purposes of a hydrogen gas cell assembly in an analytical laboratory are to check the accuracy of other pH electrodes, in particular the errors of glass-reference electrode measuring equipment, but also the magnitude of liquid junction potentials and the accuracy and stability of reference standard solutions. It should be recalled that the hydrogen gas electrode is the primary standard against which all other electrode potentials are measured. Cell assemblies are available commercially.

The Quinhydrone Electrode

p-Benzoquinone and p-hydrobenzoquinone form a reversible oxidation-reduction electrode in which hydrogen ions participate:

$$p\text{-}OC_6H_4O + 2H^+ + 2e^- = p\text{-}HOC_6H_4OH \qquad (22\text{-}11)$$

Consequently, the electrode potential is a function of pH and of the ratio of the concentrations (strictly, the activities) of the quinone and its hydroquinone:[4,8]

$$E = E^0 - 0.000198T(pH) + \frac{0.000198T}{2} \log \frac{[OC_6H_4O]}{[HOC_6H_4OH]} \qquad (22\text{-}12)$$

Normally the test solution is saturated with quinhydrone, a sparingly soluble (0.018 M) compound composed of one mole each of quinone and hydroquinone, and a large inert electrode of bright platinum or gold is immersed into it. Contact with some of the solid quinhydrone is desirable. Extensive dissociation (approximately 93 percent) of the dissolved quinhydrone automatically fixes the concentration ratio of components at unity and, if the ionic strength of the solution is not too high, the electrode will show a proper pH response:

$$E = 0.6998 - 0.0591pH \qquad (\text{at } 25°C) \qquad (22\text{-}13)$$

The quinhydrone electrode is quickly prepared, develops its potential rapidly, and is not readily poisoned. The pH response is close to the theoretical value at pH values from 1 to 8. In more alkaline media hydroquinone may be oxidized by dissolved oxygen and, being a weak acid, it begins to dissociate. Results of fair accuracy can be obtained to about pH 9.0. In solutions which are poorly buffered, the upper limit is approximately pH 8.0. In strongly acidic solutions, quinone is capable of accepting a proton. The pH response is also impaired slightly by the presence of high concentrations of electrolytes (>0.1 M) which affect unequally the activities of the two species in the solution. This defect can be overcome by saturating the solution with either quinone or hydroquinone as well as with quinhydrone.

The quinhydrone electrode is capable of yielding very reproducible potentials for fundamental studies and it can be used in many nonaqueous media, including alcohols, acetone, and formic acid. One of its analogs, the chloranil electrode, is more resistant to oxidation and has been outstanding for studies and acid-base titrations in glacial acetic acid. The components are tetrachloroquinone and tetrachlorohydroquinone. No quinhydrone is formed, there are no salt errors, and the cell emf is independent of solvent, provided the solid phases are invariant.

The Antimony Electrode

Of the various metal-metal oxide electrodes that have been described, the antimony-antimonous oxide electrode has proved to be the most satisfactory for pH measurement.[10,13] It consists of high purity electrolytic antimony cast in stick-form. An invisible coating of the very slightly soluble oxide always seems to be present as a surface film. When used in the form of a billet electrode, a short stick of the metal is cemented into a glass tube so that the metal projects about 0.5 cm. Electrodes are available commercially.

The electrode reaction is usually written as follows:

$$Sb_2O_3(s) + 6H^+ + 6e^- = 2Sb(s) + 3H_2O \qquad (22\text{-}14)$$

Various forms of antimony(III) may exist in solution, but if equilibrium between electrode and solution exists, the potential of the electrode is a function of the solution pH, and is given approximately by

$$E = E^0 - k(p\text{H}) \simeq E^0 - 0.0591\, p\text{H} \qquad (\text{at } 25°\text{C}) \qquad (22\text{-}15)$$

The standard potential of the antimony electrode is not very reproducible, nor is the slope of the emf-pH curve the theoretical value or even rectilinear. Since the potential differs from one electrode to another, it is necessary to standardize each antimony electrode by means of solutions of known pH and under the same experimental conditions to which the electrode will be subjected in use.

It is a rugged electrode and, in certain designs, is used industrially for continuous plant service, in particular, in the range from pH 1 to 10 for control and routine estimation of pH where an accuracy of ± 0.2 pH unit is adequate. The electrode finds use in electrometric acid-base titration, especially in basic nonaqueous systems where the glass electrode fails to function satisfactorily.[14] The potential of the antimony electrode is affected by dissolved oxygen, by oxidizing and reducing agents, and there is a marked sensitivity to complexing agents, notably fluoride ion, certain amino acids, and the anions of hydroxy acids. The electrode is not applicable in solutions containing more than a trace of copper, silver, or other metals more electropositive than antimony in the electrochemical series of the elements.

The Glass Electrode

The glass electrode, actually a membrane electrode, comprises a thin walled bulb of pH-responsive glass sealed to a stem of non-pH-responsive, high-resistance glass. In this manner the pH response is confined entirely to the area of the special glass membrane, eliminating any variance caused by the depth of immersion. A typical electrode is illustrated in Fig. 22-2. If intended for use

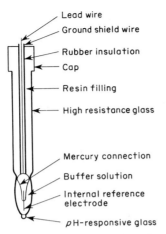

Fig. 22-2. Cut-away drawing of a typical glass electrode.

outside a shielded electrode compartment, the stem of the electrode is shielded and a shielded lead is provided which should be grounded.

Both surfaces of the glass membrane are pH-responsive. Changes in the electrical potential of the outer membrane surface are measured by means of an external reference electrode and its associated salt bridge. An electrolyte of high buffer capacity ($\beta \geq 0.05$) fills the inside of the glass membrane —a 0.025 M solution of hydrochloric acid or sulfuric acid, or a saturated chloride solution buffered with acetate, citrate, or other suitable buffer system. Into this electrolyte dips an inner reference electrode, generally a calomel or silver-silver chloride electrode. The complete pH cell is

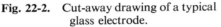

Internal reference electrode	Internal electrolyte	Glass membrane	Standard reference or unknown solution	External reference electrode

The potential of the glass electrode is given by

$$E = E_e + 0.000198T(pH - pH_r)$$ (22-16)

where pH_r is the pH of the reference solution contained within the glass bulb (often pH 7.00) and E_e represents the combination of junction potentials, variations in the reproducibility of the reference electrodes, and deviations in the response of the two glass surfaces (asymmetry potential). Upon standardization of the pH cell assembly with a reference buffer solution pH_s, the pH is measured by the operational definition, here repeated,

$$pH = pH_s + (E - E_s)/0.000198T$$ (22-17)

The mechanism by which hydrogen ions affect the potential of the glass membrane is not well understood. The cations, which are largely the alkali metals and alkaline earth metals, occupy holes in the three-dimensional network of silicon and oxygen atoms in which there is a residual negative charge. They are held in position by electrostatic forces which are centered on the neighboring oxygen atoms but are free to some extent to move from one site to another under the influence of an electrical field. The ease of their motion depends upon the strength of the electrostatic forces and upon the relative sizes of the ions and the sites they occupy. Consequently, glasses

can be tailored to some degree to produce a desired combination of characteristics: *p*H response, hygroscopicity, electrical resistance of the membrane,
chemical durability, and workability.[5,12] Early electrodes were fabricated
from a soda-lime glass, the eutectic of the ternary system: SiO_2-CaO-Na_2O
(e.g., Corning 015 and Schott 4073). Above *p*H 9, however, these electrodes
displayed a rather serious error in the presence of the ions of the alkali metals
accompanied by a definite attack of the silicon-oxygen lattice at the glass
surface. Glasses with considerably smaller alkaline error have been developed,
largely by substitution of lithium for the sodium content, and replacement of
calcium by barium or strontium. An M_2O_3 oxide, such as lanthanum oxide,
can replace all or part of the alkaline earth content with favorable effects.

The activity of water in the solution appears to play an important role
in the development of the *p*H response of a glass membrane. If the ionic
strength is extremely high, or if a nonaqueous solvent is present, the measured
potential deviates from the expected value. A direct relationship between
hygroscopicity of the glass, which undergoes certain dimensional changes and
swells noticeably, and *p*H response has been demonstrated. All glass electrodes
must be conditioned for a time by soaking in water or in a dilute buffer solution, even though they may be used subsequently in media that are only partly
aqueous. During conditioning there is an exchange of hydrogen ion from the
solution with alkali ions from the glass surface, and a swelling of the glass
surface occurs. Hydration-dehydration of the lattice is usually reversible;
nevertheless, continual leaching (chemical attack) of the alkali metal ions
ultimately impairs the response of the electrode because of the increase in
electrical resistance across the membrane. In normal use the period of service
extends from nine months to two years.

The glass electrode displays an amazing versatility. Involving no electron
exchange, it is the only hydrogen ion electrode uninfluenced by oxidizing and
reducing agents. Nor is it disturbed by common electrode poisons. However,
the glass membrane reaches equilibrium with the test solution slowly (response
time is normally several seconds) and the surface of the glass is easily contaminated by adsorbed ions and particulate matter which delay the attainment of
equilibrium between electrode and solution. The high electrical resistance
(5–500 MΩ) necessitates measuring circuits with high input impedance, and is
accompanied by a large temperature coefficient of resistance which changes
exponentially with temperature. Chemical durability and electrical resistance
are linked together. Electrodes durable against chemical attack at elevated
temperatures have excessive electrical resistances when the temperature is
lowered. Conversely, electrodes that are robust at low temperature will
corrode rapidly in solutions at high temperatures. Consequently, electrodes
are designed specifically for certain ranges of temperature and for certain
ranges of *p*H. Frequently a general purpose electrode is useful from $-5°$ to
60°C in acids and dilute alkalis with a negligible error to a *p*H of 11. In more

alkaline solutions the observed values of pH are too small and must be corrected from nomographs supplied by the manufacturer. The error at the higher pH range increases with increase of the concentration of alkali metal ions, especially sodium ion. Above pH 12 these corrections become so large that readings are invalidated. Electrodes fabricated from lithia glasses are available for high pH measurements and measurements in the presence of sodium ion. For measurements above 60°–80° a special glass is used which will withstand 100° continuously, with intermittent use up to 130°; however, below 35° these glasses are sluggish in response. Even in highly alkaline solutions at the boiling point some of these electrodes will show only 0.2 pH deviation at pH 13.7 in 1 M sodium hydroxide.

Commercial glass electrodes are fabricated in a wide variety of sizes and shapes and for many special applications. Syringe and capillary electrodes require only one or two drops of solution, even as little as 1 mm³ volume in ultramicro work, while others will penetrate soft solids or are designed for measurements on smooth surfaces. The normal-size electrode operates with a volume of solution from 1 to 5 ml. Polyalcohols added to the solution in the reference electrode, and mercury inside the glass membrane to make direct contact with the glass, permit measurements of semifrozen materials at −30°C. Glass electrodes of special construction are available for operation under pressure conditions.

Electrometric Measurement of pH

To achieve a reproducibility of ±0.02 pH unit, the assigned limit of certainty of many reference buffer standards and including unavoidable variations in liquid-junction potentials, an instrument is needed which will be sensitive and reproducible to 1.2 mV. Negligible current must be drawn during the measurement if changes in the ion concentration at the electrode surface are to be avoided, and no error is to arise from the voltage drop across the inherent resistance of the pH cell. With high-resistance glass electrodes, the current should be 10^{-12} amp or less (see Example 21-1 on page 548). These limitations restrict the choice of instrument to a potentiometer for a hydrogen-gas electrode, a quinhydrone electrode, or an antimony electrode, and a high-impedance, electron-tube voltmeter (VTVM) for a glass electrode (and also suitable for the other electrodes).

VTVM with indicating scales in pH values are calibrated in voltage units for a glass-reference electrode pair on the basis of the relationship for the emf of a pH cell, as given by Eq. 22-5. This relationship is based on the presumption that the external and internal reference electrodes for glass electrode assemblies are the same type, and of like concentrations, which is customary practice in commercial assemblies from a given manufacturer, but assemblies from different fabricators may not be interchangeable. The apparent emf/pH slope will be 59.15 mV per pH unit at 25°C; a temperature compensator on pH meters varies the instrument's definition of a pH unit from 54.20 mV at 0° to 66.10 mV at 60°.[7]

Battery-operated instruments utilize a d-c amplifier either in a direct-reading circuit with a deflection meter or to amplify the off-balance current from a compensation (potentiometer) circuit. Negative feedback is frequently used to ensure linearity of the meter reading and to gain stabilization. Circuitry using dynamic condensers (vibrating reed) or choppers with subsequent amplification of the a-c signal has extended the sensitivity (to 0.1 mV) of emf measurements through resistances of 500 MΩ. Provision for connection of an automatic temperature compensator (a thermistor) immersed in the test solution gives the instruments great flexibility.[9]

Potentiometer-Amplifier Circuit

One of the simplest circuits for pH measurements with glass electrodes incorporates an ordinary potentiometric circuit with a single electron tube in a null-type amplifier circuit, as shown in Fig. 22-3. A battery sends a constant

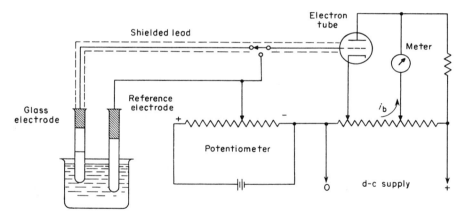

Fig. 22-3. Schematic potentiometer-amplifier circuit.

current through the slidewire, establishing a voltage difference across it as in any potentiometer, and through the meter as shown by the arrow i_b. In operation, the emf developed by the glass and reference electrode cell is opposed by an emf from the precision potentiometer. Any off-balance is observed as a deflection on the meter in the amplifier. The contactor is moved along the slidewire until a point is found at which the meter needle shows no net deflection and stands in its center position due to the tube current flowing through the meter in opposition to the current i_b. The circuit is balanced initially with the slidewire contactor at pH 7 and connected directly to the grid of the electron tube (see Eq. 22-17). The slidewire is marked off in pH units, and read directly. The electronic amplifier thus serves only as null-point indicator.

Instruments of this type are compact, portable, and inexpensive. Often the reading scale extends only from 2 to 12 pH units; reproducibility is perhaps ± 0.1 pH unit. A typical miniaturized pH meter of this type is made by Analytical Measurements, Inc.

More sophisticated instruments will incorporate a second stage of amplification to improve the sensitivity of detection, and additional features in the circuit to compensate for temperature variations, zero-drift error, and to permit standardization of the reading scale in either millivolts or pH units. A schematic diagram of an instrument of this type—the first pH meter to be marketed—is shown in Fig. 22-4. The role of each of the adjustments and circuit components perhaps can best be appreciated in terms of the sequence of operations involved in the standardization and calibration of the instrument.

1. With the ganged switch in position 1, the grid of the input stage is connected to the contactor on slidewire R_1. The contactor is moved until the meter needle stands in its center position. Note that R_1 is the center portion of a potentiometer circuit which involves the same dry cells that supply the current through the filaments of the tubes. This operation selects an arbitrary "null" position on the meter, analogous to the mechanical adjustment of a D'Arsonval galvanometer, and compensates for aging of the batteries and changes in tube characteristics.

2. The rheostat marked "temperature adjust," which shunts the "pH scale" slidewire, is set to the value of the solution temperature, thereby altering the coefficient of the logarithmic term in Eq. 22-17. With the ganged switch in position 2, one side of the Weston standard cell is attached to the cathode of the input tube (through the contactor on R_1) and the grid of this tube is attached to the pH slidewire. Actually the Weston cell is in opposition to the potentiometer involving the pH slidewire, battery E_b, and rheostat R_2, with the amplifier serving as the current-measuring galvanometer. The rheostat R_2 is adjusted until the meter returns to its center position. Now the slidewire scale is standardized in the correct number of millivolts per inscribed pH unit.

3. In the final step, the electrode assembly is immersed in a pH reference buffer and the pH slidewire is set at the value of the pH standard. With the ganged switch in position 1, a button is depressed which connects the glass electrode to the grid of the input tube. All this time the reference electrode has been connected to the contactor on the pH slidewire. Now the "zero adjust" rheostat (also called the "asymmetry control") is adjusted until the meter returns to its center position. The inscribed pH scale is thereby brought into juxtaposition with the actual pH value by the zero adjust resistance which serves to lengthen one end of the pH scale while shortening by an equal amount the other end. Any changes in the asymmetry potential of the glass electrode are also compensated.

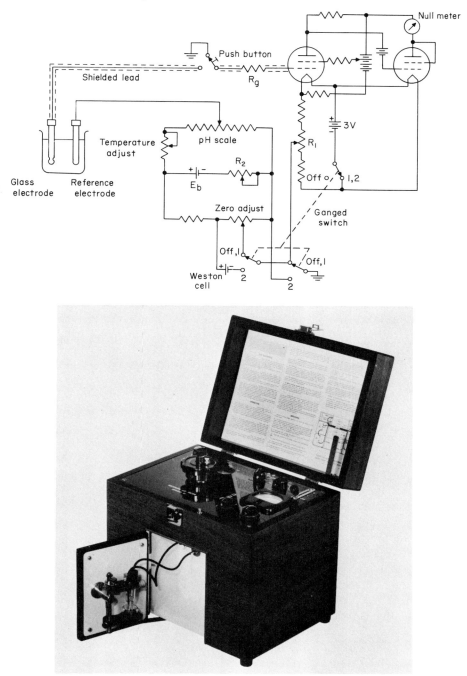

Fig. 22-4. Schematic circuit diagram and control panel of the Beckman model G *p*H meter. (Courtesy of Beckman Instruments, Inc.)

The slidewire in these instruments is also marked off in units of 100 mV and can be used in potentiometric methods other than pH measurements. The limiting factor in measurements with null-detector circuits is the slidewire accuracy which is generally at least 0.1 percent. Because these circuits are subject to zero drift and require circuit readjustments frequently, they are unsuited to long-time unattended operation. Representative commercial instruments include the Beckman models G and GS, the Coleman Compax model 20, the Photovolt model 125, and the Metrohm model E-388.

Direct-Reading pH Meters

The negative feedback principle is widely used in the design of direct-reading pH meters. Figure 22-5 shows the important features of such a circuit. The glass electrode is connected to the grid of the electrometer tube T_1. This increases the negative potential of the grid and so reduces the current through T_1. Therefore the voltage drop across the plate resistance r_p of this tube decreases and the voltage at the plate increases. Since this plate is connected to the grid of T_2, the voltage increase is imposed on this grid of T_2, the second stage in the amplifier. After the third stage, the voltage increase at the cathode of the output tube is registered on the meter A. An inverse sequence of events occurs if the negative potential of the grid of T_1 is decreased.

The overall effect is that the voltage change across the meter will show an increase or decrease in value as the plate voltage at T_1 changes. Current then passes through the meter and the feedback resistor to the circuit ground. The voltage developed across the feedback resistor is applied to the reference electrode through a "temperature adjust" rheostat or other type of temperature compensation. The feedback voltage is opposite in polarity to the voltage signal from the glass and reference electrodes. When the voltage across the feedback resistor reaches a value equal to the voltage signal between the glass and reference electrodes, a steady current is maintained in the output circuit and the meter indication is directly proportional to the signal voltage. In addition, the asymmetry control is in series with the electrodes. Thus, any voltage that may be produced by the electrodes can be bucked out by the asymmetry control so the meter will read the changes of pH from the initial buffer standardization.

A direct-reading instrument has few manipulative steps and is adaptable to continuous recording or control of industrial operations or processes. Temperature compensation can be provided by causing the feedback current to flow through a temperature-sensitive resistor located in the input circuit to supply the balancing voltage. If this resistor is placed in the solution to be measured, temperature compensation can be achieved automatically.

Direct-reading instruments may employ a d-c amplifier or an a-c amplifier to develop the balancing voltage. The former requires batteries, but such instruments are quite compact and portable. With either, long-time un-

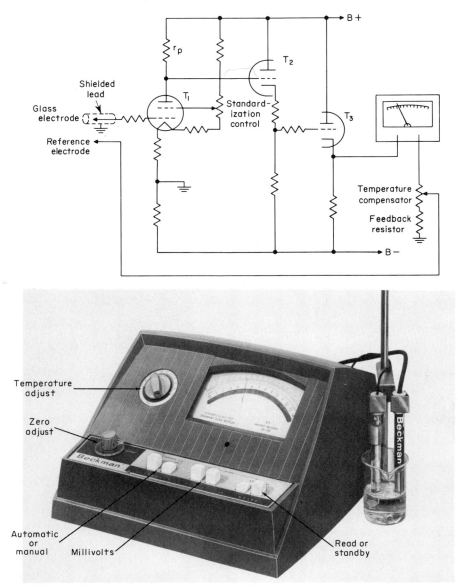

Fig. 22-5.   Schematic circuit diagram of the pH amplifier portion of the direct-reading Beckman pH meter. (Courtesy of Beckman Instruments, Inc.)

attended operation is possible. Readings are unaffected by zero-drift, grid current, or tube changes due to aging or replacement. With practically no extra cost the a-c instruments provide recording, controlling or retransmitting of data. Reproducibility and accuracy are not as good as with null-circuits because meter scale accuracies are usually of the order of 1 percent. Representative d-c instruments include the Beckman model N-1, the Philips PR 9401, and the Pye portable meter. Among the a-c instruments are the Beckman Zeromatic, the Coleman model 18A, the Photovolt models 85, 110 and 115, and Electronic Instruments model 23A.

In the "chopper-type" feedback circuits, the direct *difference* voltage is chopped and amplified as alternating voltage, but the output is rectified by a phase-sensitive circuit, and the direct-balancing voltage which is obtained is fed back into the input circuit in opposition to the electrode assembly voltage, thus providing the difference voltage (Fig. 22-6). The input voltage

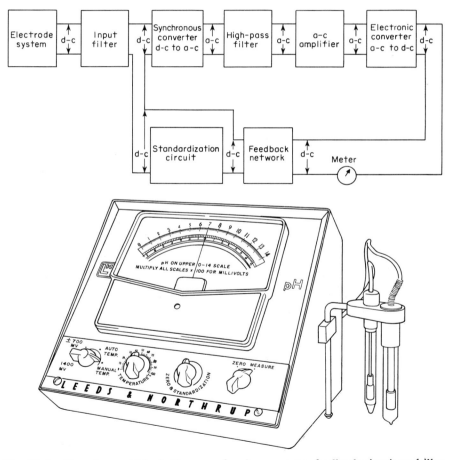

Fig. 22-6. Drawing and block diagram of a chopper-type, feedback circuit and illustration of Leeds & Northrup model 7401 *pH* Indicator. (Courtesy of Leeds & Northrup, Inc.)

is indicated by a suitable meter measuring the feedback current. The electromagnetic chopper is a reed vibrating in response to the presence of an alternating current electromagnet and which alternately makes and breaks contact with a pair of contactors connected to the ends of a center-tapped primary transformer winding. The secondary winding is the input to the amplifier. Instruments of this type include the Leeds & Northrup model 7401 and the Metrohm model E 300.

Other variations include the use of a vibrating capacitor in place of a conventional electrometer tube input. Some meters are equipped with pushbutton controls. A useful feature found in more expensive meters is expanded ranges covering 0.5, 1, or 2 pH units over the full meter scale thus permitting expanded range readings to 0.001 pH unit.

Calibration of pH Meters

In calibrating a pH meter, it is advisable to use the standard reference solution whose pH value most closely approximates that of the test solution. This minimizes the contribution of the liquid-junction potential to the readings, particularly in strongly acidic solutions. A check with a second reference buffer, such that the two buffers bracket the pH of the test solution, should be done to ensure proper functioning of the cell assembly and measurement equipment, and to verify conformity of the pH response with the theoretical Nernst slope. In effect, then, the pH value of the test solution is determined by interpolation. The response of a pH indicator electrode is usually linear with pH over the interval between reference standards, about 2 pH units. Over this pH interval a 10° temperature variation will result in an error of less than 0.07 pH unit.

A glass electrode exhibits a reasonably rapid response to rapid and wide changes of pH in buffered solutions. However, valid readings are obtained more slowly in poorly buffered or unbuffered solutions, particularly when changing to these from buffered solutions, as after standardization. The electrodes should be thoroughly washed with distilled water after each measurement and then rinsed with several portions of the next test solution before making the final reading. Poorly buffered solutions should be vigorously stirred during measurement; otherwise the thin layer of solution at the glass-solution interface tends toward the composition of the particular kind of pH-responsive glass. Suspensions and colloidal material should be wiped from the glass surface with a soft tissue.

Measurement of Acidity with Indicators

To perform colorimetric measurements of pH one requires a set of buffer solutions, an indicator or series of indicators whose ranges overlap, and some device for matching colors. Visual colorimeters have been considered in Chapter 3, and buffer solutions in an earlier section of this chapter.

Theory of Indicator Behavior

Indicators are substances which, in solution, change color according to the degree of acidity or alkalinity. In many instances they will be incompletely dissociated acids or bases in which the dissociated form differs in structure from the undissociated form.

Several hundred indicators are known, but many of them are unreliable. Ideally an indicator should exhibit a sharp color change over a narrow pH range. Most indicators have two colors, one in the extreme acidic condition and the other in the extreme alkaline condition. Of these, the members of the sulfonephthalein series are best. They are brilliant in color, are soluble in water owing to the presence of sulfonic acid groups, and possess a sharp color change usually encompassing 1.5 pH units. Some indicators have only one (visible) color and lose it completely when acid or alkaline. The phthaleins, such as phenolphthalein, and various nitrophenols are examples. Only a

Table 22-3 | *Indicators and Their pH Ranges*

INDICATOR	pH RANGE	pK_{HIn}	WAVELENGTH OF ABSORPTION MAXIMUM, mμ	COLOR CHANGE (ACID-ALKALINE)
o-Cresol red (acid range)	0.2 to 1.8			Red–yellow
Thymol blue (acid range)	1.2 to 2.8	1.75	544	Red–yellow
Tropeolin 00	1.3 to 3.2		527	Red–yellow
2,4-Dinitrophenol	2.4 to 4.0			Colorless–yellow
Methyl yellow	2.9 to 4.0	3.31	508	Red–yellow
Methyl orange	3.1 to 4.4	3.40	506	Red–orange
Bromophenol blue	3.0 to 4.6	4.05	592	Yellow–blue
Alizarin sodium sulfonate	3.7 to 5.2			Yellow–violet
α-Naphthyl red	3.7 to 5.0			Red–yellow
Bromocresol green	4.0 to 5.6	4.68	614	Yellow–blue
Methyl red	4.4 to 6.2	4.95	533	Red–yellow
Bromocresol purple	5.2 to 6.8	6.3	591	Yellow–purple
Chlorophenol red	5.4 to 6.8	6.0		Yellow–red
Bromothymol blue	6.2 to 7.6	7.1	617	Yellow–blue
p-Nitrophenol	5.0 to 7.0			Colorless–yellow
Phenol red	6.4 to 8.0	7.9	558	Yellow–red
Neutral red	6.8 to 8.0	7.0	533	Red–yellow
Cresol red (alkaline range)	7.2 to 8.8	8.2	572	Yellow–red
α-Naphtholphthalein	7.3 to 8.7			Rose–green
Tropeolin 000	7.6 to 8.9			Yellow–rose
Thymol blue (alk. range)	8.0 to 9.6	8.9	596	Yellow–blue
Phenolphthalein	8.0 to 10.0	9.4	553	Colorless–red
α-Naphtholbenzein	9.0 to 11.0			Yellow–blue
Thymolphthalein	9.4 to 10.6	10.0	598	Colorless–blue
Nile blue	10.1 to 11.1			Blue–red
Alizarin yellow	10.0 to 12.0			Yellow–lilac
Diazo violet	10.1 to 12.0			Yellow–violet
Nitramine	11.0 to 13.0			Colorless–orange brown

restricted number of indicators are used; Table 22-3 lists some of the properties of frequently used indicators.

Each indicator changes color over its own particular limited range of
pH values—the pH range of the indicator, as given by the expression

$$pH = pK_{HIn} + \log\frac{[In^-]}{[HIn]} + \log\frac{f_{In-}}{f_{HIn}} \tag{22-18}$$

where In^- represents the dissociated form and HIn the undissociated form
of the indicator (which could also exist as HIn^- or HIn^+), and f_{In-} and
f_{HIn} the activity coefficients of the respective forms. Equation 22-18 implies
that the color of an indicator in solution will depend upon the relative concentrations of In^- and HIn, and is governed by the concentration of hydrogen
ions. The behavior is not so simple, actually. When a change in color is
observed, the color change has its origin in the structural change that ac-
companies, or is induced by, dissociation. Consider the color change of
phenol red, a member of the sulfonephthalein series of indicators, as represented by the following equilibria:

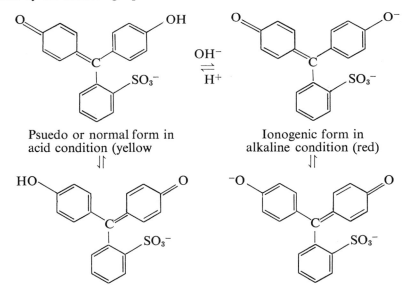

Psuedo or normal form in
acid condition (yellow

Ionogenic form in
alkaline condition (red)

The ionogenic form possesses a color and constitution different from the color
and structure of the psuedo or normal form. The color of each structure
arises from the resonance between the two tautomeric structures of the ionogenic and normal form.

The perception of one form of an indicator in the presence of another
colored form depends upon the observer's power to detect changes of tone or
shade in mixtures of two colors. The actual transformation interval to an

average observer assumes no less than 9 percent of one form together with 91 percent of the other form. In units of pH, the range of an indicator is approximately $pK_{HIn} \pm 1$, or 2 pH units.

Mixtures of indicators, called universal indicators, can be prepared. One mixture is composed of phenolphthalein, methyl red, dimethylaminoazo-benzene, bromthymol blue, and thymol blue. It changes through a series of colors, starting with red at pH 2 and passing through orange at pH 4, yellow at pH 6, green at pH 8, to blue at pH 10. Accuracy never exceeds one pH unit, but a universal indicator is useful for rough preliminary tests of pH. Test papers impregnated with mixed indicators are available.

Methods of Color Comparison

The usual method of pH color comparison for routine measurements is by direct reading. The sample solution containing a known concentration of indicator is compared with solutions of known pH value, each containing the same quantity of indicator. In the Taylor slide comparator (Fig. 22-7) and the

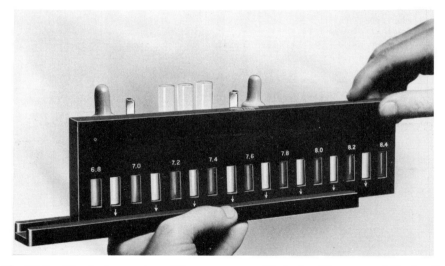

Fig. 22-7. The hydrogen ion slide-comparator (Taylor). (Courtesy of Taylor Instrument Co.)

B.D.H. capillator, the solutions for comparison are put up in small glass vials. Each set of solutions covers a range of pH values in steps, namely, 0.2 pH units. The solutions to be tested and the standard are examined together by transmitted light. When the color is matched, the test solution has the same pH as the standard. When not matched exactly, the color can be adjudged to lie between two standard solutions and, perhaps, the position in the interval estimated within 0.05 *p*H unit. Since each indicator can be used only over a limited range, a number of sets of vials are needed.

The reliability of the color and *p*H of buffered solutions after a period of time is open to some doubt. More permanent artificial color standards are available in the form of glass color filters. A comparative color wheel contains a series of color standards which duplicate in intervals of 0.2 *p*H unit the colors of one indicator (Fig. 22-8). The entire unit is held up to a light

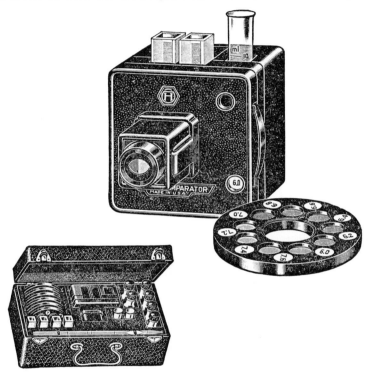

Fig. 22-8. Visual *p*H comparator (Hellige). (Courtesy of Hellige, Inc.)

source and the operator views the sample and color standard through either a split field eyepiece (Hellige) or two round holes with an opal screen as background. The wheel is rotated until the color of one of the glass standards matches the test solution. The latter is contained in a rectangular glass cell, to which has been added a specified amount of indicator solution. Units of these types are compact, portable, and easily operated by nontechnical personnel.

For precise work the spectrophotometer (Chapter 4) is employed. The concentration ratio, In^-/HIn, of Eq. 22-18 is determined from the spectral absorbance for the test solution and for solutions containing an identical concentration of indicator converted completely to its acidic form and to its basic form. If the indicator constant is unknown, a practical value for it may be determined by spectrophotometric measurements of the indicator ratio in solutions of known pH, as illustrated by Fig. 22-9.

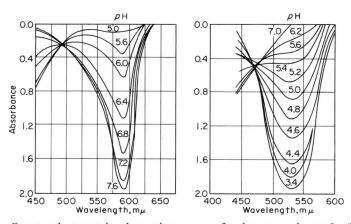

Fig. 22-9. Spectrophotometric absorption curves for bromcresol purple (left) and methyl red (right).

Limitations of Indicator Methods

Nearly all indicator procedures are secondary pH methods, inasmuch as the numbers obtained depend ultimately upon pK_{HIn} or pH values established with the hydrogen electrode. The effect of salts, changes of temperature, uncertainty of color matching, and lack of adequate buffering may introduce uncertainties of 0.2–0.4 pH unit or more in particularly unfavorable environment.

If the test solution is not adequately buffered, introduction of impurities from containers or the atmosphere may produce an appreciable change of pH. Even the addition of the indicator, itself an acid or base, will alter the pH. The latter source of error is minimized by use of isohydric indicators—an indicator solution adjusted in advance to approximate the pH of the test solution.

Proteins and colloidal materials influence the color of an indicator because of the preferential adsorption of one of the indicator forms. The error varies with individual indicators.

Salt effects can be quite serious. Two equally colored solutions need not necessarily have the same pH, provided their ionic strengths are not the same. Salt content of unknown and reference solution should be closely matched, and the ionic strength 0.2 or less. Addition of salt may also affect the light absorbing properties (hue or color tone) of one or both forms of the indicator.

The sign of the salt error is predictable if the charge type of the indicator is known. When the ionic strength is increased by the addition of neutral salts, the activity coefficients of ions decrease, whereas those of uncharged species remain substantially unity. Hence the last term of Eq. 22-18 will decrease upon addition of salt if HIn is either uncharged or a negatively charged indicator acid and will increase if In is uncharged (that is, an indicator base whose acidic form is represented by HIn^+). Neglect of salt effects leads to too high an apparent pH in the first instance and to too low an apparent pH in the second. Unfortunately, the sulfonephthaleins in their alkaline transformation ranges fall into the category of In^{-2}, for which rather large errors are found. For ionic strengths above 0.2, the behavior of the activity coefficient of different ionic species displays individual differences, and the salt error is difficult to predict and is very irregular. If one were to vary the concentration of a buffer mixture and determine the pH both by means of a hydrogen electrode and by the colorimetric method, absolute agreement would occur only at the concentration of buffer employed in preparing the standard. Above this concentration the colorimetric method would give results that are slightly higher than those secured by the hydrogen electrode, and conversely. This is illustrated by the results given in Table 22-4.

| Table 22-4 | *Effect of Varying the Concentration of a Buffer Mixture* |

MOLAR CONCENTRATION	HYDROGEN ELECTRODE pH	COLORIMETRIC pH	DIFFERENCE: ELECTROMETRIC − COLORIMETRIC
0.20	6.33	6.40	−0.07
0.10	6.42	6.45	−0.03
0.05†	6.50	6.50	0.00
0.0200	6.57	6.55	+0.02
0.015	6.62	6.55	+0.07
0.00	6.68	6.55	+0.13

†Standard solution.

Addition of alcohol or less polar solvents decreases the ionization of water and also affects the dissociation of dissolved indicators. Indicators standardized for use in aqueous solution will indicate an acidity in mixed solvents which is higher than the true acidity if the indicator is an acid type, and lower than the true acidity if the indicator is a base type. The true acidity must be somewhere between these two extremes.

Dichroism is observed with some indicators. The visual color of the indicator appears to be one color when viewed in thin layers or in low concentrations, and a second color in deep layers or high concentration. Dichroism often arises from the fact that the indicator molecule has two bands of transmission in the spectrum but the wavelengths in the two bands do not penetrate equally well through the solution. The quality of illuminant is obviously important. Bromphenol blue is particularly poor in this respect.

LABORATORY WORK

Preparation of Standard Buffer Solutions

To prepare the standard buffer solutions recommended by the National Bureau of Standards (U.S.), the indicated weights of the pure materials in Table 22-5 should be

Table 22-5	Compositions of Standard Buffer Solutions, National Bureau of Standards

(Air weights of salt per liter of buffer solution.)

STANDARD	WEIGHT OF SALT, GRAMS
$KHC_2O_4 \cdot H_2C_2O_4 \cdot 2H_2O$, 0.05 M	12.70
Potassium hydrogen tartrate, about 0.034 M	Saturated at 22°–28°C
Potassium hydrogen phthalate, 0.05 M	10.21
Phosphate:	
$\quad KH_2PO_4$, 0.025 M	3.40
$\quad Na_2HPO_4$, 0.025 M	3.55
Phosphate:	
$\quad KH_2PO_4$, 0.008665 M	1.179
$\quad Na_2HPO_4$, 0.03032 M	4.33
$Na_2B_4O_7 \cdot 10H_2O$, 0.01 M	3.81
$Ca(OH)_2$, about 0.0203 M	Saturated at 25°C

dissolved in a good grade of water, either freshly distilled or deionized, and diluted to 1 liter. The excess of solid potassium hydrogen tartrate and calcium hydroxide must be removed, the latter by filtration through a sintered glass filter (No. 3 porosity). Water for preparation of alkaline solutions should be boiled and protected from carbon dioxide while cooling, or should be purged with CO_2-free air. Entrance of CO_2 into borax and calcium hydroxide buffers must be avoided. The buffer solutions may be stored in polyethylene or Pyrex bottles. The solutions should be replaced every two months, or sooner if formation of mold is noticed. A crystal of thymol may be added as preservative.

The tartrate, phthalate, and phosphates may each be dried for 2 hr at 110°C. Potassium tetroxalate and calcium hydroxide need not be dried. Fresh-looking crystals of sodium tetraborate should be used. Calcium hydroxide supplied by the Bureau of Standards should be used; alternatively, directions for its preparation should be followed carefully.

The preparation of the buffer solutions of Clark and Lubs should be self-evident from the information given in Table 22-6.

| Table 22-6 | *Buffer Solutions of Clark and Lubs at 25°C* (Values on the conventional activity *p*H scale defined by the National Bureau of Standards)† | | |

*p*H	*x*	BUFFER VALUE, β

For *x* ml 0.2 *M* HCl plus 25 ml 0.2 *M* KCl diluted to 100 ml

*p*H	*x*	BUFFER VALUE, β
1.00	67.0	0.31
1.20	52.8	.24
1.40	26.6	.19
1.60	16.2	.077
1.80	10.2	.049
2.00	6.5	.030
2.20	3.9	.022

For *x* ml 0.1 *M* HCl plus 50 ml 0.1 *M* potassium acid phthalate diluted to 100 ml

*p*H	*x*	BUFFER VALUE, β
2.20	49.5	—
2.40	42.2	0.036
2.60	35.4	.033
2.80	28.9	.032
3.00	22.3	.034
3.20	12.9	.026
3.40	10.4	.023
3.60	6.3	.018
3.80	2.9	.015
4.00	0.1	.014

For *x* ml 0.1 *M* NaOH plus 50 ml 0.1 *M* KH phthalate diluted to 100 ml

*p*H	*x*	BUFFER VALUE, β
4.20	3.0	0.017
4.40	6.6	.020
4.60	11.1	.025
4.80	16.5	.029
5.00	22.6	.031
5.20	28.8	.030
5.40	34.1	.025
5.60	38.8	.020
5.80	42.3	.015

For *x* ml 0.1 *M* NaOH plus 50 ml 0.1 *M* KH_2PO_4 diluted to 100 ml

*p*H	*x*	BUFFER VALUE, β
5.80	3.6	—
6.00	5.6	0.010
6.20	8.1	.015
6.40	11.6	.021
6.60	16.4	.027
6.80	22.4	.033
7.00	29.1	.031
7.20	34.7	.025
7.40	39.1	.020
7.60	42.4	.013
7.80	44.5	.009
8.00	46.1	—

Table 22-6 (cont.) | *Buffer Solutions of Clark and Lubs at 25°C*

pH	x	BUFFER VALUE, β
For x ml 0.1 M NaOH plus 50 ml of a mixture 0.1 M with respect to both KCl and H_3BO_3 and diluted to 100 ml		
8.00	3.9	—
8.20	6.0	0.011
8.40	8.6	.015
8.60	11.8	.018
8.80	15.8	.022
9.00	20.8	.027
9.20	26.4	.029
9.40	32.1	.027
9.60	36.9	.022
9.80	40.6	.016
10.00	43.7	.014
10.20	46.2	—

†[From V. E. Bower and R. G. Bates, *J. Research Natl. Bur. Standards* (U.S.), **55**, 197 (1955)].

Preparation of Indicator Solutions

To prepare solutions of the sulfonephthalein indicators, grind 0.1 g of the dye in a clean mortar with the quantities of 0.05 M sodium hydroxide given in Table 22-7, and dilute with distilled water to 200 ml for a 0.05 percent stock solution.

Table 22-7 | *Preparation of Sulfonephthalein Indicator Solutions*

INDICATOR	MOLECULAR WEIGHT	Ml 0.05 N NaOH per 0.1g OF INDICATOR
Thymol blue	456	4.3
m-Cresol purple	382	5.3
Bromphenol blue	670	3.0
Bromcresol green	698	2.9
Methyl red	269	7.4
Chlorphenol red	423	4.7
Bromcresol purple	540	5.3
Bromthymol blue	624	3.2
Phenol red	354	5.7
Cresol red	382	5.3
Tetrabromphenol blue	986	2.0

Water will dissolve methyl orange and alizarin yellow; phenolphthalein and thymolphthalein will dissolve in alcohol.

Platinizing an Electrode

A thoroughly cleaned platinum electrode is immersed in the platinizing solution (3 percent platinic chloride solution containing 0.025 percent lead acetate) and connected to the negative terminal of a 3-V d-c power supply; a piece of platinum wire is attached to the positive terminal as the anode. The current is allowed to flow until the surface of the electrode is covered with a thin, dull grayish coating (about 10 sec). The platinized electrode is rinsed and used to electrolyze a dilute solution of sulfuric acid, being made alternately the cathode and anode at intervals of 15 sec for several reversals, stopping when it has been the cathode.

The electrode should be immersed in distilled water or in dilute sulfuric acid when not in use. Replace within 7 to 21 days. The electrode should never be allowed to dry out.

Preparation of a Calomel Electrode

Calomel prepared by chemical precipitation, or by an electrolytic method, very finely divided and intimately mixed with a dispersion of mercury globules, is spread as a thin layer over the surface of mercury. Lastly, the solution of potassium chloride, of chosen concentration and saturated with mercurous chloride, is added slowly and with minimum disturbance to the calomel layer over the mercury.

To prepare a saturated solution of potassium chloride, place the salt in warm distilled water in a beaker and stir thoroughly with repeated addition of salt until no more will dissolve. Then stir enough calomel to saturate the solution. A small quantity is sufficient, since it is not very soluble. Cool the solution to room temperature. It should contain undissolved potassium chloride and calomel.

E X P E R I M E N T 2 2 - 1   COLORIMETRIC pH MEASUREMENTS WITH BUFFERS

1. Determine the approximate pH of the test solution with the aid of test papers or by tests of small portions of the unknown with various indicators or with a drop of "universal" indicator.

2. Select from Table 22-3 an indicator which exhibits an intermediate color in the pH region of the unknown.

3. Prepare a series of buffer solutions in the proper range and spaced at 0.2 pH intervals. The buffer mixtures of Clark and Lubs are given in Table 22-6.

4. Add an accurately measured amount of indicator: 0.50 ml of 0.05 percent indicator solution for each 10 ml of solution. Add buffer solution to the 10.0-ml mark in test tubes marked for 10-ml content. Unmarked tubes may be used by careful measurement of indicator and buffer volumes. Each tube should be labeled near the top with the correct pH value. Add the same amount of indicator used in each of the standard buffer solutions to a clean tube, and dilute to the mark with a portion of the test solution. All solutions are swirled until they are homogeneous; never mix by inverting and closing the tube with a finger or the palm of the hand.

5. Observe the tubes against a white background in diffuse daylight. Estimate the pH of the unknown to the nearest tenth of a pH unit by comparing it successively with pairs of standards differing by 0.2 pH unit. A match with the first or last standard in any series should never be taken as an accurate determination.

E X P E R I M E N T 2 2 - 2   MEASUREMENT OF pH WITH THE HYDROGEN ELECTRODE

Place two platinized electrodes in the electrode holder (Fig. 22-1). Add sufficient standard buffer solution to cover a portion of the electrode surfaces. Bubble hydrogen from a tank (via a purification train, if necessary) slowly through the solutions.

Measure the difference of potential between the two hydrogen electrodes with a potentiometer or vacuum tube voltmeter. If the difference exceeds a few tenths of a millivolt, the electrodes should be cleaned and replatinized.

Measure the difference of potential between one of the hydrogen electrodes and the reference electrode. Calculate the theoretical potential of the hydrogen electrode in the buffer solution. Subtract the calculated value from the measured value. The result is the potential of the reference electrode. Thus all errors due to liquid-junction potential, the partial pressure of hydrogen gas, temperature, etc., are included with the value of the reference electrode and the buffer solution becomes the standard for measurement.

Replace the standard buffer solution with the unknown solution. Bubble hydrogen through the solution for several minutes and then measure the potential difference between the hydrogen electrode and the reference cell. Use the value obtained above for the potential of the reference cell and calculate the pH of the unknown.

Note. To hasten attainment of the final equilibrium potential of a hydrogen electrode, electrolyze the electrode (as cathode) immediately prior to a pH measurement. Use a dilute sulfuric acid solution as electrolyte. Rinse the electrode thoroughly with distilled water before insertion into the unknown.

E X P E R I M E N T 22-3   MEASUREMENT OF pH WITH THE QUINHYDRONE ELECTRODE

1. Place about 20 ml of a standard buffer solution in a 50-ml beaker. Add 0.1 g of quinhydrone, and stir for 1 min. Some quinhydrone should remain undissolved.

2. Immerse a clean, bright platinum electrode into the solution along with a reference electrode.

3. Measure the difference of potential between the two electrodes with a potentiometer or vacuum tube voltmeter. Calculate the apparent potential of the reference electrode from the pH of the standard buffer.

4. Replace the standard buffer with the unknown and repeat steps 1 through 3. Use the apparent value of the reference electrode found in step 3, and the potential difference measured, to calculate the pH of the unknown.

E X P E R I M E N T 22-4   MEASUREMENT OF pH WITH AN ANTIMONY ELECTRODE

1. Prepare three standard buffer solutions whose pH values lie between 4 and 10.

2. Place 25 ml of one of the standard buffer solutions in a 50-ml beaker and immerse a reference electrode and a stick of antimony which has been cleaned with abrasive paper.

3. Measure the difference of potential between the two electrodes with a potentiometer or a vacuum tube voltmeter.

4. Repeat steps 2 and 3 with each of the other standard buffer solutions.

5. Plot the observed difference of potential vs the pH of standard buffer solutions on a sheet of graph paper.

6. Replace the standards with the unknown. Repeat step 3. Read the pH of the unknown from the graph constructed in step 5.

Note. If the electrode readings show a continual drift, soak the antimony electrode overnight in a buffer solution.

Problems

1. Compare the hydrogen, quinhydrone, antimony, and glass indicator electrodes with respect to (*a*) construction, (*b*) nature of the response, (*c*) useful range, (*d*) interferences, (*e*) general utility under all operating conditions, and (*f*) usefulness in solvents other than water.

2. Which indicator electrodes could be used to measure the *p*H of these systems? (*a*) carbonated beverages, (*b*) chromium-plating baths, (*c*) sulfite-process paper-pulp slurries, (*d*) plating baths containing HBF_4, (*e*) water in swimming pools, (*f*) tomato catsup, (*g*) sites of dental caries, (*h*) 0.1 *M* solutions of ferrous sulfate from acid pickling baths.

3. In what ratios would solutions of 0.1 *M* KH_2PO_4 and 0.1 *M* K_2HPO_4 be mixed to give buffers of the following *p*H values, respectively : 6.4; 6.8; 7.3?

4. The pK_a of bromcresol purple indicator is 6.3. Determine the *p*H values that may be simulated by viewing pairs of tubes containing indicator as shown, per 10 ml:

Number of Drops of Indicator per Tube								
Acid tubes	9	8	7	6	5	4	3	2	1
Basic tubes	1	2	3	4	5	6	7	8	9

5. A hydrogen electrode/saturated calomel electrode pair dipped into a given solution at 25°C. gives an equilibrium reading of 0.5832 V, the calomel cell being positive in the external circuit relative to the hydrogen electrode. Calculate the *p*H of the solution.

6. If the E^0 value for the quinhydrone electrode is 0.699 V, what value should be observed for the quinhydrone electrode vs the saturated calomel electrode in a solution of *p*H 4.3 at 25°C.?

7. What emf would be expected for saturated calomel vs the hydrogen electrode at the stoichiometric point in the titration of 25.00 ml of 0.4000 *N* acetic acid with 0.4000 *N* sodium hydroxide?

8. In a determination of the indicator dissociation constant for phenol red, the following data were obtained: A_s in 0.01 *M* sodium hydroxide was 1.760; A_s in 0.05 *M* potassium hydrogen phthalate, 0.005; and A_s in a buffer of *p*H 7.5 was 0.575. The concentration of indicator and the thickness of the cell were the same in every measurement. The wavelength employed corresponded to the absorption maximum of the basic form of the indicator, 560 mμ. Calculate pK_{HIn} for phenol red.

9. The sodium ion correction nomograph for general purpose glass electrodes manufactured by Beckman Instruments, Inc. is shown in Fig. 22-10. (a) Estimate the corrected *p*H for these measurements:

Solution number	A	B	C	D
*p*H scale reading	13.50	11.25	12.00	12.10
Temperature, °C	25	30	25	40
$[Na^+]$	0.05	0.2	0.1	0.02

(b) Below what *p*H value is the *p*H correction less than 0.02 *p*H unit at $[Na^+]$ = 0.2? At $[Na^+]$ = 1.0? (c) To render negligible the *p*H correction at *p*H 10.9, below what value must the sodium ion concentration be maintained? *Ans.* (a) Solution A has corrected *p*H = 14.12.

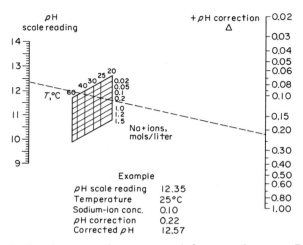

Problem 22-9. Sodium ion correction nomograph for general purpose Beckman glass electrodes. (Courtesy of Beckman Instruments, Inc.)

10. Why is it necessary to protect carefully a potassium acid phthalate buffer solution from contamination with acids or alkalis?

11. Would the error in pH_s be significant if potassium acid tartrate solution were not completely saturated?

12. Why are alkaline reference buffer solutions subject to larger errors due to temperature changes than are acid buffers?

13. Why does the pH_s value of borax buffer solutions change so considerably with temperature? (Hint: Consider polymeric species of boric acid.)

14. Compare the relative merits of the colorimetric and electric methods of pH measurement in regard to (a) cost, (b) operator skill, (c) continuous readings and control of industrial operations, (d) frequency of recalibration, (e) durability or permanence of system, (f) auxiliary solutions and equipment needed, (g) freedom from salt error, protein error, etc., and (h) portability.

Bibliography

American Society for Testing Materials, "Symposium on pH Measurement," *Spec. Tech, Publ.*, **73** (1947); **190** (1957).

Bates, R. G., *Determination of pH*, Wiley, New York, 1964.

Britton, H. T. S., *Hydrogen Ions*, 4th ed. Chapman & Hall, London, 1955.

Clark, W. M., *The Determination of Hydrogen Ions*, 3rd ed. Williams & Wilkins, Baltimore, 1928.

Kolthoff, I. M., *Acid-Base Indicators*, 4th ed. Macmillan, New York, 1937.

Kolthoff, I. M., and H. A. Laitinen, pH *and Electro-Titrations*, 2nd ed. Wiley, New York, 1941.

Lingane, J. J., *Electroanalytical Chemistry*, 2nd ed., Interscience, New York, 1958.

Literature Cited

1. Bates, R. G., *Determination of* pH, Wiley, New York, 1964.
2. Bates, R. G., *J. Res., Natl. Bur. St. (U.S.)* **66A,** 179 (1962).
3. Bates, R. G., and V. E. Bowers, ibid. **53,** 283 (1954).
4. Biilman, E., *Ann. chim.*, **15,** 109 (1921).
5. Cary, H. H., and W. P. Baxter, U.S. Patent 2,383,709.
6. Clark, W. M., *The Determination of Hydrogen Ions*, 3rd ed., Williams & Wilkens, Baltimore, 1928.
7. Clark, W. R., and G. A. Perley, *Am. Soc. Testing Mater., Spec. Tech. Publ.*, **190,** 34 (1957).
8. Granger, F. S., and J. M. Nelson, *J. Am. Chem. Soc.* **43,** 1401 (1921).
9. Lewin, S. Z., *J. Chem. Educ.*, **36,** A477 (1959); ibid. **36,** A595 (1959); ibid. **36,** A663 (1959).
10. Perley, G. A., *Anal. Chem.*, **11,** 316, 319 (1939).
11. Perley, G. A., *J. Electrochem. Soc.*, **92,** 485 (1948).
12. Perley, G. A., *Anal. Chem.*, **21,** 391, 394, 559 (1949).
13. Roberts, E. J., and F. Fenwick, *J. Am. Chem. Soc.*, **50,** 2125 (1928).
14. Stock, J. T., and W. C., Purdy, *Chem. Rev.*, **57,** 1159 (1957).

Separations By Electrolysis

Electrolytic methods can be applied to the quantitative removal and determination of one or more different metallic ions from solution or may be used, with carefully controlled conditions, to effect a separation of ions of one metal from those of several other metals. The discussion of the technique of determining a substance in solution by measuring the quantity of electricity required to effect its complete reaction in an electrolysis cell is reserved for Chapter 24.

Laws and Units

Before discussing electrolytic separations, it is essential to recall certain fundamental laws and facts related to electrolysis. The *coulomb* (Q) is the quantity of electricity that will cause the deposition or removal of 0.001118 g of silver at an electrode. An *ampere*, the unit of current, is 1 Q/sec. The *ohm* (Ω) is the unit of resistance—a column of mercury 106.3 cm long at 0°C weighing 14.4521 g and of uniform cross section has a resistance of 1 Ω. The *volt* or unit of electromotive force (emf) causes a current of 1 amp to flow through a resistance of 1 Ω.

Ohm's law gives the relation between current, resistance and electromotive force:

$$i = E/R \tag{23-1}$$

where i is in amperes, E in volts, and R in ohms.

The current in amperes per square centimeter of electrode surface is the usual definition of *current density*. It is a very important consideration in electrolytic operations. If it is too great, the processes of diffusion and stirring may be too slow to transport material to the electrode surface and some other process, such as the liberation of hydrogen from water, consumes a major part of the current at the working electrode.

The *faraday* (F), 96,487 Q, is the amount of electricity equivalent to Avogadro's number of electrons transferred in either an oxidation or a reduction process. Because this quantity of electrons must be removed to oxidize a gram equivalent of any substance and the same number of electrons must be taken to reduce a gram equivalent, a faraday is that quantity of electricity used in transforming a gram equivalent of any substance at an electrode.

The two laws of electrolysis, usually referred to as Faraday's laws, can be stated as follows:

1. The quantity of a given substance that is liberated at an electrode is proportional to the quantity of electricity that is passed through the system.

2. The amounts of different substances that are deposited by the same quantity of electricity are proportional to the chemical equivalent weights of these substances.

These statements are true only if the current efficiency does not vary and is 100 percent for the substance being measured.

Equipment for Electrolytic Separations

In order to make electrolytic separations, it is necessary to have a source of direct current, an adjustable resistance, a cell for electrolysis, including the electrodes, and usually some means for stirring the solution. In order to measure the current and applied voltage, an appropriate ammeter and voltmeter are needed. The schematic arrangement of the equipment is shown in Fig. 23-1. The direct current is most conveniently supplied from storage batteries

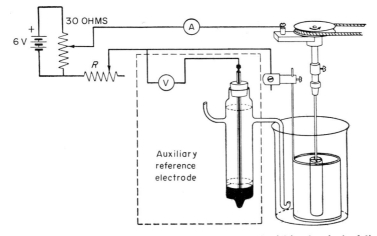

Fig. 23-1. Equipment for electrodeposition. Enclosed within the dashed lines is the additional equipment required for measuring the electrode potential.

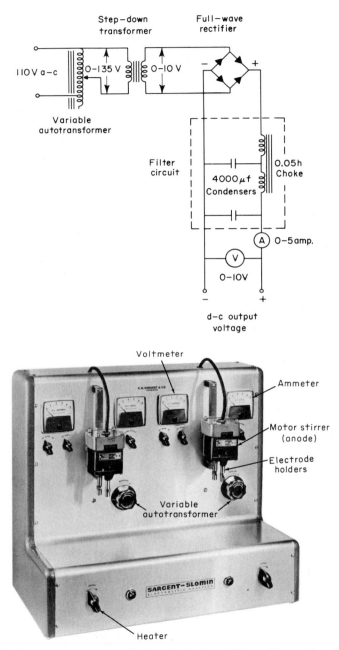

Fig. 23-2. Direct-current power supply for electrodeposition. *Upper*, the electrical circuit; *lower*, exterior view showing the controls. (Courtesy, E. H. Sargent & Co.)

because they give a steady voltage. However, compact commercial power supplies are available that operate from alternating current to supply the direct current. A schematic diagram of one unit is shown in Fig. 23-2. A fixed transformer steps the voltage down to 6 or 10 V, and the current is then passed through a selenium rectifier bridge of the full- or half-wave type, and finally through a filter circuit. The latter, a combination of an inductance or choke and a capacitor, converts the pulses of raw d-c output from the rectifiers into a more or less smooth flow of direct current. A filter circuit which leaves the ripple remaining at 1 percent or less is satisfactory. The variable autotransformer is used to control the voltage applied to the stepdown transformer, and thereby the rectified output voltage.

The electrolysis cell is frequently a tall-form beaker, covered with a split watch glass to exclude dirt and to minimize loss of solution through spray during the electrolysis. The cathode is generally a cylinder (perhaps corrugated) of platinum gauze or a perforated platinum foil. Anodes may be a coiled wire, a platinum paddle, or a second gauze electrode smaller in diameter than the cathode. A gauze construction presents the largest surface area consistent with adequate mechanical strength. The effective area will be the total foil area or the length of wire, calculated from the number of meshes and dimensions of the electrode, multiplied by πd, where d is the diameter of the wire. Effective stirring of the electrolyte is usually essential. This can be accomplished by a motor stirrer and a glass impellor, a magnetic stirrer and rotating bar magnet, or with the anode rotating within the cathode. The last method is commonly used where commercial equipment is employed.

After the electrolysis is complete, the deposited metal must be removed from the solution without contaminating the solution if further analyses are to be made on the solution, and without loss of the deposited metal if this deposit is to be weighed or analyzed. If the deposit has been made on a platinum electrode and is to be weighed, the electrode must be washed thoroughly as it is removed from the solution. Furthermore, because of the voltaic cell which is present and which would cause dissolution of the deposited metal if the applied voltage were interrupted, the electrode should be washed without breaking the electric circuit. This is best done by slowly lowering the electrolysis cell from the electrodes while washing the electrodes with a stream of water from a wash bottle. The electrodes are then rinsed with alcohol or acetone prior to drying them at an elevated temperature. The weight of the deposit is obtained by weighing the electrode before and after deposition.

Basic Principles

Let us assume a typical electrogravimetric cell. A pair of relatively large platinum electrodes is immersed in the electrolyte, and a voltage is applied

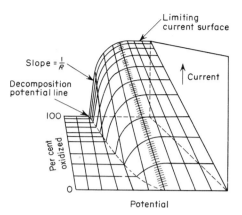

Fig. 23-3. Three-dimensional representation of a reversible oxidation-reduction system as it applies to electroanalysis. After W. H. Reinmuth, *J. Chem. Educ.*, **38**, 149 (1961).

across them. At first, as the applied voltage is gradually increased, virtually no current (except a small residual current) is observed to flow through the cell. However, as a particular point on the voltage axis is reached (Fig. 23-3), a noticeable reaction will be observed and a current begins to flow through the cell. This particular value of applied voltage is called the decomposition potential with respect to the particular electrode reaction. As soon as the decomposition potential is exceeded, continuous electrolysis of the solution is sustained. With further increase in applied voltage the current increases linearly in accordance with Ohm's law. Ideally, the slope of the curve is the reciprocal of the resistance between the terminals of the electrolytic cell. Actually, the current is soon limited by the rate of mass transfer of electroactive material to the electrode surface. The mass transfer coefficient is dependent on the rate of stirring, cell and electrode geometries, diffusion coefficient of the electroactive species, and the like. As the concentration of electroactive species in solution decreases, so also does the limiting current plateau. The decomposition potential simultaneously shifts to more cathodic (if reducible species are involved) or anodic (if oxidizable species are involved) values.

To determine what voltage must be applied to a cell to cause electrolysis, it is necessary to know first what reactions will occur at the two electrodes. If these reactions are known, it is possible to calculate the potential of each electrode and thereby determine the emf of the galvanic cell which exerts its potential in opposition to the applied voltage. For example, in the electrolysis of 0.100 M $CuSO_4$ in 1 N H_2SO_4 with platinum electrodes, the reaction at the cathode will be

$$Cu^{+2} + 2e^- \rightarrow Cu^0 \tag{23-2}$$

and at the anode

$$2H_2O \rightarrow O_2 + 4H^+ + 4e^- \tag{23-3}$$

Using the Nernst equation to calculate the potential of the copper electrode,

$$E = 0.337 + 0.0296 \log (0.100) = 0.308 \text{ V} \tag{23-4}$$

For the other electrode at which oxygen is evolved,

$$E = 1.229 + \frac{0.0591}{4} \log \frac{[O_2][H^+]^4}{[H_2O]^2} \tag{23-5}$$

This expression can be simplified by realizing that the term $[O_2]$ is the same as the partial pressure of oxygen gas in the atmosphere (approximately 0.21), and that the concentration of water is essentially constant. Then,

$$E = 1.229 + 0.0148 \log p_{O_2}[H^+]^4 \qquad (23\text{-}6)$$

In 1 N H_2SO_4, the potential is about 1.22 V.

The cell emf is the algebraic difference of the electrode potentials of the two half-cells comprising the electrolytic cell. The spontaneous reaction which will occur in this cell is

$$2Cu^\circ + O_2 + 4H^+ = 2Cu^{+2} + 2H_2O \qquad (23\text{-}7)$$

This corresponds to subtracting Eq. 23-4 from Eq. 23-5; therefore, the emf of the galvanic cell is $1.22 - 0.31 = 0.91$ V. Correspondingly, the emf of the electrolytic cell is -0.91 V. When the applied voltage is exactly 0.91 V, no current will flow through the cell in either direction, which is, of course, the principle of potentiometric measurements. As soon as the applied voltage is in excess of the galvanic cell emf, the iR drop, and the sum of any overpotential effects,

$$E_{\text{applied}} = E_{\text{cell}} + iR + \omega_{\text{anode}} + \omega_{\text{cathode}} \qquad (23\text{-}8)$$

current is forced to flow through the electrolytic cell and the reaction expressed by Eq. 23-7 proceeds from right to left. The maximum value of the current is governed by the cell resistance and mass transfer conditions.

Completeness of Depositions

The emf that is applied to an electrolytic cell must be sufficient to insure the removal of the desired electroactive species to an extent adequate for the purpose of the experiment. Take the deposition of silver for example. As the silver deposits, the concentration of silver ions in solution decreases, and, according to the Nernst equation,

$$E = 0.80 + 0.0591 \log [Ag^+] \qquad (23\text{-}9)$$

the potential at which silver deposits becomes more negative. The values in Table 23-1 represent the changes in cathode potential for various fractions

Table 23-1	Electrode Potential as a Function of Silver-Ion Concentration	
CONCENTRATION OF SILVER ION, M	FRACTION OF ORIGINAL REMAINING, %	CATHODE POTENTIAL, V
1×10^{-1}	100	0.74
1×10^{-2}	10	0.68
1×10^{-3}	1	0.62
1×10^{-4}	0.1	0.56
1×10^{-5}	0.01	0.50

of the original silver concentration, which was 0.1 M in our example. The cathode potential changes very nearly 59 mV for each tenfold decrease in the concentration of the silver ion remaining undeposited (and, in general, $59/n$ mV for metallic ions). Assuming that the anode process proceeds at a constant level and that the iR drop is essentially constant, the decomposition potential of the solution should vary by a like amount.

If only a very minute amount of a metal is to be deposited on platinum, perhaps a fraction of a microgram, then the amount of deposit may not be enough to form a mono-layer of atoms, and hence the activity of the metal phase cannot be assumed to be constant. Rogers and Stehney[13] discuss the theory of depositions in such situations.

Overpotentials

When a current flows across an electrode-solution interface, it is normally found that the electrode potential changes from the reversible value it possesses before the passage of current. The difference between the measured potential (or cell emf) and its reversible value is the overpotential (also called over-voltage). The electrodes are said to be polarized. Both cathodic and anodic processes exhibit overpotential, and it is affected by many factors. When an anodic process shows an overpotential effect, the applied potential necessary to cause electrolysis will always be a more positive value than the calculated potential and, for cathodic processes, overpotential causes the applied potential to be more negative than the calculated value. Although overpotential phenomena complicate the calculation of the applied voltage necessary for electrolysis to occur, its effect makes feasible certain separations that would not be expected from standard electrode potentials.

Various types of overpotential may be distinguished. In some electrode processes a film of oxide or some other substance forms on the electrode surface and sets up a resistance to the passage of current across it. What may be termed an ohmic-psuedo-overpotential is also observed when the capillary tip used in measuring the potential of an electrode is at an appreciable distance from the electrode surface. The latter effect only becomes appreciable at high current densities or low concentrations.

A second type of overpotential is due to concentration changes in the vicinity of the electrode and is consequently referred to as *concentration overpotential*. Whenever a finite current flows across an electrode-solution interface, the concentration of the electroactive species at the electrode surface is somewhat altered from its concentration in the bulk of the solution. The reason is that the species at the electrode surface is not replenished at a rate commensurate with the current demand. Consequently, the potential of the cathode will exhibit a more negative value as the voltage applied to the electrolytic cell is increased. Generally, the metal ion concentration at the electrode interface is only 1 percent of the bulk concentration; thus, the concentration overpotential is approximately $0.118/n$ V. In practice, concentration overpotential is minimized by the use of electrodes with large surface areas and by keeping electrolysis currents small, although the latter stipulation is not conducive to rapid electrolysis. The rate of mass transfer is aided by mechanical stirring and increase in temperature of the solution.

Although concentration changes are probably the most important source of overpotential accompanying the deposition of a metal, small overpotentials arise from other causes. As a general rule, the overpotential of a metal upon itself is not large (about 0.01 V) at low current densities. This is not true, however, for such hard metals as cobalt, nickel, iron, chromium, and molybdenum. In an ammoniacal solution the deposition potential of copper on a platinum electrode is considerably lower than on a silver electrode. Consequently, in the separation of silver from copper in an ammoniacal solution, if the silver is plated on a platinum electrode and if toward the end of the electrolysis the level of the solution is raised, copper will plate on the bare platinum surface exposed.

Complexation may affect the overpotential in either direction, because the rate of exchange of electrons between the electrode and complex species may be greater or less than the rate of exchange with the aquated ion. For example, aquo nickel ions show an overpotential of about 0.6 V at a mercury surface, whereas complexes of nickel with thiocyanate or pyridine, although actually shifting the equilibrium electrode potential more negative, show a decrease in overpotential which more than compensates for the shift in the equilibrium potential.

The evolution of gases at an electrode is usually associated with an overpotential significantly larger than concentration overpotentials. It is particularly marked in the evolution of hydrogen and oxygen, and is called the *gas overpotential*. Some values of the overpotential of hydrogen on various surfaces are given in Table 23-2. The anodic overpotential of oxygen on smooth platinum in acid solutions is approximately 0.4 V.

Gas overpotential depends on several factors: (a) *Electrode material.* At a given current density, overpotential for many metal surfaces seems to decrease roughly in a parallel manner to the thermionic work function of the electrode material. (b) *Current density.* An increase in current density invariably increases the overpotential up to a limiting value. (c) *Electrode condition.* Whether smooth or rough, bright or platinized, the overpotential at a given current density decreases if the electrode surface is roughened. This is due partly, if not entirely, to an increase in the effective area and the consequent decrease in the actual current density. (d) *Temperature.* As the temperature is raised, overpotential diminishes. For most electrodes the temperature coefficient is about 2 mV/degree. (e) *The pH.* At low current densities the overpotential is independent of the pH. At high acid concentrations and with some metals there appears to be some dependence on pH.

Table 23-2 | *Hydrogen Overpotential on Various Cathodes*

Electrolyte is $1M$ H_2SO_4. Overpotential given in volts.

CATHODE	FIRST VISIBLE GAS BUBBLES	CURRENT DENSITY	
		0.01 amp cm^{-2}	0.1 amp cm^{-2}
Antimony	0.23	0.4	—
Bismuth	0.39	0.4	—
Cadmium	0.39	~0.4†	—
		—	1.2
Copper	0.19	0.4	0.8
Gold	0.017	0.4	1.0
Lead	0.40	0.4	1.2
Mercury	0.80	1.2	1.3
Platinum (bright)	~0	0.09	0.16
Silver	0.097	0.3	0.9
Tin	0,40	0.5	1.2
Zinc	0.48	0.7‡	—

[From J. J. Lingane, *Electroanalytical Chemistry*, 2nd ed., Interscience, New York, 1958, page 209 (by permission.)]
†0.005 M H_2SO_4
‡0.01 M Zn $(C_2H_3O_2)_2$

The hydrogen overpotential is large on metals such as bismuth, cadmium, lead, tin, zinc, and especially mercury. With a mercury cathode, a number of useful separations become possible, as will be discussed in a later section. Overpotential of hydrogen on cadmium and zinc is important in electrolysis because it permits their determination in an aqueous solution.

Processes at the Anode

The behavior at an anode is, in general, analogous to that at a cathode. The process associated with the smallest oxidation potential, whether it be dissolution of the metallic anode to form cations or the discharge of anions, will take place first. Subsequent anodic processes will follow in order of increasing oxidation potential. The discharge of anions involves a consideration of sulfide, halide and hydroxyl ions only. For other anions, the hydroxyl ion, derived from the water at the surface of the anode, or water itself, will be preferentially discharged, leading to the evolution of oxygen. Consequently, for solutions of metal salts other than halides or sulfides, the decomposition potential will depend primarily upon the metal ion. Equations 23-3 and 23-6 will express the anodic reaction.

Under suitable conditions, PbO_2, MnO_2, and Tl_2O_3 can be deposited at the anode and thereby separated from nearly all other metallic ions. Halide ions can be deposited on a silver anode—selectively if the anode potential is controlled.

Electrogravimetry

Constant-Current Electrolysis

Electrolysis has long been carried out with the current kept more or less constant with time by adjusting the voltage applied to the cell. The technique can be represented by the intersection of the system surface with a plane parallel to the base, or zero-current plane, of Fig. 23-3. No control is exerted over the cathode potential; rather, a predetermined current is forced through the electrolytic cell regardless of mass transport conditions. The electrochemical process with the most positive reduction potential will occur first at the cathode, then the next most positive electrochemical process, etc. Thus, if a current is passed through a solution containing cupric, hydrogen, and zinc ions, copper will be deposited first at the cathode. As the copper deposits, the reduction potential of the cupric ions becomes more negative, requiring periodic changes in the applied emf to more negative values as the electrolysis proceeds. More significantly, the rate at which cupric ions can be brought to the electrode surface will eventually fall under the rate required by the current forced through the cell; that is, the reduction of cupric ions alone will not hold the current at the desired level. Further increases in the applied emf will then result in a rapid change of cathode potential to a point where it equals that of hydrogen ions, and liberation of hydrogen gas begins (Fig. 21-11). From this point on an increasing fraction of the current is devoted to the evolution of hydrogen, although the cathode potential will become relatively stable at a level fixed by the electrode potential and the overpotential for the evolution of hydrogen gas. This second process would be intolerable were it to involve another metal deposit; even so, the continual evolution of gas at the electrode is unsuited for adherent deposits.

Since, in the foregoing example, the hydrogen-ion concentration remains virtually constant in a solution during the evolution of hydrogen at the cathode and oxygen at the anode, the potential of the cathode cannot become sufficiently negative for the deposition of the zinc ions to commence. It should be evident, then, that metallic ions with a positive reduction potential may be separated, without external control of the cathode potential, from metallic ions having negative reduction potentials. However, for this separation to be successful, the hydrogen overpotential on the cathode plus the reversible reduction potential of the hydrogen ions must be less than the negative reduction potential of any of the metallic ions that are to remain in solution. For example, cupric ions in a solution containing 1 M hydrogen ions may be separated from all metallic ions whose reduction potentials are more negative than about -0.4 V—the hydrogen overpotential on a copper electrode for relatively large current densities. Additional selectivity can be achieved through use of masking agents or potential buffers, or control of pH.

Example 23-1

Under what conditions would it be possible to initiate the deposition of zinc onto a copper-clad electrode from a solution that is 0.01 M in zinc ions? Also, what conditions are necessary for quantitative removal of zinc?

From the Nernst equation, the deposition potential for zinc is

$$E = -0.76 + 0.03 \log (0.01) = -0.82 \text{ V}$$

and this value increases to -0.94 V when 0.01 percent remains in solution. Turning to the expression for the evolution of hydrogen, we can evaluate the minimum pH necessary to allow the deposition of zinc to commence, assuming that the overpotential of hydrogen on copper to be 0.4 V:

$$E = 0.0 + 0.059 \log [H^+] + (-0.4) = -0.82$$

from which the pH is calculated to be 7. Although it might be expected that the pH would have to be raised to about 8.5 to remove the zinc quantitatively, this is true only if the amount of zinc is insufficient to coat completely the electrode surface exposed to the solution. As soon as the electrode becomes coated with zinc metal, the overpotential of hydrogen rises to the value on a zinc surface and, consequently, the deposition of zinc proceeds to completion at pH 7 approximately. In practice, an ammoniacal buffer is employed, partly to take advantage of the superior deposit from zinc ammine ions.

Separations with Controlled Electrode Potentials

To carry out the electrolytic separation of two metals whose deposition potentials differ by an adequate amount, yet which lie on the same side of hydrogen, provision must be made to control the electrode potential. This is achieved by introducing an auxiliary reference electrode and placing the tip of the salt bridge adjacent to the working electrode. The potential of the working electrode is determined by measuring the emf of the cell established by the electrode and the reference electrode, from which the potential of the working electrode (herein assumed to be the cathode) can be calculated:

$$E_{\text{cathode}} = E_{\text{cell}} - E_{\text{reference}} \qquad (23\text{-}10)$$

A potentiometer or vacuum-tube voltmeter serves to measure the cell emf. The extra items of equipment, enclosed within the dashed lines of Fig. 23-1, are the only changes required in the conventional apparatus for electrodeposition by the constant-current method.

With the isolation of the term: $E_{\text{cathode}} + \omega_c$, from the cell emf, controlled-potential electrolysis may cleanly separate two elements, put an element into a particular oxidation state, or synthesize an organic compound. The potential of the cathode (or anode in oxidation reactions) is controlled so that it never becomes sufficiently negative to allow the deposition of the next element.

In practice, the controlled potential should be $0.118/n$ V more negative than the final equilibrium electrode potential to correspond to the hundred-fold difference that usually prevails in concentration between the electrode surface and the bulk concentration. This control of the electrode potential is achieved by adjusting the voltage applied to the electrolysis cell—manually with a battery and a variable resistor, manual adjustment of the autotransformer at the input of commercial electroanalyzers, or electronically with a potentiostat. The current steadily decreases as the metallic ions are removed, but the maximum current permissible is used at all times and thus the electrolysis proceeds at its maximum rate. The electrolysis is discontinued when the current has fallen to a constant low value, usually 10 or 20 ma. The intersection of the system surface with a plane parallel to the zero-potential plane in Fig. 23-3 shows the course of the current and the percent reduced (or oxidized) during the electrolysis.

A variety of electronic circuits are available which are capable of decreasing or increasing automatically the applied emf in order to maintain a constant electrode potential. The schematic circuit of one instrument is shown in Fig. 23-4. It can be used in conjunction with the power supply shown in Fig. 23-2.

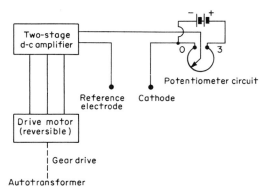

Fig. 23-4. Schematic circuit diagram of an automatic potentiostat.

In use, the electrode potential is set at any desired value from 0 to 3 V vs the reference electrode. The reference half-cell is then balanced against the working electrode through a potentiometer. When the voltage of the working electrode changes from the preset potential, a current flows in the potentiometer circuit. This current, amplified by a d-c amplifier, activates one of two relays that control the reversible motor that adjusts the contactor of the autotransformer (Fig. 23-2). If the electrode potential is low, one of the relays operates the autotransformer to increase the electrode potential. If it is high, the other relay turns the motor in reverse to decrease it until the difference signal has been reduced to zero.

An approximate value of the limiting electrode potential can be calculated from the Nernst equation, but lack of knowledge concerning the overpotential term for a system severely limits its usefulness. A more reliable method involves the determination of the limiting potential empirically from current-potential curves. The current-potential curve is determined for each reaction under exactly the same conditions that will prevail in the actual analysis. The potential of the working electrode is increased in regular increments by increasing the voltage applied to the cell. The current is observed at each value of the electrode potential. To minimize any change in the concentration around the electrode, the cell circuit should be closed only long enough to secure the current measurement. Schematic current-cathode potential curves for the reduction of cupric ions are shown in Fig. 21-11. Ordinary polarograms obtained with the dropping mercury electrode serve excellently to define the conditions for electrolysis with a large mercury cathode. Usually these will be about 0.1–0.15 V more negative than the polarographic half-wave potential.

Consider, for example, a solution which is 0.1 M in cupric ions and 0.01 M in lead and tin ions. A diagram of the course of the electrolysis of these metals in hydrochloric acid medium and using platinum electrodes is shown in Fig. 23-5.[3] If hydrazine is present, the potential at which the oxidation of hydrazine will occur will be approximately 0.4–0.6 V vs SCE. This anode potential, shown as the lower solid line in Fig. 23-5, will remain fairly constant because

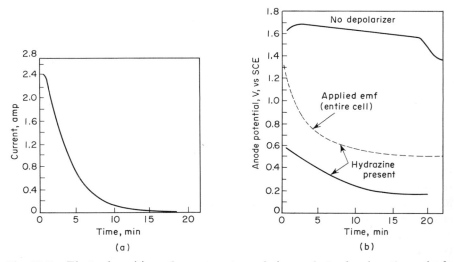

Fig. 23-5.   Electrodeposition of copper onto a platinum electrode when the cathode potential was maintained at -0.35 V vs SCE. (a) Current decay with time. (b) Anode potential in absence and presence of hydrazine; also the change in total applied emf with time when hydrazine was present. Adapted from J. J. Lingane, *Anal. Chim. Acta*, **2,** 589 (1948) and J. J. Lingane and S. Jones, *Anal. Chem.*, **23,** 1804 (1951).

the factors that affect this reaction do not change appreciably. Copper will be deposited first on the cathode at a potential of about 0.0 V vs SCE from the reduction of the $CuCl_3^{-2}$ and $CuCl_2^-$ ions. (The overpotential term is roughly 0.10–0.15 V for the currents initially employed.) Thus, the emf required for electrolysis will be about 0.6 V plus any ohmic drop. As copper is deposited, the concentration of the chlorocuprous complex ions decreases and the potential of the cathode becomes more negative. When the copper concentration is lowered to about 10^{-5} M, the potential of the cathode is -0.40 V vs SCE. Actually, the copper concentration need only be lowered to about 10^{-4} M for the removal to be quantitative and, consequently, the cathode potential is usually controlled at -0.35 V vs SCE. At -0.40 V vs SCE the lead and tin will start to deposit. Thus, if the potential of the cathode can be controlled so that it never becomes more negative than -0.35 V vs SCE, no lead or tin will be deposited, whereas the deposition of copper from chloride medium is virtually complete.

After the copper is separated, the tin plus lead can then be separated on the copper-clad electrode by controlling the potential of the cathode at another value which is slightly less negative than that required for the liberation of hydrogen gas. In the presence of tartrate ions and at pH 4.5–5.0, only lead ions will be deposited, because the tartrate complex of tin(IV) is sufficiently stable to prevent the codeposition of tin.[9]

Separations with controlled electrode potentials are very satisfactorily done with a mercury cathode. By including a silver or some other coulometer in series with the electrolysis cell, it is comparatively simple to perform a series of separations and analyses without replacing the mercury cathode between successive separations and, perhaps, without weighing any electrodes.

Halides may be determined by electrolyzing their solutions between a platinum cathode and a silver anode. By controlling the anode potential, the gain in weight of the anode is equal to the weight of the particular halide in the original solution.

The use of controlled electrode potentials is now quite prevalent in preparative organic chemistry. If a certain organic compound can undergo a series of reductions (or oxidations), each at a definite potential, it is then possible to reduce the starting material selectively and efficiently to some desired compound by controlling the potential of the cathode during the reduction. Because this procedure for organic compounds produces essentially only the desired product, it is much more economical than most reductions or oxidations performed chemically, where side reactions producing undesired products usually occur.

Constant Voltage Electrolysis

If we consider all the terms embodied in Eq. 23-8 for the separation of copper and lead ions at the cathode, with oxygen liberated at the anode, the copper is practically completely deposited at an applied voltage of 1.91 V:

$$E_{applied} = (1.23 + 0.40) - (0.21 - 0.01) + 0.50$$

where the ohmic drop is assumed to be 0.50 V. The lead will not begin to deposit until the applied voltage exceeds 2.28 V. Consequently, the separation of copper from lead can be accomplished by an electrolysis at any constant applied voltage between these two values.

This technique assumes that the ohmic drop and the overpotential terms in Eq. 23-8 remain constant. However, as a consequence of the cell reaction, the copper concentration diminishes and the hydrogen-ion concentration increases. This results in both E_{anode} and $E_{cathode}$ becoming more negative. From the Nernst equation the theoretical cathode potential will change from 0.31 to 0.19 V if the corresponding cupric ion concentration changes from 0.1 to 10^{-5} M. On the other hand, the anode potential will have decreased only slightly. The greater conductance of the hydrogen ion decreases the cell resistance and affects the iR term. Finally, the overpotential terms are dependent on the current density and cannot be expected to remain constant when the current tends to vary. These variations render it difficult to control the cathode potential within as close limits as is possible by the controlled potential method.

The electrolysis process can be represented by the intersection of the system surface in Fig. 23-3 with a slanted plane. When the current is zero, the cell emf is equal to the applied voltage. During the electrolysis, as the cathode potential becomes more negative, the copper concentration becomes depleted to the point where the supply of cupric ions at the cathode surface is insufficient to meet the current demand. When this occurs, the current must of necessity decrease, ultimately falling to zero. Thus, the deposition of lead does not occur, but this advantage is achieved at the cost of diminished current at any time. Hence a longer time is required for complete electrolysis in comparison with the controlled potential method.

Composition of the Electrolyte

It is clearly possible to separate one metal from another if the respective deposition potentials are sufficiently far apart and, in constant-current electrolysis, if one potential is more negative than that required for the evolution of hydrogen. When two metals have similar discharge potentials, sometimes the electrolyte composition can be altered sufficiently for separation to be possible. By addition of a masking agent which forms a complex with one of the metal ions, the discharge potential for this ion usually becomes more negative. Take, for example, an alkaline solution of copper and bismuth ions to which cyanide ions are added. The cupric ions are reduced to the monovalent state and form the complex cuprocyanide ion:

$$Cu^+ + 3CN^- \rightleftharpoons Cu(CN)_3^{-2}; \qquad K_f = 10^{27} \qquad (23\text{-}11)$$

In this environment the discharge potential of the cuprocyanide ion is -1.05 V when 1 M cyanide ion is present. By contrast, the addition of cyanide hardly affects the deposition potential for bismuth, and if tartrate ions are present to keep the bismuth in solution, quantitative separation from copper is possible.

The temperature dependence of a series of homologous metal complexes sometimes provides a means for separating discharge potentials. For example, in the case of nickel and zinc in ammoniacal solution, the deposition potentials are similar at 20°C, being -0.90 and -1.14 V, respectively, but differ markedly at 90°, now being -0.60 and -1.05 V. In general the less dissociated the complex at room temperature, the greater the change in the degree of dissociation as the temperature rises.

Potential Buffers

Suitable oxidation-reduction systems which are preferentially reduced at the cathode, or oxidized at the anode, may be employed to limit and maintain a constant potential at the electrode. The name "potential buffer" is applied to this type of electrolyte because of its functional resemblance to pH buffers. For example, the uranium(III)/(IV) system has been used to prevent the cathode potential from exceeding approximately -0.5 V, the reduction potential of the uranium system. As the cathode potential attains this value, there is increased competition of the uranium(IV) reduction reaction with the deposition process. The reduced uranium(III) ions are reoxidized at the anode and remain in the electrolyte to continue the cyclic process. Eventually the entire current flow through the electrolytic cell is consumed in the reduction of uranium(IV) at the cathode and the oxidation of uranium(III) at the anode. One application of the uranium couple has been to prevent the deposition of chromium and manganese at a mercury cathode while permitting copper, tin, lead and nickel to deposit in the normal manner.

Nitrate ions have long been employed in the constant current deposition of copper and lead dioxide to prevent the formation of metallic lead at the cathode. Nitrate ions are less easily reduced than copper ions, and sufficiently so that the cupric ions can be quantitatively removed; yet nitrate ions are more easily reduced than lead ions. At the anode, on the other hand, plumbous ions are oxidized to lead dioxide more easily than hydroxyl ions to oxygen, thus,

$$Pb^{+2} + 2H_2O \rightarrow PbO_2 + 4H^+ + 2e^- \tag{23-12}$$

for which the electrode potential is 1.46 V, whereas the liberation of oxygen, occurs at about 1.70 V. Chloride ions must be absent for several reasons: Chloride ions are oxidized more easily ($E^0 = 1.36$ V), the overpotential of chlorine gas is less than that for the deposition of PbO_2, and formation of $PbCl_3^-$ is appreciable.

The successful deposition of copper from chlorocuprous ions, and the prevention of the competing oxidation of these ions to cupric ions at the anode, are due to the buffering action of hydrazine. The oxidation of hydrazine,

$$N_2H_5^+ \rightarrow N_2 + 5H^+ + 4e^- \tag{23-13}$$

for which the electrode potential is 0.17 V, takes place in preference to chloro-cuprous ions,

$$CuCl_3^{-2} \rightarrow Cu^{+2} + 3Cl^- + e^- \qquad (23\text{-}14)$$

for which the electrode potential is 0.51 V. As long as hydrazine is present in excess, the anodic oxidation of chloride ions and copper(I) will be prevented. Without any hydrazine, the anode potential remains at a relatively high value between the chlorocuprous-copper and the water-oxygen couples, as shown in Fig. 23-5.

Physical Characteristics of Metal Deposits

It is important to conduct the electrolysis under conditions which insure that the deposit is pure, adherent to the electrode, and quantitative. This requires consideration of the factors that influence the nature of the deposit—current density, the chemical nature of the ion in solution—that is, complexed or as an aquated ion, the rate of stirring, the temperature, and the presence of depolarizers to minimize the evolution of gases.

The optimum conditions for achieving the best deposit vary from one metal to another. Adherence to the electrode is the most important physical characteristic of a deposit. Generally a smooth deposit and adherence are congruent. Flaky, spongy, or powdery deposits adhere only loosely to an electrode. Simultaneous evolution of a gas is often detrimental. Continual evolution of bubbles on the electrode surface disturbs the orderly growth of the crystal structure of a metal deposit, and porous and spongy deposits may be obtained. Once under way, these continue because the current density is high at points on an otherwise smooth surface, and this is conducive to ir-regular, tree-like growths. The discharge of hydrogen frequently causes the film of solution in the vicinity of the cathode to become alkaline, with the consequent formation of hydrous oxides or basic salts.

The chemical nature of the ion in solution often has an important influence on the physical form of the deposited metal. For example, a pure, bright, and adherent deposit of copper can be obtained when electrolyzing a nitric acid solution of cupric ions. By contrast, a coarse, tree-like deposit of silver is obtained under similar conditions. If a suitable deposit of silver is to be obtained, the electrolysis must be carried out from a solution in which the silver ions are complexed as $Ag(CN)_2^-$. Similarly, the best deposits of iron are obtained from an oxalate complex and those of nickel from an ammonia com-plex. Halide ions facilitate the deposition of some metals, probably because the overpotential is lower for metal halide ions than for aquated metal ions. Complex ions also exhibit what is known as "throwing power" to a considerable degree—that is, the property of a solution by virtue of which a relatively uniform deposit of metal may be obtained on irregular surfaces.

The time required for electrodeposition is shortened if the electrode is rotated or the electrolyte stirred vigorously. As an adjunct to the normal diffusion process and mass transfer conditions, it lowers the concentration overpotential and enables a higher current density to be employed without deleterious results.

Increase in temperature has two effects which oppose each other. Diffusion is favored. On the other hand, hydrogen overpotential is decreased and the stability of many complex ions is decreased.

Factors Governing Current

When the electrode potential is controlled so that only a single reaction can occur, the decrease of the current is a reliable criterion of the progress of the electrolysis. The current-time curve usually obeys the relation

$$i_t = i_0 e^{-kt} \qquad \text{or} \qquad 2.3 \log (i_0/i_t) = kt \qquad (23\text{-}15)$$

where i_0 is the initial current and i_t the current at time t. If $t = t_{1/2}$ when $i/i_0 = 1/2$, then

$$t_{1/2} = \frac{2.3}{k} \log 2 = 0.69/k \qquad (23\text{-}16)$$

Deposition is quantitative after 10 half-lives, or when $i = 0.001\ i_0$.

A plot of Eq. 23-15 on semilog coordinates produces a straight line, from which the value of k can be evaluated. Lingane[8] has shown that the constant k is given by

$$k \text{ (in min}^{-1}) = \frac{0.43\, DA}{\delta V} \qquad (23\text{-}17)$$

where A is the electrode area in centimeters squared, V is the electrolyte volume in milliliters, D is the rate of diffusion of the reacting ion expressed in square centimeters divided by minutes, and δ is the thickness of the diffusion layer surrounding the electrode expressed in centimeters. Equation 23-17 provides a logical basis for the selection of experimental conditions to achieve rapid electrolysis. The electrode area should be as large as possible and the solution volume as small as possible. This explains the advantage of tall-form beakers and large, cylindrical, gauze electrodes. Stirring and elevated temperatures reduce the thickness of the diffusion layer, and an increase in temperature also increases the diffusion coefficient. The current at concentration C is given by

$$i = \frac{nFACD}{\delta} \qquad (23\text{-}18)$$

The Mercury Cathode

Cathodes comprising a pool of mercury or an amalgamated platinum or brass gauze electrode warrant special consideration. The mercury cathode is not generally used to determine any of the metals plated out because of the difficulties involved in weighing and drying the mercury before and after the determination. However, it is one of the most useful aids for the removal of certain base metals, even in considerable quantities, that interfere in the determination of elements high in the electromotive series. Two factors set mercury apart from other electrode materials. Many of the metals depositing on mercury can form an alloy (amalgam) with the mercury. Owing to the alloy formation the deposition potentials of these metals on mercury are displaced from their normal value in the positive direction with respect to reduction potentials. Their deposition is also aided by the fact that the hydrogen over-potential on mercury is particularly large. As a result the deposition from a fairly acid solution is possible for such metals as iron, nickel, chromium, zinc, and even manganese under certain conditions.

In its simplest form the mercury cathode cell consists of a shallow pool of mercury covering the bottom of a beaker. Electrical contact to the mercury is made by a glass-enclosed platinum wire, either immersed in the mercury pool or sealed through the base of the container. The cell designed by Melaven,[11] shown in Fig. 23-6, is a slightly more refined form and is in common use. The cathode consists of 35 to 50 ml of pure mercury in a modified separatory funnel. The apparatus has a conical base fitted with a three-way stopcock. One arm of the stopcock is connected to a leveling bulb that controls the level of the mercury in the cell; the other permits removal of the electrolyte. With a beaker, this removal is accomplished by siphoning. The anode is a platinum wire in the form of a spiral. Agitation is accomplished by a mechanical stirrer or a stream of air.

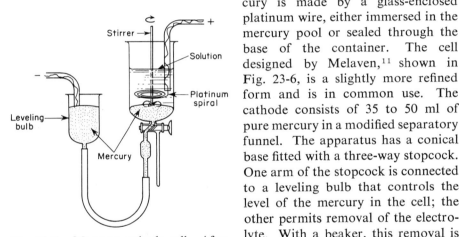

Fig. 23-6. Mercury cathode cell. After A. D. Melaven, *Ind. Eng. Chem.*, *Anal. Ed.*, **2**, 180 (1930).

Simple, unitized cells have been designed.[6] A sturdy, compact, self-contained immersion electrode is shown in Fig. 23-7. This cell is a glass dish about 30 mm in diameter by 15 mm high, from the side of which extends a glass tube carrying the wire for electrical contact. A flat, spiral anode completes the cell. The unitized electrode is easily removed from the electrolyte and washed with a stream of wash solution quickly enough to prevent appreciable dissolution of the deposited metals. The consumption of mercury is a minimum, usually 5 ml per electrolysis, and the simplicity with which duplicate assemblies are interchanged encourages frequent substitution of fresh mercury. This increases the efficiency of a separation and decreases the time for elec-

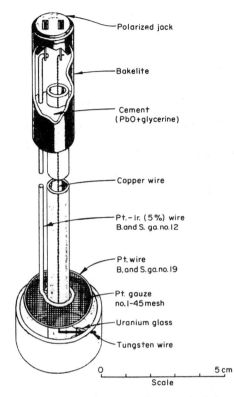

Polarized jack

Bakelite

Cement
(PbO+glycerine)

Copper wire

Pt.– Ir. (5%) wire
B.and S. ga.no.12

Pt. wire
B.and S.ga.no.19

Pt. gauze
no.I–45 mesh

Uranium glass

Tungsten wire

0   5 cm
Scale

Fig. 23-7. Unitized mercury cathode cell. After H. O. Johnson, J. R. Weaver, and L. Lykken, *Anal. Chem.*, **19**, 481 (1947).

trolysis. Finally, the difficulty from loss of mercury in handling and from dispersion during electrolysis is minimized.

Specially designed mercury cathode equipment patterned after the above designs is available commercially and can be used in conjunction with ordinary electrolysis apparatus.

Vigorous stirring materially shortens the electrolysis. Agitation can be accomplished by any type of mechanical stirrer or by a stream of air. Rapid countercurrent stirring of the mercury and the electrolyte at the deposition interface favors a more efficient deposition and constantly exposes fresh mercury to the electrolyte. This can be provided by a magnetic stirring bar floating on the mercury surface, or by letting the impeller blades be only partially immersed in the mercury. A commercial unit has been devised in which a magnetic circuit provides the stirring, the electrolyte and the mercury becoming the two independent rotors of a d-c motor.[1] In addition, the magnetic field

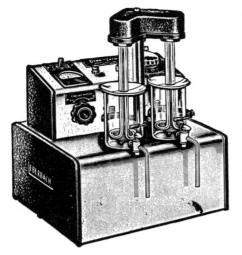

Fig. 23.8. The Dyna-Cath, a commercial mercury cathode instrument. (Courtesy of Eberbach & Son.)

immediately removes deposited ferromagnetic materials from the mercury-solution interface and retains them beneath the surface of the mercury. The instrument is pictured in Fig. 23-8.

The electrolyte is usually a 0.1–0.5 M solution of sulfuric acid or perchloric acid. Nitric and hydrochloric acids are avoided; the reduction of nitrate lowers the current efficiency for the reaction of interest, and the anode may be attacked in the presence of chloride.

A current density of 0.1–0.2 amp cm^{-2} is common, but substantially higher current densities have been used in cells with appropriate cooling devices to remove heat developed by the resistance of the electrolyte, as is done in the Dyna-Cath (Fig. 23-8). The amount of metal removed is proportional to the current and the area of the mercury surface.

In most cases the constant-current technique serves excellently as the separation method for the elements shown in Table 23-3. Most uses of the mercury cathode concern the removal of an interfering element or elements

Table 23-3					*Electrolysis With A Mercury Cathode in* 0.3 N *Sulfuric Acid Solution*												
H																	He
Li	Be											B	C	N	O	F	Ne
Na	Mg											Al	Si	P	S	Cl	Ar
K	Ca	Sc	Ti	V	Cr	Mn	Fe	Co	Ni	Cu	Zn	Ga	Ge	As	Se	Br	Kr
Rb	Sr	Y	Zr	Nb	Mo	Tc	Ru	Rh	Pd	Ag	Cd	In	Sn	Sb	Te	I	Xe
Cs	Ba	La	Hf	Ta	W	Re	Os	Ir	Pt	Au	Hg	Tl	Pb	Bi	Po	At	Rn
Fr	Ra	Ac															
			Ce	Pr	Nd	Pm	Sm	Eu	Gd	Tb	Dy	Ho	Er	Tm	Yb	Lu	
			Th	Pa	U	Np	Pu	Am	Cm	Bk	Cf	Es	Fm	Md	No	Lw	

[G. E. F. Lundell and J. I. Hoffman, *Outlines of Methods of Chemical Analysis*, John Wiley & Sons, Inc., New York, 1938, p. 94.]

†On the periodic chart of the atoms the theoretical separation possibilities have been indicated for the mercury cathode. The elements enclosed by solid line (———) are quantitatively deposited in the mercury. Those surrounded by a dotted line (·····) are quantitatively separated from the electrolyte but not quantitatively deposited in the mercury. Elements enclosed by a wavy line (〰〰) are incompletely separated from the electrolyte.

before the determination of a substance that remains in the electrolyte. In this respect it has been extensively applied to facilitate the determination of aluminum, titanium, vanadium, and magnesium in a wide variety of materials. The element most commonly deposited is iron. The mercury cathode has also been used to effect the reduction of an element or compound to a lower oxidation state in solution. Other applications are enumerated in review articles.[10,12]

Internal Electrolysis

Internal electrolysis is the term applied by Sand[14] to electrogravimetric analyses which employ an attackable anode. The latter is connected directly to the cathode. In reality the arrangement is nothing but a short-circuited galvanic cell. It is convenient in some applications because the electrolysis proceeds spontaneously without the application of an external voltage and the choice of an attackable anode limits the cathode potential without elaborate instrumentation or the operator's attention. However, the driving force—that is, the difference between the potential of the system plating at the cathode and the dissolution of the anode—is small, and in consequence, the cell resistance is a critical factor in determining the rate of metal deposition. The application of the method is restricted to small amounts of material if the time of electrolysis is not to be excessively long.

The selection of an anode is made with a knowledge of the reversible potentials of the various metal ion-metal couples. A typical application is the removal of small amounts of copper and bismuth from pig lead.[2] Since the reduction potential of lead is sufficiently far apart from the reduction potentials of the copper and bismuth systems, the anodes can be constructed from helices of pure lead wire. The arrangement of equipment is shown in Fig. 23-9.

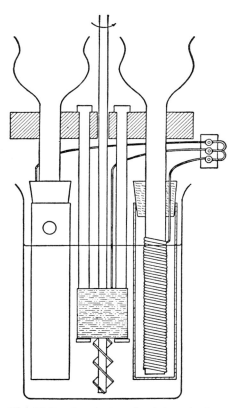

Fig. 23-9. Apparaturs for internal electrolysis.

Dual anodes are often used to provide a larger electrode area. These are inserted within a porous membrane (Alundum shell) in order to isolate them from the sample and forestall any direct plating on the lead itself. A platinum gauze electrode is placed between the anode compartments. The electrolysis is begun by short-circuiting the cathode to the anode.

To keep the ohmic resistance small, the anode solution must have a high concentration of electrolyte. In addition it must contain a higher concentration of the ions formed from the dissolution of the anode (i.e., lead ions in the example) than does the catholyte containing the dissolved sample. The anode reaction will be the dissolution of the lead; the cathode reaction the deposition of copper. The cell can be represented as

$$- Pb^0 \mid Pb^{+2} \mid\mid Cu^{+2} \mid Cu^0(Pt) +$$

Because the cell operates spontaneously, the cathode is the positive electrode. Short-circuited as the cathode and anode are, the only dissipation of energy is in the form of the ohmic resistance, which in turn limits the maximum current flow through the cell:

$$iR = -E_{Pb^{+2},Pb^0} + E_{Cu^{+2},Cu^0} + \frac{0.0591}{2} \log \frac{[Cu^{+2}]}{[Pb^{+2}]} \qquad (23\text{-}19)$$

For an anolyte solution that is 1 M in Pb^{+2} ion, and inserting standard electrode potentials, Eq. 23-19 becomes

$$iR = 0.22 + 0.0296 \log [Cu^{+2}] \qquad (23\text{-}20)$$

With this arrangement the electrode potential of the cathode cannot exceed -0.12 V. Only those metal ions will deposit whose electrode potentials are more positive than this value. In the sample taken, as the electrolysis progresses, the concentration of copper(II) ions diminishes and the electrode potential of the cathode becomes more negative until it becomes equal to the anode potential (or the decomposition potential of another substance is exceeded). At no time will the decomposition potential of lead at the cathode be exceeded. There is no danger of lead contamination due to the concentration-overpotential factor, because the rate of cathodic deposition is controlled by the rate of anodic dissolution.

The anode need not always be constructed of the material that constitutes the matrix of the sample. For selective reduction of several trace constituents in zinc, for example, four separate samples would be dissolved for the separation of traces of silver, copper, lead, and cadmium. In the first, an attackable anode of copper would permit the complete removal of silver but control the cathode potential below the deposition potentials of the others. Similarly, a lead anode would make it possible to remove silver plus copper; a cadmium electrode would remove silver, copper, and lead; and with a zinc anode, all four elements would be removed.

The amount of deposit is generally limited to quantities not exceeding 25 mg. Although larger quantities have been handled, the deposit is apt to be spongy and some of the metal ions may diffuse to the anode during the longer time required for complete electrolysis. Little attention is required during an analysis except to flush the anolyte compartments once or twice. Halide solutions may be employed without removing the halide ion and without adding an anodic depolarizer. Average running time is 30 min per sample.

Electrography

The electrographic method, developed by Glazunov[5] and Fritz,[4] is a useful microanalytical tool for accurately identifying and determining substances. The method consists in anodically dissolving a minute amount of the test substance onto a piece of bibulous paper or, for more accurate rendition, gelatin-coated paper which has been soaked in a suitable electrolyte. The test sheet is held under pressure between the sample surface, the anode, and a suitable cathode surface. The latter may be a flat square electrode for flat surfaces, a long narrow electrode for use on metal ribbons, or sponge rubber covered with aluminum foil for uneven surfaces of sample. The unit is connected to a battery of dry cells and a current is allowed to flow for several seconds. A general laboratory circuit is shown in Fig. 23-10. While the current is flowing, ions leave the surface of the specimen and migrate into the permeable test sheet. Their presence can be made manifest, if they are colorless, by treating the

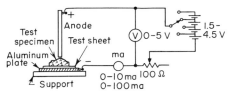

Fig. 23-10. Schematic arrangement of equipment and electrical circuit for electrographic analysis.

test sheet with selective reagents. Distinctive identifying colors result and appear in an exact chemical and physical image of the surface.

The magnitude of the current required and its duration can be approximated from the second law of Faraday:

$$it = \frac{96,487 A dn}{W} \tag{23-21}$$

where i = current in amperes

t = duration of the current in seconds

A = area of the specimen surface in centimeters squared

W = atomic weight of the element dissolving and forming n-equivalents per gram-atom

d = the minimum weight of material needed for detection by the method chosen in grams per square centimeter.

In general, 50 μg of most metals will produce brilliantly colored products when the reaction is confined to an area of 1 cm.[2] These conditions would require a current of 15 ma and an exposure time of 10 sec. For multicomponent samples the current may be carried almost entirely by ions of highest mobility, with the result that the pattern will be underexposed with respect to the poorly conducting constituents. This difficulty may be partially remedied by moistening the specimen with a mineral acid instead of a neutral electrolyte and by eluting the interfering ions prior to spot testing.

The test sheet may be moistened with only a neutral electrolyte, such as sodium nitrate or sodium chloride; or it may be impregnated with a reagent for the metal or metals to be detected, such as potassium ferricyanide for iron and ammonium sulfide for copper and silver. With neutral electrolytes the print must be further developed by immersion in a developing reagent that forms a reaction product of distinctive color. Individual patterns can be secured by developing successive prints with different selective reagents —for example, α-benzoinoxime for copper, dimethylglyoxime for nickel, and α-nitroso-β-naphthol for cobalt from a sulfide mineral surface which has been electrographed with an ammonia solution. The test sheet should be fine-grained and held in close contact with the surface to be tested. By this method, in contrast with contact printing, lateral diffusion or "bleeding" is minimized. Prints are sharp and permit many fine features to be detected.

The electrographic method is applicable only to materials that are conductors of the electric current. It can be applied for the inspection of lacquer coating and of plated metals for pinholes and cracks in their surface. It can be used for many alloy identifications, such as the differentiation of lead-containing brass from ordinary brass, nickel in steel, and the distribution of metal constituents within an alloy. In the biological field the method is applicable to the localization of those constituents which are normally present within the tissue in an ionic state. One important advantage of this method, besides those of simplicity and rapidity, is the fact that so little of the sample is consumed; it remains essentially unaltered. Portable field kits have found extensive use in inspection and sorting work, in the laboratory as well as in the stockroom and in mineralogical field work.

Analogous to the anodic oxidation transfer is the cathodic reduction of certain anions of tarnish or corrosion films on metals. These are often tied up as basic insoluble salts and are not detectable in simple contact printing. Electrolytic reduction will free these ions.

By controlling the time, pressure, and current in a series of transfers, quantitative determinations can be made by comparing the color intensity of the pattern of an unknown sample with a series of patterns produced by known amounts of the metallic ion.

Electrophoresis

Electrophoresis is the migration of large molecules and small aggregates of molecules under the influence of an electric field applied to a medium in which the particles are suspended. Proteins, viruses, clay suspensions, rubber emulsions, and colloidal particles are some examples of substances that carry a charge or about which an electrical double layer exists and which may be separated into pure components by this technique.

In general, the material to be separated is suspended in a water solution where the pH and the electrolyte concentration are controlled carefully. In order to minimize the factors that cause random migration (e.g., convection currents) in free electrophoresis and thereby permit separations that would otherwise be impossible, the suspensions of the material to be separated are placed on paper or some other supporting medium which provides a capillary mesh to hold the solution. Hence, adsorption and partition effects plus molecular sieving action are superimposed upon the electric field effects. Each end of the supporting medium, soaked in buffer, dips into a trough containing an electrode and a quantity of the buffer solution (Fig. 23-11).

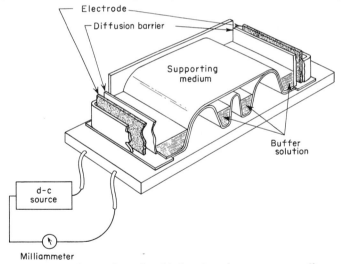

Fig. 23-11. Electrophoresis with free-hanging support medium.

Carbon electrodes are separated from the solution by plastic diffusion barrier plates or tubes. When a solution of the test material is applied to the center of the supporting medium and a voltage is applied across the length of the medium, its components will migrate towards one or the other of the electrodes. After a certain time, particles having a similar ratio of charge to size will have migrated to a specific section of the medium where their migration velocity is equal and opposite to the rate of flow of the solution and they no longer advance. Their direction and rate of travel are a function of electrophoretic mobilities and isoelectric points and will furnish a clue to their identity. Remixing cannot occur and the fractions are available for both qualitative and quantitative examination.

In operation, separations can be accomplished horizontally on the cooled surface of the support base—plastic or polyethylene covered glass—to minimize temperature gradients. If it is not desirable to have the paper or cellulose acetate strips in contact with the base, a central bridge is placed under the paper. When separations are made in starch paste or silica gel, the solid media are confined to the table surface by sides which extend above the surface and by removable gates placed across the ends. Evaporation of solvent is minimized by covering the supporting medium with a glass plate or sheet of polyethylene film, or by maintaining the apparatus in an atmosphere saturated with the solvent.

A power unit is required which is capable of supplying up to 750 V direct current from a full-wave rectifier, the output of which is filtered to leave 0.1 percent or less ripple.

Serum electrophoresis is widely used as a clinical diagnostic aid. Certain types of disease are evident simply by looking at a serum pattern. Enzyme fractions can be quantitatively analyzed by electrophoresis. Carbohydrates may be separated in 30 min, with separations equally as good as those attained with partition chromatography. Purity of dye lots can be quickly checked.

After compounds have been separated by electrophoresis, they may be determined in several ways. If dyes are used, the strip may be scanned using a photoelectric scanning device. Individual bands may be dissolved in a solvent and determined by suitable methods. Radioisotopes can be scanned.

Electrochromatography

Separations performed by simultaneous flow of an electrolyte and electrical migration transverse to the solvent flow in a stabilizing medium are called electrochromatography or curtain electrophoresis. In this method the solution to be examined is introduced continuously by capillary flow through a wick at the top (and usually near the center) of the supporting medium.[15] This medium, held vertically, may be a sheet of soft, thick industrial filter paper, a layer of starch, a bed of very small glass beads or resin particles, supported between two plates of glass or other material. The eluting electrolyte flows downward by gravity through the supporting medium. The electrical field is applied at right angles to this flow by means of a wick arrangement whereby the lower corners of the paper dip into the electrode compartment, or by means of a pair of side electrodes that clamp onto the vertical edges of the sheet. In the latter arrangement the electrodes may be flat platinum foils, or they may consist of platinum wires mounted in cellophane tubes which are held against the paper sheet by clamps and through which buffer solution flows continuously to make electrical contact and to wash away electrolysis products.

The direction of migration of any component is determined by the rates at which it travels in the descending buffer (adsorption and partition forces) and in the electric field between the electrodes. The components therefore diverge and are collected in a series of closely spaced containers arranged at appropriate points along the serrated bottom edge of the support. The schematic arrangement of the equipment is shown in Fig. 23-12.

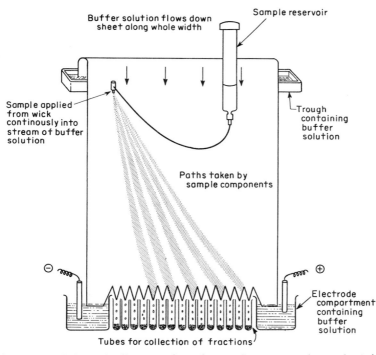

Fig. 23-12. Schematic diagram of continuous flow, paper electrophoresis cell.

Electrochromatography provides a means for the continuous resolution of compounds. By proper selection of pH of the electrolyte, compounds can be fractionated into three groups. Neutral compounds move straight down the paper, whereas positively charged species migrate toward the negative electrode, and conversely, the negatively charged components migrate toward the positive electrode. Pronounced differences in equivalents of charge per molecule can lead to distinct migration paths even among species of the same charge type. In the presence of complex-forming reagents, many cations exhibit anionic properties, and with different reagents the order of separations can be changed (Fig. 23-13).

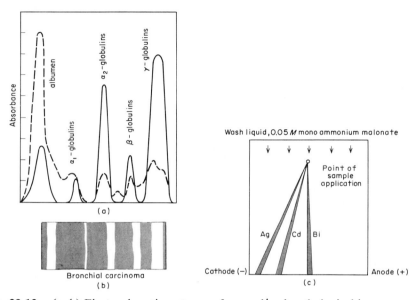

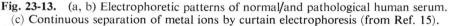

Fig. 23-13. (a, b) Electrophoretic patterns of normal/and pathological human serum. (c) Continuous separation of metal ions by curtain electrophoresis (from Ref. 15).

LABORATORY WORK

General Instructions

Platinum electrodes are expensive and, if of gauze construction, somewhat delicate and must be handled carefully. They are cleaned by heating in 5 M nitric acid, to which a reductant is added when dealing with a deposit of lead dioxide — a little hydrogen peroxide. Before weighing, the electrode is passed through the oxidizing flame of a burner to remove any grease picked up from hands.

At the end of an electrolysis, lower the solution away from the electrodes without interrupting the current, and wash the electrode surface as it becomes exposed with a stream of wash water. Remove the electrode containing the deposit from its holder and rinse with ethanol or acetone, then dry for several minutes in an oven at 80°C. Weigh the electrode plus deposit.

The electrolyte is generally composed of nitrates or sulfates because halides in acid solution give active halogens which attack the anode unless a proper depolarizer is present — for example, hydrazine in chloride solutions. Tin, silver, zinc and bismuth damage the platinum and, in such separations, the cathode is copper-clad before depositing these metals.

EXPERIMENT 23-1   CONTROLLED CATHODE SEPARATIONS

A. Determination of Copper in Brass[3,7]

Transfer a 0.5-g sample of brass (weighed accurately) to a 200-ml tall-form beaker. Dissolve in 10 ml of concentrated HCl plus 5 ml of water to which concentrated nitric acid is added dropwise until dissolution is complete. In an alternative method, add 10 ml of 1:1 HCl and, in small portions, 5 ml of 30 percent hydrogen peroxide. Boil the solution to expel the oxides of nitrogen and chlorine (or excess hydrogen peroxide).

Dilute the solution to 25 ml, and add 4 g of hydrazine hydrochloride. Heat the solution to 95°C and maintain it at this temperature until the dark green color changes to a light olive-green indicating considerable reduction to the chlorocuprous complex ion.

Place the beaker in position in the electrolysis apparatus and add water until the electrodes are covered completely. Place the tip of the salt bridge from the reference electrode on the outside and near the middle of the cathode.

Turn on the electrolysis current and adjust the applied emf to maintain the cathode potential at -0.35 V vs SCE. The initial current should range from 2 to 4 amp. Copper may not deposit for several minutes or until all the cupric ions have been reduced to the chlorocuprous ion and, indeed, the reference electrode may at first be negative to the cathode. Copper will commence to plate out when the cathode potential is about -0.2 V. As the deposition of copper proceeds, continuously adjust the applied emf to maintain the cathode potential at the limiting value. Continue the electrolysis until the current decreases to 10–20 ma.

B. Determination of Tin plus Lead in Brass

To the solution from which copper has been removed, add 1 g of hydrazine hydrochloride, and insert a copper-clad electrode (weighed accurately). Adjust the applied emf to -0.60 V vs SCE initially, but after the electrode becomes coated with a deposit of tin and lead, raise the applied emf to -0.70 V. Continue the electrolysis until the current decreases to a constant value and remains steady for 10 min. Before removing the electrodes, carefully neutralize the solution to pH 5–6 with aqueous ammonia.

C. Successive Determination of Copper, Bismuth, Lead, and Tin in Brass[9]

This separation is conducted in a tartrate solution. Dissolve the sample as described in part A. Add 100 ml of 0.1 M sodium tartrate solution and sufficient 5 M sodium hydroxide solution to adjust the pH at 5.0. Add 4 g of hydrazine hydrochloride and recheck the pH. Warm the solution to 70°C and proceed with the electrolysis.

Copper is deposited at -0.30 V vs SCE, bismuth at -0.40 V (or copper plus bismuth at -0.40 V), and lead at -0.55 V initially and raising to -0.60 V after the electrode becomes coated with lead. The solution remaining from the lead deposition is acidified to destroy the tartrate complex of tin(IV), and tin is determined at -0.60 V initially and raising to -0.65 V after the electrode becomes coated with tin.

The amount of lead must not exceed 100 mg per 200 ml at a pH of 5 because larger amounts precipitate as the tartrate.

EXPERIMENT 23-2   SEPARATION OF COPPER BY INTERNAL ELECTROLYSIS

Assemble the apparatus as shown in Fig. 23-9. For anodes, wind pure lead wire, 10 to 12 gauge, around the stem of a thistle tube which has been shortened to 6 in. in length, to form a compact helix. Leave a sufficient length of wire to connect to the common binding post. Each anode compartment is a porous alundum shell (extraction thimble obtained from the Norton Company, RA 84 or 360, 19 × 90 mm). The solution is stirred by a glass corkscrew stirrer or with a magnetic stirrer and bar.

Transfer aliquots containing 10–30 mg of copper into 400-ml beakers. To each, add 3 ml concentrated nitric acid and 3 ml of concentrated sulfuric acid. Dilute to 200 ml. Warm the solution to 70°C.

Fill the anode compartments with a solution composed of nitric acid (3 percent v/v) and lead nitrate (5 percent w/v) and insert the anode compartments and the platinum cathode into the sample. Add 0.3 g of urea and short-circuit the electrodes.

Electrolyze for 15 min and then flush out the anode compartments with lead nitrate–nitric acid solution. Continue the electrolysis until the copper is completely deposited, as indicated by failure to plate on a fresh surface when the solution level is raised. Lower the beaker, and rinse the electrode with a stream of distilled water. Remove the cathode, dry, and weigh.

E X P E R I M E N T   2 3 - 3   REMOVAL OF METALS AT THE MERCURY CATHODE

Transfer aliquots containing approximately 0.5 g of iron (or copper, nickel, or other heavy-metal ion) to a 180-ml tall-form beaker. Dilute to about 80 ml. Add 1 ml of concentrated sulfuric acid.

Fill the cathode compartment with fresh mercury and insert the unitized assembly into the beaker. Adjust the current to 5 amp. After 15 min raise the unitized electrode assembly and rinse with a stream of distilled water. Replace the mercury with fresh mercury and electrolyze for another interval. Repeat the cycle at 15-min intervals the first three times and then at 30-min intervals until the removal of the metal ions is considered complete.

Notes. An auxiliary motor stirrer rotating slowly at the level of the mercury surface, or a magnetic stirrer bar floating on the surface, will speed the rate of deposition.

It is not necessary to change the mercury when using the Melaven cell.

The instructor may wish to have the student follow the removal of the metal ions by means of spot tests or other methods.

E X P E R I M E N T   2 3 - 4   ELECTROGRAPHIC SPOT TESTING

A schematic diagram of an electrograph is given in Fig. 23-10. The sample is made the anode, in contact with a sheet of hardened filter paper, such as Schleicher & Schull Nos. 575 or 576 or Whatman No. 50, and backed by a thick, soft, backing paper such as S & S No. 601 or blotting paper.

General Directions. Moisten the pad of the printing medium and backing paper with electrolyte, blot lightly, and place on the aluminum base plate with the printing surface upward. Place the specimen on the paper and make contact by bringing the other electrode onto the specimen by hand pressure or by a clamp. Close the electrical circuit for the length of time calculated by Equation 21. Generally an exposure of 10 seconds with a current of 15 ma/cm² of surface area is sufficient.

Examination of a Print of Pure Metal. Moisten the pad with an electrolyte consisting of 0.5 M sodium carbonate solution plus 0.1 M sodium chloride solution. After printing, remove the upper sheet and cut it into four parts. Hold one part over a beaker of warm, concentrated aqueous ammonia, hold the second part over a beaker of warm, concentrated hydrochloric acid, and hold the third part over a warm surface until dry. Compare the original color and the colors of the treated portions of the test sheet with those listed in Table 23-4.

Use of Color-Producing Reagents.

1. Solder lugs may be lead- or tin-dipped. A test sheet impregnated with a 0.5 M ammonium molybdate solution yields a blue color with tin; a zinc sulfide test paper, subsequently treated with warm, yellow ammonium polysulfide, reveals lead as a black stain.

2. A specimen of steel may be examined for nickel and chromium. A test sheet moistened with a saturated solution of barium hydroxide plus a 1 percent alcoholic

Table 23-4	Colors of Transfer Products of Certain Metals[†]			
METAL	ELECTROLYTE: 0.5 M Na₂CO₃ + 0.1 M NaCl	FUMING OVER		EXPOSURE TO HEAT AND LIGHT
		NH₃	HCl	
Copper	Greenish blue	Deep blue	Green-yellow	Green-blue
Silver	Colorless	—	—	Black
Iron	Brown	Brown	Orange-yellow	Brown
Nickel	Light green	Light violet	Green	Light green
Cobalt	Dirty brown	Brown	Blue	Deep blue
Molybdenum	Deep blue-violet	Gray	Gray	Gray
Chromium	Yellow	Yellow	Yellow	Yellow

[†]H. W. Hermance and H. V. Wadlow, "Electro Spot Testing and Electrography," in *Am. Soc. Testing Materials, Spec. Tech. Pub.*, **98**, 25 (1950).

dimethylglyoxime solution yields yellow barium chromate and red nickel dimethylglyoxime when these metals are present.

3. A flat laboratory spatula, labeled stainless, may be tested for pinholes in the coating over the underlying iron. A test sheet impregnated with 0.5 M potassium ferricyanide solution yields blue dots where holes exist in the coating unless the chromium plate has an underlying layer of nickel.

EXPERIMENT 23-5   ELECTROCHROMATOGRAPHY

Use a commercial apparatus or assemble the cell as illustrated in Fig. 23-12. Place a sheet of Eaton-Dikeman grade 301 paper, 0.05 in. thick (or grade 320, 0.1 in. thick), 24 in. $\times$ 24 in., over a glass plate or block of solidified polystyrene foam. Lay a strip of platinum foil along each vertical edge and connect each electrode to the terminals of a power supply capable of app'ying continuously 160–400 V with a current flow of 25–100 ma. The top edge of the paper should extend above the block or plate at least 2 in. so that the edge can be folded over and immersed in the background electrolytic solution.

When the background solution has traversed the length of the paper, small pointed paper strips are touched to the bottom edge (if special serrated paper is not used). The voltage is applied and the mixture to be separated is added by capillary flow through a paper wick or a drag pen. If desired, a polyethylene sheet can be hung over the face of the supporting medium to reduce evaporation.

Suggested inorganic mixtures:[15]

1. Silver and cupric ions, each 0.005 M. Wash liquid is 0.01 M EDTA in 1 M aqueous ammonia. Potential, 200 V. Ions located with yellow ammonium sulfide.

2. Cobaltous and ferric ions, each 0.005 M. Wash liquid is 0.05 M malonic acid in 0.1 M acetic acid. Potential, 50 V. Ions located as above.

3. Silver, cadmium, and bismuth, each 0.005 M. Wash liquid is 0.05 M monoammonium malonate. Potential, 162 V. Ions located as above.

EXPERIMENT 23-6   PAPER ELECTROPHORESIS

A number of experiments in paper electrophoresis, using the Shandon Unikit, are described in J. G. Feinberg and I. Smith, *Chromatography and Electrophoresis on Paper*, Shandon Scientific Co., Ltd., London, 1962. Typical experiments include the following, run at 250–400 V on Whatman No. 1 filter paper, 30 × 10 cm. The individual components are spotted (one drop of each solution) along a line across the center of the strip and with the spots 2 cm from an edge and each other. The buffer solution is placed in the electrode compartments, and the paper strip is uniformly wetted with the buffer except in the vicinity of the component spots. After insertion of the ends of the strip in the appropriate buffer compartment, the remainder of the paper is carefully moistened and the electrophoresis begun without delay.

A. Separation of three indicators (Congo red, phenol blue, and bromphenol blue) with either an acidic or a basic buffer. Indicator concentration is 0.05 percent in ethanol. The acidic buffer is 0.1 M in acetic acid and 0.04 M (3.1 g/liter) in ammonium acetate. The basic buffer is 0.1 M in ammonia and 0.04 M in ammonium acetate. Run for 1–2 hr.

Note the direction of electromigration of the indicators in each buffer.

B. Separation of fluorescein, tartrazine, and malachite green (0.1 percent in water) with one of the buffers described in part A. Run for 1–2 hr.

Note the direction of migration of each spot.

Problems

1. At what value should the cathode potential be controlled if one desired to separate silver from a 0.005 M solution of cupric ions? If the initial silver concentration is 0.05 M, how long should the deposition take, assuming $\delta = 2 \times 10^{-3}$ cm; $D = 7 \times 10^{-5}$ cm^2 sec^{-1}; $V = 200$ ml; and $A = 150$ cm^2? *Ans.* (a) 0.26 V vs NHE; (b) Approximately 10.0 min to remove 99.9 percent of the silver.

2. Copper and nickel can be separated by a constant current procedure provided the pH is carefully controlled. Calculate the minimum pH necessary to initiate the deposition of nickel from a 0.005 M solution. Assume that the current is 1 amp, $A = 150$ cm^2, and remember that the electrode will be covered with the copper deposit.

3. Under the conditions of Problem 2, how completely will the copper have been removed up to the point when hydrogen gas is initially liberated?

4. What is the initial cathode potential when cadmium deposits from a solution 0.01 M in cadmium?

5. What weights of each of the following would be deposited by 3.378 coulombs? (a) Cu^0 from Cu^{+2}, (b) PbO$_2$ from Pb^{+2}, (c) Cl$^-$ as AgCl at a silver anode, (d) Sn^0 from SnCl$_4$. *Ans.* (c) 1.24 g.

6. A solution is initially 0.01 M in silver ion and 0.5 M in cupric ion at 25°C. (a) What cathode potential is needed theoretically for the complete deposition of silver? (b) What cathode potential may be required considering concentration polarization? (c) How much silver remains in the solution when the cathode potential has been brought to 0.45 V vs NHE? *Ans.* (a) 0.50 V, (c) $pAg = 5.93$.

7. Under a given set of electrolysis conditions, 0.500 g of silver was deposited at the cathode and oxygen liberated simultaneouly at the anode. Calculate the number of millimoles of hydrogen ion added to the solution. If the solution volume were 200 ml, what would be the change in pH, assuming initially that the solution was neutral and unbuffered? *Ans.* $\Delta pH = 5.37$ units.

8. In an electrolytic determination of bromide ion from 100 ml of solution, the silver anode, after electrolysis was completed, was found to have gained 0.8735 g. (a) Calculate the molarity of bromide in the original solution. (b) Calculate the potential of the silver electrode at the beginning of the electrolysis, assuming the solubility product of AgBr is 4×10^{-13}. *Ans.* (a) 0.109 *M*, (b) 0.124 V.

9. A solution which is 0.1 *M* in zinc sulfate, and buffered at *p*H 4 with an acetate buffer, is to be electrolyzed using a copper-clad cathode. If the overpotential of hydrogen on copper is 0.75 V at the current density to be used, and that of oxygen on the platinum anode is 0.50 V, (a) calculate the decomposition potential of the solution, assuming that the *iR* drop is 0.5 V. (b) Will the decomposition potential change as the electrolysis proceeds? (c) How much zinc will remain in solution at the point when hydrogen gas begins to be liberated?

10. At a current density of 0.01 amp cm^{-2} the overpotential of hydrogen gas on cadmium is 0.4 V. Would it be possible to deposit cadmium quantitatively in a solution buffered at *p*H = 2? *Ans.* Not completely since the cadmium ion concentration is lowered only to 10^{-4} *M*.

11. The cathode potential is controlled 0.05 V less negative than the value at which tin would be deposited from a 0.005 *M* solution. (a) Calculate the molarity of copper ions remaining in a sulfate solution. (b) Estimate the quantity of undeposited copper in a solution 1.0 *M* in HCl and containing hydrazine hydrochloride.

12. If lead is used as the soluble anode in the internal electrolysis of a lead solution containing a small amount of copper, what would be the final concentration of copper in solution if the lead concentration is 0.2 *M*?

13. By means of suitable calculations, show why zinc can be successfully plated onto a copper-clad electrode from a solution buffered at *p*H = 7, whereas the deposition would not occur if smooth platinum electrodes were substituted. Assume a current density equivalent to the appearance of first visible gas bubbles.

14. Suggest an electrographic method for detecting the presence of copper filings on an ax blade suspected of being used to cut telephone cables. The method should be adaptable to courtroom demonstration before a jury of laymen.

15. Suggest a field method for the detection of fool's gold (FeS_2).

16. For a typical laboratory deposition of 0.200 g copper onto a platinum electrode (area 160 cm^2) from 200 ml of 0.5 *M* tartrate solution adjusted to *p*H 4.5 and containing hydrazine, calculate the time required to reduce the copper concentration (a) to 1 percent of its original value and (b) to 0.1 percent. Starting at an initial value of 2.6 amp the current decreased to 1.3 amp after 2 min, to 0.65 amp after 4 min, and to 0.33 amp after 6 min.

17. In Problem 16, assuming that the diffusion coefficient of the tartrate complex is approximately 2×10^{-5} cm^2 sec^{-1}, estimate the thickness of the diffusion layer about the electrode.

18. A solution is 0.1 *M* in cadmium ion and 0.01 *M* in hydrogen ion. (a) What is the difference between the two cathode potentials? (b) To this solution is added sufficient ammonia to convert the cadmium to $Cd(NH_3)_4^{+2}$ and to make the solution 0.57 *M* in free NH_3 and 0.10 *M* in NH_4^+. Assuming that the volume of the solution is unchanged, what is the difference between the two cathode potentials? The formation constant for $Cd(NH_3)_4^{+2}$ is 4×10^8.

19. In an ammoniacal solution, 0.10 *M* in both NH_3 and NH_4^+, would the deposition of copper be complete if the cathode potential were limited at -0.40 V vs SCE? The formation constant of $Cu(NH_3)_2^+$ is 1.5×10^6. *Ans.* No, a cathode potential of -0.64 V vs SCE would be required.

20. Outline a procedure for the successive determination of lead, cadmium, and zinc in metallurgical materials, such as flue dust from zinc refineries, composed chiefly of the oxides of these three metals.

21. During the determination of silver in silver solder, the cupric ammine complex undergoes reduction to the cuprous ammine complex. What difficulty is thereby introduced into the electrodeposition of silver from the silver ammine complex? The formation constant of $Ag(NH_3)_2^+$ is 1.5×10^7; see Problem 19 for other information.

22. For the determination of cyanide ion, Baker and Morrison [*Anal. Chem.*, **27** 1306 (1955)] employed a silver and platinum electrode pair, connected together through a microammeter, immersed in 1 M NaOH solution to which the cyanide sample is added. (a) Write the cell representing the reaction and (b) the electrode reactions involved. (c) Why does a reaction, nevertheless, proceed spontaneously?

23. During the deposition of copper from a chloride medium and in the presence of hydrazine hydrochloride as anodic depolarizer, the following current readings were obtained for corresponding times:

3.00 amp = 1.00 min	1.2 amp = 7.0 min	0.075 amp = 13.0 min
3.00 amp = 2.00 min	0.8 amp = 8.0 min	0.052 amp = 14.0 min
2.85 amp = 3.00 min	0.50 amp = 9.0 min	0.036 amp = 15.0 min
2.70 amp = 4.00 min	0.30 amp = 10.0 min	0.027 amp = 16.0 min
2.2 amp = 5.0 min	0.18 amp = 11.0 min	0.020 amp = 17.0 min
1.8 amp = 6.0 min	0.12 amp = 12.0 min	0.016 amp = 18.0 min
		0.016 amp = 20.0 min

(a) Graph the results on semilog paper. (b) From the descending slope of the graph, determine the value of the constant k (see Eq. 23-15). (c) Estimate the time required to reduce the copper concentration to 0.1 percent of its original value (after all the residual copper(II) ions are reduced to the chlorocuprous complex ion). *Ans.* (b) $k = 0.46$ min^{-1}; (c) Approximately 15 min.

Bibliography

Bier, M., *Electrophoresis*, Academic Press, New York, 1959.

Charlot, G., J. Badoz-Lambling, and B. Tremillon, *Electrochemical Reactions*, Am. Elsevier, New York, 1962.

Lingane, J. J., *Electroanalytical Chemistry*, 2nd ed., Interscience, New York, 1958.

Rechnitz, G.A., *Controlled Potential Analysis*, Pergamon, London, 1963.

Sand, H. J. S., *Electrochemistry and Electrochemical Analysis*, Blackie, London, 1940.

Schleicher, A., *Elektroanalytische Schnellmethoden*, 3rd ed., F. Enke, Stuttgart, 1947.

Literature Cited

1. Center, E. J., R. C. Overbeck, and D. L. Chase, *Anal. Chem.*, **23**, 1134 (1951).
2. Clarke, B. L., L. A. Wooten and C. L. Luke, *Trans. Electrochem. Soc.*, **76**, 63 (1939).
3. Diehl, H., *Electrochemical Analysis with Graded Cathode Potential Control*, G. Frederick Smith Chemical Co., Columbus, Ohio, 1948.
4. Fritz, H., *Z. anal. Chem.*, **78**, 418 (1929).
5. Glazunov, A., *Chim. Ind.*, Special Number (Feb. 1929), 425.
6. Johnson, H. O., J. R. Weaver, and L. Lykken, *Anal. Chem.* **19**, 481 (1947).
7. Lingane, J. J., *Ind. Eng. Chem., Anal. Ed.* **17**, 640 (1945).
8. Lingane, J. J., *Anal. Chim. Acta*, **2**, 591 (1948).
9. Lingane, J. J., and S. Jones, *Anal. Chem.*, **23**, 1804 (1951).
10. Maxwell, J. A., and R. P. Graham, *Chem. Rev.*, **46**, 471 (1950).
11. Melaven, A. D., *Ind. Eng. Chem., Anal. Ed.*, **2**, 180 (1930).
12. Page, J. A., J. A. Maxwell, and R. P. Graham, *Analyst*, **87**, 245 (1962).
13. Rogers, L. B., and A. F. Stehney, *J. Electrochem. Soc.*, **95**, 25 (1949).
14. Sand, H. J. S., *Analyst*, **55**, 309 (1930).
15. Strain, H. H., *Anal. Chem.*, **30**, 228 (1958).

CHAPTER 24

Coulometric Methods

Coulometric methods of analysis are based on the exact measurement of the quantity of electricity that passes through a solution during the occurrence of an electrochemical reaction. The substance of interest may be oxidized (or reduced) at one of the electrodes (primary coulometric analysis) or may react quantitatively in solution with a single product of electrolysis (secondary coulometric analysis). In either case, the fundamental requirement of coulometric analysis is that only a single (overall) reaction take place for which the electrode reaction used for the determination proceeds with 100 percent current efficiency.

Coulometric methods eliminate the buret and the preparation and storage of standard solutions. In their place the electron becomes the primary standard and titrant. The reactant is generated in controlled amounts within the electrolytic cell. The quantity of reactant formed between the beginning and the interruption of current at the end is directly related to the net charge transferred, Q, and can be computed directly from Faraday's law. Only the time of electrolysis t and the current i must be determined. If the current varies, the integral $\int i \, \partial t$ replaces the simple product $Q = it$. More versatile than most electrogravimetric methods, coulometric methods can be applied to determinations in which the reactant is difficult to obtain as, for example, gaseous or volatile materials such as chlorine, bromine or iodine; also, unstable chemicals such as titanium(III), chromium(II), or copper(I). The method is particularly useful in the range from milligram to microgram quantities and is capable of great accuracy. It adapts well to the tendency toward automation of routine analyses or to remote control as in the analysis of radioactive material.

The electrode processes may be carried out by two distinctly different techniques—with controlled potential of the working electrode (potentiostatic coulometry) or with constant current (amperostatic coulometry).

Measurement of Net Charge Transfer

Whenever one faraday of electricity, 96,487 Q, passes through an electrolyte, it causes chemical changes in $1/n$ gram-ions or $1/n$ gram-molecular weights of reactant, where n is the number of electrons involved per mole of reactant.

Example 24-1

If a constant current of 10.00 ma passes through a chloride solution for 200 sec, what weight of chloride reacts with the silver anode?

The net charge transferred is

$$Q = it = (10 \times 10^{-3} \text{ amp})(200 \text{ sec}) = 2.00 \text{ Q}$$

or

$$\frac{2.00}{96,487} = 2.075 \times 10^{-5} \text{ faradays (or moles) of chloride ion}$$

Since $n = 1$ for the reaction,

$$Ag^0 + Cl^- \rightarrow AgCl + e^-$$

2.075×10^{-5} equivalents of chloride ion formed AgCl. In weight, the amount is

$$(2.075 \times 10^{-5})(35.45) = 0.735 \times 10^{-3} \text{ g (or 0.735 mg)}$$

If the electrolysis is carried out at controlled potential, the current will decrease logarithmically as a function of time according to the expression

$$i = i_0 e^{-kt} \tag{24-1}$$

This gives the curve shown in Fig. 24-1. The net charge transfer is given by the integral

$$Q = \int_0^\infty i \, \partial t \cong \int_0^t i_0 e^{-kt} \, \partial t \tag{24-2}$$

Since the functional dependence of current on time is almost always complex, the value of the integral is found graphically by measuring the area under the current-time curve or by using a current-time integrating device. Since it is obviously impossible to carry out the electrolytic generation to infinite time, in practical analysis the electrolysis is terminated when the current has diminished to approximately 0.1 percent of the initial current, i.e., $i/i_0 \leq 0.001$. When the logarithm of the current is plotted as a function of time, the intercept at $t = 0$ is i_0 and the slope is $-k/2.3$ (see Eq. 23-17 on page 631). The limit-

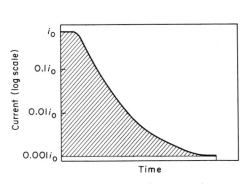

Thermometer

Gases liberated

Measuring buret

Electrolyte

Leveling bulb

Electrodes

Fig. 24-1. Schematic of current-time relationship in controlled-potential coulometry. Shaded area indicates the graphical method of integration.

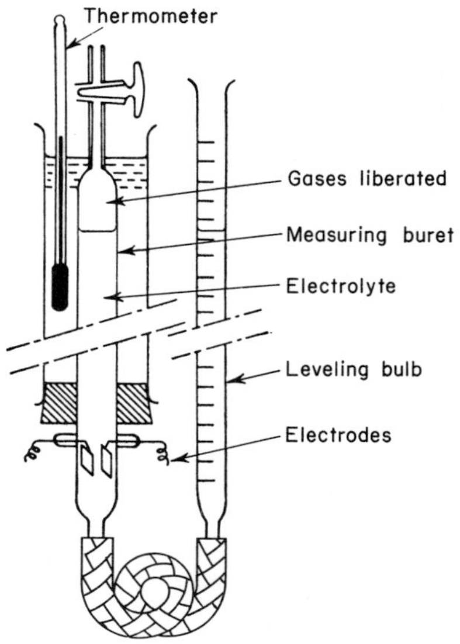

Fig. 24-2. Gas coulometer. After J. J. Lingane, *J. Am. Chem. Soc.*, **67**, 1916 (1945).

ing value of Q as t becomes large is i_0/k. Often an appreciable residual (background) current i_r is observed with the supporting electrolyte alone, and the current decays only to the value of the residual current. The net charge transferred becomes $Q - i_r t$.

Coulometers

The electrolytic method for determining the current-time integral employs a standard chemical coulometer in series with the electrolysis cell. With electrogravimetric coulometers, the change in weight of one electrode is a measure of the charge transferred. The coulometer is simply a second electrolytic cell in which an electrochemical reaction is known to proceed with 100 percent current efficiency, as, for example, the deposition of silver or copper. A modern version of the electrogravimetric coulometer is the coulometric coulometer.[4] After completion of the coulometric step, the coulometer is included in another circuit, by means of which a perfectly constant current is passed through the coulometer in the opposite direction. In this way the electrodes are returned to their original condition. The time required for this, multiplied by the current, gives the number of coulombs consumed in the actual determination. For example, if the reaction involved reduction of copper(II) to metallic copper, the deposit is redissolved anodically and the end point is indicated by a sharp change in electrode potential from the value for copper to that for the discharge of oxygen (see Electrolytic Stripping). This method is particularly suited for analyses on a microscale.

Lingane has described two gas coulometers. In one the total volume of hydrogen and oxygen liberated in the electrolysis of an aqueous solution of 0.5 M potassium sulfate is collected in a thermostatted gas-measuring buret.[6] Its lower limit of accuracy is 10 Q. For the range from 5 to 20 Q, 0.1 M hydrazine sulfate is used as electrolyte. Nitrogen is evolved at the anode and hydrogen at the cathode. The net coulometer reaction is

$$N_2H_5^+ = N_2 + 2H_2 + H^+ \tag{24-3}$$

The total volume of nitrogen and hydrogen evolved is measured in a 5-ml buret.[8] A typical arrangement of the gas coulometer is shown in Fig. 24-2. In using a gas coulometer, one must adjust liquid levels before, during, and after the electrolysis, but the coulometer thereby furnishes a semicontinuous indication of the progress of the reaction. After correction of the gas volume to standard conditions of pressure and temperature, 16,810 ml of gas corresponds to one faraday (96,487 Q) theoretically; the actual volume per coulomb is 0.1739 ml at standard conditions.

Integrators

A simple electromechanical integrator is constructed by connecting the ends of a series resistor (in the current circuit) to one of the coil windings of a low-inertia integrating motor—essentially a d-c motor built for 0.25–1.5-V operation in which friction and heat losses have been reduced to a minimum. The speed of shaft rotation is a linear function of the applied voltage—derived from the current flowing through the series resistor. Rotation of the armature shaft is followed by a mechanical counter.[1]

Electronic integration, although calling for the use of complicated equipment, enables one to integrate even small charge transfers and, in accuracy, leaves nothing to be desired. In fact, the main limitation (0.01 percent) with electronic equipment arises from background signal. Voltage-to-frequency converters measure the voltage drop over a standard resistor and feed the output to a scaler, from which the current-time integral is obtained as a number of counts. For example, an input signal of one volt may be converted to an output signal of 10,000 counts per second. The operational amplifier-capacitor integrator is similar to those used in analog computors. Response time to current changes is as fast as 10 μsec. Usable range extends from 10 μa to 10 ma. A typical circuit is included in Fig. 24-3.

Coulometry with Controlled Potential of the Working Electrode

In controlled potential coulometry, four instrumental units are involved—a coulometer, a d-c current supply, a potentiostat, and an electrolytic cell. The test material is reduced (or oxidized) directly at the working electrode,

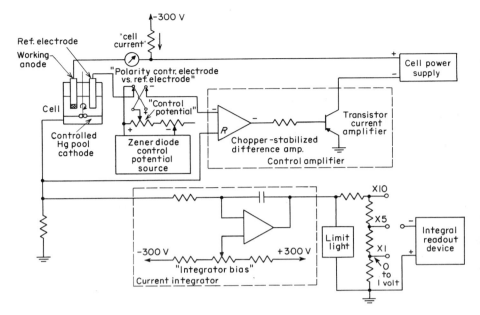

Fig. 24-3. Electronic controlled-potential coulometric titrator block diagram, switched for reduction. After M. T. Kelley, H. C. Jones, and D. J. Fisher, *Anal. Chem.*, **31**, 488 (1959). (Courtesy of *Analytical Chemistry*.)

and the charge transfer during this process is integrated by a coulometer. In order that only the desired reaction may take place, the potential of the working electrode is controlled within 1–5 mV of the limiting electrode potential with the aid of a potentiostat. As the desired constituent reacts at the working electrode, the current decreases from a relatively large value at the beginning to essentially zero at the completion of the reaction (Fig. 24-1).

Electronic Coulometric Titrator

In the apparatus of Kelley, Jones and Fisher (marketed by Indiana Instruments Co. and NUMEC Instruments & Controls Corp.) the potential of the working electrode is controlled by a stabilized difference amplifier combined with a transistor current amplifier.[5] The electrolysis current is integrated by a stabilized amplifier and the integral is read out as a voltage. The block diagram, switched for reduction, is shown in Fig. 24-3. The command signal to the control amplifier is the algebraic sum of the control potential from the control potential source and the potential of the controlled electrode with respect to the solution, as seen through the reference electrode. The control potential is a selected fraction of the constant potential across a silicon voltage (Zener) diode. The current integrator is an analog computor circuit.

Titrations are made in an inert atmosphere provided by a nitrogen blanket.

For controlled anode-potential oxidations, such as those of iodide or iron(II), platinum electrodes are used, and the cathode is isolated by a salt bridge and frit barrier. For controlled cathode-potential reductions, such as those of uranium(VI) or copper(II), the anode is a platinum wire that is isolated by a sulfuric acid salt bridge and frit barrier and the cathode is a mercury pool. Thorough agitation of the mercury-solution interface is necessary to obtain a high initial current by providing adequate mixing of the solution to replenish ions depleted by electrolysis. A standard reference electrode, positioned as close to the working electrode as possible, is used to monitor the potential of the working electrode. The titration is terminated when the current drops to a predetermined fraction of the initial current or to the residual current from the supporting electrolyte.

Methodology

To apply controlled-potential coulometry, current-potential diagrams must be available for the oxidation-reduction system to be determined and also for any other system capable of reaction at the working electrode. As discussed in earlier chapters, in any sample system where two or more ions are capable of oxidation (or reduction) at a working electrode, that which requires the least free energy for transformation will determine the electrode process. For this to be compatible with the requirement of 100 percent current efficiency in generation, it is necessary to control the potential of the working (generating) electrode within specified limits.

These limits can be understood better from an example. Consider a mixture of antimony(V) and antimony(III) in a supporting electrolyte containing 6 M HCl plus 0.4 M tartaric acid (Fig. 24-4).[3] Plots of Q vs cathode potential show plateaus centered at -0.21 and -0.35 V vs SCE. First, one prereduces the supporting electrolyte at -0.35 V. Then the sample is introduced and the system deaerated. Finally the reduction is started, at -0.21 V for $Sb^{+5} \rightarrow Sb^{+3}$, followed at -0.35 V for $Sb^{+3} \rightarrow Sb^0$. Initially, electrolysis proceeds at a constant rate (initial current $= i_0$) until the potential of the working electrode reaches the limited value, in this case -0.21 V vs SCE. At this point the potentiostat takes over, and the current through the cell gradually decreases until all antimony(V) has been reduced to antimony(III). This pattern is repeated at -0.35 V.

Current-potential diagrams (also denoted "coulograms") are obtained by plotting current against cathode-reference electrode potential (rather than cathode-anode potential which would include the large (and variable) iR drop in the cell). The necessary data can be obtained by setting the potentiostat to one cathode-reference electrode potential after another in sequence, allowing only enough time at each voltage setting for the current indicator to balance. Alternatively, the reduction (or oxidation) is performed in the usual manner except that periodically throughout the electrolysis the potential

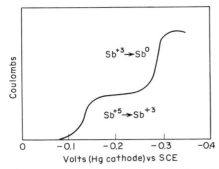

Fig. 24-4. Electrolytic reduction of antimony(V) by two-step process in 6 M HCl plus 0.4 M tartaric acid. After L. B. Dunlap and W. D. Shults, *Anal. Chem.*, **34**, 499 (1962). (Courtesy of *Analytical Chemistry*.)

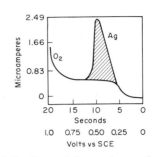

Fig. 24-5. Potential scanning method for silver. The lower curve is the residual current of the supporting electrolyte, ending in the discharge of oxygen. After S. S. Lord, R. C. O'Neill and L. B. Rogers, *Anal. Chem.*, **24**, 209 (1952). (Courtesy of *Analytical Chemistry*.)

is adjusted to a value which causes cessation of current flow. The net charge transferred up to this point and the electrode potential are noted and the electrolysis then continued. Curves plotted from a series of points establish optimum electrode potentials because they relate extent of reaction with electrode potentials under actual titration conditions and electrode material.

By controlling the potential of the electrode at a suitable value, it is possible to reduce a metal completely to a lower valency state, and then, by controlling at a more positive potential, the metal can be oxidized quantitatively to a higher valency state on allowing the current to reach its background value. For example, at -0.15 V with a mercury electrode, reduction of uranium (IV to III) and chromium(III to II) occur simultaneously. If a pre-electrolysis is carried out at -0.55 V, only uranium(III) is oxidized. Although the reaction does not occur with 100 percent current efficiency, it is complete. When all uranium(III) has been removed from the solution, chromium is determined by oxidation to chromium(III) with a 100 percent yield at -0.15 V.

Indirect methods are possible. In the determination of plutonium in the presence of iron, the first step is the reduction of plutonium(VI) to plutonium (III) and partial reduction of iron(III) to iron(II) at a platinum electrode in a sulfuric acid electrolyte. When this is followed by oxidation of the mixture to plutonium(IV) and iron(III), the net reaction is the reduction of plutonium (VI) to plutonium(IV). Interference caused by the presence of uranium is thereby avoided.[10] Also, the reaction which occurs at a mercury electrode,

$$Hg^0 + Y^{-4} = HgY^{-2} + 2e^- \qquad (24\text{-}4)$$

may be used to follow a number of electrochemical reactions wherein a metal, M^{+n}, is not electroactive:

$$M^{+n} + HgY^{-2} + 2e^- = Hg^0 + MY^{-4+n} \qquad (24\text{-}5)$$

An excess of HgY^{-2} is added to the solution of M^{+n} (Y^{-4} is the symbol for the anion of EDTA). The current is limited by the diffusion of M^{+n} to the electrode, and becomes zero at the end point.

Controlled-potential coulometry suffers from the disadvantages of requiring relatively long electrolysis times and expensive equipment, although it proceeds virtually unattended with automatic coulometers. However, direct indication of optimum conditions for successive reactions are easily obtained. No indicator electrode system is necessary, since the magnitude of the final current is sufficient indication of the degree of completion of the reaction. Although the concentration limits vary for each individual case, the upper limit is about 2 milliequivalents and the lower limit is about 0.05 microequivalent. The latter limit is largely set by the magnitude of the residual current and the many factors that affect it.

Potential Scanning

Extreme sensitivities have been achieved in the potential scanning method. The methodology is illustrated in the method for silver.[7] In the plating cycle, silver is plated at a controlled potential, thus concentrating it. Then the deposit is dissolved by changing the potential continuously. The current-time (or potential) curve, shown in Fig. 24-5, has a peak near the half-wave potential for silver. Standards and blanks are deposited and then dissolved under identical conditions. The method is employed exclusively in micro-analysis; the lower limit is about 10^{-8} M. Often, for practical reasons and because of current efficiencies, only a fraction of the total metal is deposited; identical plating times for standards and samples ensures proportionality. Results are obtained from calibration curves of net charge transferred vs concentration of metal.

Constant-Current Methods

In contrast with controlled-potential methods, constant-current procedures require only a knowledge of the current and the elapsed time to determine the net charge transfer. Since both current and time can be measured with high accuracy and relatively simple equipment, this method of coulometry is both accurate and simple.

Equipment

The schematic diagram of a coulometric setup for constant-current methods is illustrated in Fig. 24-6. The major problem is adequate stabilization of the constant-current supply in the range of from 1 to 200 ma. Fairly constant current can be obtained from batteries with a series-regulating resistance. Either a 45-V B battery or a 12-V storage battery with a large series (ballast) resistor R_1 is used to maintain constancy of current. If sufficiently large, virtually all the iR drop appears across it, whereas the voltage drop across the

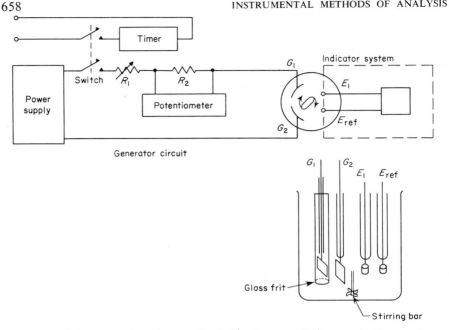

Fig. 24-6. Schematic of equipment (and titration vessel) for constant-current coulometry. R_1 is series (ballast) resistor; R_2 is precision resistor; G_1 and G_2 are
generator electrodes (one isolated behind a frit barrier); E_1 and E_{ref} are electrodes
for end-point detector system.

cell varies from 0.5 to 3 V. This resistor is also varied to adjust the cell current
to the desired level. Usually a current is selected that allows the electrolysis
to be completed within 10 to 200 sec. To maintain the series resistance in
thermal equilibrium and minimize adjustments of the cell current, it is advisable to employ a switching arrangement whereby the electrolytic cell is
replaced by a dummy resistance (high-wattage type, approximately 20 Ω)
during the intervals between analyses.

The current can be indicated approximately by a calibrated milliammeter,
and measured precisely by means of the voltage drop across a precision
resistor incorporated directly in series with the electrolytic cell. The voltage
drop across the resistor can be measured very precisely with a manual or a
recording potentiometer when the voltage drop is about one volt. Under
these conditions the error in the current measurement is about 0.002 percent.

Time measurements are normally made with a precision electric stop-clock.
A single switch control actuates both the timer and the electrolysis current.
Times accurate to 0.01 sec are possible with modern electric chronometers.

One commercial source of equipment (E. H. Sargent & Co.) which maintains a constant current in any of several selected ranges is shown in Fig. 24-7.
It comprises basically a power supply of the conventional a-c rectifier and

filter type to provide a d-c voltage with a maximum of about 300 V, sufficient for work with high-resistance electrolytes. Current which is drawn from this power supply by connection to the cell electrode system passes through a

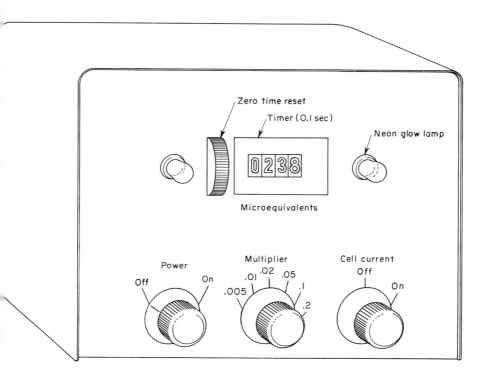

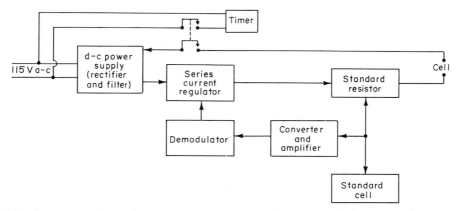

Fig. 24-7. Sargent coulometric current source block diagram (and front panel). (Courtesy of E. H. Sargent & Co.)

series-regulating tube and a precision resistor, which is one of several selected by a current selector switch. The size of this resistor is so chosen that, at the specified current level, an iR drop or voltage is developed which is equal to the potential of a standard cadmium cell. Any instantaneous error or difference resulting from a change in current due to line voltage or cell resistance variation is converted to an a-c signal, amplified many times, and reconverted to a d-c signal which is applied to the series regulator. Other commercial units are available from Fisher Scientific Co., Allied Electronics, Ltd., and A.E.I. (Woolwich), Ltd.

Generating electrodes must be of sufficient area to permit a low enough current density to keep electrode polarization within the limits necessary for 100 percent current efficiency. Currents normally employed require a substantial electrode surface area (10 cm^2 or larger), and often utilize a half-cylinder of sheet or gauze platinum. The nonworking electrode must be isolated in most cases by a salt bridge and frit barrier. The latter arrangement, however, increases the internal resistance of the cell and entails larger energy losses, so that a potentiostat may have difficulty in stabilizing the potential properly.

Detection of the End Point

Various methods are used for detection of the end point. It can be found by means of normal colored indicators, provided the indicator itself is not electroactive, or by instrumental methods—potentiometry, amperometry, and photometry. No correction for volume changes is necessary when plotting the results if internal generation of titrant is employed. Potentiometric and photometric indication find use in acid-base and redox titrations, while amperometric procedures are applicable to redox and precipitation reactions and, in particular, for these systems as the solutions become more dilute.

Electrolytic Stripping

The removal (stripping) of deposits has been used to measure the thickness of plated metals and of corrosion or tarnish films. In the case of oxide tarnish on the surface of metallic copper, the specimen is made the cathode and the copper oxide is reduced slowly with a small, but constant, known current to metallic copper. When the oxide film has been quantitatively reduced, the potential of the cathode changes rapidly to the discharge potential of hydrogen. The equivalence point is taken as the point of inflection of the voltage-time curve, as illustrated in Fig. 24-8. From the known current i, expressed in milliamperes, and the elapsed time t, in seconds, the film thickness T, in angstrom units, can be calculated from the known film area A in centimeters squared, and the film density ρ according to the equation

$$T = \frac{10^5 Mit}{AnF\rho} \qquad (24\text{-}6)$$

where M is the gram-molecular weight of the oxide comprising the film. From mixed films of oxide and sulfide on a metal, two inflection points are obtained. Similar methods have been described for the determination of the relative amounts of stannous and stannic oxides on a tinplate surface.

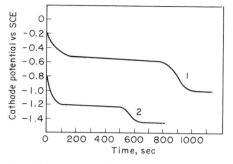

Fig. 24-8. Cathodic reduction of tarnish films on copper. Curve 1, cuprous oxide; Curve 2, cuprous sulfide.

Analogous anodic dissolution is used to determine the successive coatings on a metal surface. Iron is sometimes clad with a tin undercoating for adhesion and a copper-tin surface layer for protection from corrosion. The two coatings will exhibit individual potential breaks. In a similar manner, the thickness of chromium plate on iron, copper, or nickel, and of zinc or nickel plate on either copper or iron can be determined. The method may also be used whenever the substance to be determined can be deposited before hand so as to adhere to a solid electrode or to form an amalgam with a mercury electrode. Sensitivity is high. Accuracy is limited by the residual current and by the fact that the last traces of deposit do not dissolve uniformly from the surface.

Primary Coulometric Titrations

In primary coulometric titrations at constant current the substance to be determined reacts directly at the electrode. Consequently, no other substance should be able to be electrolyzed at the working electrode until much higher potentials are attained, usually at least 0.5 V from the desired value. Since the potential of the working electrode is not controlled, this class of titrations is limited generally to reactants which are nondiffusible.

One major area of application involves the electrode material itself participating in an anodic process as, for example, the reaction of mercaptans, sulfhydryl groups, and ionic halide ions with silver ions generated at a silver anode. For chloride samples the initial reaction may be

$$Cl^- + Ag^0 \rightarrow AgCl + e^- \tag{24-7}$$

followed by

$$Ag^0 \rightarrow Ag^+ + e^- \tag{24-8}$$

as soon as the limiting current (supply of chloride ions to the anode) has become smaller than the current forced through the electrolytic cell. At this point the silver ion generated anodically diffuses into the solution, and precipitation occurs with the chloride ions left in solution. Of course, the result of the two reactions is identical. The end point of the titration is ascertained amperometrically. Commercial titrators for biological and industrial samples based on this method are available (Aminco-Cotlove, Buchler Instruments). Combustion by the oxygen flask method precedes the titration step for nonionic halides in organic compounds. Mercaptan samples are dissolved in a mixture of aqueous methanol and benzene to which aqueous ammonia and ammonium nitrate are added to buffer the solution and to supply sufficient electrolyte to lower the solution resistance.

Secondary Coulometric Titrations

In secondary coulometric titrations an active intermediate is first generated quantitatively by the electrode process and this then reacts directly with the substance to be determined. The standard potential of the auxiliary system has to lie between the potential of the system to which the substance to be determined belongs and the potential at which the supporting electrolyte or a second electroactive system undergoes an electrode reaction.

A knowledge of current-potential curves aids the analyst in choosing the auxiliary system. Current-potential curves for systems pertinent to the coulometric determination of iron(II) at constant current are illustrated in Fig. 24-9. To complete the titration within a reasonable period of time, usually 10–200 sec, a finite current must be selected, say i_0. The necessary

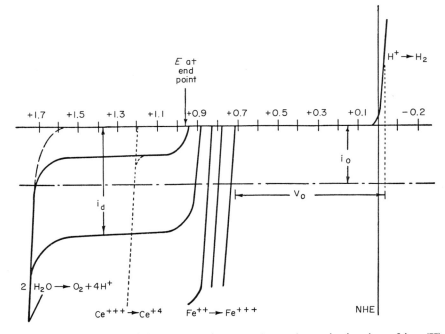

Fig. 24-9. Current-potential curves pertinent to the coulometric titration of iron(II) with cerium(III) as the auxiliary system.

applied emf will result in a voltage drop across the cell given by V_0 for the initial concentration of iron(II) present in the solution. At the beginning, iron(II) is oxidized directly at the anode:

$$Fe^{+2} \rightarrow Fe^{+3} + e^- \tag{24-9}$$

As the concentration of iron(II) decreases with the progress of the oxidation, the current will tend to decrease. However, since the current is being maintained constant, the voltage must be increased continually until ultimately the decomposition potential of water is exceeded. If i_0 is selected sufficiently small to delay the other anodic oxidation, the time required for a determination will become too long for practical consideration. One alternative, of course, is to control the anode potential at a value below the decomposition potential of the undesired reactant, as was discussed in an earlier section.

Interposition of an auxiliary system between the potentials at which iron(II) and water are oxidized is the basis of secondary coulometric titrations. No interfering electrode reaction can occur if the potential of the working electrode, in this case the anode, is prevented from reaching the value that would occasion initiating the decomposition of water. Limitation of such potential drift is achieved by having a precursor of the secondary titrating agent present in relatively high concentration. In our example a large excess of cerium(III) is added to the solution. Now as soon as the limiting current of iron(II) falls below the value of the current forced through the cell, that is, $i_0 > i$ limiting, the cerous ion commences to undergo oxidation at the anode in increasing amounts until it may be the preponderant anode reactant. Since the ceric ion formed reacts instantly and stoichiometrically with the iron(II)

$$Ce^{+4} + Fe^{+2} \rightarrow Ce^{+3} + Fe^{+3} \tag{24-10}$$

the total current ultimately employed in attaining the oxidation of iron(II) is the same as would have been required for the direct oxidation. Because there is a relatively inexhaustible supply of cerous ions, the anode potential is stabilized at a value less than the decomposition potential of water. The end point is signalled by the first persistence of excess ceric ions in the solution and may be detected the ordinary way with a platinum-reference electrode pair, or photometrically at a wavelength at which ceric ion absorbs strongly.

Errors due to impurities in the supporting electrolyte or in the auxiliary substance can be avoided by performing a pretitration, then performing the sample titration, or a succession of titrations, in the same supporting electrolyte.

Exploitation of titrants that for one reason or another are difficult to use in conventional titrimetry are among the virtues of secondary coulometric methods. Electrolytic generation of hydroxyl ion has some advantages over conventional methods. Very small amounts of titrant can be prepared, and in a carbonate-free condition. To analyze dilute acid solutions, such as would result from adsorption of acidic gases, the cathode reaction

$$2H_2O + 2e^- \rightarrow H_2 + 2OH^- \tag{24-11}$$

generates the hydroxyl ion. Of course, in the initial stages it is also possible for the hydrogen ion to react directly at the cathode,

$$2H_3O^+ + 2e^- \rightarrow 2H_2O + H_2 \tag{24-12}$$

but in the vicinity of the end point, the secondary generation predominates. The anode reaction must also be considered. If a platinum anode is used, it must be isolated in a separate compartment, for hydrogen ions would be liberated at its surface. Alternatively, a silver anode may be used within the electrolytic cell in the presence of bromide ions, for then the anode reaction is

$$Ag^0 + Br^- \rightarrow AgBr + e^- \tag{24-13}$$

and the silver and bromide ions are fixed as a coating of silver bromide on the electrode surface.

Halogens generated internally, and particularly bromine, have found widespread application, especially in organic analysis. In contrast with certain difficulties encountered in the use of bromate-bromide mixtures by conventional volumetric procedures, coulometry is much simpler.[11] Bromates are not soluble in many organic solvents, and many organic samples are not soluble in water. However, sodium and lithium bromides are quite soluble in various organic solvents in which brominations can be conducted.

The complexing ability of EDTA has been exploited in the coulometric titration of metal ions. The method depends on the reduction of the mercury(II) or cadmium chelate of EDTA and the titration, by the anion of EDTA that is released, of the metal ion to be determined. If the direct reaction of metal with EDTA is too slow, excess of the EDTA anion is generated and then the excess is back-titrated by cadmium generated at a cadmium-amalgam electrode.

Dual intermediates can be used whenever the substance to be titrated does not react rapidly with the auxiliary system or, at least, when the reaction rate is not as rapid as the generation rate. An excess of titrant is generated and permitted to react for the necessary time. Then the polarity of the working electrode is reversed and a back-titration is conducted with a second auxiliary system. In this manner an excess of bromine can be titrated with electrically generated chlorocuprous ion,

$$Cu^{+2} + 3Cl^- + e^- \rightarrow CuCl_3^{-2} \tag{24-14}$$

$$Br_2 \text{ (in excess)} + 2CuCl_3^{-2} \rightarrow 2Cu^{+2} + 2Br^- + 6Cl^- \tag{24-15}$$

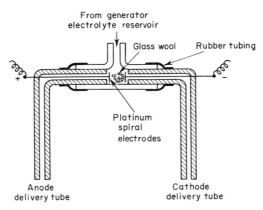

Fig. 24-10. Double-arm electrolytic cell for external generation of titrant. After D. D. DeFord, J. N. Pitts, and C. J. Johns, *Anal. Chem.*, **23**, 938 (1951). (Courtesy of *Analytical Chemistry*.)

External Generation

Internal generation methods possess limitations. Oftentimes conditions conducive to optimum generation of reactant and to rapid reaction with the substance to be titrated are not compatible. Or the sample may contain two or more substances which are capable of undergoing reactions at the electrode and which are not different sufficiently in electrode potential to permit use of an auxiliary system. For example, the titration of acids by electrically generated hydroxyl ion is precluded in the presence of certain other reducible substances. These limitations are circumvented when the reagent is generated in an electrolytic cell that is isolated from the solution to be titrated, and the desired electrolytic product is allowed to flow via a capillary tube into the test solution.

Cross-sectional views of a double-arm[2] and a single-arm generator cell[9]

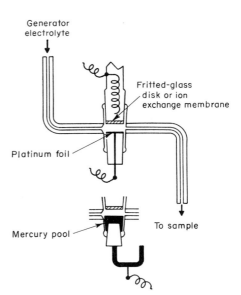

Fig. 24-11. Single-arm generator cell with working electrode either of platinum or a mercury pool. After J. N. Pitts et al., *Anal. Chem.*, **26**, 628 (1954). (Courtesy of *Analytical Chemistry*.)

are illustrated in Figs. 24-10 and 24-11. The supporting electrolyte is fed continuously from a reservoir into the top of the generator cell. The incoming solution is then divided at the T-joint, in the two-arm design, so that about equal quantities flow through each of the arms of the cell. Platinum electrodes are sealed on either side of the T-joint. The products of electrolysis are swept along by the flow of solution through the arms and emerge from the delivery tips on either side. A beaker containing the sample to be titrated is placed beneath the appropriate delivery tip. Thus, determinations performed with external generation of titrant hardly differ from normal volumetric methods in essentials; the only difference is that the titer is referred to unit of time and not unit of volume. Naturally, one-half of the liquid continuously discharged is conducted to waste. When a solution of Na_2SO_4 is supplied, H_2SO_4 is formed at the anode and NaOH at the cathode. For bromination, a solution of KBr is used.

The single-arm generator cell is useful for the generation of reagents in those cases in which mixing of the cathode and anode electrolysis products can be tolerated. The working electrode can be made of platinum or it can be a mercury pool. The other electrode compartment is isolated by a frit barrier. The flow of supporting electrolyte is usually 6 ml/min, or larger.

The titration of azo dyes with titanium(III) illustrates the advantage of external generation. At room temperature the rate of reaction of titanous ion with the dye is slow. Yet on raising the temperature hydrolysis of titanium(IV) and bubble formation at the electrode surface lead to low current efficiencies. However, if the titanium(III) is generated at room temperature and then delivered to the hot dye solution, optimum conditions prevail for each step. A mercury-pool cathode or an amalgamated working electrode is used to take advantage of the favorable hydrogen overpotential on mercury.

LABORATORY WORK

General Instructions

Assemble the titration apparatus as shown in Fig. 24-6. Connect a 45-V B battery through a 5000-Ω potentiometer (or bank of fixed resistors of different values), a 3000-Ω limiting resistor, the current-measuring device, the generator electrodes, and an ON-OFF switch. Measure the current with a calibrated 0–10 milliammeter or determine the iR drop across a precision 100-Ω resistor (for currents not exceeding 10 ma) with a student potentiometer. Time measurements made with a stopwatch or stopclock will provide results of moderate accuracy.

Arrange the generator electrodes and indicator system as shown in Fig. 24-12. Positioning the generator electrode from which the reactant is derived adjacent to the indicator electrode, in the direction of stirring, gives a more rapid warning of the approach of the end point. For photometric indication, the electrolysis cell is positioned in the photometer in place of the usual cuvette.

When using amperometric indication for the end point, plot the amperometric signal vs time. The end point will be signalled by an abrupt change in the amperometric current, which may be taken as the end point, or the coulometric titration may be terminated momentarily, the amperometric current and generation time noted, and then the generation continued for perhaps an additional 5–10 sec. This series of steps is repeated until 4 or 5 readings are obtained beyond the end point, which is then established by extrapolation of the two branches of the plot.

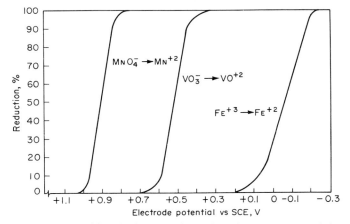

Fig. 24-12. Coulograms of iron(III), vanadium(V) and manganese(VII) in 1 *M* phosphate medium at *p*H 2 with a platinum cathode. (Courtesy of B. W. Conroy and O. Menis, NUMEC, Apollo, Pa.)

Pretitration of the supporting electrolyte should be done to remove impurities and to familiarize oneself with the end point signal. Then the sample is added and the titration continued until the end point signal reappears.

E X P E R I M E N T   2 4 - 1   ELECTRICALLY GENERATED HYDROXYL ION

Place 100 ml of 0.05 *M* KBr solution (6 g/liter) in a 200-ml tall-form beaker. Add several drops of an appropriate indicator, or insert glass-calomel electrodes for potentiometric indication. The generator electrodes may be a platinum foil cathode (10 cm^2) and a helix of silver (No. 6 gauge) wire as anode (or a second platinum foil electrode isolated by a frit barrier).

Turn on the stirrer and generator current. Adjust the current by means of the potentiometer (or bank of resistors) to 10 ma or less. Titrate to the theoretical *p*H at the end point (adding a trace of acid, if necessary), then discontinue the current. Add the sample, then turn on the current and timer simultaneously. Adjust the variable rheostat whenever necessary to maintain the current at the selected value throughout the titration. Select an aliquot of the sample that will require about 200 sec (for example, 10–20 ml of 0.001 *N* acid, transferred with a pipet; or microsyringe if more concentrated acids are employed).

After every titration clean the anode with emery cloth or by dipping it into concentrated aqueous ammonia (or potassium cyanide solution). Several consecutive samples may be titrated without renewing the supporting electrolyte.

E X P E R I M E N T   2 4 - 2   ELECTRICALLY GENERATED BROMINE

Place 100 ml of 0.2 *M* KBr solution (24 g/liter) and 3 ml of 18 *M* H$_2$SO$_4$ in a 200-ml tall-form beaker. The generator electrodes are two platinum foil electrodes (10 cm^2 or larger in area). If amperometric indication is employed, insert a small platinum electrode and a large-area calomel and apply 0.2 V positive with respect to the SCE. Pretitrate to an end-point signal, then add 1.00 ml of 0.005 *M* As$_2$O$_3$ solution (0.987 g/liter) and titrate until the same signal is repeated.

EXPERIMENT 24-3   ELECTROLYTICALLY GENERATED CERIC ION

Place 40 ml of 0.1 M cerous ammonium sulfate and 10 ml of 9 M H_2SO_4 in the electrolysis cell. Insert a platinum foil working electrode in the cell and isolate a second platinum foil electrode (the cathode) inside a tube with a fritted glass end and filled with 1.5 M H_2SO_4. Purge the supporting electrolyte with nitrogen gas for 10 min, and maintain a stream of gas through the electrolyte during the titration.

Add a sample of ferrous ammonium sulfate and titrate at 50 ma. The end point is ascertained potentiometrically with a platinum-calomel electrode pair or amperometrically with a platinum indicator electrode. A pretitration is recommended.

EXPERIMENT 24-4   ELECTRICALLY GENERATED IODINE

Place 50 ml of 0.1 M KI solution (16.6 g/liter) and 20 ml of 0.25 M Na_2HPO_4 solution (36 g/liter) in the electrolysis cell. Add a few drops of 0.005 M As_2O_3 solution (0.987 g/liter) and pretitrate to the end point (starch-iodide color, amperometric indication, or potentiometric indication).

Add 1.00 ml of 0.005 M As_2O_3 solution and titrate once more to the end point signal.

EXPERIMENT 24-5   ELECTRICALLY GENERATED SILVER ION

For the titration of bromide and iodide, the supporting electrolyte is 0.5 M KNO_3 (51 g/liter). The working electrode (anode) can be a clean silver foil (10 cm²) or a silver rod;* the cathode is a platinum foil electrode. For the titration of chloride, the supporting electrolyte is a nitric-acetic acid system (38 ml concentrated HNO_3 and 200 ml glacial acetic acid per liter) plus 0.05 percent gelatin.

Use 5.00–15.00 ml of 0.025 M KBr (2.975 g/liter), or 0.025 M KCl (1.864 g/liter), solution when the generating current is 30 ma. For amperometric indication, a large-area SCE may be short-circuited to the platinum indicator electrode through a suitable galvanometer.

EXPERIMENT 24-6   EXTERNAL TITRATION

Assemble an external generator, double-arm cell as shown in Fig. 24-10.

Connect a source of direct current, approximately 200 ma with 0.1 percent or less ripple, through a precision resistor, the pair of generator electrodes, and if necessary, a 1250-Ω (100-W) rheostat and a 125-Ω (20-W) rheostat.

Feed a solution of the supporting electrolyte continuously into the generator cell to provide a delivery rate of 6 ml/min from each delivery tip. Use a 600- or 800-ml beaker for the titration.

Suggested supporting electrolytes: 1.0 M sodium sulfate solution (adjusted to pH 7) for generation of hydroxyl or hydrogen ions; 0.05 M potassium iodide solution in 0.1 M boric acid (to neutralize the hydroxyl ion produced at the cathode) for generation of iodine; and 0.05 M potassium bromide in 0.1 N sulfuric acid for generation of bromine.

*Any previous coating of silver halide must be completely removed (see Experiment 24-1).

Problems

1. The initial current is 90.0 ma and decreases exponentially with $k = 0.0058$ sec^{-1}; the titration time is 714 sec. How many milligrams of uranium(VI) are reduced to uranium(IV)?

2. When an integrating motor was calibrated, these results were obtained:

CURRENT, ma	SHUNT RESISTANCE, Ω	TIME, sec	COUNTS, N
10.02	2220	600	9102
20.03	1110	600	9180
30.00	770	600	9458
50.00	475	600	9773

Calculate the microequivalents per count. *Ans.* 1.98×10^{-5} microequivalents per count at 30.00 ma.

3. The calibration factor of an integrating motor is 0.00267 microequivalents per count. Calculate the normality of an acid solution, 10.0 ml of which produced 40.72 counts during a titration. *Ans.* 0.01087 N.

4. These results were obtained during the titration of three successive 1.00-ml aliquots of As_2O_3 solution with electrically generated iodine at pH 8 and using amperometric indication of the end point. Graph the results and determine the normality of the As_2O_3 solution. The microequivalents of iodine generated are followed by the amperometric signal in microamperes: Pretitration—0.00 microequivalents = 0.4 μa; 5.10 = 0.7; 9.90 = 1.3; and 15.0 = 1.7. First aliquot—15.0 = 0.4; 50.0 = 0.4; 100.0 = 0.4; 149.5 = 1.3; 154.5 = 2.0; 160.0 = 2.6; 164.9 = 3.0. Second aliquot—164.9 = 04.; 200.0 = 0.4; 250.0 = 0.4; 273.8 = 1.0; 277.4 = 2.2; 280.8 = 2.7; 286.1 = 3.2. Third aliquot— 286.1 = 0.4; 350.0 = 0.4; 400.0 = 0.4; 402.0 = 0.8; 406.3 = 2.6; 411.0 = 3.1; 416.1 = 3.8. *Ans.* 0.133 ± 0.003 N.

5. In coulometric titrations, a milliampere-second corresponds to how many grams of (a) hydroxyl ions, (b) antimony (III to V), (c) chloride ions, (d) copper (II to 0), (e) arsenious oxide (III to V). *Ans.* (e) 5.13×10^{-7} g.

6. A 0.5 M K_2SO_4 solution in a gas coulometer gave 22.33 ml of hydrogen plus oxygen at the end of an electrolysis; temperature was 24.0°C in the water jacket and the pressure was 740 mm. The partial pressure of water over the electrolyte is 22 mm at 24°C. How many coulombs were involved in the electrolysis? *Ans.* 111.7 Q.

7. Calculate the concentration of acid in a 10.0-ml aliquot which required a generation time of 165 sec for the appearance of the pink color of phenolphthalein. The voltage drop across a 100-Ω resistor was 0.849 V.

8. Sketch the current-potential curves that would pertain to each of these coulometric systems; (a) The titration of acids with electrically generated hydroxyl ion in a potassium bromide electrolyte and using a silver anode. (b) The generation of excess bromine in a potassium bromide electrolyte, followed by the generation of copper(I) to react with the unused bromine. (c) The titration of zinc with generated ferrocyanide ions.

9. In the coulometric determination of permanganate ion by generating ferrous ion from ferric, the permanganate was all reduced to manganous ion by a constant current of 2.50 ma acting for 10.37 min. Calculate the molarity of the permanganate if the initial volume was 25.00 ml.

10. In an electrolytic determination of bromide from 100.0 ml of solution, the quantity of electricity, as read on a mechanical current-time integrator, was 105.2 Q. Calculate the weight of bromide ions in the original solution. Calculate the potential of the silver electrode that should be employed throughout the electrolysis. $K_{\text{sp AgBr}} = 4 \times 10^{-13}$.

11. The following measurements were made in a coulometric titration of arsenic(III) ions with generated bromine.

> Generation time: 132.6 sec
> Calibrated resistance: 100 Ω
> *iR* drop across resistance: 0.620 V

Calculate the amount of arsenic present in the sample.

12. Using generating currents of 1 to 10 ma, and corresponding titration times of about 300 to 100 sec, what range in weights of mercaptans may be present in a solution volume of 50 ml? The reaction is $Ag^0 + RSH \rightarrow AgSR + H^+ + e^-$.

13. In Fig. 24-12 are shown the coulograms of iron(III), manganese(VII) and vanadium(V) for their reduction in 1 *M* phosphate medium at *p*H 2 with a platinum cathode. Outline a procedure for the determination of each element in a mixture of the others by controlling the cathode potential.

14. Assuming that the coulograms for iron and vanadium, shown in Fig. 24-12, are reversible, outline a constant-current procedure for the determination of iron(II) in the presence of vanadium(IV).

15. From the information contained in Fig. 24-12, outline a procedure for the determination of the amounts of vanadium(V) and vanadium(IV) in a mixture containing the two oxidation states.

Bibliography

Abresch, K., and I. Claassen, *Die coulometrische Analyse*, Verlag Chemie, Weinheim, 1961.

Charlot, G., J. Badoz-Lambling, and B. Tremillon, *Electrochemical Reactions*, Elsevier, Amsterdam, 1962.

Kies, H. L., *J. Electroanal. Chem.*, **4**, 257 (1962).

Lewis, D. T., *Analyst*, **86**, 494 (1961).

Lingane, J. J., *Electroanalytical Chemistry*, 2nd ed., Interscience, New York, 1958.

Tutundzic, P. S., *Anal. Chim. Acta*, **18**, 60 (1958).

Literature Cited

1. Bett, N., W. Nock, and G. Morris, *Analyst*, **79**, 607 (1954).
2. DeFord, D. D., J. N. Pitts, and C. J. Johns, *Anal. Chem.*, **23**, 938 (1951).
3. Dunlap, L. B., and W. D. Schults, *Anal. Chem.*, **34**, 499 (1962).

4. Ehlers, V. B., J. W. Sease, *Anal. Chem.*, **26,** 513 (1954); S. W. Smith and J. K. Taylor, *J. Res. Natl. Bur. Std.* (U.S.) **63C,** 65 (1959).
5. Kelley, M. T., H. C. Jones, and D. J. Fisher, *Anal. Chem.*, **31,** 489 (1959).
6. Lingane, J. J., *J. Am. Chem. Soc.*, **67,** 1916 (1945).
7. Lord, S. S., R. C. O'Neill, and L. B. Rogers, *Anal. Chem.*, **24,** 209 (1952).
8. Page, J. A., and J. J. Lingane, *Anal. Chim. Acta*, **16,** 175 (1957).
9. Pitts, J. N., et al., *Anal. Chem.*, **26,** 628 (1954).
10. Shults, W. D., *Anal. Chem.*, **33,** 15 (1961).
11. Swift, E. H., and co-workers, *Anal. Chem.*, **19,** 197 (1947); **22,** 332 (1950); **24,** 1195 (1952); **25,** 591 (1953); and *J. Am. Chem. Soc.*, **70,** 1047 (1948); **71,** 1457, 2717 (1949).

Polarography

The polarographic method of analysis is based on the current-voltage curves arising at a microelectrode when diffusion is the rate-determining stage in the discharge of ions. The conditions are those resulting in concentration overpotential. Quantitative and qualitative analyses of substances are possible if the substance in question is capable of undergoing cathodic reduction or anodic oxidation. Substances present in concentrations ranging from 10^{-5} to 0.01 M can be determined.

Basic Principles

An electrode is considered to be polarized when it adopts a potential impressed upon it with little or no change of the current. Take, for example, a platinum electrode dipping into a solution of copper(II) ions which is also 0.1 M in sulfuric acid. When short-circuited with a calomel reference electrode, the platinum electrode will assume the potential of the calomel electrode with no flow of current. The platinum electrode is polarized, and it will remain polarized until an emf is impressed across the two electrodes that is sufficient to exceed the decomposition potential of the cupric ions. When the impressed voltage does exceed the decomposition potential, copper deposits on the platinum. Until this potential is attained, there is no reversible electrode reaction. After some copper has plated out, the electrode becomes depolarized and its potential is determined by the Nernst equation,

$$E = E^0 + \frac{0.0591}{2} \log [Cu^{++}] \qquad (25\text{-}1)$$

So long as the electrode is ideally depolarized, passage of current does not cause the potential to deviate from its reversible value.

Figure 25-1 gives idealized current-voltage curves of copper(II) ion solutions at varying concentrations. (See also Fig. 21-11.) Starting out with a well-stirred solution of 0.05 M copper (II) and impressing a voltage across the platinum electrode and reference electrode, the current-voltage curve will be traced by curve OAB. No current will be observed to flow until the applied emf exceeds the decomposition potential of a solution of 0.05 M copper. At point A, copper commences to plate out on the electrode and current starts to flow. As the voltage is increased further, the current increases linearly in accordance with Ohm's law. On the other hand, if the voltage is reduced from B to A, the current will

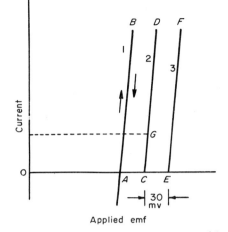

Fig. 25-1. Current-voltage curves without polarization. Curve 1: 0.05 M copper; Curve 2: 0.005 M copper; Curve 3: 0.0005 M copper.

diminish gradually to zero as the deposit of copper dissolves from the platinum electrode. Similarly, for smaller concentrations of copper the current-voltage traces will be given by curves OCD and OEF. In each case, the decomposition potential will be shifted along the voltage axis to a more negative value by 30 and 60 mV, respectively, as expected from Eq. 25-1.

The picture changes if the experiment is repeated without stirring the solution and with a microelectrode (an electrode with a small area of contact with the test solution). Consider, for example, a concentration of 0.005 M cupric ion at an impressed emf corresponding to D in Fig. 25-1. If the voltage is held constant, the current will start to flow at a value corresponding to D but will decrease rapidly to some value G as the concentration of copper ions at the microelectrode surface becomes depleted by deposition. The current, represented by G, is characteristic of the rate at which fresh cupric ions are supplied to the microelectrode by diffusional processes alone. A concentration gradient is established between the electrode surface and the bulk of the solution. Owing to the relative slowness of diffusion, the concentration of the ions at the electrode surface C_0 is lowered and differs from that in the bulk of the solution C. Consequently there will be a concentration gradient in passing from the electrode to the electrolyte, since the only way by which ions can get into the region around the microelectrode is by diffusion from the bulk of the solution.

The rate of diffusion of a particular ionic species is proportional to the difference between these two concentrations, and is given by Fick's law

$$\frac{\partial s}{\partial t} = \frac{AD}{\delta}(C - C_0) \tag{25-2}$$

where A = exposed area of the electrode surface
$\quad\quad D$ = diffusion coefficient of the ion
$\quad\quad \delta$ = thickness of the hypothetical diffusion layer about the micro-
$\quad\quad\quad$ electrode.

As the region around the microelectrode becomes depleted of electroactive ions, that is, as C_0 approaches zero, the rate of diffusion becomes proportional to the concentration in the bulk of the solution, C. This is another characteristic property of a completely polarized electrode, and serves as the basis for quantitative analyses.

When equilibrium is established at a microelectrode, the rate of discharge of the ions by the current will be equal to the rate of diffusion to the electrode, as given by Eq. 25-2. If i is the current and A is unity, then the rate of discharge of ions is equal to i/nF, where n is the number of electrons involved in the discharge process and F, the faraday, is the quantity of electricity carried by one equivalent. Therefore,

$$\frac{i}{nF} = \frac{D}{\delta}(C - C_0) \tag{25-3}$$

and

$$i = \frac{DnF}{\delta}(C - C_0) \tag{25-4}$$

The general form of Eq. 25-4 is such that for relatively small values of the current, the concentration overpotential is small, and as the applied emf is increased beyond the decomposition potential, the current exhibits the normal rise as shown between A and H in Fig. 25-2. However, as the voltage is in-

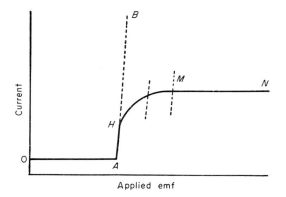

Fig. 25-2. Current-voltage curve with polarization.

creased, a stage is reached at which the concentration overpotential increases rapidly and the current reaches a limiting value as given by Eq. 25-4 when $C_0 \ll C$. This is the portion of the curve in Fig. 25-2 designated by MN, a region called the *limiting current plateau* because it represents the limiting or maximum rate at which the particular ion species can be discharged under the given experimental conditions. As the concentration in the bulk of the solution increases, so does the limiting current.

Polarographic Circuit

The dropping mercury electrode assembly and schematic apparatus for polarography is shown in Fig. 25-3. The anode is a layer of mercury at the bottom of flask A, and the cathode is mercury dropping from a reservoir

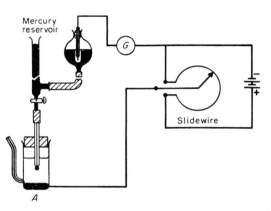

Fig. 25-3. The dropping mercury electrode assembly and schematic apparatus for polarography.

through the end of a capillary tube at a rate of about 1 drop every 3 sec. The anode and cathode are joined to the positive and negative terminals of a potentiometer slidewire. This enables a variable potential difference to be applied between the anode and cathode. The current is indicated by the galvanometer G.

The cathodic and anodic processes in a cell of this type are conveniently separated by making one of the electrodes very large compared with the other. The current density across the larger electrode is lower than that at the smaller electrode; the latter is more readily polarizable and is hence the determining electrode in the current-voltage relation. Furthermore, since the anode has a large area and the current is generally very small, of the order of microamperes, the concentration polarization at this electrode will be negligible and its potential may be regarded as constant.

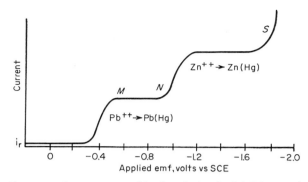

Fig. 25-4. Current-voltage curves of lead and zinc in 0.1 M potassium chloride.

Figure 25-4 shows a typical cathodic current-voltage curve, often called a polarogram, of lead and zinc in 0.1 M potassium chloride. The first wave on the polarogram is the reduction of lead ion to form a very dilute amalgam on the surface of the mercury drops,

$$Pb^{++} + 2e^- + Hg \rightarrow Pb(Hg) \qquad (25\text{-}5)$$

and the second wave is the similar reduction of zinc ion. Until the decomposition potential of lead ions is attained, only a very small residual current is observed. The commencement of the lead reduction is signaled by an increase in current, at first gradual, then almost linear in the mid-portion, and again slower, until the current finally attains the limiting value controlled by the diffusion process. Between M and N no further change in current occurs until the impressed voltage exceeds the decomposition potential of zinc ion, where-upon the zinc wave develops and the same process is repeated. The final current rise at S results from the reduction of potassium ions in the supporting electrolyte.

Since the area of the mercury drop is very small, the actual current is only about 1–100 μa. Consequently the concentration changes in the bulk of the test solution are negligible and several polarograms can be recorded or run in succession without any detectable difference in limiting current.

The Components of the Limiting Current

Although it is the diffusion current of an electroactive substance in solution that gives the characteristic polarographic wave, there are other possible con-tributions to the total limiting current that may also influence the current-voltage curve. In the deduction of the limiting current, Eq. 25-4, it was as-sumed that the ionic species which is being discharged is brought up to the electrode by diffusion only. In general, however, some of the ions will be trans-ported to the electrode, or away from it, by the normal process of transference. In addition, a small residual current and sometimes an adsorption current and a kinetic current all contribute to the observed limiting current. To render polarography truly quantitative, each of these currents, in addition to the desired diffusion current, must either be eliminated or else a correction must be applied to the measured limiting current.

Migration Current

Electroactive material is able to reach an electrode both by electrostatic attraction and diffusive forces. Cations will move toward the cathode under the influence of the electric field and the effect is to cause an apparent increase in the cathodic diffusion current. If the cation were in the form of a negatively charged complex, such as $Cd(CN)_4^=$, the effect would be an apparent decrease in the diffusion current. The whole effect of migration current, as it is denoted, can be eliminated simply by adding a relatively large quantity of an inert electrolyte which does not interfere with the electrode process. For example, suppose a solution contains 0.1 M potassium chloride in addition to 0.01 M cadmium ion. The current is carried through the cell impartially by all the ions present; the fraction carried by each depends upon its relative concentration, compared with other ions, and its transference number. In this case, approximately 90 percent of the current will be transported to the cathode by the potassium ions. If the concentration of potassium ions is increased until they represent greater than 99 percent of the total cations present, the relative currents carried by the other cations are reduced practically to zero. Chloride ions carry the current in the opposite direction. Since the potassium ions cannot be discharged at the cathode until the impressed voltage becomes rather large, large numbers of them will remain as a cloud around the cathode. This positively charged cloud restricts the potential gradient to a region so very close to the electrode surface that there is no longer an electrostatic attraction operative to attract other reducible ions from the bulk of the solution. With an appropriate excess of *supporting electrolyte* (as a salt like potassium chloride is called) the migration current is eliminated. Often a supporting electrolyte will be a buffer mixture for controlling the pH.

Diffusion Current

From the laws governing the conditions of diffusion at a dropping mercury electrode and the periodic growth and fall of the drop, the theoretical equation for the diffusion current obtained is

$$i_d = 607 n D^{1/2} C m^{2/3} t^{1/6} \qquad (25\text{-}6)$$

where i_d = average current in microamperes during the life of the drop

n = the number of faradays of electricity required per mole of the electrode reaction

D = diffusion coefficient of the reducible or oxidizable substance in the units $cm^2 \ sec^{-1}$

C = concentration in millimoles per liter

m = rate of flow of mercury from the dropping electrode capillary expressed in the units mg sec^{-1}

t = drop time in seconds, usually measured at the half-wave potential.

Originally derived by Ilkovic,[4] Eq. 25-6 generally is referred to by his name.

Polarographic Maxima

Current-voltage curves obtained with the dropping mercury electrode are frequently distorted by more or less pronounced maxima. These maxima vary in shape from sharp peaks to rounded humps (Fig. 25-5). In all cases the current rises sharply, but instead of developing into a normal diffusion current, it increases abnormally until a critical value is reached and then rapidly decreases to a limiting value corresponding with the normal diffusion current plateau. No rigid explanation has been proposed. Maxima are especially prevalent

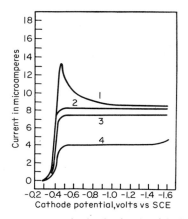

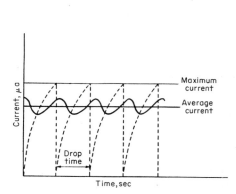

Fig. 25-5. Maxima obtained with lead and its suppression by gelatin. 0.001 M lead nitrate in 0.1 M potassium nitrate with (1) none, (2) 0.01, (3) 0.1, and (4) 1 percent gelatin. After I. M. Kolthoff and J. J. Lingane, *Polarography*, Interscience Publishers, Inc., New York, 1952, Vol. I, p. 165.

Fig. 25-6. Schematic representation of actual current-time curves and observed galvanometer oscillations. *Dashed line:* actual current-time curve; *solid line:* observed galvanometer oscillations about the average current.

when the decomposition potential is considerably removed from the electro-capillary zero of mercury.

Whatever the cause, maxima must be eliminated in order to obtain the true diffusion-current plateau. They can usually be suppressed by surface-active agents such as dye ions or colloids. Gelatin is often used, but the amount present in the solution must be carefully controlled and should lie between 0.002 and 0.01 percent. Less is useless, and more will suppress the diffusion current. Agar and methyl cellulose are also employed, and among dyestuffs, methyl red and acid and basic fuchsine have been used. Generally the proper amount of suppressor is added to every polarographic solution during the preparative step as a precautionary measure.

The magnitudes of the maxima depend on the drop time, becoming smaller the slower the drop time.

Factors Governing the Diffusion Current

The Ilkovic equation indicates that the diffusion current should increase directly with the sixth root of the lifetime of a drop. The curves shown as dashed lines in Fig. 25-6 can actually be obtained with a galvanometer possessing a very fast response. Galvanometers usually employed have a 3- to 6-sec time period and therefore are unable to follow the periodic growth and fall of the current with each individual drop. The saw-toothed waves actually observed, as represented by the solid line in Fig. 25-6, correspond to the oscillations about the true average current to which the Ilkovic equation refers. Thus, in measuring the diffusion current, one should measure the average of the galvanometer oscillations rather than the maximum or minimum "throw."

In order to obtain the true diffusion current of a substance, a correction must be made for the residual current. The most reliable method for making this correction is to evaluate in a separate polarogram the residual current of the supporting electrolyte alone. The value of the residual current at any particular potential of the dropping electrode is then subtracted from the total current observed. In practice, an adequate correction can be obtained by extrapolating the residual current portion of the polarogram immediately preceding the rising part of the polarogram, and taking as the diffusion current the difference between this extrapolated line and the current-voltage plateau. Both methods are illustrated in Fig. 25-7. The extrapolation method is useful when the polarogram comprises several waves. In this case the diffusion current plateau of a preceding wave may be extrapolated.

The Ilkovic equation points out two facts of great importance: (1) The ob-

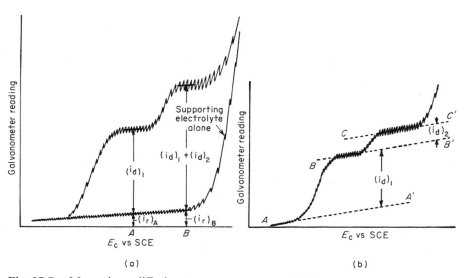

Fig. 25-7. Measuring a diffusion current: *A*, exact method; *B*, extrapolation method.

served diffusion current is directly proportional to the concentration of electro-active material. This relationship is the foundation of quantitative polaro-graphic analysis. (2) The diffusion current is proportional to the product $m^{2/3}t^{1/6}$. This permits a correlation to be made among diffusion currents obtained with different capillaries or with the same capillary at different applied potentials or under different pressure on the dropping mercury. When the Ilkovic equation is rearranged as follows,

$$I_d = 607nD^{1/2} = \frac{i_d}{Cm^{2/3}t^{1/6}} \qquad (25\text{-}7)$$

I_d is called the diffusion current constant. The quantities m and t depend on the dimensions of the dropping capillary electrode and on the pressure exerted on the capillary orifice due to the height of the mercury column attached to the electrode. An increase in pressure will not alter the size of the individual drops, which is a function of the capillary bore, but it will increase the number of drops forming in a given time and consequently the total electrode area exposed to the solution. The diffusion current will be proportional to the square root of the net pressure of mercury after correction for the back pressure due to the interfacial tension between the mercury and the solution. A mercury reservoir of large area is attached to the mercury column to prevent any change in height of the column during a series of analyses.

The drop time t varies as a function of the emf impressed across the polarographic cell. Actually the drop time follows very closely the electrocapillary curve of mercury, as shown in Fig. 25-8. The electrocapillary curve expresses

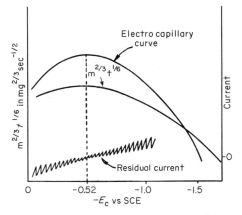

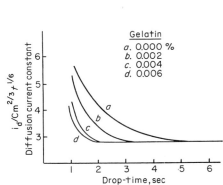

Fig. 25-8. Comparison of the capillary characteristics and the electrocapillary curve for mercury with increasing negative potential. The magnitude of the residual current is shown on the lower curve.

Fig. 25-9. Effect of gelatin and drop time on the diffusion current constant, I_d for 0.00014 M nickel nitrate in 0.1 M potassium chloride. After F. Buckley and J. K. Taylor, *Trans. Am. Electrochem. Soc.* **87**, 463, (1945).

the relation between the potential of mercury and the surface tension at a mercury electrolyte solution interface. As the emf is increased, the drop time first increases, then passes through a maximum at about -0.52 V, and decreases rapidly with increasing negative cathodic potential. The product $m^{2/3}t^{1/6}$ is less affected because it is influenced by the sixth root of t only; and, for practical purposes, may be assumed constant over the range of cathode potential from 0 to -1.0 V, but at more negative potentials its decrease is more rapid and must be taken into account.

The influence of temperature on the diffusion current is quite marked, particularly as the diffusion coefficient of many ions changes 1 to 2 percent per degree in the vicinity of 25.0°C, the standard temperature chosen for polarographic work. This implies that the temperature of the solution in the polarographic cell must be controlled to 0.5°C or less.

Certain discrepancies between the diffusion current constant, as derived from the Ilkovic equation, and experimental data have been reported. The predicted linear relation between the numerator and the terms in the denominator of Eq. 25-7 is not strictly obeyed owing to neglect of the fact that the diffusion is towards a curved surface. For absolute values, the Ilkovic equation should be multiplied by a factor: $(1 + xD^{1/2}t^{1/6})m^{1/3}$. The value of x is approximately 32.[9]

Gelatin or some other maximum suppressor has a very pronounced effect on the critical drop time below which the Ilkovic equation fails, as shown in Fig. 25-9. Without gelatin the Ilkovic equation fails with drop times less than 4 or 5 sec. As gelatin is added, the critical drop time decreases to the neighborhood of 1.5 sec. At faster drop rates there is appreciable stirring of the solution and a significant variation in the thickness of the diffusion layer which produces an abnormally large current. In practice, with drop times between 2 and 5 sec, 0.005–0.01 percent of gelatin present and 0.5 M or larger concentration of supporting electrolyte, the Ilkovic equation is valid within ± 2 percent.[1]

If the polarographic solution is agitated in any manner, the effective thickness of the diffusion layer is diminished. While this increases the observed diffusion current and would be advantageous with some types of electrodes, the dropping electrode requires a quiescent solution. Unless the drops fall under their own weight when they are completely formed, no reproducible diffusion current can be obtained. The electrode assembly should be shock-mounted for protection from vibration.

The nature and viscosity of the solvent medium also influence the diffusion current. The diffusion coefficient D varies inversely with the viscosity coefficient of the polarographic solution. Ionic species will vary in size and consequently in their rate of diffusion, depending on whether they are present as aquo complexes or some other type. The effect of complex formation is shown by the data in Appendix B. In some cases the nature of the complex species determines whether or not a satisfactory polarographic wave will be obtained.

With stannic ions, for example, no reduction is obtained in nitrate or perchlorate media in which only an aquo complex exists, whereas well-defined waves are found in chloride solutions in which the predominant species is $SnCl_6^=$.

Kinetic Currents

The possibility that either one or both of the oxidation states of the electroactive material might be in chemical equilibrium with other substances must be considered. If so, the diffusion current may be governed by a slow reaction process taking place at the surface of the dropping electrode and preceding the rapid electron exchange. The electrolytic removal of material from the electrode/solution interface unbalances the equilibrium, which is restored at a measurable rate. The rates of these reactions in many instances control the magnitude of the resulting current. Such currents may produce either a large maximum on the current-voltage curve or an abnormally large apparent diffusion current. The former is termed a catalytic and the latter a kinetic current.

The kinetic current will be proportional to the rate constant and to the volume of the interface, and thus is a direct function of the mercury drop size but is independent of the velocity of mercury flow from a given capillary. Kinetic currents have been observed mainly in the organic field, particularly during the reduction of certain carboxylic acids and their anions.

The Half-Wave Potential

The electroactive material in polarography is characterized by its half-wave potential. This is the potential at the point of inflection of the current-voltage curve, one-half the distance between the residual current and the final limiting current plateau, as shown in Fig. 25-10. The significance of the half-wave potential will be evident from consideration of an oxidation-reduction system:

$$ox + ne^- \rightleftarrows red \qquad (25\text{-}8)$$

The reversible potential of the system as it exists at the electrode-solution interface of the drop will be recorded on the polarogram. This electrochemical equilibrium may be represented mathematically as follows:

$$E = E^0 + \frac{0.0591}{n} \log \frac{[ox]_i}{[red]_i} \qquad (25\text{-}9)$$

where the subscripts denote concentrations at the electrode-solution interface.

Assume, for example, that the solution at the electrode surface consists entirely of the oxidized form before the commencement of the current-voltage curve. As soon as the applied emf is made large enough to reduce some of the oxidant, the concentration of oxidant at the electrode surface begins to decrease. Some ions will move in from the bulk of the solution as the concentration gradient builds up between the electrode surface and the bulk of the solution. The observed current depends upon the rate of diffusion established

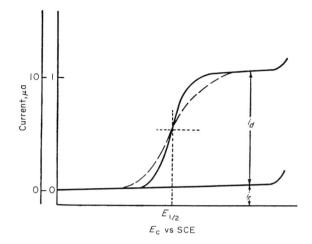

Fig. 25-10. Significance of the half-wave potential. Concentration of reducible ion, represented by the dashed line, is tenfold larger than the concentration represented by the solid line.

by the concentration gradient, and can be expressed similarly to Eq. 25-4, as follows:

$$i = K([ox] - [ox]_i)D_{ox}^{1/2} \qquad (25\text{-}10)$$

where K includes capillary characteristics and the n, m, and t terms from the Ilkovic equation. When the current attains the limiting value represented by the diffusion-current plateau, the concentration of oxidant at the electrode-solution interface will be reduced to zero, and

$$i_d = K[ox]D_{ox}^{1/2} \qquad (25\text{-}11)$$

Solving Eq. 25-10 for $[ox]_i$, and then combining with Eq. 25-11,

$$[ox]_i = \frac{i_d - i}{KD_{ox}^{1/2}} \qquad (25\text{-}12)$$

For metals that form amalgams with the dropping electrode, the concentration of metal amalgam is directly proportional to the current on the current-voltage curve, and, in fact, generally the concentration of reductant formed is proportional to the observed current, so

$$i = K[red]_i D_{red}^{1/2} \qquad (25\text{-}13)$$

Solving for $[red]_i$ and substituting the result into Eq. 25-9 along with Eq. 25-12, the potential of an oxidation-reduction system can be expressed as

$$E = E^0 + \frac{0.0591}{n} \log \frac{i_d - i}{i} + \frac{0.0591}{n} \log \left(\frac{D_{red}}{D_{ox}} \right)^{1/2} \qquad (25\text{-}14)$$

By definition, the half-wave potential is the point where

$$i = i_d - i \qquad \text{or} \qquad i = \tfrac{1}{2}i_d \qquad\qquad (25\text{-}15)$$

thus,

$$E_{1/2} = E^0 + \frac{0.0591}{n} \log\left(\frac{D_{\text{red}}}{D_{\text{ox}}}\right)^{1/2} \qquad\qquad (25\text{-}16)$$

Consequently, the polarographic half-wave potential is related to the standard reduction potential of the oxidation-reduction system. As does the latter, it depends on the ratio of the oxidized to the reduced state, but it differs somewhat from the latter depending upon the magnitude of the diffusion coefficients. Also, any overpotential of a metal upon mercury will be included in the measured half-wave potential. Nevertheless, the half-wave potential is a characteristic property of the given oxidation-reduction system and can be used for its identification.

Basic Instrumentation

Indicator Electrodes

The dropping electrode consists of a mercury drop which forms at the end of a capillary tube of 0.03 to 0.05 mm interior diameter. The drops are formed under constant pressure and detach themselves at a constant time interval. The reason why the small mercury drop is so widely used is its unique property of giving exactly renewable surfaces. If a polarogram be run forward and reverse, the average current passing through the polarographic solution is a function of the applied emf only and is independent of time and of the direction of the polarizing voltage. No other electrode has this property, except the streaming-mercury electrode.[2]

Use of a dropping electrode has several advantages. (a) Its surface area is reproducible with any given capillary. (b) The constant renewal of the electrode surface eliminates passivity or poisoning effects. (c) The high overpotential of hydrogen on mercury renders possible the deposition of substances difficult to reduce, as for example, the alkali ions. (d) Mercury forms solid solutions (amalgams) with many metals and thereby lowers their reduction potential. (e) The diffusion current assumes a steady value immediately and is reproducible. The dropping mercury electrode is useful over the range $+0.4$ to -2.8 V, referred to the normal hydrogen electrode. Above 0.4 V, mercury dissolves and gives an anodic wave. At potentials more negative than -1.5 V, visible hydrogen evolution occurs in acid solutions, and the usual supporting electrolytes begin to discharge. For polarographic studies at and beyond -2 V it is necessary to use as supporting electrolytes ions having higher reduction potentials than the alkali metals. The only compounds satisfactory for this purpose are the quaternary ammonium salts and hydroxides (Fig. 25-11).

Although the dropping mercury electrode is the most versatile electrode used in polarography, the relatively large charging current which is always present excludes the possibility of extending the range of conventional polarography to dilutions less than 10^{-5} M. However, high-sensitivity derivative instruments may be 200 times more sensitive and will compensate for the effect of the charging current. The dissolution potential of mercury limits its usefulness with most oxidizing systems. Noble-metal electrodes having a relatively high overpotential of oxygen can be employed for following polarographic reactions which take place at voltages where mercury oxidizes. Platinum microelectrodes, for example, can be used over the range +0.9 to −0.1 V vs the normal hydrogen electrode. However, solid microelectrodes possess several disadvantages: (a) The current does not become constant upon impressing an emf until after a wait of several minutes, and then slowly decreases with time. (b) The current-voltage curve changes when the applied emf is reversed or when

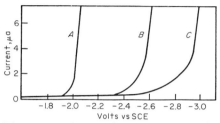

Fig. 25-11. Supporting electrolytes for use in the region of high-reduction potentials: *A*, sodium hydroxide; *B*, tetramethylammonium hydroxide; *C*, tetrabutyl-ammonium hydroxide.

the rate at which the voltage is increased varies. (c) Electrode pretreatment influences the value of the current and the half-wave potential. (d) The temperature coefficients of the observed diffusion currents are higher than with a dropping electrode.

On the other hand, rotation of a solid microelectrode increases the current as much as twentyfold over that of a dropping electrode, and a steady current is obtained immediately. Increasing the rate of rotation produces larger currents, but also decreases the likelihood of obtaining a limiting current plateau. Rotating microelectrodes find considerable use in amperometric titrations, but are not suited to single measurements of current owing to lack of reproducibility.

Reference Electrodes

A mercury pool at the bottom of the polarographic cell is the simplest form of a reference electrode. Since the layer of mercury has a large area and the current is generally very small, the concentration overpotential at this electrode is negligible and its potential may be regarded as constant. In chloride solutions it maintains the potential of the calomel electrode of the particular chloride ion concentration. While convenient, the mercury pool never possesses a definite, known potential. In the absence of chloride ions or other depolarizing electrolyte, and particularly in nonaqueous solutions, the potential does not attain a constant value. Moreover, in the presence of substances capable of forming complexes with mercury, the dissolution potential of mercury will be shifted to more negative reduction potentials, thus compressing the useful range of the dropping electrode. In order to eliminate the possibility of unknown or nonreproducible anode potentials, it is necessary to replace the mercury pool with a separate reference electrode connected to the polarographic cell through a conventional salt bridge. The saturated calomel electrode (SCE) is commonly employed, and it is almost universal practice in polarography to express half-wave potentials with reference to this electrode.

Conventions on Plotting Current-Voltage Curves

The conventional method of plotting current-voltage curves is shown in Fig. 25-12. The applied emf is plotted along the abscissa, reading in increasing negative values to the right. Current is plotted in the vertical direction. By convention, currents resulting from cathodic reductions are considered to be positive, and those from oxidations are considered to be negative. Taking the saturated calomel electrode as the point of reference, the zero on the voltage axis is actually 0.246 V on the normal hydrogen scale of reduction potentials.

When only the supporting electrolyte is present in the polarographic cell, the observed current-voltage curve is shown by Curve 1 in Fig. 25-12. The rapid increase in anodic current below $+0.2$ V vs the SCE is caused by the dissolution of the mercury drop; and the rapid increase in cathodic current above -1.8 V results either from the discharge of hydrogen ions or the cation

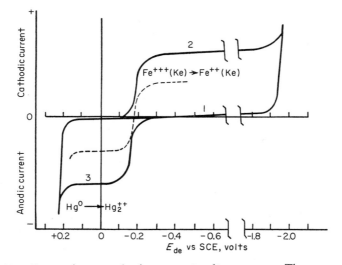

Fig. 25-12. Conventions on plotting current-voltage curves. The supporting electrolyte, Curve 1, contained 0.5 M sodium citrate and 0.005 percent gelatin and was adjusted to pH 5.6. Curve 2 is the cathodic reduction of ferric citrate complex. Curve 3 is the anodic oxidation of ferrous citrate complex. The dotted curve is a composite cathodic-anodic wave of a mixture of equal amounts of ferric and ferrous iron in citrate medium.

constituting the supporting electrolyte. In between these two potentials the electrode is perfectly polarized and only a small residual current flows. Addition of an electroactive material will alter the picture. Curve 2 on Fig. 25-12 results from the addition of a small amount of ferric ions in the form of a tartrate complex and is a typical cathodic wave. On the other hand, if an equal amount of ferrous ions is added, also as a tartrate complex, the anodic wave results (shown as Curve 3). A mixed wave is obtained when both oxidation states are present in the bulk of the solution—the dashed portion on Fig. 25-12. Assuming no difference in the diffusion coefficients of ferrous and ferric complexes, the cathodic diffusion current of Curve 2 will equal the anodic diffusion current on Curve 3, and the mixed wave will have the same height. In any mixed wave the amount of each oxidation state present will be proportional to the difference in current between the respective current plateau and the residual current obtained in the absence of either oxidation state.

Except for a small iR correction due to the sign of the current in each case, the half-wave potentials of the three curves will be identical. In fact, any serious deviation among the half-wave potentials is an indication that the electrode reaction is not proceeding reversibly.

Instruments

A large selection of commercial instruments is available. Less expensive models require manual control and point-by-point plotting of current-voltage curves. A schematic diagram of an instrument of this type is shown in Fig. 25-13; below is an illustration of the instrument. The Sargent-Heyrovsky model XII Polarograph, patterned after the original instrument that was developed

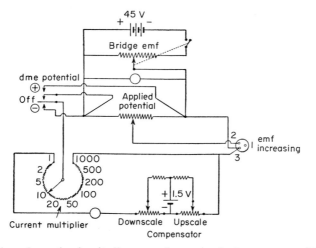

Fig. 25-13. The schematic circuit diagram of a manual instrument. (The Sargent Polarograph, model III, courtesy of E. H. Sargent & Co.)

by Heyrovsky and Shikata,[3] is similar in circuit design but features photographic recording of the current-voltage traces. A motor drives a drum which carries the slidewire and the photographic paper. The light beam of the galvanometer is reflected onto the paper through a fixed slit. The Fisher model 65 Elecdropode (Fig. 25-14) operates from 110-V a-c line without using

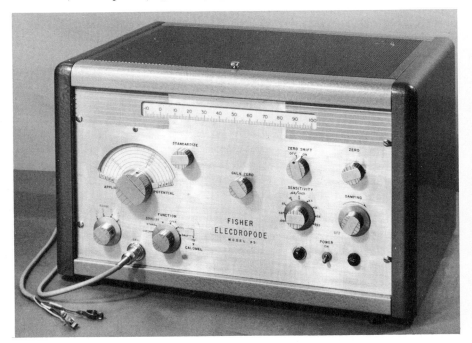

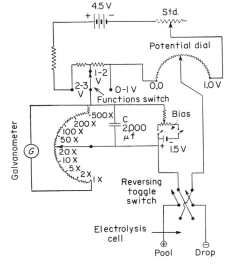

Fig. 25-14. The Fisher Elecdropode and schematic circuit diagram. (Courtesy of Fisher Scientific Co.)

batteries or vacuum tubes. A silicon zener diode provides the necessary potential control. Sensitivities of these instruments range from 0.025 to 0.003 μa per division (on galvanometer scale). Automatic pen-recording instruments such as Sargent model XXI, Leeds & Northrup, Tinsley, are considerably more expensive. They are ideal for routine control and research purposes.

Though it is convenient to have available a completely assembled and self-contained instrument, an instrument can be easily assembled from readily available components.[5] A typical circuit is shown in Fig. 25-15. A suitable potentiometer is a circular slidewire or a 10-turn Heliopot potentiometer, the resistance of which should be 50–100 Ω. The potential drop across the slidewire is adjusted to any desired value by inserting one or two dry cells and regulating the voltage by means of a radio potentiometer of from 100 to 300 Ω placed in series. A 0- to 3-V voltmeter readable to ± 0.01 V adequately measures the voltage span. To measure the current, a galvanometer ranging in sensitivity between 0.005 and 0.01 μamp/mm scale deflection is satisfactory. The shunt for the galvanometer can be an Ayrton shunt or two ordinary 1000-Ω resist-

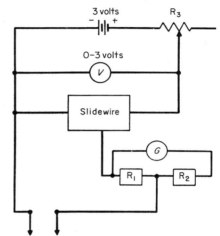

Fig. 25-15. Basic circuit for obtaining current-voltage curves.

ance boxes connected as shown. Keeping the total resistance at some fixed value, for example, $R_1 + R_2 = 1000$, the sensitivity of the galvanometer circuit will be given by $(S_g R_1)/(R_1 + R_2)$, where S_g is the sensitivity of the galvanometer alone.

General Analytical Considerations

Spacing of Multiple Wave Formations

When two or more reducible substances are present in a solution, a minimum separation of 200 mV between half-waves is considered necessary for clear, unambiguous interpretation of curves. If the difference is less, the waves must be spaced farther apart by some means. When a wave in advance of the substance to be determined is due to a major component of the sample (even though separated by a sufficient difference in half-wave potential), a preliminary separation of one or the other is usually necessary. The removal of a major component does not have to be quantitative if it is done only to minimize the magnitude of its wave.

Sometimes the interfering substance may be removed by precipitation. In the separation of zinc and nickel, which have nearly identical half-wave potentials in neutral chloride solution, an alkali hydroxide can be employed as the supporting electrolyte. Zincate ions are reducible, whereas nickel is precipitated as the hydroxide. A portion of the clear supernatant liquid is taken for analysis. In separations of this type the possibilities of adsorption and coprecipitation must always be considered.

In many instances interferences from overlapping waves can be eliminated by proper choice of supporting electrolyte. This is done often by incorporating a suitable complex-forming agent in the supporting electrolyte. Taking nickel and zinc again as an example, the two waves are adequately separated in a 1 N ammonium-aqueous ammonia buffer and appear at -1.06 and -1.33 V, respectively, vs the SCE.

A case often encountered is the simultaneous determination of two constituents which are present in very different concentrations. If the minor constituent is reduced at a lower potential, it is quite simple to record this wave at suitable current sensitivity, and subsequently to reduce the sensitivity to record the wave due to the major constituent. When the predominant constituent produces a wave well in advance of the others, it should be removed. Electrolysis at a controlled potential is convenient. The limiting cathode potential can be ascertained from an examination of the polarographic waves, particularly if a mercury cathode is employed. Subsequently the minor constituents in the sample are determined in the residual solution. Difficulties of this type can also be eliminated by means of a compensator or bias circuit built into the polarographic circuit. The compensator consists merely of an auxiliary battery and potential divider arrangement designed to send through the galvanometer a current opposing the normal diffusion current arriving from the polarographic cell. In operation the interfering wave is allowed to develop completely, then the compensator adjusted until the galvanometer deflection is reduced to the original null position. Now the sensitivity of the galvanometer can be increased to measure the wave of the minor constituent. A typical compensator or bias circuit is incorporated in the schematic circuit shown in Fig. 25-13.

In practice, when the wave given by a major constituent has been suppressed by means of a compensator circuit, the galvanometer oscillations retain their same magnitude as formerly on the diffusion current plateau. When the sensitivity is increased the oscillations also increase, as shown in Fig. 25-16. To avoid oscillations of excessively large amplitude, a condenser can be connected across the galvanometer terminals to damp the oscillations. The proper size (generally a 1000- to 2000-μf, electrolytic type) can be calculated[7] or determined experimentally. Improper damping will distort the current readings. By combining a compensator circuit with condenser damping, usually two constituents whose concentrations are in the ratio of 50 to 1 may be determined.

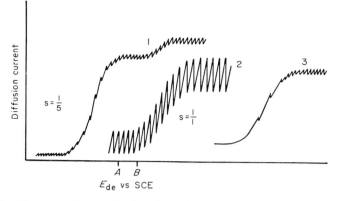
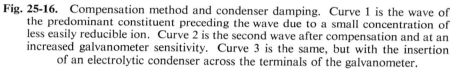

Fig. 25-16. Compensation method and condenser damping. Curve 1 is the wave of the predominant constituent preceding the wave due to a small concentration of less easily reducible ion. Curve 2 is the second wave after compensation and at an increased galvanometer sensitivity. Curve 3 is the same, but with the insertion of an electrolytic condenser across the terminals of the galvanometer.

Removal of Dissolved Oxygen

Oxygen is easily reduced at the dropping electrode. It takes place in two steps: at -0.1 and at -0.9 V vs the SCE. Consequently, it becomes necessary to remove dissolved air from most analysis solutions. This is commonly done by bubbling an inert gas, hydrogen or nitrogen, through the solution for 10–15 min immediately before recording the polarogram. Use of gas dispersion tubes materially shortens the time. Commercial nitrogen or hydrogen can be used without further purification except when all traces of oxygen must be removed. These traces can be removed by passing the tank gas first through chromous sulfate in 1 N sulfuric acid or through an ammoniacal solution containing strips of copper metal. Each solution is followed by a water rinse.

Measurement of Wave Heights

To evaluate a polarogram quantitatively, the height of each wave must be measured. With a well-defined polarographic wave whose limiting current plateau parallels the residual current curve, measurement of the diffusion current is relatively simple. In the exact procedure the actual residual current curve is determined separately with the supporting electrolyte alone. Subtracting the residual current from the average value of the current on the diffusion-current plateau (both measured at the same voltage) provides the diffusion current. For subsequent electroactive substances, the diffusion current would be found by subtracting both the residual current and all preceding diffusion currents. Fig. 25-7 A illustrates the method of measurement.

Simpler, though less exact, is the extrapolation method. The portion of the residual-current curve preceding the initial rise of the wave is extrapolated and a line parallel to it is drawn through the average value of the galvanometer oscillations on the succeeding diffusion-current plateau, as shown in Fig. 25-7 B. Preceding diffusion-current regions can be utilized as pseudo-residual current curves for succeeding waves.

For ill-defined waves the point method is to be preferred. By this method the wave height is defined as the vertical distance at the half-wave potential between the straight lines approximating the residual and diffusion current regions. The procedure is illustrated in Fig. 25-17. Follow in order of the

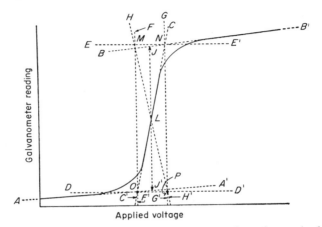

Fig. 25-17.   Measurement of wave height by the point method.

alphabetical sequence the construction of the various lines and the box *MNOP* from which the half-wave potential *L* is estimated. By this method of measurement no linear response between wave height and concentration can be expected.

Applications to Organic Compounds

Reversible organic reductions are confined largely to quinones and a few other functional systems such as the phenylene diamines, which resemble quinones in forming resonating systems. Most of the applications to organic compounds have involved irreversible reductions; a sampling of the organic functional groups which have been found reducible are listed in Table 25-1.

Awareness of the extent to which organic functional groups can be converted to an active polarographic group can markedly extend the method. A number of examples are enumerated in Table 25-2. Generally, the polarographic method will not distinguish between members of a homologous series, except perhaps between the first member and the remainder. However, the shift of half-wave potential with structure and substitution, as well as with pH and ionic strength, often alter conditions so that analysis is made possible. For example, the reduction potential of the disulfide group linked to a phenyl group is -0.5 V vs SCE and to an alkyl group is -1.25 V.

Table 25-1	Organic Functional Groups Which Are Reducible					
>C=O	ketone	—C≡N	nitrile	—NO₂	nitro
—CHO	aldehyde	—N=N—	azo	—NO	nitroso
>C=C<	alkene	—NO=N—	azoxy	—NHOH	hydroxylamine
φ—C≡C—	aryl alkyne	—O—O—	peroxy	—ONO	nitrite
>C=N—	azomethine	—S—S—	disulfide	—ONO₂	nitrate

Also dibromides, aryl halide, alpha-halogenated ketone or aryl methane, conjugated alkenes and ketones, polynuclear aromatic ring systems, and heterocyclic double bond.

Table 25-2	Organic Functional Group Analysis of Nonpolarographic Active Groups

FUNCTIONAL GROUP	REAGENT	ACTIVE POLAROGRAPHIC GROUP
Carbonyl	Girard T and D	Azomethine
	Semicarbazide	Carbazide
	Hydroxylamine	Hydroxylamine
Primary amine	Piperonal	Azomethine
	CS₂	Dithiocarbonate (anodic)
	Cu₃(PO₄)₂ suspension	Copper(II) amine
Secondary amine	HNO₂	Nitrosoamine
Alcohols	Chromic acid	Aldehyde
1,2-Diols	Periodic acid	Aldehyde
Carboxyl	(Transform to thiouronium salts)	—SH (anodic)
Phenyl	Nitration	—NO₂

Oxygen Determinations

Several compact portable units are available for the determination of dissolved oxygen. The oxygen sensing probe is an electrolytic cell with gold (or platinum) cathode separated from a tubular silver anode by an epoxy casting. The anode is electrically connected to the cathode by electrolytic gel, and the entire chemical system is isolated from the environment by a thin gas-permeable membrane (often Teflon). A potential of approximately 0.8 V (from a solid-state power supply) is applied between the electrodes. The oxygen in the sample diffuses through the membrane, is reduced at the cathode with the formation of the oxidation product—silver oxide—at the silver anode. The resultant current is proportional to the amount of oxygen reduced. To counteract temperature effects, a thermistor is built into the sensor. The analyzer unit operates over the range from 0.2 to 50 ppm of dissolved oxygen. Gases that reduce at -0.8 V will interfere; these include the halogens and SO_2, and H_2S contaminates the electrodes.

Evaluation Methods

Direct Comparison

The direct comparison method calls for recording the current-voltage curves of a standard solution of the test ion under the same conditions as the unknown. Then, using the Ilkovic equation in the simplified form, the diffusion current quotient, i_d/C, can be computed. When divided into the height of the unknown wave, it yields the concentration of test ion in the unknown. The unknown will be most accurately determined when the concentration of the comparison standard is about the same as that of the unknown, particularly if a nonlinear relation exists or is suspected to exist between wave height and concentration. The quantity of standard can be estimated by remembering that the diffusion current of simple ions in neutral or acid solution is about 4 μa per milliequivalent of reducible ion.

Relative measurements of this type do not demand knowledge of the exact capillary characteristics, only that they remain constant during the comparison. Likewise, temperature need not be controlled at any fixed value, merely maintained the same for all solutions. Immersion of the solution cells in a large container of water is adequate. However, it is important that the composition of the supporting electrolyte and the amount of maximum suppressor added be identical for the unknown and the comparison standard.

Table 25-3	*Calibration Data for Aluminum by Direct Comparison and Absolute Method*

The table presents various concentrations of aluminum in 0.2N sodium acetate of pH 4.7 plus 0.6 millimolar Pontachrome Violet SW. $m^{2/3}t^{1/6} = 2.31$. Diffusion currents (second wave) are measured at a potential of -0.6 volt vs. S.C.E. and corrected for the diffusion current of unreacted dye measured at -0.35 volt.

ALUMINUM, MILLIMOLAR	i_d, MICROAMPERES		i_d/C, MICROAMPERES MMOLE^{-1} LITER	$I_d = \dfrac{i_d}{Cm^{2/3}t^{1/6}}$
	OBSERVED	CORRECTED		
0	0.050†	—	—	—
0.00925	0.165	0.115	12.4	5.36
0.01850	0.256	0.216	12.2	5.28
0.0370	0.495	0.445	12.0	5.19
0.0550	0.660	0.610	12.2	5.28
0.0740	0.892	0.842	11.4	4.93
0.111	1.39	1.34	12.0	5.20
0.148	1.82	1.77	12.0	5.19
0.185	2.21	2.16	11.7	5.04
0.222	2.64	2.59	11.7	5.05
0.259	3.17	3.12	12.0	5.19
		Average	12.0 ± 0.2	5.17 ± 0.10

†Correction for observed zero current.
[From H. H. Willard and J. A. Dean, *Anal. Chem.*, **22**, 1264 (1950).]

When analyzing a large number of similar samples, it may be convenient to construct a calibration graph from which concentrations of future unknowns may be read. Several points on the graph should be verified each time a set of samples is run.

A typical set of data illustrating the direct comparison method is assembled in Table 25-3 and partially used to construct Fig. 25-18.

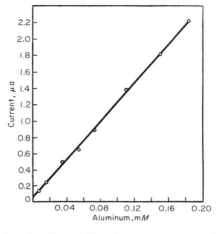

Fig. 25-18. Calibration curve for aluminum. Data from Table 25-3.

Standard Addition

If a single analysis is to be performed, it is possible to dispense with the preparation of a known solution which is the exact duplicate of the test solution. The polarogram of the unknown solution is recorded, then a known volume of a standard solution of the test ion is added and the polarogram repeated. From the increase in the diffusion current, the original concentration can be computed by interpolation. For the unknown solution,

$$i_d = KC_x = h \qquad (25\text{-}17)$$

and after the addition of v ml of a standard solution, whose concentration of test ion is C_s to V ml of unknown,

$$KC_x\left(\frac{V}{V+v}\right) + KC_s\left(\frac{v}{V+v}\right) = H \qquad (25\text{-}18)$$

Solving for the concentration of the unknown,

$$C_x = \frac{-vC_s h}{hV - H(V+v)} \qquad (25\text{-}19)$$

For maximum precision the amount of standard solution added should be sufficient to about double the original wave height. (See also page 343 in Chapter 11.)

Internal Standard Method

The internal standard method, also called the "pilot ion" method, is based on the fact that the relative wave heights of two electroactive substances in a particular supporting electrolyte are constant for equal concentrations and independent of capillary characteristics. Even small temperature differences between analyses can be tolerated. In practice, one element is used to standardize the dropping assembly and all the other diffusion-current constants for other elements are measured relative to this same ion. Thus, it is only necessary to add a known concentration of the reference ion to an unknown; and from the wave heights of the unknown and the reference ion, the concentration of the unknown can be computed:

$$C_x = \frac{i_x (I_d)_s}{i_s (I_d)_x} \cdot C_s \qquad (25\text{-}20)$$

This method simplifies work when different capillary systems must be used. Only a single standard solution is required for a series of test substances once the internal standard ratio, $(I_d)_s / (I_d)_x$, has been established. Whenever the nature or the concentration of the supporting electrolyte is altered in any manner, the ratio must be determined anew. The method has only limited application because only a small number of ions give sufficiently well-defined waves for use as internal standards. In multicomponent mixtures there may not be sufficient difference among existing half-wave potentials to introduce another wave.

Absolute Method

The absolute method utilizes Eq. 25-7. The diffusion current constant, I_d, is independent of the individual capillary but varies with the composition of the supporting electrolyte. The temperature must be rigidly controlled at 25°C, all boundary conditions under which the Ilkovic equation is valid must be adhered to, and the capillary characteristics must be determined for each dropping assembly employed. In addition, the galvanometer must be accurately calibrated, since the method employs absolute current measurements. Thus, although quantitative work without a calibration curve or a standard solution is possible, in many cases the conditions and the solutions are not sufficiently defined for this method to yield results with any degree of accuracy. Column 5 of Table 25-3 contains a typical set of calculated values of the diffusion current constant.

LABORATORY WORK

Assembling the Equipment and Solutions

Prepare a dropping mercury electrode assembly similar to the one shown in Fig. 25-3. Fill the leveling bulb half-full of clean mercury. Insert a 7- to 10-cm length of capillary and open the stopcock or release the screw hose-clamp. Raise the leveling bulb until drops of mercury begin to form at the tip of the capillary.

Allow the drops to form continuously during the entire laboratory period. When a laboratory period is completed, rinse the capillary with distilled water and then dry by blotting with filter paper. Insert the capillary through an inverted cone of filter paper and clamp vertically over a small beaker. Lower the leveling bulb until the drops cease to form.

MERCURY IS POISONOUS. Use a large tray under the dropping electrode assembly and be sure to clean up all spilled mercury.

Cover the bottom of the electrolysis cell with a $\frac{1}{8}$-in. layer of mercury. Pour in enough solution to fill the cell within a $\frac{1}{2}$-in. from the top, and place the cell in position so that the capillary is dipping into the solution. Adjust the height of the mercury reservoir until the drops detach themselves from the capillary every 2–4 sec.

In place of the mercury pool, an external reference electrode may be connected to the cell by means of a salt bridge. The area of the mercury surface should be at least 10 cm².

Removal of Dissolved Oxygen. Connect the gas-inlet tube to a tank of nitrogen, and bubble gas through the solution for 10 min. Removal of oxygen is complete within 1 to 2 min when a filter stick is used to disperse the nitrogen. When necessary or desired, traces of oxygen which may be present in tank gases can be removed by passing the gas through a gas-washing bottle filled with a solution of chromous chloride, or alkaline pyrogallol, or ammoniacal cuprous chloride and a second washing bottle filled with distilled water to remove any spray.

Gelatin Solution, 0.2 percent. Dissolve 0.2 g of gelatin in 100 ml of freshly boiled water that has been cooled to 60°. Add a small crystal of thymol and stopper firmly with a rubber stopper.

Adjustment of the galvanometer Index. Flip the toggle switch marked LAMP to ON and bring the galvanometer index to the desired position by rotating the COMPENSATOR control UPSCALE or DOWNSCALE.

Use of the Sensitivity Switch. The markings on the CURRENT MULTIPLIER are factors by which the galvanometer deflections must be multiplied to obtain the reading for full sensitivity, 1. If the galvanometer index goes off-scale as the current-voltgage curve is recorded, decrease the galvanometer sensitivity by turning the CURRENT MULTIPLIER switch to a larger number.

Selection of the Applied emf. Rotate the EMF switch clockwise to connect the batteries in the bridge circuit. Continue the rotation clockwise until the voltage desired is applied across the bridge. If a VOLTMETER is located on the front panel, it indicates the total voltage applied across the slide wire.

Plotting the Current-voltage Curve. Set the CURRENT MULTIPLIER to 10, the APPLIED POTENTIAL dial to 0, the VOLTMETER reading to 1.0 V, the toggle switch marked DME to "−", and the toggle switch marked GALV to "+". Increase the applied emf by rotating the APPLIED POTENTIAL dial in steps of 25 or 50 (0.025 or 0.050 V). Record the maximum (or preferably the average) galvanometer index reading each time.

When the APPLIED POTENTIAL dial reaches 1000 (1.000 V), return it to 500 and advance the BRIDGE EMF control until the voltmeter reads 2.00 V. Again increase the applied emf by rotating the APPLIED POTENTIAL dial from 500 (now 1.000 V) to 1000 (2.000 V). The span of the APPLIED POTENTIAL dial is now 0–2 V.

Use of the Compensator. The COMPENSATOR control may be used to balance out a large diffusion current when it precedes the current-voltage curve of an ion of interest. Adjust the BRIDGE EMF and APPLIED POTENTIAL dial to a value at which the interfering current-voltage curve is completely developed, then rotate the COMPENSATOR control DOWNSCALE until the galvanometer index is brought back to the reading that corresponded to the residual current. Decrease the CURRENT MULTIPLIER setting and plot the current-voltage curve at the increased galvanometer sensitivity.

Note. In these generalized instructions names of operational controls may differ among the various instruments. Compare the manufacturer's directions with his circuit diagram and the diagram in Fig. 25-13.

EXPERIMENT 25-1   EVALUATION METHODS: DIRECT COMPARISON

1. Prepare a series of standard solutions, each containing 20 ml of 1 M potassium chloride, 2.5 ml of 0.2 percent gelatin, and these quantities of 0.01 M cadmium sulfate solution: 25, 20, 15, 10, 5, 2, and 0 ml. Dilute to the mark in 100-ml volumetric flasks and mix well.

2. Pour the strongest solution into the electrolysis cell and run the polarogram from 0.4 to 0.8 V negative to the pool or reference electrode. For the remainder of the standards, determine only the current flowing before the cadmium wave develops and the diffusion current of the fully developed wave.

3. Transfer aliquots of the unknown solution containing 0.10 to 0.25 mM of cadmium into 100 ml volumetric flasks. Add 20 ml of 1 M potassium chloride and 2.5 ml of 0.2 percent gelatin and dilute to volume. Measure the residual current and the diffusion current as before.

4. Plot a calibration curve on a sheet of graph paper. The ordinate will be the diffusion current in microamperes or arbitrary scale divisions and the abscissa the corresponding cadmium concentration. Correct all observed diffusion current values by subtracting the value of the residual current found for the blank or by the extrapolation method. (Both are illustrated in Fig. 25-7.) From your calibration curve determine the concentration of the unknown.

Note. At the discretion of the instructor, other metal salt solutions may be substituted for cadmium sulfate.

EXPERIMENT 25-2   EVALUATION METHODS: STANDARD ADDITION

1. Pipet into a 100-ml. volumetric flask 10 ml of the unknown cadmium solution. Add 20 ml of 1 M potassium chloride solution, 2.5 ml of 0.2 percent gelatin solution, and dilute to the mark. Mix well.

2. Transfer a known volume of the solution to the electrolysis cell. Run the current-voltage curve from 0.4–0.8 V negative with respect to the reference electrode.

3. Estimate the concentration of the unknown from the fact that the diffusion current of aquo ions in neutral or acid solution is about 4 μa per milliequivalent of reducible ion. Pipet into the electrolysis cell a volume of standard cadmium solution which contains approximately the same amount of cadmium that is estimated to be present in the original solution but multiplied by the fraction $\frac{25}{100}$ or $\frac{50}{100}$, whichever numerator corresponds to the volume transferred to the electrolysis cell in the preceding step.

4. Run the current-voltage curve as before. Calculate the concentration of the unknown solution from Eq. 25-19.

EXPERIMENT 25-3   EVALUATION METHODS: INTERNAL STANDARD
                   METHOD

1. Pipet into a 100-ml volumetric flask 10 ml of a cadmium stock solution and 10 ml of a zinc stock solution, each about 0.01 M. Add 20 ml of 1 M potassium chloride solution, 2.5 ml of 0.2 percent gelatin solution, and dilute to the mark. Mix well.

2. Transfer a portion of the solution to the electrolysis cell. Run the current-voltage curves between 0.4 and 1.5 V negative with respect to the reference electrode. Determine the diffusion current for the cadmium and the zinc wave, respectively.

3. Pipet into a separate 100 ml volumetric flask 10 ml of the unknown cadmium solution and 10 ml of the same zinc stock solution. Add 20 ml of 1 M potassium chloride solution, 2.5 ml of 0.2 percent gelatin solution, and dilute to the mark. Mix well.

4. Transfer a portion of the second solution to an electrolysis cell. Run the current-voltage curves between -0.4 and -1.5 V as before. Determine the diffusion current for the cadmium and zinc waves. Calculate the concentration of the unknown solution from Eq. 25-20 and with the information obtained in steps 2 and 4.

Note. If the experiment seems somewhat artificial to the student, suggest that the drop rate of the mercury issuing from the capillary be altered between steps 2 and 4. Also suggest to the student that he calculate the concentration of the unknown solution by substituting the values for the diffusion current constant of the cadmium and zinc ions into Eq. 25-20. Appendix B lists these constants.

EXPERIMENT 25-4   CATHODIC, ANODIC, AND MIXED CURRENT-VOLTAGE CURVES

1. To a series of three 150-ml beakers add 50 ml of 1 M sodium citrate solution and 2.5 ml of 0.2 percent gelatin solution. Remove dissolved oxygen from the second and third solution before proceeding.

2. To the first beaker add 10 ml of 0.01 M ferric ammonium sulfate solution; to the second add 10 ml of 0.01 M ferrous ammonium sulfate solution; and to the third add 5 ml each of the ferrous and ferric solutions. Adjust each solution to pH 5.6. Transfer the contents of each beaker to 100-ml volumetric flasks and dilute to the mark. Mix well.

3. Run the current-voltage curves from $+0.2$ to -0.5 V with respect to the reference electrode. To plot the anodic portions of each curve reverse the connections to the galvanometer or initially adjust the galvanometer index to the mid-point of its scale when only the supporting electrolyte is in the electrolysis cell. To employ positive values of applied emf reverse the leads to the dropping electrode and pool or reference electrode. The series of current-voltage curves will resemble Fig. 25-12.

Notes

The ferrous ammonium sulfate solution must be prepared fresh each time using water that has been de-aerated. Even with these precautions a small cathodic wave due to ferric ion may appear on the current-voltage curve.

The half-wave potentials of the three curves will not be exactly the same unless a correction is made for the iR drop within the electrolysis cell. If this correction is attempted, remember the signs of the diffusion currents: positive for cathodic currents and negative for anodic currents.

EXPERIMENT 25-5   ANALYSIS OF A COPPER-BASE ALLOY[6]

Lead, tin, nickel and zinc are to be determined by the standard addition method. The major portion of the copper is removed from the dissolved sample, and lead is determined in one aliquot of the residual solution and tin in a second aliquot. Nickel and zinc are determined on a second sample from which copper, tin, and lead have been removed. Suitable solutions will be available if copper and tin plus lead were deposited electrolytically at controlled cathode potentials (see Experiments 23-1A and 23-1B) Synthetic solutions that simulate the metal contents of the alloy may be employed if the electrolytic separations were not carried out. In the latter event a pseudo-alloy solution is prepared that contains 4–20 mg each of lead and tin, 2–4 mg of nickel, and 4–100 mg of zinc, in a total volume of 100 ml.

Lead. Transfer a 25-ml aliquot of the synthetic solution to a 100-ml volumetric flask. Add 4.8 g of sodium hydroxide pellets, 2.5 ml of 0.2 percent gelatin, and dilute to the mark. Mix well. Transfer exactly 25 ml of the solution to the electrolysis cell. Run the current-voltage curve from 0.6 to 0.9 V negative with respect to a SCE (approximately 0.5–0.8 V negative with respect to a mercury pool in contact with 1 M sodium hydroxide solution).

Estimate the concentration of lead in the 25 ml aliquot from the fact that the diffusion current is about 4 μa per milliequivalent of lead. Evaluate the amount of lead present by the standard addition method.

Tin. Transfer a 25-ml aliquot of the synthetic solution to a 100-ml volumetric flask. Add 21 g of ammonium chloride, 6.6 ml of 12 M hydrochloric acid, and dilute to about 90 ml. Shake until all the salt has dissolved, warming if necessary. Add 2.5 ml of 0.2 percent gelatin solution and dilute to the mark. Mix well. Transfer exactly 25 ml of the solution to the electrolysis cell, Run the current-voltage curve from 0 to 0.7 V negative with respect to a SCE.

Estimate the amount of tin in the 25-ml aliquot from the diffusion current of the second wave. Subtract the diffusion current previously found for lead alone, since the half-wave potential of lead is virtually coincident with that of the second tin wave in the 4 M ammonium chloride plus 1 M hydrochloric acid-supporting electrolyte. Evaluate the amount of tin present by the standard addition method.

To correct the diffusion current of the second tin wave for the contribution of the coincident lead wave, multiply the diffusion current of lead found in the sodium hydroxide-supporting electrolyte by 1.036 and subtract the result from the total diffusion current due to tin plus lead. The factor 1.036 is the ratio of the diffusion current constants of lead in the ammonium chloride-hydrochloric acid medium and the sodium hydroxide medium, namely 3.52/3.40.

Nickel and Zinc. Transfer a 25-ml aliquot of the synthetic solution from which tin and lead are absent to a 100-ml volumetric flask. Add 25 ml of a supporting electrolyte stock solution, which contains 43 g of ammonium chloride and 270 ml of concentrated aqueous ammonia, made up to 1 liter. Add 1 g of sodium sulfite, 2.5 ml of 0.2 percent gelatin solution, and dilute to the mark. Mix well and allow to stand 10 minutes to let the sulfite react with the dissolved oxygen. Transfer exactly 25 ml of the solution to the electrolysis cell. Run the current-voltage curves from 0.8 to 1.6 V negative with respect to the SCE.

If the height of the first wave due to nickel ions is much smaller than that of the second wave due to zinc ions, run a second current-voltage curve from 0.8 to 1.3 V negative with respect to the SCE at an increased galvanometer sensitivity.

Estimate the amounts of nickel and zinc in the 25 ml aliquot from the respective diffusion currents, and evaluate the amount of nickel and zinc present by the standard addition method.

Notes. When working with the alkaline-supporting electrolytes, one observes a large diffusion current that begins at zero applied emf. Proceed as follows: Adjust the applied emf to 0.6 V negative to the reference electrode and return the galvanometer index to zero by means of the diffusion current compensator (or bias control).

If the residual solutions from the electrodeposition experiments are employed, transfer the residual solutions to 250-ml volumetric flasks and dilute to the mark. Use 50 ml aliquots in each of the above steps.

Problems

1. Compare the evaluation methods with respect to (a) applicability to routine analyses of similar type samples, (b) applicability to routine analyses of samples of widely varying composition but for the analysis of a few constituents by polarography, and (c) applicability to occasional analyses of a wide variety of samples and for a wide variety of constituents.

2. Discuss the factors that may contribute to the observed polarographic limiting current of a single ion in addition to the diffusion current. How may all the undesirable factors be eliminated?

3. Polarographic curves resemble potentiometric titration curves. When might polarography yield useful data not obtainable by potentiometric methods?

4. The data below were obtained at 25°C. with cadmium ion in a supporting electrolyte composed of 0.1 M potassium chloride and 0.005 percent gelatin. Galvanometer deflections were measured at -1.00 V vs SCE. The galvanometer sensitivity was stated as 0.0055 μa/mm; the current multiplier was set at 50. $t = 2.47$ sec; $m = 3.30$ mg sec^{-1}.

Cd^{++}, mM	i_d, mm
0.00	4.5
0.20	11.0
0.50	21.0
1.00	34.5
1.50	54.0
2.00	70.5
2.50	86.5

Plot the calibration curve on a sheet of graph paper with the ordinate the diffusion current in microamperes (or arbitrary scale divisions) and the abscissa the corresponding cadmium concentration. From the calibration curve determine the concentration of an unknown solution, prepared similarly, which has a diffusion current of 39.5 mm after correction for the residual current.

5. Exactly 25.0 ml of the unknown solution, which gave a diffusion current of 39.5 mm in Problem 4, has been transferred to the polarographic cell. To this solution is added exactly 5.0 ml of 0.0100 M cadmium solution. The corrected diffusion current is now 88 mm. Calculate the concentration of the unknown cadmium solution.

6. At the time the unknown cadmium solution was prepared in Problem 4 a second solution was also prepared, identical in all respects except that it also contained zinc ions, 10.0 ml of 0.0100 M zinc in a total volume of 100 ml. The corrected diffusion current was 32 mm for the zinc wave. Calculate the concentration of the unknown cadmium solution by the internal standard method. Obtain the necessary diffusion current constants from Appendix B.

7. Calculate the concentration of cadmium in the unknown solution of Problem 4 by the absolute method. Necessary data will be found in Problem 4 and Appendix B.

Bibliography

Delahay, P., *New Instrumental Methods in Electrochemistry*, Interscience, New York, 1954.

Heyrovsky, J., *Polarographischer Praktikum*, J. Springer, Berlin, 1948.

Kolthoff, I. M., and J. J. Lingane, *Polarography*, 2d ed., Interscience, New York, 1952.

Meites, L., *Polarographic Techniques*, Interscience, New York, 1955.

Milner, G. W. C., *The Principles and Application of Polarography*, Wiley, New York, 1957.

Müller, O. H., *The Polarographic Method of Analysis*, 2d ed., Chemical Education Publishing Co., Easton, Pa., 1951.

Müller, O. H., in *Physical Methods of Organic Chemistry*, 3rd ed., A. Weissberger (Ed.), Vol. I, Part IV, Chapter 48, Interscience, New York, 1960.

Schmidt, H., and M. von Stackelberg, *Modern Polarographic Methods* (translated by R. E. W. Maddison), Academic Press, New York, 1963.

Literature Cited

1. Buckley, F., and J. K. Taylor, *Trans. Am. Electrochem. Soc.*, **87**, 463 (1945); also *J. Res. Natl. Bur. Std.* (U.S.), **34**, 97 (1945).
2. Heyrovsky, J., and J. Forejt, *Z. physik. Chem.*, **193**, 77 (1943).
3. Heyrovsky, J., and M. Shikata, *Rec. trav. chim.*, **44**, 496 (1925).
4. Ilkovic, D., *Coll. Czech. Chem. Commun.*, **6**, 498, (1934).
5. Lingane, J. J., *Anal. Chem.*, **21**, 47 (1949).
6. Lingane, J. J., *Ind. Eng. Chem., Anal. Ed.*, **18**, 429 (1946).
7. Lingane, J. J., and H. Kerlinger, *Ind. Eng. Chem., Anal. Ed.*, **12**, 750 (1940).
8. Lingane, J. J., and B. A. Loveridge, *J. Am. Chem. Soc.*, **66**, 1425 (1944); ibid., **72**, 438 (1950); L. Meites and T. Meites, ibid., **73**, 395 (1951); H. Strehlow and M. von Stackelberg, *Z. Elektrochem.*, **54**, 51 (1950).

C H A P T E R | 26

Amperometric Titration Methods

The polarographic method can be used as the basis of an electrometric titration method comparable with the potentiometric, the conductometric, and the photometric methods. In this case the voltage applied across the indicator electrode and reference electrode is kept constant, and the current passing through the cell is measured and plotted against the volume of reagent added. Hence the name *amperometric titration*.

The current is measured, in general, on a diffusion-current region of a current-voltage curve. On such a region the current is independent of the potential of the indicator electrode because of an extreme state of concentration polarization at the electrode. Since at the electrode surface the concentration of material undergoing electrode reaction is maintained at a value practically equal to zero, the current is limited by the supply of fresh material to the electrode surface by diffusion. The rate of diffusion, and hence the current, is proportional to the concentration of diffusing substance in the bulk of the solution.

This technique can best be described by an example—the titration of a reducible substance, lead ion, with a non-reducible reagent, sulfate ion. A polarogram of a solution containing lead ions is represented by Curve A in Fig. 26-1. If the voltage is held at any value on the diffusion current plateau, the current will be represented by i_0. The titrant exhibits no diffusion current at the applied emf. Increments of titrant remove some of the electroactive lead ions. As the concentration of lead ions decreases, the current decreases to i_1, i_2, i_3, and finally i_r, at which point the lead ions have completely reacted and

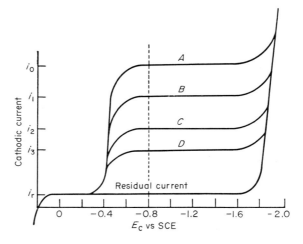

Fig. 26-1. Successive current-voltage curves of lead ion made after increments of sulfate ion were added.

the only current flowing is a residual current characteristic of the supporting electrolyte.

If successive values of the diffusion current are plotted against the volume of titrant added, the result is a straight line which levels off at the end point (Fig. 26-2). The intersection of the extrapolated branches of the titration curve gives the end point.

When both titrant and unknown give diffusion currents at the applied

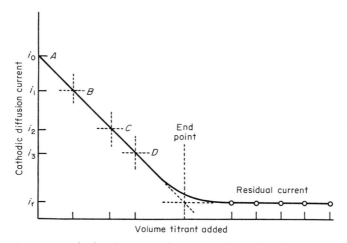

Fig. 26-2. Amperometric titration curve for the reaction of lead ions with sulfate ions. See Fig. 26-1 for corresponding current-voltage curves. Performed at $E = -0.8$ V vs SCE.

voltage chosen, the current will drop to the end point, then increase again to give a V-shape titration curve, as seen in Fig. 26-3. If the original material

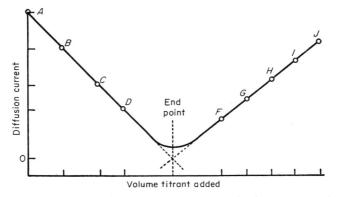

Fig. 26-3. Type of amperometric titration curve when both reactant and titrant give diffusion currents; e.g., the titration of lead ions with dichromate ions performed at $E = -0.8$ V vs SCE. See also Fig. 26-5.

does not react electrolytically, but the titrant does, a horizontal line, rising at the end point, results. This is shown in Fig. 26-4.

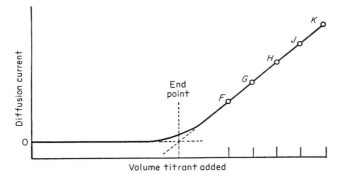

Fig. 26-4. Type of amperometric titration curve when only titrant gives a diffusion current; e.g., the titration of lead ions with dichromate ion performed at $E = 0.0$ vs SCE. in an acetate buffer of $pH = 4.2$. See also Fig. 26-5.

Methodology

If the optimum value at which to maintain the titration voltage is not known, the polarograms are determined for the materials involved, an appropriate voltage selected, and the titration carried out. As sometimes happens, a choice between two applied emf values can be made. In the titration of lead with dichromate the titration can be conducted by choosing as the voltage a value E_1 at which dichromate ions are reduced, but not lead ions. The current-voltage curves are shown in Fig. 26-5, in which the titration curve is a horizontal line,

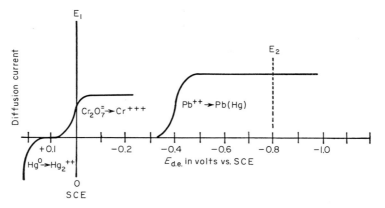

Fig. 26-5. Current-voltage curves of dichromate and lead ions shown schematically.

rising at the end point. It resembles Fig. 26-4. By shifting the cathode potential to E_2, both dichromate and lead ions are reduced. The current will drop to the end point, then increase again to give a V-shape titration curve.

In practice, the reversed L-shape type of curve, illustrated by Fig. 26-4, is preferred. Since the titrant in this case produces no current, it can be added continuously at a moderate rate until the end point is passed. This will be noted by a permanent increase in the diffusion current. Then three or four additional readings, taken after successive increments of excess titrant have been added, will establish the rising branch of the curve.[3]

Strictly speaking, a correction for dilution is necessary to attain a linear relation between current and volume of titrant, but by working with a reagent which is tenfold more concentrated than the solution being titrated, the correction becomes negligibly small. Incompleteness of reaction in the vicinity of the end point usually will not detract from the results provided reaction equilibrium is attained rapidly during the titration. Points can be selected between 0 and 50 and 150 to 200 percent of the end-point volume for the construction of the two branches of the titration curve. In these regions the common ion effect will repress dissociation and solubility of precipitates.

Apparatus

The equipment for conducting amperometric titrations is simple. Although it may be the same as for polarography, several simplifications are possible. The potential of the indicator electrode need only be selected within 0.1 V if it lies on a limiting current region of a current-voltage curve. Often the potential of a reference electrode will lie in the permissible range, so that it is necessary only to short-circuit the indicator electrode through a suitable current-measuring instrument to a reference electrode of relatively large area. A number of suitable reference electrodes are listed in Table 20-2.

No thermostat is necessary. The temperature of a solution will seldom vary appreciably during the short time, 10 min or less, necessary to conduct a titration.

The indicator electrode may be a dropping mercury electrode or a rotating metal microelectrode.[5] The latter is simple to construct. It consists of a short length of wire, usually platinum, protruding 5–10 mm from the wall of a piece of glass tubing. The latter is bent at right angles a short distance from the end of the stem so as to sweep an area of the solution with the wire. It is illustrated in Fig. 26-6. The electrode is mounted in the shaft of a motor and rotated at a constant speed of about 600 rpm. By using a rotating electrode, the diffusion layer thickness is decreased, thereby increasing the sensitivity and the rate of attainment of a steady diffusion state. The limiting current may be up to 18 or 20 times larger than that with a dropping electrode; it is proportional to the $\frac{1}{3}$ power of the number of revolutions per minute above 200 rpm.[7] A stationary electrode with a magnetic stirrer to pass the solution by the electrode exhibits the same response as a rotated electrode.

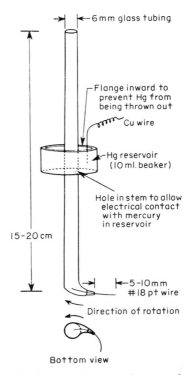

Fig. 26-6. Rotating platinum microelectrode.

The larger currents attained with a rotating electrode allow correspondingly smaller concentrations to be measured without loss of accuracy. Also the absence of drops disengaging themselves at regular intervals eliminates the charging current observed with a dropping electrode, which in turn permits the use of ordinary rugged microammeters. However, many systems whose oxidation potentials or reduction potentials lie in the range of the platinum microelectrode do not give limiting currents with a rotating electrode. And where the discharge of hydrogen interferes, a dropping mercury electrode, with its larger value of hydrogen overpotential, must be used.

The removal of oxygen is generally mandatory over most of the useful range of the dropping electrode. Nitrogen or hydrogen gas must be bubbled through the solution preceding the titration and for a minute or two after the addition of each increment of titrant. The oxidation of mercury limits the anodic range of the dropping electrode, but when applicable, the rotating electrode extends the useful range to about $+0.9$ V vs the SCE, at which point the oxidation of water to oxygen commences.

Successive Titrations

Iodide, bromide, and chloride can be successively titrated in mixtures with silver, using the rotating electrode.[4] In a 0.1–0.3 N solution of ammonia only silver iodide will precipitate when a silver solution is added. The indicator reaction is the reduction of the complex diammine silver ion. Consequently, the potential of the rotating electrode must be made negative enough to plate out silver, but must not be negative enough to give an appreciable current due to the reduction of dissolved oxygen. The range of permissible potential is strictly limited, as is evident from an examination of the current-voltage curves of diammine silver reduction and oxygen reduction using a silver-plated micro-electrode in an ammoniacal solution (Fig. 26-7). Fortunately the mercury/ mercuric iodide/potassium iodide reference electrode happens to lie in the permissible range (-0.23 V vs SCE) and can be short-circuited through the

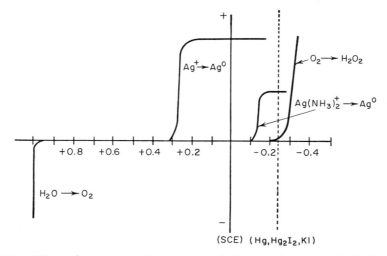

Fig. 26-7. Schematic current-voltage curves of silver and oxygen obtained with a rotated microelectrode.

current-measuring device to the rotating electrode. During the titration of iodide the current remains constant at zero, or nearly so, until the iodide ions are consumed, and then rises. After three or four points have been recorded past the end point, the solution is acidified to make it 0.8 N in nitric acid. Immediately the silver ions added in excess and now released from the ammine complex combine with the bromide ions and precipitate as silver bromide, and the current drops to zero.

The titration of bromide and chloride is carried out at a less negative potential, for in these titrations the indicator reaction is the deposition of silver from aquo-silver ions. Since the potential of the saturated calomel electrode lies in the limiting current region, it also may be short-circuited to the rotating electrode. Chloride does not interfere with the titration of bromide because silver chloride particles cause a cathodic current even in the presence of a large excess of chloride. Therefore a second rise in the current indicates the end point of the bromide titration. A chloride end point can be obtained by adding gelatin, which suppresses the current due to silver chloride, and continuing the titration until the current again rises after the chloride end point. A composite of these titration curves is shown schematically in Fig. 26-8.

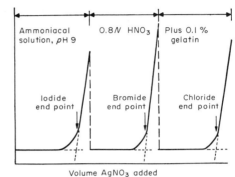

Fig. 26-8. A composite of the consecutive titration curves for a mixture of iodide, bromide and chloride.

Titrations to Zero Current

With systems in which both the oxidant and reductant yield a diffusion current, the titration curve obtained is of the type shown in Fig. 26-9. In such systems as the titration of ferric ion with titanous solution, a voltage E is impressed upon the indicator electrode, so that the diffusion current for the reduction of ferric ion is set up at the start of the titration. As the ferric ion concentration is decreased linearly, the current decreases in a similar fashion and reaches zero at the end point. When the end point is passed, a diffusion current caused by the oxidation of the titanous ion is set up. A change in slope caused by the difference in diffusion coefficients is usually evident as the lines cross the zero axis. Actually the zero axis is the value of the residual current for the supporting electrolyte, and usually will be different from zero.

Titrations of this type without any chemical reaction are also possible.[6] Cupric ions and stannous ions in a tartrate medium at pH 4 possess the current-

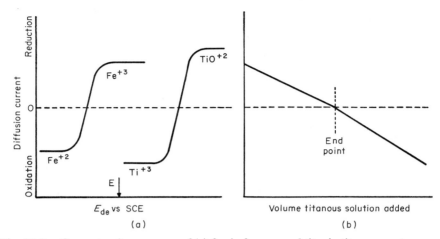

Fig. 26-9. Current-voltage curves of (a) ferric-ferrous and titanic-titanous systems and (b) amperometric titration system for ferric iron titrated with titanous solution at $E_{d.e.}$ = point E on the graph.

voltage curves schematically represented in Fig. 26-10. At an applied potential midway between the half-wave potential of the cathodic cupric/copper wave and the anodic stannous/stannic wave, the diffusion currents of both waves are fully developed. Titrating with a solution of cupric ions, the anodic diffusion current of the stannous system will be compensated by the increasing cathodic current of the cupric system. The net diffusion current will be zero at the end point.

Two Indicator Electrodes

In a modification of the usual or classical amperometric system, two similar platinum electrodes can be immersed in the titration cell. A small and constant voltage is applied to these electrodes as in the classical method. For the method to be applicable, the only requirement is that a reversible oxidation-reduction system be present either before or after the end point.

In a titration with two indicator electrodes, and when the reactant involves a reversible system, a small amount of electrolysis takes place. The amount of oxidized form reduced at the cathode is equal to that formed by oxidation of the reduced form at the anode. Both electrodes are depolarized until either the oxidized or the reduced member of the system has been consumed by a titrant. After the end point, only one electrode remains depolarized if the titrant does not involve a reversible system. The solution at this juncture resembles a one-electrode method connected to a depolarized (reference) electrode. Current flows until the end point. At and after the end point the current is zero or close to zero.

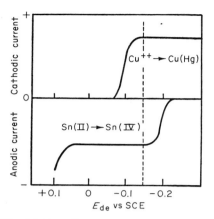

Fig. 26-10. Current-voltage curves for cathodic reduction of cupric ions and anodic oxidation of stannous ions, both in tartrate medium at $pH = 4$.

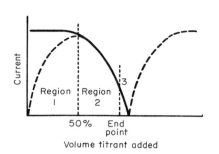

Fig. 26-11. Amperometric titration lines using two indicator electrodes. The dashed line in Region 1 is followed when the reactant is poorly poised initially; after the end point, when the titrant also forms a reversible oxidation-reduction system.

The method was introduced years ago under the name "dead stop end .point."[1] The reverse of this type of end point, and the more desirable in practice, might be called "kick off" and resembles a reversed L-shaped amperometric curve. When both the system titrated and the reagent are reversible oxidation-reduction systems, the current is zero or close to zero only at the end point, and a V-shape titration curve results.

Three regions appear in a titration curve when two indicator electrodes are employed.[2] Take for example the iodine-iodide system being titrated with thiosulfate. If a considerable quantity of iodide is in solution, the system will be well poised and the current maintains a steady value (Region 1 on Fig. 26-11). As the titration progresses and the concentration of iodine gets smaller, the concentration overpotential (polarization) at the cathode begins to play a role and the current tends to become diffusion controlled. Now the current tends to vary in proportion to the concentration of iodine remaining in the bulk of the solution. The characteristics of the line giving the change of current from the point where the system is well poised to the vicinity of the end point is represented as Region 2. Near the end point the line becomes straight as in a titration with one indicator electrode at constant applied emf. No current flows after the end point, since the thiosulfate-tetrathionate system is not a reversible couple and insufficient emf is applied to cause the oxidation of iodide ions at the anode and the discharge of hydrogen (or dissolved oxygen) at the cathode.

If the system involving the reactant is poorly poised, as it is when no iodide ions are initially present in the solution, the current at the start of the titration

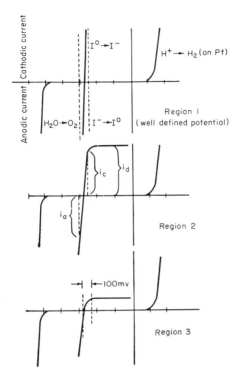

Fig. 26-12. Schematic current-voltage curves for two indicator electrodes corresponding to regions on Fig. 26-11; iodine titrated with thiosulfate with excess iodide present.

will be essentially zero. The current will rise as iodide ions are formed and will reach a maximum when the degree of completion of the titration is 50 percent. This portion of the curve is represented by the dashed lines in Region 1 of Fig. 26-11. The remainder of the titration curve will follow the descending branch.

Both one and two indicator electrode methods become identical if the applied emf in the two-indicator method is made large enough to yield a diffusion-controlled current early in the titration. Whereas some workers recommend only sufficient applied emf to balance the back emf—approximately 20 millivolts in the iodine titration—the diffusion current is not completely developed until the applied emf is 100 mV or greater, as shown in Fig. 26-12. With larger values of applied emf the value for the iR term remains negligibly small over a larger region, and thus the titration line remains straight over a longer distance in the vicinity of the end point. In effect, this places the system under a diffusion-controlled condition well in advance of the end point. A second effect is to increase the current sensitivity; but this can be varied at will by varying the size of the electrodes and the speed of stirring.

Comparison with Other Titration Methods

Several advantages of amperometric methods are immediately apparent. The equipment is simple. Since it is a relative method, there are fewer disturbing variables, as contrasted with polarography. Electrode characteristics are unimportant. There is no need to determine the capillary characteristics of a dropping electrode. Use of rotating electrodes is possible, and in fact, desirable when applicable. The lack of current oscillations when using rotating electrodes makes it possible to use rugged microammeters for measurement of the current. Accuracy is higher than in polarography because each branch of the titration curve effectively is the average of the recorded points. An error in the end point is primarily determined by the accuracy of the titrant delivery.

The method possesses greater sensitivity than conductometric and potentiometric titrations. In fact, amperometric methods are best for determining traces with good precision. Concentrations from 0.1 to 0.0001 M, and even in favorable cases to 0.000,001 M can be measured with ease and accuracy.

Applications of amperometric methods are more general than classical potentiometric methods and polarography. Many systems do not possess a measurable equilibrium potential but can be electrolyzed under an applied emf. However, even if one reactant is not oxidizable or reducible, the titration can be conducted by utilizing the oxidation-reduction characteristics of the other reactant. This method is one of the few generally applicable to precipitation reactions.

LABORATORY WORK

E X P E R I M E N T 26-1   TITRATION OF LEAD WITH DICHROMATE

1. Transfer 25 ml of 0.02 M lead nitrate solution to a polarographic cell. Add 25 ml of a supporting electrolyte, which is approximately 0.1 M in potassium nitrate, 0.17 M in acetic acid, and 0.06 M in sodium acetate. The pH should be about 4.2. (The weights of the three ingredients in the supporting electrolyte are 10, 10, and 5 g per liter, respectively.) Add 2.5 ml of 0.2 percent gelatin solution. Remove dissolved oxygen.

2. Determine the current-voltage curve of lead from 0 to 1.0 V negative, using a dropping mercury electrode and an external saturated calomel electrode of large area (> 10 cm²).

3. Plot the current-voltage curve on a sheet of graph paper.

4. Apply 0 V across the electrodes; i.e., short the dropping electrode directly through a galvanometer and shunt. Titrate with 0.05 M potassium dichromate solution from a 10-ml buret. Take readings every 0.5 ml until the galvanometer registers a definite deflection, and then take readings every 0.25 ml until several points have been obtained beyond the equivalence point.

5. Run a current-voltage curve on the solution containing excess potassium dichromate. Plot the curve on the sheet of graph paper used in step 3.

6. Repeat step 4 with the cathode at 1.0 V negative with respect to the SCE.

7. Repeat steps 4 and 6 with 0.002 M lead nitrate solution and 0.005 M potassium dichromate solution.

8. On a second graph, plot the two pairs of curves of current vs volume of titrant for steps 4, 6, and 7.

Note. See Fig. 26-5 for the current-voltage curves of lead and chromium, and Figs. 26-3 and 26-4 for the general shape of the titration curves.

E X P E R I M E N T 26-2   TITRATION OF ARSENIC WITH BROMATE

1. Transfer 25 ml of 0.001 N arsenious oxide to the polarographic cell. Add 5 ml of 12 M hydrochloric acid and 20 ml of 0.125 M potassium bromide (15 g/liter). Center a button-type platinum electrode in the cell (a 150-ml beaker) and insert the arm of the salt bridge from a saturated calomel electrode whose surface area exceeds 10 cm².

Insert a stirring bar and adjust the stirring rate between 200 and 600 rpm without producing a vortex.

2. Apply 0.2 V positive to the rotating platinum electrode (which is the anode in this titration). Titrate with 0.05 N potassium bromate solution from a 10-ml buret. At first the galvanometer will be deflected only slightly, and 1-ml increments may be added. When a definite galvanometer deflection occurs, decrease the size of the increments to 0.25 ml and secure several readings after the equivalence point.

3. Run the current-voltage curve of bromine from 0.3 V negative to 0.9 V positive vs the SCE. The excess bromate reacts with the bromide ions in the presence of hydrogen ions to form free bromine, the electroactive species undergoing reduction at the rotating platinum electrode.

4. Repeat step 2 with duplicate samples to ascertain the precision attainable by this titration method.

EXPERIMENT 26-3   USE OF TWO-INDICATOR ELECTRODE SYSTEM (DEAD STOP METHOD)

1. Transfer 5 ml of 0.01 N iodine solution to a 150-ml beaker. Add 0.1 g of potassium iodide and dilute to about 60 ml.

2. Apply 0.1 V across two similar platinum wire (or foil) electrodes. Pass the solution by the electrodes with a magnetic stirrer. Titrate with a 0.01 N sodium thiosulfate solution from a 10-ml buret. Take readings every 0.5 ml until the galvanometer index remains constant through four or five additions. Plot the results on graph paper.

In place of a conventional instrument, connect an A battery of 1.5 V through 0.1-MΩ and 7000-Ω resistors in series. Connect two similar platinum-wire electrodes to the terminals of the 7000-Ω resistor. In series with the cathode, insert a galvanometer with a sensitivity of about 0.1 $\mu a/mm$.

The titrant may be sodium arsenite; if it is, the pH of the solution must be adjusted between 4 and 9 with a suitable buffer.

Problems

1. Compare polarographic determinations with amperometric titrations with respect to (a) relative accuracy, (b) permissible range of applied potential usable, and (c) applicability of each method in regard to tppes of ions and range of concentrations.

2. Cupric ions form a precipitate with alpha-benzoinoxime in an ammoniacal solution. The $Cu(NH_3)_4^{++}$ present in a supporting electrolyte consisting of 0.05 M ammonia and 0.1 M ammonium chloride is reduced stepwise, giving polarographic waves at -0.2 and -0.5 V vs SCE. Alpha-benzoinoxime gives a polarographic wave with $E_{1/2} = -1.6$ V vs SCE. Deduce the shape of the amperometric titration curve that will be obtained at applied voltage of -0.8 V vs SCE, and also the sketch of the titration curve obtained at -1.7 V. Which potential would be preferred under normal circumstances? When nickel and zinc ions are also present in the titrating solution, which potential would be preferred?

3. Contrast amperometric titration methods with potentiometric titration methods.

Bibliography

Delahay, P., *Newer Instrumental Methods in Electrochemistry*, Interscience, New York, 1954.

Kolthoff, I. M., and J. J. Lingane, *Polarography*, 2nd ed. Interscience, New York, 1952.

Literature Cited

1. Foulk, C. W., and A. T. Bawden, *J. Am. Chem. Soc.*, **48,** 2045 (1926).
2. Kolthoff, I. M., *Anal. Chem.*, **26,** 1685 (1954); P. Delahay, *Newer Instrumental Methods in Electrochemistry*, Interscience, New York, 1954, pp. 258–264.
3. Kolthoff, I. M., and Y. D. Pan, *J. Am. Chem. Soc.*, **61,** 3402 (1939); ibid., **62,** 3332 (1940).
4. Laitinen, H. A., W. P. Jennings, and T. D. Parks, *Ind. Eng. Chem., Anal. Ed.*, **18,** 355, 358 (1946).
5. Laitinen, H. A., and I. M. Kolthoff, *J. Phys. Chem.*, **45,** 1051 (1941).
6. Lingane, J. J., *J. Am. Chem. Soc.*, **65,** 866 (1943).
7. Tsukamoto, T., T. Kambara, and I. Tachi, *Proc. First Intern. Polarographic Congr.*, *I,* 525 (1951).

Conductance Methods

Electrolytic Conductivity

Electrolytic conductivity is a measure of the ability of a solution to carry an electric current. Solutions of electrolytes conduct an electric current by the migration of ions under the influence of an electric field. Like a metallic conductor, they obey Ohm's law. Exceptions to this law occur only under abnormal conditions—for example, very high voltages or high-frequency currents. Thus, for an applied electromotive force E, maintained constant but at a value which exceeds the decomposition voltage of the electrolyte, the current i flowing between the electrodes immersed in the electrolyte will vary inversely with the resistance of the electrolytic solution R. The reciprocal of the resistance $1/R$ is called the conductance, and is expressed in reciprocal ohms, or mhos.

The standard unit of conductance is specific conductance κ, which is defined as the reciprocal of the resistance in ohms of a 1-cm cube of liquid at a specified temperature. The units of specific conductance are the reciprocal ohm-cm (or mho/cm). The observed conductance of a solution depends inversely on the distance d between the electrodes and directly upon their area A:

$$\frac{1}{R} = \kappa \frac{A}{d} \tag{27-1}$$

The electrical conductance of a solution is a summation of contributions from all the ions present. It depends upon the number of ions per unit volume of the solution and upon the velocities with which these ions move under the influence of the applied electromotive force. As a solution of an electrolyte is diluted, the specific conductance in Eq. 27-1, will decrease. Fewer ions to carry the electric current are present in each cubic centimeter of solution. However, in order to express the ability of individual ions to conduct, a function called the *equivalent conductance* is employed. It may be derived from Eq. 27-1, where A is equal to the area of two large parallel electrodes set 1 cm apart and holding between them a solution containing one equivalent of solute. If C_s is the concentration of the solution in gram equivalents per liter, then the volume of solution in cubic centimeters per equivalent is equal to $1000/C_s$, so that Eq. 27-1 becomes

$$\Lambda = 1000 \frac{\kappa}{C_s} \qquad (27\text{-}2)$$

At infinite dilution the ions theoretically are independent of each other and each ion contributes its part to the total conductance, thus

$$\Lambda_\infty = \Sigma(\lambda_+) + \Sigma(\lambda_-) \qquad (27\text{-}3)$$

where λ_+ and λ_- are the ionic conductances of cations and anions, respectively, at infinite dilution. Values for the limiting ionic conductances for many ions in water at 25°C are given in Table 27-1. The ionic conductance is a definite

Table 27-1		Equivalent Conductances of Ions at Infinite Dilution at 25°C	

CATIONS	λ_+	ANIONS	λ_-
H^+	350	OH^-	198
Li^+	39	F^-	55
Na^+	50	Cl^-	76
K^+	74	Br^-	78
NH_4^+	73	I^-	77
Ag^+	62	NO_3^-	71
Mg^{+2}	53	IO_4^-	55
Ca^{+2}	60	HCO_3^-	45
Sr^{+2}	59	Formate	55
Ba^{+2}	64	Acetate	41
Zn^{+2}	53	Propionate	36
Hg^{+2}	53	Butyrate	33
Cu^{+2}	54	Benzoate	32
Pb^{+2}	73	Picrate	30
Co^{+2}	55	SO_4^{-2}	80
Fe^{+2}	54	CO_3^{-2}	69
Fe^{+3}	68	$C_2O_4^{-2}$	74
La^{+3}	70	CrO_4^{-2}	82
Ce^{+3}	70	PO_4^{-3}	80
$CH_3NH_3^+$	59	$Fe(CN)_6^{-3}$	101
$N(Et)_4^+$	33	$Fe(CN)_6^{-4}$	111
$N(Bu)_4^+$	19		

[From B. E. Conway, *Electrochemical Data*, Elsevier, Amsterdam, 1952, p. 145; and from R. A. Robinson and R. H. Stokes, *Electrolyte Solutions*, Butterworths, London, 1955, p. 452.]

constant for each ion in a given solvent, its value depending only on the temperature. Since these are actually equivalent conductances, symbols such as $\frac{1}{2}Ba^{++}$ are sometimes employed.

Example 27-1

The equivalent conductance at infinite dilution of H_2SO_4 is

$$\Lambda_\infty = 350 + 80 = 430 \text{ ohm}^{-1} \text{ cm}^2$$

The molar conductance is given by

$$(2)\,(350) + (2)\,(80) = 860 \text{ ohm}^{-1} \text{ cm}^2$$

The conductivity of solutions is quite temperature-dependent. An increase of temperature invariably results in an increase of ionic conductance, and for most ions this amounts to about 2 percent per degree. For precise work, conductance cells must be immersed in a constant-temperature bath. It is customary to select 25°C for measurements in the United States, although generally 18°C is preferred in Europe. For relative measurements, as in titrations, the conductance cell need only attain thermal equilibrium with its surroundings before proceeding with conductance measurements.

Instrumentation

Measurement of Conductance

Conductivity measurements usually involve determination of the resistance of a column of solution. The passage of direct current through an electrolyte causes changes in the electrolyte. Hence it is necessary to work with current pulses of very short duration or with alternating current. Following the suggestion of Kohlrausch in 1868, the measurement of resistance is usually made with a rapidly alternating current of low intensity at frequencies in the audio range. Some variation of the four-arm Wheatstone bridge, shown in Fig. 27-1, is generally employed. The a-c source S may be a low-voltage tap on a 60-cycle transformer or a vacuum tube or transistor oscillator for higher frequencies (often 1000 cps). The cell C is in the arm $\overline{ab}$, and a resistance R_2 constitutes the arm $\overline{ac}$. The arms $\overline{bd}$ and $\overline{dc}$ are in the form of a calibrated slidewire resistor, R_5, and end resistors R_3 and R_4. Point d is a sliding contact which is moved back and forth until no signal can be observed in the detector D, an a-c

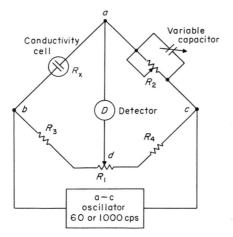

Fig. 27-1. Schematic circuit for measurement of the resistance of an electrolyte.

voltage-sensitive device such as an a-c galvanometer, earphone, cathode-ray oscilloscope, or an electron ray "eye" tube. The bridge is then balanced. To place the balance point d roughly midway between b and c, the resistance in R_2, often of the decade type, is adjusted so as to be approximately equal to that of the electrolyte in the cell C. A condition of balance of the Wheatstone bridge is that

$$\frac{R_2}{R_x} = \frac{\overline{dc}}{\overline{bd}} \tag{27-4}$$

Since the conductance cell contains electrodes separated by a dielectric, there may be appreciable cell capacitance. Provision is generally made for balancing out this capacitance by means of a variable capacitor in parallel with resistance R_2. It is adjusted arbitrarily until the detector gives a sharply defined balance point.

A typical commercial conductivity bridge is shown in Fig. 27-2. Bridge

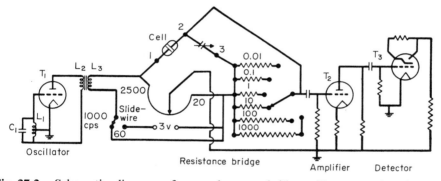

Fig. 27-2. Schematic diagram of a conductance bridge. (Courtesy of Industrial Instruments, Inc.)

current is supplied at 50 or 60 cps from the 110-V main through a voltage-reducing transformer, or at 1000 cps from a vacuum tube oscillator. High bridge frequencies are desirable when measuring low resistances. Grid current for the vacuum tube T_1 is supplied by the oscillator coil L_1 in parallel with the condenser C_1. The output coil L_2 in the plate circuit, which is coupled inductively with L_3, serves to convey the oscillations to the conductance bridge. One arm of the Wheatstone bridge is the slidewire graduated roughly logarithmically from 20 to 2500 Ω, whose contactor is a lead from the balance-indicating circuit. Balance is obtained with operation of 6 decades of resistors 0.01 to 1000 Ω each. Each decade represents a factor of 10, the decimal point in the slidewire reading. The bridge covers the range 0.2 to 2,500,000 Ω. When used with conductivity cells of appropriate cell constants, the entire range of electrolytic conductivity from deionized water to concentrated strong acids is covered.

For some applications of conductance measurements, in particular conductometric titrations, a source of inconvenience has always been the necessity of having to convert resistance readings into conductance units. In a more elaborate model of the conductivity bridge (Fig. 27-3) readings can be made directly in either ohms or micromhos. This has been achieved by reliance upon the nonlinear transfer characteristics of a specific electron tube. In the changeover from ohms to mhos the main slidewire is connected as either the adjacent or opposite arm of the bridge, with respect to the unknown.

Conductance Cells

In the design of conductance cells for precision measurements a number of factors must be taken into consideration. However, for many purposes two parallel sheets of platinum fixed in position by sealing the connecting tubes into the sides of the measuring cell are adequate. Also satisfactory are two sheet-platinum electrodes or wands immersed in the solution and held by ordinary clamps (Fig. 27-3A). These arrangements make the measured resistance independent of sample volume and proximity to surface.

There are practical limits of measured electrolytic resistance for any desired accuracy and sensitivity. The optimum appears to be in the vicinity of 500–10,000 Ω when errors are to be ± 0.1 percent. In solutions of low conductance, the electrode area A should be large and the plates spaced (d) close together; for highly conducting solutions, the area should be small and the electrodes far apart. The platinum electrodes are almost always lightly plated with platinum black to reduce the polarizing effect of the passage of current between the electrodes.

For a given cell with fixed electrodes, the ratio d/A is a constant, called the cell constant Θ. It follows that

$$\kappa = \frac{1}{R}\left(\frac{d}{A}\right) = \frac{\Theta}{R} \qquad (27\text{-}5)$$

For conductance measurements a cell is calibrated by measuring R when the cell contains a standard solution of known specific conductance, and Θ is then computed by means of Eq. 27-5. The electrolyte almost invariably used for this purpose is potassium chloride. Values of the specific conductance of potassium chloride solutions are given in Table 27-2. For conductometric titrations the

Table 27-2	Specific Conductances of Potassium Chloride Solutions

| GRAMS KCl/kg OF SOLUTION | κ IN Ω^{-1} cm^{-1} | |
	18°C	25°C
71.1352	0.09784	0.11134
7.4191	0.01117	0.01286
0.7453†	0.001221	0.001409

[From the data of G. Jones and B. C. Bradshaw, *J. Am. Chem. Soc.*, **55**, 1780 (1933).]
†Virtually 0.0100 *M*.

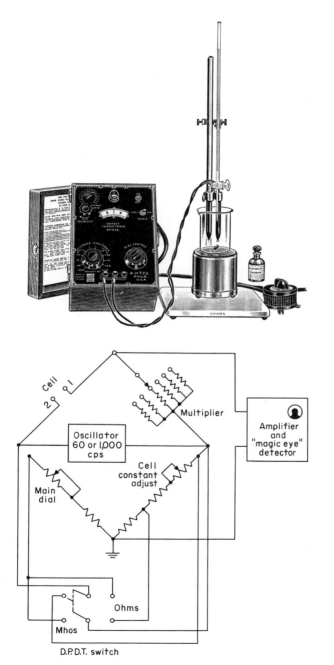

Fig. 27-3. Serfass direct-reading conductance bridge and titration assembly and schematic diagram of the bridge. (Courtesy of Industrial Instruments, Inc.)

absolute conductance need not be known, merely relative conductances as the titration progresses.

Example 27-2

When a certain conductance cell was filled with 0.0100 M solution of KCl, it had a resistance of 161.8 Ω at 25°C, and when filled with 0.005 M NaOH it had a resistance of 190 Ω.

The cell constant is
$$\Theta = (0.001409)\ (161.8) = 0.2281 \text{ cm}^{-1}$$
The specific conductance of the sodium hydroxide solution is

$$\kappa = \frac{\Theta}{R} = \frac{0.2281}{190} = 0.00120 \text{ ohm}^{-1} \text{ cm}^{-1}$$

and the equivalent conductance is

$$\Lambda = \frac{(1000)\ (0.00120)}{0.005} = 240 \text{ cm}^2 \text{ equiv}^{-1} \text{ ohm}^{-1}$$

Various types of conductivity cells are commercially available. The dip cell (Fig. 27-4) is the simplest to use whenever the liquid to be tested is in an open container. It is merely immersed in the solution to a depth sufficient to cover the electrodes and the vent holes. Liquid volumes of 5 ml or less suffice for small-diameter dip cells. A pair of individual platinum electrodes on glass wands is useful in conductance titrations. Epoxy cells are used for high-temperature work in corrosive solutions except concentrated oxidizing acids. Pipette cells permit measurements with small volumes of solution—as little as 0.01 ml in some designs.

Temperature Compensation

Conductivity varies with temperature as well as with electrolyte concentration. The temperature coefficient of conductance of electrolyte solutions in water is almost always positive and of a magnitude from about 0.5 to 3 percent per degree Centigrade. A practical means of providing temperature compensation is to introduce into the bridge circuit a resistive element which will change with temperature at the same rate as the solution under test. In different forms, this temperature compensator arm of the bridge can be a rheostat calibrated in temperature and requiring manual adjustment or a thermistor and fixed resistive network in thermal contact with the test solution, to provide automatic compensation. Regardless of the means employed, accurate compensation for temperature changes requires that the temperature coefficient of resistance of the compensator match that of the test solution.

Direct Concentration Determinations

Although the electrical conductance of a solution is a general property and is not specific for any particular ion, a number of analyses can be made by means of a measurement of conductivity. In general, the success of a measurement

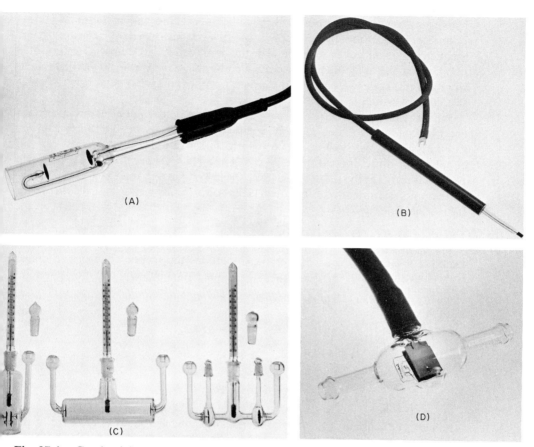

Fig. 27-4. Conductivity cells. (a) Dip type cell for medium conductance solutions; cell constants from 0.5 to 2. (b) Individual wands for conductometric titrations. (c) Fill type cell for laboratory work to contain the sample under test and to be immersed in a temperature bath. (d) Flow-through cell; cell constants from 0.01 to 0.2. (Courtesy of Industrial Instruments, Inc.)

depends upon relating the property of the sample that it is sought to estimate to the conductance of some highly conducting ion. For example, free caustic remaining in scrubbing-tower solutions can be estimated by observing the decrease in conductance of the solution. This is possible even in the presence of the salts formed upon neutralization of the alkali, because the conductance of the hydroxyl ion is approximately fivefold greater than that of any other anion. Similarly, the unusually high conductance of the hydrogen ion permits an estimation of the free acid content in acid pickling baths. The changing conductivity resulting from the absorption of gaseous combustion products in suitable solutions is frequently employed for the determination of carbon, hydrogen, oxygen and sulfur individually, in organic and in inorganic compounds. The change in conductivity is always measured in relation to an identical solution not in contact with the combustion products. On the other hand, when checking the purity of distilled or deionized water, steam distillates, rinse waters, boiler waters, or in regeneration of ion exchangers, it is the total salt content which is sought.

For all these purposes very compact and inexpensive conductance bridges are available with scales calibrated directly in pounds per gallon, parts per million, grains per gallon, or percent. For example, instruments can be supplied for direct indication such as 1–12 lb Na_2CO_3 per 100 gal., 0–40 parts per thousand salinity, 0.4–10% H_2SO_4, 0.4–12% NaOH, and 96–99.5% H_2SO_4. These units are intended for industrial monitoring as well as for following an industrial process.

Example 27-3

The scale of a conductivity bridge is inscribed from 0.005 to 2.0% H_2SO_4 in approximately a logarithmic manner. For these solutions the specific conductance ranges from about 0.00044 to 0.176 Ω^{-1} cm^{-1}. What range of resistances are involved and what cell constant is compatible.

The resistance values will range from

$$R = \frac{\theta}{0.00044} = 22,800$$

to

$$R = \frac{\theta}{0.176} = 56.9$$

A suitable cell constant is 10.0 cm^{-1}; the resistance ranging from 57 to 22,800 Ω. A cell constant of 20 cm^{-1} would also be suitable. A smaller cell constant would provide too low a resistance for the stronger acid solutions.

A cell with constant 10 cm^{-1} would have electrodes of moderate area and some distance apart; perhaps electrodes 0.5 cm^2 in area and spaced 5 cm apart.

Direct-reading conductivity meters are also available. These instruments apply a stabilized a-c voltage to the conductivity cell and a series resistor, rectify the voltage drop across the series resistor, and measure the resultant d-c signal. As long as the resistor in series with the cell is smaller in resistance, the d-c signal will be directly related to the cell resistance. Continuous indication is provided on a linear meter scale.

Conductometric Titrations

In this method the variation of the electrical conductivity of a solution during the course of a titration is followed. It is not necessary to know the actual specific conductance of the solution; any quantity proportional to it is satisfactory. This may result in considerable simplification of equipment. The titrant is introduced by means of a buret, and the conductance readings corresponding to various increments of titrant are plotted against the latter. Figure 27-5 illustrates the conductometric titration of hydrochloric acid with sodium hydroxide. As seen from Eq. 27-3, the measured conductance is a linear function of the concentration of ions present. In the example, the falling branch represents the conductance of the hydrochloric acid still present in the solution, together with that of the sodium chloride already formed. The rising branch represents the conductance of the excess base present after neutralization, together with that of the sodium chloride. Since the variation of conductance is linear, it

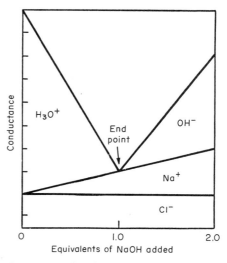

Fig. 27-5. Titration of hydrochloric acid with sodium hydroxide.

is sufficient to obtain six or eight readings, covering the range before and after the end point, and draw two straight lines through them. The point of intersection of the two branches gives the end point.

If the reaction is not quantitative, there is curvature in the vicinity of the end point. Hydrolysis, dissociation of the reaction product, or appreciable solubility in the case of precipitation reactions, will give rise to this type of curvature. At a sufficient distance on either side away from the end point, from 0 to 50 percent and between 150 and 200 percent of the equivalent volume of titrant, sufficient common ion is present to repress these effects, and the branches are straight lines. By extrapolating these portions of the lines, the position of the end point can be determined.

The acuteness of the angle at the point of intersection of the two branches will be a function of the individual ionic conductances of the reactants. In Fig. 27-5 the falling branch was steep because it involved the replacement of hydrogen ion ($\lambda_+ = 350$) by sodium ions ($\lambda_+ = 50$), and a large difference exists between the two conductances. Similarly, the rising branch on this curve is relatively steep also, but not as steep as the falling branch, because the conductance of the hydroxyl ion ($\lambda_- = 198$) is considerably smaller than the corresponding value for the hydrogen ion.

The titrant should be at least ten times as concentrated as the solution being titrated in order to keep the volume change small. If necessary, a correction may be applied:

$$\left(\frac{1}{R}\right)_{\text{actual}} = \left(\frac{V + v}{V}\right)\left(\frac{1}{R}\right)_{\text{observed}} \qquad (27\text{-}6)$$

where V is the initial volume and v is the volume of titrant added up to the particular conductance reading.

In principle, all types of reactions can be employed. The method can be used with very dilute solutions, about 0.0001 M. On the other hand, since every ion present contributes to the electrolytic conductivity, large amounts of extraneous electrolytes should be absent. In the presence of large amounts of such electrolytes, the change in conductance accompanying a reaction would be a very small part of the total conductance and would be difficult to measure with accuracy. For this reason oxidation-reduction reactions usually cannot be performed, since the solutions are generally well buffered or strongly acid.

Under optimum conditions the end point in conductometric titrations can be located with a relative error of approximately 0.5 percent. A single titration requires about 10 min.

Acid-Base Titrations

The conductometric titration of an acid with a base, each completely dissociated, is illustrated by Fig. 27-5 for the titration of hydrochloric acid with sodium hydroxide:

$$(H^+ + Cl^-) + (Na^+ + OH^-) \rightarrow (Na^+ + Cl^-) + H_2O \qquad (27\text{-}7)$$

The highly conducting hydrogen ions initially present in the solution are replaced by sodium ions having a much smaller ionic conductance, while the concentration of chloride ions remains constant except for the small dilution by the titrant. The conductance of the solution at any point on the descending branch of the titration curve is given by the expression

$$\frac{1}{R} = \frac{1}{10000}(C_H\lambda_H + C_{Na}\lambda_{Na} + C_{Cl}\lambda_{Cl}) \qquad (27\text{-}8)$$

In terms of the initial concentration of hydrochloric acid C_i and the fraction of the acid titrated f,

$$C_H = C_i(1 - f), \qquad C_{Na} = C_i f, \qquad \text{and} \qquad C_{Cl} = C_i$$

Substituting these values into Eq. 27-8,

$$\frac{1}{R} = \frac{C_i}{10000}[\lambda_H + \lambda_{Cl} + f(\lambda_{Na} - \lambda_H)] \qquad (27\text{-}9)$$

As a result of the term within the parentheses in Eq. 27-9, the conductance of the solution diminishes up to the equivalence point. Beyond the equivalence point the conductance increases in direct proportion to the excess base added.

Example 27-4

Let us assume that one is titrating 100 ml of 0.01 N HCl solution with 0.1 N NaOH in a cell whose constant is 1.0 cm^{-1}. Under these conditions the initial conductance is

$$\frac{1}{R} = \frac{0.01}{(1000)\,(1)}\,(350 + 76) = 0.00426\ \Omega^{-1}$$

In this dilute solution, little error is introduced by assuming that the actual ionic conductances are essentially those at infinite dilution when dealing with completely ionized materials.

When the titration is 0.9 complete,

$$\frac{1}{R} = \frac{0.01}{(1000)\,(1)}\,[350 + 76 + (0.9)\,(50 - 350)]$$

$$= 0.00156 \; \Omega^{-1}$$

and, correcting for the dilution caused by the titrant,

$$\frac{1}{R} = \frac{(100 + 9)}{100}\,(0.00156) = 0.00170 \; \Omega^{-1}$$

At the equivalence point, there exists a solution of sodium chloride whose conductance is

$$\frac{1}{R} = \frac{0.01}{(1000)\,(1)}\,(76 + 50)\,(110/100) = 0.00139 \Omega^{-1}$$

When the equivalence point has been exceeded by 10 percent,

$$\frac{1}{R} = \frac{0.01}{(1000)\,(1)}\,[126 + (0.1)\,(248)]\,(111/100) = 0.00167 \Omega^{-1}$$

If the strong acid is titrated with a weak base, e.g., an aqueous solution of ammonia, the first part of the conductance-titration curve, representing the removal of hydrogen ion and replacement by ammonium ion, will be very similar to the descending branch of Fig. 27-5, since most cations have similar ionic conductances. After the equivalence point is passed, however, the conductance will remain almost constant, since a solution of ammonia has a very small conductance compared with that of ammonium chloride (Fig. 27-6).

$$(H^+ + Cl^-) + NH_3 \rightarrow NH_4^+ + Cl^- \qquad (27\text{-}10)$$

Titrations of weak acids or weak bases are somewhat more difficult. Acetic acid, for example, is present partly in the form of H^+ and CH_3COO^-, but largely as nonionized molecules. The proportions of each are regulated by the law of mass action. Initially the solution has a low conductance. As neutralization proceeds, the common ion formed, i.e., the acetate ion, represses the dissociation of the acetic acid so that an initial fall in conductance may occur. With further addition of sodium hydroxide the conductance of the sodium and acetate ions soon exceeds that of the acetic acid which they replace, and so the curve passes through a minimum and thereafter the conductance of the solution increases. The shape of the initial portion of these conductance curves will vary with the strength of the weak acid and its concentration, as indicated in Figs. 27-6 and 27-7.

When a weak acid is titrated with a weak base, the initial portion of the conductance titration curve follows the pattern described above. Beyond the equivalence point, there is no change in the conductance because of the very

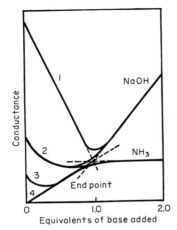

Fig. 27-6. Conductometric titration curves of various acids by sodium hydroxide and ammonia. The numbered curves are (1) HCl, (2) acid, pK_a of 3, (3) acid, pK_a of 5, and (4) acids, $pK_a > 7$.

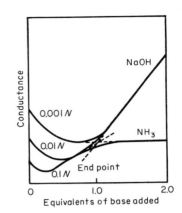

Fig. 27-7. Conductometric titration curves of acetic acid ($pK_a = 4.75$) at various concentrations.

small conductance of the excess free base. The intersection of the two branches is sharper than for a corresponding titration of a weak acid with a strong base.

Pronounced hydrolysis in the vicinity of the equivalence point makes it necessary to select the experimental points for the construction of the two branches considerably removed from the equivalence point. It will be observed in Fig. 27-7 that for dilute solutions of weak acids no linear region is obtained preceding the equivalence point, and therefore no reliable point of intersection seems possible. Addition of ethanol or other solvent with a smaller dielectric constant than water often reduces the dissociation of the weak acid sufficiently to yield a region of linear conductance preceding the equivalence point. When this does not suffice, two other experimental modifications may aid in the location of the equivalence point. In one procedure, titrations are conducted with duplicate portions of test solution, using an aqueous solution of ammonia as one titrant and a strong base as the other titrant, both titrants equivalent in normality. The conductance curves preceding the equivalence point are practically identical in shape, but beyond the equivalence point the curves will have quite different slopes. After superimposing the fore-portions, the intersection of the two branches beyond the equivalence point establishes the end point, as shown in Fig. 27-7. In the second procedure, sufficient ammonia is added to neutralize about 80 percent of the weak acid; then the titration is carried out with standard sodium hydroxide. If the conductance were plotted during the addition of the aqueous solution of ammonia, the curve would resemble those discussed. As long as any of the original acid is present the curve will continue to parallel the shape shown in Fig. 27-6, but when all the acid has been consumed, the ammonium ion formed commences to react with the hydroxyl ion, thus

$$(NH_4^+ + CH_3COO^-) + (Na^+ + OH^-) \rightarrow$$
$$NH_3 + H_2O + Na^+ + CH_3COO^- \quad (27\text{-}11)$$

and the conductance falls owing to the replacement of the ammonium ion ($\lambda_+ = 73$) by the sodium ion ($\lambda_+ = 50$). When the replacement is complete, the conductance abruptly increases, as shown in Fig. 27-8, and is then parallel to the corresponding part of Fig. 27-5 after the equivalence point.

The determination of a very weak acid or a very weak base is merely an extension of the titration of weak acids or weak bases. Take, for example, the titration for boric acid ($pK_a = 9.2$) with sodium hydroxide, as shown in Fig. 27-6. Initially the conductance is very small, since boric acid is dissociated to a negligible extent in aqueous solution. During the titration the reaction

$$HBO_2 + (Na^+ + OH^-) \rightarrow Na^+ + BO_2^- + H_2O \quad (27\text{-}12)$$

occurs, and the conductance increases linearly with the formation of borate and the addition of sodium ions. Beyond the equivalence point, further addition of sodium hydroxide introduces hydroxyl ions and there is a further increase of conductance. The inflection point will not be particularly sharp; in fact, it is often impossible to locate accurately the intersection of the two

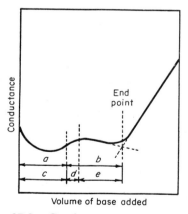

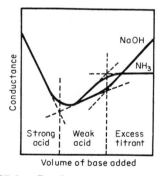

Fig. 27-8. Conductometric titration of a weak acid employing preliminary addition of ammonia followed by sodium hydroxide: (a) volume of NH_3 added; (b) volume of NaOH added up to the end point; (c) amount of acid neutralized by the NH_3; (d) amount of acid neutralized by the NaOH; and (e) displacement of NH_3 from NH_4^+ formed in (c).

Fig. 27-9. Conductometric titration of a mixture of a strong acid and a weak acid. Example: oxalic acid.

branches. This is true when the acid becomes so weak that extensive hydrolysis occurs throughout the reaction and the nonlinear portion extends from the end point to the initial point. Only if the product of the ionization constant and the acid concentration exceeds 10^{-11} can the titration be performed.

One of the valuable features of the conductance method of titration is that it permits the analysis of a mixture of a strong and a weak acid in one titration. Fig. 27-9 illustrates the neutralization of oxalic acid ($pK_1 = 1.2$; $pK_2 = 4.3$), representative of a strong acid and a moderately strong acid present in equivalent amounts. The initial decrease in conductance is due to the removal of hydrogen ions supplied by the relatively complete dissociation of $H_2C_2O_4$. This is followed by an increase in conductance as the weak acid, $HC_2O_4^-$, is consumed and replaced by $C_2O_4^=$ ions and the cation of the titrant. A rounded section joins these two branches, since the pK_a values are too close to each other and consequently the neutralization of the second acid begins while that of the first is being completed. When the neutralization of the second acid is complete, there is an increase in conductance when sodium hydroxide is the titrant due to the sodium and hydroxyl ions. Substitution of ammonia as the titrant results in a greater rise in conductance on the middle portion of the titration curve and little further change in conductance after the second end point. The first point of intersection gives the amount of strong acid in the mixture, and the difference between the first and second is equivalent to the amount of weak acid. Practical applications include the determination of mineral acids in vinegar and the titration of sulfonic acid groups followed by either carboxylic or phenolic groups in mixtures of organic acids.

The conductance method is also useful in the titration of the conjugate base of a weakly ionized acid, and vice versa. For example, organic acid salts such as acetates, benzoates, and nicotinates can be titrated with a standard solution of a completely ionized acid. As long as the ionization constant of the displaced acid or base divided by the original salt concentration does not exceed approximately 5×10^{-3}, the displaced acid will not contribute to the total conductance. The descending branch in the middle portion of Fig. 27-8 illustrates the nature of the titration curve that will be obtained.

Determinations by Precipitations and Through Formation of Complexes

Mercuric nitrate and perchlorate have found use as reagents for complexometric reactions. These salts exist almost entirely in the form of free ions. If a solution of a cyanide is added, the reaction

$$(Hg^{++} + 2ClO_4^-) + 2(K^+ + CN^-) \rightarrow Hg(CN)_2 + 2(K^+ + ClO_4^-) \quad (27\text{-}13)$$

occurs. Before the equivalence point, 1 mercuric ion is replaced by 2 potassium ions. The conductance varies only slightly. Beyond the end point the addition of potassium and cyanide ions causes the conductance to increase. In this class of reactions the slopes of the branches of the curve are determined both by the change in the ionic conductances of the ions present and by any change in the total number of electrical charges carried by the ions in solution. For these reasons, an acetate salt is preferable when titrating an anion, and a lithium salt when titrating a cation.

Even in favorable cases, results obtained through electrical conductivity tend to be less accurate than in acid-base systems. In precipitations, all the factors influencing the formation of the precipitate and the nature of the product must be considered just as in ordinary gravimetric methods. A slow rate of precipitation, excessive solubility of the insoluble materials, and all types of adsorption or occlusion difficulties make it difficult if not impossible to locate the equivalence point with any degree of accuracy.

High-Frequency Methods

A current alternating at frequencies exceeding 1 Mc/sec is affected by the conductance and capacitance of a solution within the field. The vessel containing the solution is placed in the field of an inductance coil or between the plates of a capacitor carrying the high-frequency current. Since the inductance coil or the capacitor is part of the high-frequency oscillator circuit, any changes in the composition of the solution will be reflected as changes in the oscillator, or changes in the plate and grid currents and voltages. Capacitance balance is the major factor in high-frequency measurements, whereas resistive balance was the more important in the determination of low-frequency conductivity. The unique advantage of methods based on high-frequency alternating currents is the possibility of placing the electrodes outside the vessel and out of direct contact with the solution. Significant measurements can be made without danger of electrolysis or electrode polarization, and without altering or consuming any solution.

Oscillator Circuit

The fundamental circuit of an oscillator is shown in Fig. 27-10. It consists of a capacitance C and an inductance L, plus the resistive components attributed to both. Upon adjustment of the circuit capacitance (called "tuning"), a condition will be attained which is known as resonance. When the condenser is discharged through the inductance, current will surge back and forth from the inductor to the capacitor at a frequency given by

$$f = \frac{1}{2\pi\sqrt{LC}} \tag{27-14}$$

Since the circuit always has some resistance, the current will decay rapidly. If, however, the resonant circuit of Fig. 27-10 is coupled to the input of an electronic amplifier, as shown in Fig. 27-11, the voltage impressed on the grid will alternate at the frequency given by Eq. 27-14. As a result the output voltage at the plate, which is μe_g, will also alternate at the same frequency. Now if an inductance L_2 is inserted in the plate circuit and coupled to L_1 in the grid circuit

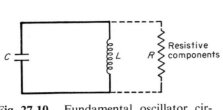

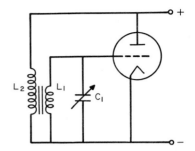

Fig. 27-10. Fundamental oscillator circuit.

Fig. 27-11. Schematic diagram of a tuned
grid oscillator circuit.

by means of a common core, the amplified plate voltage will appear across L_2.
With the windings of the coils properly arranged, coil L_2 can serve to convey
the output voltage oscillations back to the input grid circuit. Then if L_1 is
selected so that the magnitude of the feedback voltage delivered from it exactly
equals the original input grid voltage, then it can replace it. Furthermore,
the electronic circuit will continue to amplify the returned signal and oscillations will be maintained. The resonant circuit can be placed in either the grid
or plate circuit, or in both circuits and coupled through a common inductance.

High-Frequency Titrimeters

The test solution is made part of the high-frequency oscillating circuit, either
in the capacity or the induction branch. The cell may be the tube upon which
the coil is wound, with corresponding alterations in capacitance between the
windings and in inductance due to the change in permeability of the material
making up the cell, or it may be the dielectric material between the plates of a
condenser. Changes in the solution's conductivity and dielectric properties will
affect the value of the particular component in the oscillator circuit which contains the cell, and consequently alter the high-frequency conductance and
capacitance of the cell. Depending upon the particular oscillator circuit, in
some instruments this effect can be observed as a change in the plate or grid
currents, the voltages at the plate or grid, or the frequency at which resonance
occurs; in others the effect of changes in the electrolyte upon the inductance or
capacitance is offset by retuning the oscillator to the original resonant frequency. As shown in Fig. 27-12, the sample cell is in parallel with a calibrated
capacitor. In order to return to the resonant frequency it is necessary to remove
the exact amount of capacitance which was added by the sample.

Another convenient method is to measure the output frequencies of two
identical oscillator circuits, one of which contains the sample cell as part of the
oscillator capacitance (f), the other serving merely as a reference unit (f_0). The
outputs from the two units are fed into a mixer unit from which is obtained a
low-frequency difference ($f - f_0$) directly proportional to the change in the

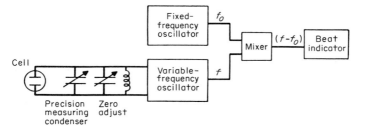

Fig. 27-12. Schematic diagram of a high-frequency titrimeter.

high-frequency capacitance of the cells. Either the difference frequency is measured directly, or after each change in the test solution the value of the variable precision condenser is altered to make up for the capacitance change in the cell. Instruments of a beat-frequency type or those involving compensatory alteration in circuit components are more stable in practice than direct-reading instruments. An instrument of the compensatory type which is commercially available is illustrated in Fig. 27-13.

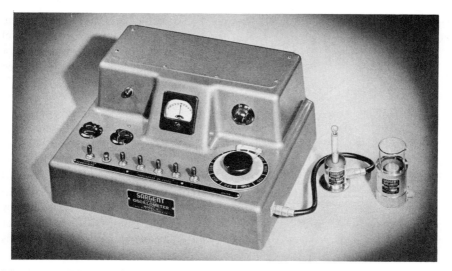

Fig. 27-13. The chemical oscillometer. Test-tube style sample holder and titration cell are shown at the right. Switches along the panel front are calibrated capacitors in parallel with a variable capacitor (main dial). (Courtesy of E. H. Sargent & Co.)

Equivalent Circuit of Cell and Solution

The vertical cross section of a typical cell is shown in Fig. 27-14A. The outside and inside surfaces of the annular space are plated with metal. When the annular space between the metal plates is filled with liquid, the high-frequency

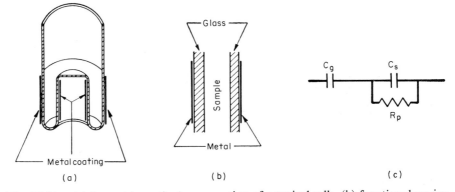

Fig. 27-14.   (a) Isometric vertical cross section of a typical cell; (b) functional equivalent of the cell; (c) equivalent circuit of cell and solution.

behavior of the system will be similar to that of a system in which the metal plates of a condenser are separated by a dielectric, comprising in this case the glass walls and the sample. The fundamental equivalent circuit of the cell may be treated as shown in Fig. 27-14C. C_s represents the capacitance across the liquid sample, and C_g is the capacitance of the glass walls of the cell. In case the solution within the cell has appreciable conductance, the approximate equivalent circuit may be represented by placing a resistance, R_p, in parallel with C_s. The resistive component of the container walls is so high as to be a negligible contribution.

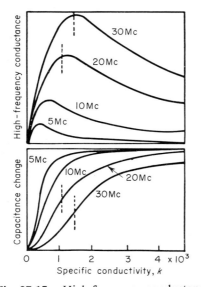

Fig. 27-15.   High-frequency conductance and capacitance change as a function of low-frequency conductivity. Zero refers to a cell filled with pure solvents.

High-Frequency Conductance Term

When the frequency at which the field between the two electrodes alternates becomes greater than 1 Mc/sec, the conductance of the solution begins to include capacitance terms in addition to the ordinary low-frequency conductance (Fig. 27-15). Consider what happens to the individual ions of an electrolyte and to polar molecules when exposed to a rapidly alternating field. Each ion or dipolar molecule tends to move or align itself in the direction of the electrode of opposite polarity. Once every cycle, the electrode polarity changes, and the ion or dipole must reverse its motion or orientation. The conductivity of the solution is the result of movement of positive and negative ions relative to their neighbors and to the solvent molecules. Each ion tends to move ahead of its ionic atmosphere with the result an unsymmetrical charge distribution forms around each central ion and exerts a retardation force on the ion in a direction opposite to its motion. However, at alternating frequencies greater than 1 Mc/sec, the central ion changes its direction of motion so quickly with every cycle of the applied field that there is little chance for the dissymmetry of the ionic atmosphere to arise. As a result the conductance increases.

The relationship between conventional low-frequency conductance measurements and high-frequency conductance, G, or the capacitance (C_p) is given by[2]

$$G = \frac{1}{R_p} = \frac{\kappa(2\pi f)^2 C_g^2}{\kappa^2 + (2\pi f)^2(C_g + C_s)^2} \tag{27-15}$$

$$C_p = \frac{C_g\kappa^2 + 2\pi f(C_g C_s^2 + C_g^2 C_s)}{\kappa^2 + (2\pi f)^2(C_g + C_s)^2} \tag{27-16}$$

where κ is the low-frequency specific conductance and the other terms have the meanings expressed by Eq. 27-14 and in Fig. 27-14. As C_g increases, i.e., thinner cell walls, the value of G increases, and when C_g approaches infinite capacitance, the high-frequency conductance approaches the low-frequency conductance as a limit. When κ approaches a very small or very large value, G approaches zero so that there is a peak for a given frequency. The position of the peak is important from the standpoint of reversals and curvature in the titration curves based on high-frequency conductance. Upon differentiating Eq. 27-15, setting the result equal to zero, and solving,

$$\kappa_{\text{peak}} = 2\pi f(C_g + C_s) \tag{27-17}$$

When C_g becomes negligibly small in comparison with C_s, the value of the high frequency conductance at the maximum increases with frequency, and

$$f_{\text{peak}} = \frac{1.8 \times 10^{12}\kappa}{D} \tag{27-18}$$

where D is the dielectric constant of the solution. From this relation it would seem that very high frequencies must be employed if solution concentrations in the range of 0.1 M are to be measured. Table 27-3 gives the concentration of electrolyte solutions giving maximum sensitivity for various oscillator frequencies.

Table 27-3	Relation of Electrolyte Concentration and Frequency for Maximum Sensitivity		
OSCILLATOR FREQUENCY, MEGACYCLES	CONCENTRATION OF MAXIMUM SENSITIVITY		
	NaCl	CaCl$_2$	HCl
5	0.0025 M	0.0013 M	0.0006 M
30	0.014	0.008	0.003
57	0.032	0.015	0.005
100	0.05	0.027	0.01
375	0.2	0.1	0.036

[From W. J. Blaedel and H. V. Malmstadt, *Anal. Chem.*, **22**, 734 (1950); J. Forman and D. J. Crisp, *Faraday Soc.* **42A**, 186 (1946).]

It is difficult to construct oscillators which will operate at frequencies much above 30 Mc and provide trouble-free service in routine laboratory use. Thus the method is severely restricted in respect to the range of concentrations of electrolytes that can be employed with a reasonable degree of instrument response.

Capacitance Changes

The change in equivalent parallel capacitance is actually the quantity measured by titrimeters of the beat-frequency type or those involving compensatory alteration in circuit components to make up for the capacitance change in the test solution. Reference to Fig. 27-15 shows that the capacitance, for dilute ionic solutions, follows an S-shape curve when plotted as a function of the low-frequency conductivity of the solution. The peak high-frequency conductance and the inflection point on the capacitance curve occur at the same low-frequency conductivity value. Consequently, Eq. 27-17 applies when speaking of the mid-point of a capacitance curve; similarly the discussion also applies to the relationship for the concentration of electrolyte solutions giving maximum sensitivity for various oscillator frequencies.

Lowering the dielectric constant of the solvent decreases C_s and results in an increased capacitance change, and at the same time shifts the inflection point to lower values of conductivity. This is advantageous for acid-base titrations in certain nonaqueous solvents.

Titration Curves

Before attempting to carry out high-frequency titrations it is advisable to determine the response of the instrument as a function of the electrolyte concentration. Each instrument with associated cell has an optimum range for which changes in the test solution will produce the maximum response. Typical high-frequency conductance and capacitance curves are shown in Fig. 27-15

The relationship between the forms of ordinary low-frequency titration curves and high-frequency curves are best shown by means of transfer plots. In Fig. 27-16, upper right and lower right, are two plots of specific conductivity at low frequency vs the corresponding response at 10 and 3 Mc, respectively. To ascertain the corresponding high-frequency titration curve from an ordinary titration curve, the high-frequency response corresponding to the specific conductivity for each volume of titrant added is found from either the 10- or the 3-Mc transfer plot and then plotted vs the respective volume of titrant. The shapes of the high-frequency titration curves are shown in the upper left and lower left of Fig. 27-16.

At 10 Mc under the conditions employed, V-shape high-frequency conductance and capacitance curves are obtained. Although similar in shape to the low-frequency curves, considerable curvature exists in the curves both near

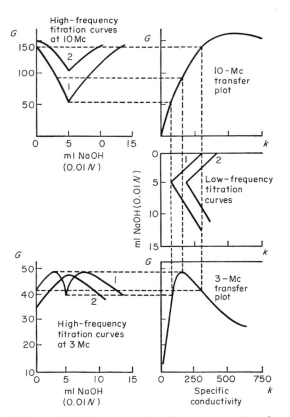

Fig. 27-16. Correlation of high-frequency titration curves to low-frequency titration curves. (1) 5 ml of 0.01 N HCl in total volume of 60 ml. (2) 5 ml of 0.01 N HCl plus 55 ml 0.001 N KCl. After C. N. Reilley and W. H. McCurdy, Jr., *Anal. Chem.*, **25**, 86 (1953). (Courtesy of *Analytical Chemistry*.)

to and considerably removed from the vicinity of the end point. This curvature is a distinct drawback and renders extrapolations uncertain.

Further difficulties arise when measuring high-frequency conductance during a titration at lower frequencies—for example, 3 Mc. The high-frequency readings lie on both sides of the peak value, and it is possible to obtain an M-shape titration curve or an inverted V-shape curve. The complexity of these curves could cause errors of interpretation.

Table 27-4 | *Dielectric Constants*

Formamide	109.5	Acetic anhydride	20.7	Acetic Acid	6.15
Water	81	1-Propanol	20.1	Ethyl acetate	6.02
Formic acid	58.5	2-Propanol	18.3	1-Butylamine	5.3
Acetonitrile	37.5	1-Butanol	17.1	Chloroform	4.806
Nitrobenzene	34.8	Ethylenediamine	14.2	Benzene	2.379
Methanol	32.6	Benzyl alcohol	13.1	Carbon tetrachloride	2.238
Ethanol	24.3	Phenol	9.78	1,4-Dioxane	2.209
Acetone	20.7	Aniline	6.89		

Acid-base, precipitation, and ion-combination reactions can be followed by high-frequency methods in the same manner as discussed for low-frequency titrations. In fact, ordinary frequencies will provide as good or better titration curves except in those few instances where it is advantageous to remove the electrodes from direct contact with the test solution or when titrations are conducted in nonaqueous solvents.[1]

Measurement of Dielectric Constant

When a nonconducting liquid is placed between the metal plates of Fig. 27-14, the system behaves as two capacitors, C_g and C_s, in series. The capacitance C_s will vary from a fixed value C_0, determined by the geometry of the cell when filled with air, to a value D dependent upon the dielectric constant of the sample; that is,

$$C_s = C_0 D \tag{27-19}$$

The value C_0 depends upon the thickness of the glass walls, the effective plate area, and the dielectric constant of the container itself. The capacitance of the cell is not a linear function of the dielectric constant, but will approach the value of C_g as a limit. Figure 27-17 is a plot of cell response with solutions of various dielectric constants. The region of linear response may be extended by inserting a variable inductance between the measuring cell and the oscillator circuit.

Table 27-4 lists the dielectric constants of some common materials. The high value for water renders it possible to determine extremely small amounts of

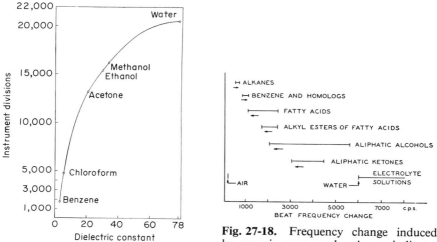

Fig. 27-17. Instrument response as a function of dielectric constant (Sargent chemical oscillometer, model V).

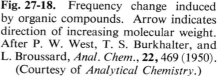

Fig. 27-18. Frequency change induced by organic compounds. Arrow indicates direction of increasing molecular weight. After P. W. West, T. S. Burkhalter, and L. Broussard, *Anal. Chem.*, **22**, 469 (1950). (Courtesy of *Analytical Chemistry.*)

water in organic liquids or moisture in granular or powdered substances. For many years a dielectric type of moisture meter for use with grains, cereals, and other powdered substances has been available commercially. The test material is uniformly packed between two parallel plates which serve as the measuring condenser.

High-frequency methods have been applied to the discrimination of organic mixtures. Organic compounds lie in rather definite groups in the range between the dielectric constant of air and water,[3] as shown in Fig. 27-18.

LABORATORY WORK

Operation of Industrial Instrument Conductivity Bridge (Serfass Conductance Bridge)

1. Connect the instrument to a 110-V a-c main. Snap the toggle switch to the ON position (and the second toggle switch to 60 CYCLES).

2. Connect leads 1 and 2 of the bridge to the conductivity cell or to a pair of platinum-foil electrodes. For solutions with high conductance, use a cell with small electrode area or electrodes far apart; for solutions with low conductance, place the electrodes closer together.

3. Transfer a suitable portion of the unknown solution to the conductivity cell (or a 250-ml beaker, if platinum-foil electrodes are used). Add distilled water until the electrodes are immersed at least 1 cm. Stir the solution with a magnetic stirrer or over-head motor stirrer.

4. Set the multiplier switch at an intermediate position (on the resistance or conductance scale) and rotate the main dial control the full length of the scale. Observe the tuning indicator (magic eye tube) and when a maximum shadow angle is obtained, the

circuit is balanced. If no shadow angle is obtained, or an indication of a shadow angle is obtained only at either extreme of the scale, set the multiplier switch at another position and again rotate the main dial control the full length of the scale.

5. If a sharp balance is not obtained, connect a decade condenser box across terminals 2 and 3. Obtain the best balance possible in the usual manner, then add capacitance from the box until the tuning indicator gives a maximum shadow angle. Then readjust the main dial control for final balance.

6. The resistance (or conductance) of the solution in ohms (or mhos) is found by multiplying the main dial reading by the value of the multiplier switch position.

7. Add the titrant from a 10-ml buret in 0.5-ml increments until at least four readings beyond the end point have been obtained. Plot the conductance of the solution (as read directly, or the reciprocal of the resistance of the solution) against the volume of titrant. Extrapolate the two segments of the titration curve. The point of intersection is the end point. Multiply all readings by the ratio $(V + v)/V$, where V is the initial volume of solution and v is the volume of titrant added up to that point.

E X P E R I M E N T 2 7 - 1   TITRATION OF A COMPLETELY IONIZED ACID

1. Transfer 50 ml of 0.01 M hydrochloric acid to a 250-ml beaker and dilute to about 100 ml. Measure the conductance. Titrate with 0.1 N sodium hydroxide added in 0.5-ml increments from a 10-ml buret. Measure the conductance (or resistance) after the addition of each increment.

2. Repeat the titration, using 0.001 M and 0.0001 M solution of hydrochloric acid and titrating with 0.01 N and 0.001 N sodium hydroxide, respectively.

E X P E R I M E N T 2 7 - 2   TITRATION OF AN INCOMPLETELY IONIZED ACID

1. Transfer 50 ml of 0.1 N acetic acid to a 250-ml beaker and dilute to about 100 ml. Measure the conductance. Titrate with 1 N sodium hydroxide added in 0.5-ml increments from a 10-ml buret.

2. Repeat the titration, using 0.01 N and 0.001 N solutions of acetic acid and titrating with 0.1 N and 0.01 N sodium hydroxide, respectively.

3. Repeat the entire series of titrations, substituting aqueous solutions of ammonia as the titrant.

4. Plot all results on one piece of graph paper. The curves should resemble Fig. 27-7.

E X P E R I M E N T 2 7 - 3   TITRATION OF INCOMPLETELY IONIZED ACID: PARTIAL NEUTRALIZATION WITH AMMONIA FOLLOWED BY TITRATION WITH SODIUM HYDROXIDE

1. Transfer 50 ml of 0.1 N acetic acid to a 250-ml beaker. Dilute to about 100 ml with distilled water. Measure the conductance.

2. Add, in 0.5-ml increments, a total of 8 ml of 0.5 N aqueous ammonia. Complete the titration with 1 N sodium hydroxide added from a 10-ml buret.

Note. The aqueous ammonia need not be standardized. The titration curve should resemble Fig. 27-8.

E X P E R I M E N T 2 7 - 4   TITRATION OF A MIXTURE OF ACIDS

1. Transfer 40 ml of 0.01 N acetic acid and 10 ml of 0.01 N hydrochloric acid to a 250-ml beaker. Dilute to about 100 ml with distilled water. Measure the conductance.

2. Titrate with 0.1 N sodium hydroxide added from a 10-ml buret. Use 0.25 ml-increments of titrant.

3. Repeat the titration, using 10 ml of 0.01 N acetic acid and 40 ml of 0.01 N hydrochloric acid.

Note. If desired, a 0.1 N aqueous ammonia solution may be used as titrant as was done in Experiment 27-2.

EXPERIMENT 27-5   PRECIPITATION TITRATIONS

1. Transfer 50 ml of 0.01 N sodium chloride to a 250-ml beaker and dilute to about 100 ml. Measure the conductance.
2. Titrate with 0.1 N silver nitrate added from a 10-ml buret.
3. Repeat the titration with 0.1 N silver acetate as titrant.
4. Plot the results on the same graph and note the slope of the two branches of the titration curve for the different titrants.

EXPERIMENT 27-6   ION COMBINATION TITRATIONS

1. Transfer 5 ml of 0.1 N potassium iodide to the conductivity cell. Dilute with distilled water to about 100 ml. Measure the conductance.
2. Titrate with 0.1 N mercuric perchlorate. A small break in the titration curve occurs when the titration is 50 percent complete due to the formation of K_2HgI_4. A much larger break occurs when the reaction

$$K_2HgI_4 + Hg(ClO_4)_2 \rightarrow 2HgI_2 + 2KClO_4$$

is complete.

Note. Prepare mercuric perchlorate by saturating a 0.1 N perchloric acid solution with red mercuric oxide.

EXPERIMENT 27-7   RESPONSE CURVES FOR A HIGH-FREQUENCY TITRIMETER

1. Fill the cell with exactly 80 ml of distilled water (or any known amount of water sufficient to cover the condenser plates or the top of an inductance coil). Start the stirrer and determine the instrument reading.
2. Add, in 1-ml increments, a total of 9 ml of 0.001 N hydrochloric acid. Determine the instrument reading after each addition.
3. Repeat step 2 using a total of 9 ml of 0.01 N acid.
4. Repeat step 2 using a total of 10 ml of 0.1 N acid.
5. Repeat steps 1 through 4 using a series of sodium hydroxide solutions.
6. Repeat steps 1 through 4 using a series of sodium chloride solutions.
7. Repeat steps 1, 3, and 4 using a series of acetic acid solutions.
8. Plot the respective instrument readings vs the normality of the solution in the titration cell after each increment was added to obtain a series of response curves characteristic of the particular high-frequency instrument employed. If a Sargent oscillometer was employed, the response curves will resemble the lower portion of Fig. 27-15.

EXPERIMENT 27-8   TITRATIONS WITH A HIGH-FREQUENCY TITRIMETER

From the response curves obtained in Experiment 27-7, select the range of optimum concentrations for conducting titrations with your particular titrimeter. Fill the titration cell with distilled water until the condenser plates are covered. Transfer an appropriate volume of solution to the cell and, with the stirrer running, add 0.5-ml increments of the titrant. Continue the addition of titrant until the end point is reached and seven or eight readings are obtained beyond it. Plot the condenser readings (or respective instrument readings) vs volume of titrant added; the intersection of the extrapolated straight-line portions of the two branches of the curve is taken as the end point of the titration.

Suggesed titrations: (1) Experiment 27-1, steps 1 and 2; (2) Experiment 27-2, steps 1 and 2; (3) Experiment 27-4; and (4) Experiment 27-5.

E X P E R I M E N T 2 7 - 9   MEASUREMENT OF DIELECTRIC CONSTANT

1. Connect the test-tube cell holder to a high-frequency instrument, such as the Sargent oscillometer. Balance the instrument with the cell empty.

2. Prepare a calibration curve of instrument response as a function of dielectric constant by successively measuring pure solutions of benzene, chloroform, acetone, ethanol, methanol, and water.

3. Determine the instrument reading of an unknown solution and report the dielectric constant of the unknown solution by reference to your calibration curve.

Note. The instructor may wish to have the student prepare a calibration curve for a binary mixture—for example, nitrobenzene and benzene or aniline and nitrobenzene—and then determine the composition of an unknown.

Problems

1. An aqueous 20% HCl solution has a specific conductance of about 0.85 Ω^{-1} cm^{-1} at 25°C. What is the measured resistance with a cell of constant (a) 100, (b) 20, (c) 10, (d) 1, (e) 0.2 cm^{-1}? Are these resistance values feasible to measure with standard conductivity bridges? *Ans.* (d) 1.177 Ω, a low value which would require relatively elaborate equipment.

2. A cell constant of 20.0 cm^{-1} is recommended for a commercial conductivity bridge designed to span the range from 1 to 18% HCl. The corresponding conductance ranges from 0.0630 to about 0.750 Ω^{-1}. What range of resistance values are involved? *Ans.* 318–26.7 Ω.

3. A meter scale is to be inscribed from 2 to 1000 ppm Na$_2$SO$_4$, and the midpoint of the logarithmic scale shall correspond to 40 ppm. Suggest a compatible set of instrument parameters; i.e., resistance range and cell constant. *Ans.* Resistance should range from 1000 Θ to 500,000 Θ. If $\Theta = 0.2$, the resistance readings will range from 200 to 10,000 Ω with 5,000 Ω at midscale. This range is feasible, and in fact, a commercial instrument is available with the cell constant 0.2 cm^{-1}.

4. Similar to Problem 3, individual instruments are to be designed for each of these systems. Compute the resistance range and a compatible cell constant. Use handbooks to locate necessary conductance values, and assume average distilled water has a specific conductance of 2×10^{-6} Ω^{-1} cm^{-1}. (a) 0%–5% HCl; (b) 0.5%–5% NH$_3$; (c) 0–60 ppm sodium formate; (d) 0–40 ppm salinity (as NaCl); (e) 96%–99.5% H$_2$SO$_4$; (f) 0.1%–10% CrO$_3$.

5. The equivalent conductance of a 0.002414 N acetic acid solution is found to be 32.22 at 25°C. Calculate the degree of dissociation of acetic acid at this concentration, and caulclate the ionization constant.

6. The specific conductance at 25°C of a saturated solution of barium sulfate was 4.58×10^{-6} Ω^{-1} cm^{-1}, and that of the water used was 1.52×10^{-6}. What is the

solubility of $BaSO_4$ at 25° in moles per liter and in grams per liter? Calculate the solubility product constant.

7. The solubility product of silver iodate at 25°C is 3.1×10^{-8}. What would be the resistance of a saturated solution of silver iodate, measured with a cell whose cell constant was 0.2 cm^{-1}? (Neglect the solvent correction.)

8. A very dilute solution of NaOH (100 ml) is titrated with 1.00 N HCl. The following resistance readings (in ohms) were obtained at the indicated buret readings: 0.00 ml, 3175; 1.00 ml 3850; 2.00 ml, 4900; 3.00 ml, 7150; 4.00 ml, 5080; 5.00 ml, 3495; 6.00 ml, 2733. Determine the normality of the solution and the weight of NaOH present.

9. In the titration of 100 ml of a dilute solution of acetic acid with 0.500 N aqueous ammonia, the following resistance readings (in ohms) were obtained at the indicated buret readings: 8.00 ml, 750; 9.00 ml, 680; 10.00 ml, 620; 11.00 ml, 570; 12.00 ml, 530; 13.00 ml, 508; 15.00 ml, 515; 17.00 ml, 521. What is the normality of the acetic acid solution?

10. In the titration of 100 ml of H_2SO_4 in glacial acetic acid with 0.500 M sodium acetate in the same solvent, the following specific conductance ($\times 10^6$) data were obtained at the indicated buret readings:

0.50 ml = 2.95	3.50 ml = 4.78	7.00 ml = 3.35
1.00 ml = 3.30	4.00 ml = 4.70	7.50 ml = 3.40
1.50 ml = 3.65	4.50 ml = 4.33	8.00 ml = 3.60
2.00 ml = 4.00	5.00 ml = 3.99	8.50 ml = 3.90
2.50 ml = 4.35	5.50 ml = 3.65	9.00 ml = 4.20
3.00 ml = 4.65	6.00 ml = 3.35	9.50 ml = 4.50

What is the molarity of the sulfuric acid solution? *Ans.* 0.0176 M; individual end point for each replaceable hydrogen.

11. The following relative conductance readings were obtained during the titration of a mixture containing an aliphatic carboxylic acid and an aromatic sulfonic acid. The titrant was 0.200 N NH$_3$.

0.00 ml = 2.01	3.10 ml = 1.16	4.50 ml = 1.51
1.00 ml = 1.75	3.20 ml = 1.19	5.00 ml = 1.51
2.00 ml = 1.47	3.50 ml = 1.23	6.00 ml = 1.52
2.50 ml = 1.33	4.00 ml = 1.40	8.00 ml = 1.53
3.00 ml = 1.19	4.20 ml = 1.47	

Calculate the number of equivalents of each acid present in the mixture.

12. Using the equivalent conductance values obtained from Table 27-1, sketch the general form of the titration curve in each of the following cases: (a) titration of $Ba(OH)_2$ with HCl; (b) titration of NH_4Cl with NaOH; (c) titration of silver nitrate with potassium chloride; (d) titration of silver acetate with lithium chloride; (e) titration of sodium acetate with HCl; (f) titration of barium carbonate with H_2SO_4 [hint: check solubility of intermediate products]; (g) titration of a mixture of a sulfonic acid and a carboxylic acid with NaOH; (h) titration of $KH_3(C_2O_4)_2$ with NH$_3$; titration of a mixture containing Na_3PO_4 and Na_2HPO_4 with HCl.

13. A commercial liquor contains nicotinic acid, ammonium nicotinate, and nicotinamide. Devise a conductometric titration for the determination of the free acid and the ammonium salt.

14. Exactly 50 ml of a 0.001 N solution of HCl is titrated with 0.01 N KOH. Calculate the conductance (and resistance) observed after the addition of 0, 25, 50, 90, 100, 110, 150, 175, and 200 percent of the equivalent amount of titrant. Assume the cell constant is 0.2 cm^{-1}. Plot the results.

15. Exactly 100 ml of a 0.1 N solution of NH_4NO_3 is titrated with 1.0 N KOH. As in Problem 14, calculate the conductance observed after the addition of the stated increments of titrant. Assume the cell constant is 0.5 cm^{-1}. Plot the results.

16. The response of the Sargent oscillometer to varying concentrations of hydrochloric acid was obtained by adding known increments of acid to exactly 100 ml of distilled water. The following instrument readings were obtained for the indicated acid additions: (A) using 0.001 N HCl. 0.00 ml = 21,297, 1.00 ml = 21,277, 5.00 ml = 21,208, 8.00 ml = 21,262, 10.00 ml = 21,327; (B) using 0.01 N HCl and continuing with the solution from set A: 1.00 ml = 21,821, 3.00 ml = 23,135, 5.00 ml = 24,429, 7.00 ml = 25,430, 9.00 ml = 26,192; (C) continuation with 0.1 N HCl: 1.00 ml = 27,330, 2.00 ml = 28,357, 4.00 ml = 28,600, 8.00 ml = 28,690, 10.00 ml = 28,700. Plot the instrument response vs molarity of HCl. Estimate the concentration of maximum sensitivity and compare with the value given in Table 27-3. The Sargent oscillometer operates at 4.89 Mc.

17. On the graph prepared in Problem 16, sketch the response curve for NaCl using the information contained in Table 27-3 and assuming in all other respects the curve parallels the one for HCl. Sketch the general form of the titration curve in each of the following cases, assuming the response curve for NaOH coincides with the curve for HCl: (a) titration of 0.01 N HCl with 0.1 N NaOH, (b) titration of 0.0005 N HCl with 0.005 N NaOH, (c) titration of 0.001 N HCl with 0.01 N NaOH. Ans. (a) Titration is not feasible because the response changes only from 28,700 at the beginning to 28,460 at the equivalence point.

18 Exactly 100 ml of a dilute HCl solution was titrated with 0.0200 N NaOH. The following oscillometer readings were obtained at the indicated buret readings:

0.00 ml = 26,552	4.00 ml = 23,538	6.00 ml = 22,940
1.00 ml = 26,036	4.50 ml = 23,047	7.00 ml = 23,631
2.00 ml = 25,328	5.00 ml = 22,585	7.75 ml = 24,174
3.00 ml = 24,506	5.50 ml = 22,631	9.00 ml = 24,930
		10.00 ml = 25,445

What is the molarity of the HCl solution? Ans. 0.00105 M.

19 Ammonia in gas streams has been determined by bubbling the gas through exactly 100 ml of 0.0400 M boric acid at a rate of 10 liters/min and measuring the change in conductance. The following data was obtained for a series of standard solutions of ammonia added to boric acid:

NH$_3$ ADDED, MILLIEQUIVALENTS	CONDUCTANCE, Ω^{-1}, ($\times 10^4$) HBO$_2$	HBO$_2$ + NH$_3$
3.665	0.55	45.55
0.715	0.55	10.65
0.0715	0.55	1.61
0.0071	0.55	0.66

Plot the calibration curve. Calculate the ammonia concentration present in each of these gas streams for which these conductance readings ($\times 10^4$) were obtained: sample A, 12.75; sample B, 6.35; sample C, 1.15; sample D, 3.45. Ans. Sample C contains 4.0 milliequivalents of NH$_3$.

20. In Problem 19 the cell constant was 0.069 cm^{-1}. Assuming that the equivalent conductance of the borate ion at infinite dilution to be about 80 cm^2 equivalent^{-1} ohm^{-1}, and that the specific conductance of the water employed was 2×10^{-6} Ω^{-1} cm^{-1}, estimate the degree of ionization of boric acid at the concentration employed, and calculate the ionization constant.

Bibliography

Britton, H. T. S., *Conductometric Analysis*, Van Nostrand, Princeton, N.J., 1934.

Kolthoff, I. M., and H. A. Laitinen, *pH and Electro Titrations*, 2nd ed., Wiley, New York, 1941.

Lingane, J. J., *Electroanalytical Chemistry*, 2nd ed., Interscience, New York, 1958.

Sherrick, P. H., G. A. Dawe, R. Karr, and E. F. Ewen, *Manual of Chemical Oscillometry*, E. H. Sargent & Co., Chicago, 1954.

Shedlovsky, T., in A. Weissberger (Ed.), *Physical Methods of Organic Chemistry*, 3rd ed., Vol. I, Part 4, Chapter 45, Interscience, New York, 1960.

Literature Cited

1. Dean, J. A., and C. Cain, Jr., *Anal. Chem.*, **27**, 212 (1955).
2. Reilley, C. N., and W. N. McCurdy, Jr., *Anal. Chem.*, **25**, 86 (1953).
3. West, P. W., T. S. Burkhalter, and L. Broussard, *Anal. Chem.*, **22**, 469 (1950)

Process Instruments and
Automatic Analysis

Methods for continuous analysis and control of on-stream process systems and automatic analyzers for routine laboratory methods will be considered in this final chapter. While it is true that specific types of automatic equipment have been used for many years to control the process stream environment—temperature, pressure, flow rate, etc.—only recently have automatic measurements of stream composition become more widespread in use. In control analyses, generally, chemical constituents have been determined on grab samples which were subsequently analyzed by conventional manual techniques with obvious shortcomings in time, economy, and human-error possibilities. More and more industrial processes, however, require constant surveillance and control at each step in the process. Instruments and methods are needed to provide a dynamic rather than historical analysis. This requires either continuous analysis, or at least rapid repetitive analysis, of starting materials, intermediate products, and the end products for the desired component. Often monitored also are various possible contaminants which could be deleterious at various stages in the process. Only by means of analyses of these types can production facilities reduce off-specification materials to a minimum. Remedial action can be taken within a few minutes (for discontinuous repetitive analyses) or immediately with continuous on-stream analyzers. By suitable feedback circuitry, the latter instruments will make necessary adjustments in a process stream to maintain the specific variable or component at a predetermined value.

Although instrument costs are high, they still represent a small amount of plant or laboratory costs. Since the limits of accuracy of both process and laboratory work can be no better than the reliability of instruments used in making measurements, high costs are easily justified. Other advantages to be gained include greater safety of operation, greater operating economy, and new evaluations. Applicability of a method which initially appears to be border-line may actually prove to be acceptable in service because continuous sampling tends to improve precision. Flowing samples are easier to protect from con-tamination.

Not every process or analytical method lends itself to automation. Applica-tion to solid samples is difficult for many types of measuring techniques now used in continuous analysis. In fact, there will probably always remain a hard core of complex chemical analyses that will totally defy automation or be too costly to automate.

Automatic Analyzers

Instruments for automatically determining specific chemical variables or process parameters will be discussed first. Some of these have received atten-tion in preceding chapters.

Continuous Analysis

Continuous analysis adopts many of the instrumental techniques which have been developed to a high degree in laboratory use and applies them to char-acteristic measurements on flowing samples in chemical processes. The features of continuous analysis are illustrated schematically in Fig. 28-1. A sample at a controlled rate is obtained from the main process stream or other source of material. When necessary, provision is made for preparing the initial sample for analysis by further operations such as the addition of reagents or filtration. The actual measurement is made by a suitable sensor or transducer. The results of the analysis are indicated in terms of the concentration of the desired component in the sample, usually by a chart recorder or other readout device.

The sample system should be designed to operate effectively despite the most unfavorable case of sample conditions. Transport lag must be eliminated and dead-ended volume reduced if events within the analyzer are to be representa-tive of the stream being monitored. Special bypass pumping devices are often needed to keep fresh sample rapidly supplied to the input of the analyzer. Care must be taken to prevent fractionation of liquid samples or the adsorption of gaseous constituents onto the tubing or fittings ahead of the analyzer. Ex-treme care is required in continuous analysis of trace quantities. Leakage of sample at a fitting or connection can cause serious back diffusion of the at-mosphere into the stream; examples include dissolved oxygen in power plant

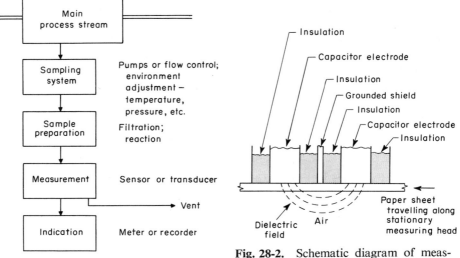

Fig. 28-1. Features of continuous analysis.

Fig. 28-2. Schematic diagram of measuring head for control of moisture in paper web. (Courtesy of Foxboro Co.)

condensate streams or the analysis for water in dry gas streams. Corrosive samples or materials under extremes of pressure or temperature may restrict latitude in the design of sample systems, especially with regard to sample cells for the various optical methods of analysis. Gas handling equipment should always include a small protective filter, preceded by a major filter if the gas contains suspended matter requiring removal. If a gas sample has a water vapor concentration high enough to cause condensation within the analyzer, or if moisture constitutes an interferent, stream drying equipment must be installed.

If several separate process streams are reasonably identical in major constituents and the concentration of desired component does not vary widely, all streams can be connected through solenoid-operated, three-way valves to a common manifold which leads to the instrument. Each stream can then be selected sequentially by a multipoint recorder at intervals of 3–5 min, giving almost continuous analysis of each stream.

Methods Based on Nonselective Properties

A number of instrumental methods have been available for some time for continuous measurement of nonselective properties such as pH, density, viscosity, conductance, capacitance, and combustibility. Selected examples will serve to illustrate these types of analysis.

The composition of binary systems where each component has a somewhat different physical parameter can be determined. A calibration curve of the parameter signal vs composition yields the correlation. For example, water in many organic materials is readily determined, since water has a dielectric constant of 80 while most organic materials have a dielectric constant between 1 and 10. Thus, the moisture content of the paper web during manufacture at speeds of up to 3000 ft/min can be measured as shown in Fig. 28-2. The measuring head is an electrical capacitor which uses the paper web as part of the measuring circuit. The dielectric constant of dry paper is about 3.

In many process streams a pseudo-binary situation exists wherein the components of the stream fall into two responsive groups. If the signal difference between the groups is large compared with the difference between the individual members of each group, a successful "group type" analysis is possible. In this manner, the concentration of aromatics in a reformate stream consisting of naphthenes, paraffins, and aromatics can be determined by refractometric methods. Other examples have been discussed in the chapters on conductance methods and methods for the analysis of gases.

Determination of the pH value of process streams is handled by heavy-duty, industrial pH analyzers which feature solid-state electronics for longer life and plug-in circuit components for quick replacement when necessary. It is important that the conditions to which the pH-responsive electrodes are subjected do not impair the performance of the electrodes, or at least affect them to such a degree that excessive maintenance is required in order to keep the system dependably operative. Extraneous material must never be allowed to scratch or to coat the pH-sensitive portion of the glass surface. Such materials can be oils, tars, suspended solids, or precipitated chemicals.

Simple, but rugged, flow colorimeters are used for continuous monitoring of process streams. A diagram of a typical installation is shown in Fig. 28-3.

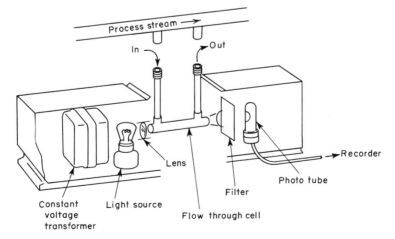

Fig. 28-3. Colorimeter-turbidimeter for process streams. (Courtesy of Beckman Instruments, Inc.)

Components consist of a well-regulated light source, a proper interference filter, a flow-through sample compartment, and a photodetector. A cylindrical shutter surrounds the source and facilitates checking and adjustment of zero and 100 percent span in plant service. Units of this type find application in measurement of color in a final product or imparted to a process stream, decoloration of a product with bleaching earth, measurement of clarity of a product in filtration or sedimentation control, and continuous detection of particles, bubbles, immiscible droplets and other suspended matter. Group analysis for aromatics, diolefins, ketones and aldehydes is handled with ultraviolet absorption instruments employing a mercury vapor lamp and suitable filters.

Absorptiometry with X rays provides a unique method for studying the fluidization of a finely divided solid by a gas, as in beds of silicon fluidized by air.

Differential Analyzers

Differential instruments permit measurements to more decimal places, even with plant equipment, than absolute measurements. Signal specificity can also be improved while lessening the extraneous influence of other parameters such as temperature variations, alteration in sample flows, and slight mismatch of electronic components. Differential methods tend also to compensate for suspended particulate matter and stray colors in the sample stream.

Differential refractometers achieve sensitivities of 4×10^{-6} refractive index unit, which is equivalent to 40 ppm of water in glacial acetic acid. Other measurements include concentration of sugar solutions and high molecular weight organic compounds, and the composition of mixed Freons for aerosol propellants.

Flow colorimeters can be improved by measuring the signal ratio from two phototubes. Zero drift is checked by purging a standard sample through the sample cell occasionally and making appropriate optical adjustments. These instruments are ideal for low levels of color and turbidities in liquids, i.e., concentrations down to 1 ppm.

Other examples of differential analyzers include infrared process analyzers, gas density balances, and thermal conductance bridges.

Specific Process Analyzers

The electrolytic hygrometer provides a specific method for the determination of water down to 1 ppm in gaseous samples. It involves continuous passage of the gas stream through an electrolytic cell—a capillary tube of Teflon, 0.12 mm in diameter, containing two intertwined platinum electrodes isolated from each other by a Teflon coil. A thin film of a hygroscopic electrolyte (phosphoric acid) coats the electrodes. A d-c potential applied between the electrodes electrolyzes any moisture absorbed into hydrogen and oxygen. The electrolysis current is directly proportional to the concentration of water in the sample.

This current becomes the linear signal which drives the indicating meter. Instruments of this type are used to monitor the moisture content of hydrogen chloride, protective atmospheres such as argon or nitrogen blankets in atomic reactors, and natural-gas pipelines to prevent formation of explosive hydrocarbon hydrates.

The Hersch galvanic cell provides an electrolytic method for the determination of low concentrations of oxygen. The gas stream passes through an electrolytic cell which consists of a silver cathode and an anode of active lead or cadmium. The electrodes are separated by a porous tube saturated with an electrolyte of potassium hydroxide. Oxygen in the gas sample is absorbed on the silver cathode and dissolves in the electrolyte as hydroxyl ions. The metallic lead or cadmium in turn is oxidized to plumbite ions or cadmium hydroxide. The magnitude of the cell current is a measure of the oxygen in the sample—a sensitivity of one part per million is attainable. Acidic substances are removed in advance by scrubbing the gas stream with caustic. Calibration is achieved by generating periodically known amounts of oxygen in a separate electrolysis cell.

Reactive sulfur compounds in a gas stream have been determined by a coulometric method. The gas stream is continuously bubbled through a solution of potassium bromide and sulfuric acid contained in the reaction cell. The reactive sulfur compounds are absorbed through reaction with electrolytic bromine present. The residual bromine concentration is automatically maintained at a constant value by means of sensing electrodes which match the rate of electrolytic generation of bromine to the absorption by reactive compound. The bromine-generating current, which is recorded, varies directly with the amount of sulfur compounds present in the sample. With timed cycles and selective absorbents preceding the reaction cell, results for hydrogen sulfide, mercaptans, and sulfur dioxide, in succession, are obtainable.

The Norelco Autrometer, a fluorescent X-ray spectrometer, accepts samples that are solid, powdered, viscous, or liquid. The method is nondestructive, and the instrument will analyze up to 24 elements in a single sequencing cycle. The Autrometer measures first the standard, then the sample for the first element, then proceeds to the second, continuing this process automatically for each of the elements preset for determination. Each 2θ angle is built into the Autrometer indexing drum. The unit adjusts to the exact angle in a few seconds each time. Programming of the desired analyses is effected at the console control. The user selectively arranges for the analysis of as many or as few elements as he desires by activating or deactivating appropriate channels through the simple twist of a knob designating each specific element. Time is less than a minute per element, whereas standard X-ray analysis would take about 15 min per element. The count (preset) is made by a bank of Dekatron tubes, calibrated to a built-in zeroing system to make the standard a 100 percent count, and held by electronics. A second count is then made by the same tubes for the unknown, referenced to the standard count, and the ratio typed out.

A number of other specific methods have been discussed in preceding chapters: process gas chromatographs, process mass spectrometers, and direct-reading emission spectrographs.

Wet-Chemical Analytical Systems

Most routine laboratory analyses require the close attention of a trained scientist or technician. With the development of automatic, wet-chemical instruments, many of these measurements can be made just as effectively and with just as much accuracy by far less skilled technicians, or by no one at all. Almost any repetitive analytical determination can be automated.

Automatic laboratory analyzers operating on two fundamentally different principles can be obtained. In one type, standard laboratory tests are used and each sample is handled as a discrete entity. Only the reagents are added and the measurements made by the device itself. The Robot Chemist (Research Specialties, Inc.) is one such analyzer. From a sample turntable the sample is introduced, diluted, and reacted with a color-producing reagent; then the resulting color is measured and the answer is printed on tape. Finally, the solution from the sample cell is removed to a waste container and the cell rinsed prior to the next determination.

In the second type of analyzer, the samples are treated in a continuously flowing system. The analytical system consists of a series of individual modules, each a separate component performing one specific function in a programmed sequence (Fig. 28-4). Modules can be interchanged and rearranged for different

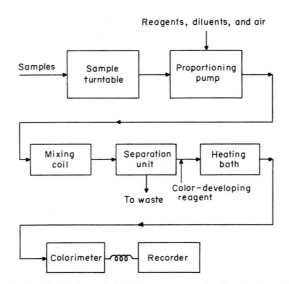

Fig. 28-4.   Typical modules in an automatic chemical analyzer.

analytical purposes. The system automatically prepares the sample, introduces it, purifies, isolates, senses, reads out, and records the concentration. As a sample-processing turntable rotates, a sampling capillary dips into each container in succession, aspirating its contents for a timed interval and feeding them into the analytical system. Between samples the capillary is raised and sucks in air for another timed interval.

The heart of the analyzer is the proportioning pump. It can handle 12 or more separate fluids (reagents, diluents, air, etc.) simultaneously while varying their delivered output in any ratio up to 79 to 1. The pump consists of two parallel stainless-steel roller chains with spaced roller thwarts that bear continuously against a spring-loaded platen. Flexible resistant tubing with different inside diameters is employed.

At each point in the system where two different liquids come together there is a mixing coil of suitable length. Digestive procedures are accomplished at $95° \pm 0.1°C$ in a continuous glass or plastic helix which provides a thin layer of fluids which quickly reach the bath temperature.

After the sample is processed, the end product is quantitated by a suitable sensing device—dual-beam spectrophotometer, fluorimeter, flame spectrometer, or titrator—and the results are printed on a continuous strip chart or on a paper tape next to an identifying sample number. Known standards are interspersed periodically to assure correctness of calibration.

Cross contamination between samples is an ever-present hazard in continuous flow systems. Air bubbles both between the individual samples and within the sample volume minimize contamination. The bubbles act as a wiping influence in the tubular system and as an unbreachable barrier between samples. Wash liquids can also be introduced.

One important difference between automatic and manual systems is that reactions do not have to be carried to completion. Because in analytical processing systems conditions are constant and unvarying within the unit, and known standards are also subjected to identical treatment, sensing of incomplete reactions provides an accurate, reproducible determination. Answers are supplied for most analyses from 10 to 100 times faster than by manually-operated methods, that is, in minutes rather than in hours or even days. Furthermore, results are not affected as they would be if the operator happened to be mentally fatigued or otherwise momentarily inattentive.

The AutoAnalyzer (Technicon Instruments) is an example of a continuous flow system. On one eight-channel instrument designed for clinical laboratories, the determination of sodium, potassium, chloride, carbon dioxide, glucose, urea nitrogen, albumin, and total protein is performed on a single 1.2-ml serum sample. In an eight-hour day, one instrument can run 120 complete analyses or 960 individual tests, not including blanks and control samples. By comparison with ordinary manual methods, this particular instrument handles the output of one technician over a period of three weeks when working manually. However, for automation to justify itself, at least 20–30 relatively simple tests of a particular type must be run a day. Before some applications become feasible, analytical methods for specific products, and with automated methods in mind, will need to be developed.

Automatic Combustion Methods

A successful automation of classical techniques for determining carbon, hydrogen, and nitrogen is achieved in the Fisher CHN Analyzer. The instrument decomposes a 1- to 5-mg sample in a modified Dumas micro-combustion train. Then it separates the combustion products by a form of gas chromatography. To measure the separated gases and record the results, electronic integration in the form of voltage-to-frequency conversion is used. The schematic diagram (Fig. 28-5) illustrates the sequence of automatic operations once the

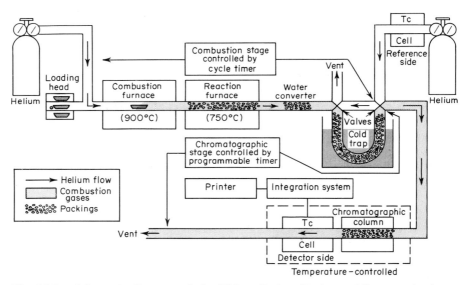

Fig. 28-5. Schematic diagram of the Fisher Carbon-Hydrogen-Nitrogen Analyzer. (Courtesy of Fisher Scientific Co.)

sample, mixed with cobaltic oxide and placed in the loading head, is moved into the quartz combustion furnace. At the "start" signal, the combustion furnace moves in and encloses the tube and boat, heating the sample quickly to about 900°C. Oxygen liberated by the cobalt oxide converts the carbon in the sample to carbon monoxide and dioxide, and the hydrogen to water. Nitrogen is released as the free gas, with some oxides. A stream of helium carries the combustion gases into a reaction furnace, operated at 750°C. Here a chemical charge completes the simultaneous oxidation and reduction of the sample gases. Hot copper reduces the nitrogen oxides to nitrogen. Copper oxide converts the carbon monoxide to dioxide. A silver-silver salt charge absorbs any halogens and sulfur. Next the gases pass through a charge of calcium carbide where water vapor is converted to acetylene. A nitrogen cold-trap freezes the sample gases and isolates them in a loop of tubing. After the combustion cycle a valve seals off the combustion train, which is then ready for another sample. The chromatographic stage is begun by lowering the cold-trap and heating the injection loop. Another stream of dry helium carries the gases (as a plug) into the chromatographic column where the three gases—N_2, CO_2, and C_2H_2—are completely separated. Most organic samples can be completely burned in 10–12 min, and the chromatographic separation requires another 10 min. Thus, a technician can run 3–5 carbon, hydrogen, and nitrogen determinations every hour; classical microanalytical methods require separate trains and 30–45 min for each element.

The entire procedure for sulfur in metals has been automated. In a programmed induction furnace the metal sample is burned in a stream of purified oxygen. The sulfur dioxide is absorbed in hydrogen peroxide and titrated to a pH 4.8 end point with an automatic titrator. All the operator does is weigh out the sample, pop it into the induction furnace, start the timed combustion cycle and, in 3–6 min, read the digital results on printed tape.

Continuous On-Stream Control Analysis

The final step in automatic process instrumentation involves transfer of the instrumentation from the control laboratory to the process stream. A continuous analyzer is attached to a sampling line and thereafter obtains automatically and continuously a reading which is proportional to the instantaneous concentration of a particular component in the flowing stream. The information provided is then used to set automatically the environmental controllers and to take any corrective action necessary in the process stream. In essence, continuous stream analyzers take over the function of the control laboratory with a considerable increase in speed and efficiency.

In some processes (for example, acetylene-from-hydrocarbon processes) certain steps are so critical that the close control available only by continuous on-stream analysis is a necessity. In other instances, continuous on-stream analysis leads to increased throughput through the ability to operate closer to safety limits and through better material utilization. Accurate continuous analysis permits the holding of a narrow specification range. It can also keep a close check on waste streams for excessive loss of valuable components or warn of the development of pollution levels in effluent streams. Analyzers can provide accurate records for accounting purposes and can be important from a legal standpoint.

A number of steps are involved in setting up on-stream control facilities. The analyst, in close collaboration with the project engineer, must determine the analytical task or tasks to be done in order to follow a process as effectively as possible. The number of constituents monitored and the number and location of checkpoints must be decided. Economic considerations and the manpower requirements for installation, calibration, and maintenance must not be overlooked. Different analytical tools may be desirable at each checkpoint. Alternate approaches, if they exist, are investigated in the control or research laboratory, and the proper equipment is selected from among the available instruments.

Since instrument companies are in possession of "know-how," the analyst usually divides the design problem between himself and the instrument company. He determines the analyses desired on a continuous basis and submits a detailed description of the stream conditions, concentration ranges, desired accuracies, etc., to one or more instrument companies. Sometimes the entire project is put in the hands of an instrument company that will not only recommend the proper analytical points and the necessary instrumentation, but also carry out the assembly of components and the actual installation.

Design Features

When an analyzer is selected for a given problem, the first step is to make certain that the particular analysis can be made by the instrument and that it has sufficient sensitivity to determine the component of interest in the range of concentrations expected. Although similar in operating principles to their laboratory cousins, process stream analyzers differ in a number of important respects. Moving the automatic instrument sensors from the laboratory to the plant gives rise to major problems confronting instrument designers. Design criteria must incorporate these features: (1) reliability, (2) operational simplicity, (3) readout as foolproof as possible, (4) ease of maintenance, and (5) flexibility for future growth.

First and foremost is reliability. Instrument downtime represents plant process downtime, or operation without control, which is very costly. Hence, long-term stability and reliability are essential characteristics. Availability of modular plug-in type construction shortens necessary repairs and goes a long way toward making the instrumentation as reliable as any of the links in the process. Operational simplicity implies a minimum of controls and infrequent attention by the operator. Preferably once every shift a cursory check is run. Thorough overhaul and inspection is carried out only during normal process downtime.

Readout and control functions must be made as foolproof as possible. Digital readout devices are utilized extensively. The environment in which the analyzer is used differs from the calm of the laboratory. Analyzers must withstand wide ambient temperature fluctuations and heavy vibrations, and they must not create explosion hazards. Often the units are completely sealed so as to operate independent of outside conditions and to withstand the onslaught of monkey-wrench mechanics.

Closed Control Loop

An automatic control system generally consists of the sensing element, the amplifier and recorder, the controller, and the final control element. These elements react upon each other and form the closed loop, as illustrated in Fig. 28-6. All are of equal importance.

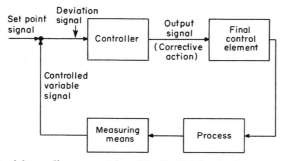

Fig. 28-6. Control loop diagram. After W. G. Holzbock, *Instruments for Measurement and Control*, 2nd ed., Reinhold, New York, 1962; p. 246.

Automatic control systems depend for their operation on deviations. Before the controller can act, a deviation in the process variable must occur. The controller, which receives the signal from the sensing element, compares it with the set point signal and responds to it with an output signal to the final control element, which produces a correction in the process. The corrective cycle terminates when the modified signal from the sensing element equals the set point signal. It is this feedback that actuates the correction.

A time lag is involved in each of the steps in the control loop: dead time and time constant. A thorough treatment of this subject will be found elsewhere.[1] It suffices to say here that dead time and the time constant of a specific process determine generally which control action to use.

In using a control instrument an analyst must develop a thorough understanding of the instrument and develop a program that can be followed by a less skilled employee, so that routine tests may be performed during each shift to verify adequately the proper functioning of the equipment. The ultimate goal is to tie on-stream process sensors to computors. Computors will calculate the final results of instrument measurements, collate the various results for each process stream, automatically print them on a report sheet, and transmit everything to the plant engineer. They will also be used to analyze measurement results and search for useful correlations not obviously discernible.

Types of Analyzers

Unlike the typical laboratory instrument which must be versatile enough to handle a wide range of problems, the process stream analyzer is usually sensitized at the factory for a particular analysis. Although it can be shifted from one problem to another, the modification must usually be made in the repair shop.

If the infrared spectrum of the component of interest has an absorption band which is relatively free from overlapping by the absorption bands of the other components present, then an infrared analyzer can be used to provide the desired analytical information through the relative intensity of the spectral band. Process infrared analyzers are discussed on page 134.

For measurements of the homoatomic molecules O_2, N_2, and H_2, instruments that are based on the principle of thermal conductivity may be used. In some hydrocarbon analyses where the total concentration of C_4's, C_5's, etc., are wanted, the continuous mass spectrometer may offer the most efficient solution. Aromatic compounds may be followed through their ultraviolet absorption bands.

The typical use of continuous analyzers in ethylene purification is shown in Fig. 28-7. Purity and recovery are monitored at five checkpoints. Other

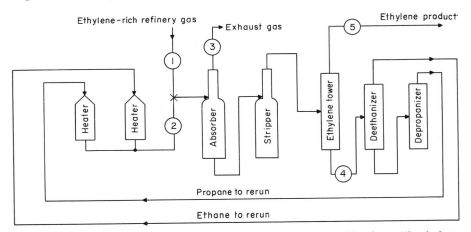

Fig. 28-7. Use of continuous infrared analyzers in ethylene purification: (1) ethylene analysis on feed stock for accounting purposes; (2) ethylene analysis beyond crackers; (3) ethylene analysis of absorber off-gas for absorber efficiency; (4) ethylene analysis in ethylene tower bottoms for fractionation tower efficiency; (5) end point analysis for ethylene purity. After P. A. Wilks, Jr., *Chem. Eng. Progr.*, **51**, 358 (1955).

stream components during ethylene manufacture and initial purification might be any mixture of these: CH_4, C_2H_6, C_3H_8, C_2H_2, CO, CO_2, and N_2. In the final purification, impurities are likely to be methane, ethane, and acetylene, whose total concentration will be less than 2 percent. Instrument readability (1 percent of scale) should correspond to 0.05 percent ethylene in the manufacture, 0.02 percent in the initial purification, and 0.005 percent in the final purification. Long-term stability (eight hours or longer) should be within 2 percent of scale.

Nondestructive methods for gauging the thickness of a homogenous material are often based on the absorption or diminution in initial intensity of an X-ray, gamma-ray, or beta-ray beam in passage through a layer. The unabsorbed radiation passes into the detector, in which the current is amplified and opposed by the signal received from a beam that passes through a stationary sample of standard required gauge. Deviations from balance activate a servo-mechanism which automatically readjusts the mill rolls more or less

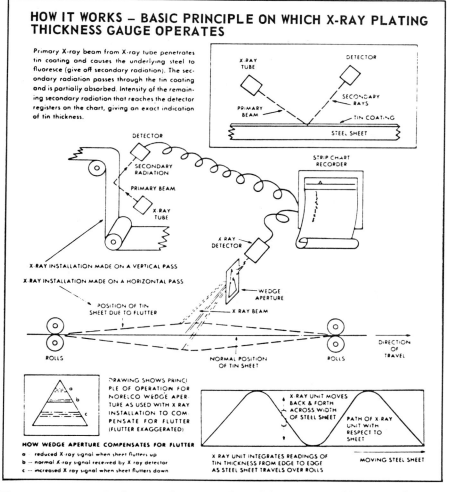

HOW IT WORKS – BASIC PRINCIPLE ON WHICH X-RAY PLATING THICKNESS GAUGE OPERATES

Primary X-ray beam from X-ray tube penetrates tin coating and causes the underlying steel to fluoresce (give off secondary radiation). The secondary radiation passes through the tin coating and is partially absorbed. Intensity of the remaining secondary radiation that reaches the detector registers on the chart, giving an exact indication of tin thickness.

X-RAY INSTALLATION MADE ON A VERTICAL PASS

X-RAY INSTALLATION MADE ON A HORIZONTAL PASS

DRAWING SHOWS PRINCIPLE OF OPERATION FOR NORELCO WEDGE APERTURE AS USED WITH X RAY INSTALLATION TO COMPENSATE FOR FLUTTER (FLUTTER EXAGGERATED)

HOW WEDGE APERTURE COMPENSATES FOR FLUTTER

a – reduced X-ray signal when sheet flutters up
b – normal X-ray signal received by X-ray detector
c – increased X-ray signal when sheet flutters down

X RAY UNIT INTEGRATES READINGS OF TIN THICKNESS FROM EDGE TO EDGE AS STEEL SHEET TRAVELS OVER ROLLS

X RAY UNIT MOVES BACK & FORTH ACROSS WIDTH OF STEEL SHEET

PATH OF X-RAY UNIT WITH RESPECT TO SHEET

MOVING STEEL SHEET

Fig. 28-8. Schematic diagram of X-ray plating thickness gauge. (Courtesy of Philips Electronic Instruments.)

tightly. This technique of gauging is now established practice for a wide variety of rolled metal sheets travelling at 800 ft/min on the rolling mill. In addition to X rays, sources of radiation are radioisotopes mounted in shielded containers. For example, the normal gauging range for Sr^{90} is 300–10,000 mg cm^{-2}. Beta gauges are employed for lower gauging ranges from 1 to 1200 mg cm^{-2} and utilize Kr^{85}, Ru^{106}, or Tl^{204}.

Operation of the X-ray tin gauge, outlined in Fig. 28-8, is based on the principle of absorption by the tin coating of fluorescent iron X rays arising from the excitation of the iron base. The iron radiation is absorbed in direct proportion to the thickness of the tin plate. Dual units simultaneously measure the tin coating on both sides of the steel strip, moving at speeds of 500–650 ft/min. Signals, reflecting the coating weight, regulate either the speed of the strip through the plating bath or the amount of current applied to the tin anodes. The wedge aperture compensates for flutter of the sheet during its travel between rollers. Usually the X-ray equipment is positioned at the point where the plated steel is ready for coiling, and flutter is a minimum.

Bibliography

Holzbock, W. G., *Instruments for Measurement and Control*, 2nd ed., Reinhold, New York, 1962.
Siggia, S., *Continuous Analysis of Chemical Process Systems*, Wiley, New York, 1959.

Literature Cited

1. Holzbock, W. G., *Automatic Control: Principles and Practice*, Reinhold, New York, 1958.

APPENDICES

Appendix A | *Standard Electrode Potentials in Aqueous Solution at 25°C†*

COUPLE		E^0 (V)
$F_2(g) + 2H^+ + 2e^-$	$\rightleftharpoons 2HF$	3.06
$S_2O_8^{-2} + 2e^-$	$\rightleftharpoons 2SO_4^{-2}$	2.01
$H_2O_2 + 2H^+ + 2e^-$	$\rightleftharpoons 2H_2O$	1.77
$MnO_4^- + 4H^+ + 3e^-$	$\rightleftharpoons MnO_2(s) + 2H_2O$	1.70
$Ce^{+4} + e^-$	$\rightleftharpoons Ce^{+3}$	1.61
$H_5IO_6 + H^+ + 2e^-$	$\rightleftharpoons IO_3^- + 3H_2O$	1.6
$BrO_3^- + 6H^+ + 5e^-$	$\rightleftharpoons \frac{1}{2}Br_2 + 3H_2O$	1.52
$MnO_4^- + 8H^+ + 5e^-$	$\rightleftharpoons Mn^{+2} + 4H_2O$	1.51
$PbO_2 + 4H^+ + 4e^-$	$\rightleftharpoons Pb^{+2} + 2H_2O$	1.455
$Cl_2 + 2e^-$	$\rightleftharpoons 2Cl^-$	1.36
$Cr_2O_7^{-2} + 14H^+ + 6e^-$	$\rightleftharpoons 2Cr^{+3} + 7H_2O$	1.33
$MnO_2(s) + 4H^+ + 2e^-$	$\rightleftharpoons Mn^{+2} + 2H_2O$	1.23
$O_2(g) + 4H^+ + 4e^-$	$\rightleftharpoons 2H_2O$	1.229
$IO_3^- + 6H^+ + 5e^-$	$\rightleftharpoons \frac{1}{2}I_2 + 3H_2O$	1.09
$Br_2 + 2e^-$	$\rightleftharpoons 2Br^-$	1.065
$VO_2^+ + 2H^+ + e^-$	$\rightleftharpoons VO^{+2} + H_2O$	1.00
$HNO_2 + H^+ + e^-$	$\rightleftharpoons NO(g) + H_2O$	1.00
$NO_3^- + 3H^+ + 2e^-$	$\rightleftharpoons HNO_2 + H_2O$	0.94
$2Hg^{+2} + 2e^-$	$\rightleftharpoons Hg_2^{+2}$	0.92
$Ag^+ + e^-$	$\rightleftharpoons Ag$	0.7991
$Hg_2^{+2} + 2e^-$	$\rightleftharpoons 2Hg(l)$	0.789
$Fe^{+3} + e^-$	$\rightleftharpoons Fe^{+2}$	0.771
$O_2(g) + 2H^+ + 2e^-$	$\rightleftharpoons H_2O_2$	0.682
$2HgCl_2 + 2e^-$	$\rightleftharpoons Hg_2Cl_2(s) + 2Cl^-$	0.63
$Hg_2SO_4(s) + 2e^-$	$\rightleftharpoons 2Hg + SO_4^{-2}$	0.615
$H_3AsO_4 + 2H^+ + 2e^-$	$\rightleftharpoons H_3AsO_3 + H_2O$	0.559
$I_3^- + 2e^-$	$\rightleftharpoons 3I^-$	0.536
$Cu^+ + e^-$	$\rightleftharpoons Cu$	0.52
$VO^{+2} + 2H^+ + e^-$	$\rightleftharpoons V^{+3} + H_2O$	0.361
$Fe(CN)_6^{-3} + e^-$	$\rightleftharpoons Fe(CN)_6^{-4}$	0.36
$Cu^{+2} + 2e^-$	$\rightleftharpoons Cu$	0.337
$UO_2^{+2} + 4H^+ + 2e^-$	$\rightleftharpoons U^{+4} + 2H_2O$	0.334
$Hg_2Cl_2(s) + 2e^-$	$\rightleftharpoons 2Hg + 2Cl^-$	0.2676

| **Appendix A** | *Standard Electrode Potentials in Aqueous Solution at 25°C†* (cont.) |

COUPLE	E^0 (V)
$BiO^+ + 2H^+ + 3e^- \rightleftharpoons Bi + H_2O$	0.23
$AgCl(s) + e^- \rightleftharpoons Ag + Cl^-$	0.2222
$SbO^+ + 2H^+ + 3e^- \rightleftharpoons Sb + H_2O$	0.212
$SO_4^{-2} + 4H^+ + 2e^- \rightleftharpoons H_2SO_3 + H_2O$	0.17
$S_4O_6^{-2} + 2e^- \rightleftharpoons 2S_2O_3^{-2}$	0.17
$Sn^{+4} + 2e^- \rightleftharpoons Sn^{+2}$	0.15
$S(s) + 2H^+ + 2e^- \rightleftharpoons H_2S$	0.14
$CuCl + e^- \rightleftharpoons Cu + Cl^-$	0.137
$TiO^{+2} + 2H^+ + e^- \rightleftharpoons Ti^{+3} + H_2O$	0.10
$AgBr(s) + e^- \rightleftharpoons Ag + Br^-$	0.095
$2H^+ + 2e^- \rightleftharpoons H_2(g)$	0.00
$Pb^{+2} + 2e^- \rightleftharpoons Pb$	−0.126
$Sn^{+2} + 2e^- \rightleftharpoons Sn$	−0.136
$AgI(s) + e^- \rightleftharpoons Ag + I^-$	−0.151
$Mo^{+3} + 3e^- \rightleftharpoons Mo$	−0.2 (approx.)
$N_2 + 5H^+ + 4e^- \rightleftharpoons N_2H_5^+$	−0.23
$Ni^{+2} + 2e^- \rightleftharpoons Ni$	−0.25
$V^{+3} + e^- \rightleftharpoons V^{+2}$	−0.255
$Co^{+2} + 2e^- \rightleftharpoons Co$	−0.277
$Ag(CN)_2^- + e^- \rightleftharpoons Ag + 2CN^-$	−0.31
$Cd^{+2} + 2e^- \rightleftharpoons Cd$	−0.403
$Cr^{+3} + e^- \rightleftharpoons Cr^{+2}$	−0.41
$Fe^{+2} + 2e^- \rightleftharpoons Fe$	−0.440
$2CO_2 + 2H^+ + 2e^- \rightleftharpoons H_2C_2O_4$	−0.49
$H_3PO_3 + 2H^+ + 2e^- \rightleftharpoons H_3PO_2 + H_2O$	−0.50
$U^{+4} + e^- \rightleftharpoons U^{+3}$	−0.61
$Cr^{+3} + 3e^- \rightleftharpoons Cr$	−0.74
$Zn^{+2} + 2e^- \rightleftharpoons Zn$	−0.763
$Mn^{+2} + 2e^- \rightleftharpoons Mn$	−1.18
$Zr^{+4} + 4e^- \rightleftharpoons Zr$	−1.53
$Ti^{+3} + 3e^- \rightleftharpoons Ti$	−1.63
$Al^{+3} + 3e^- \rightleftharpoons Al$	−1.66
$Th^{+4} + 4e^- \rightleftharpoons Th$	−1.90
$Mg^{+2} + 2e^- \rightleftharpoons Mg$	−2.37
$Ce^{+3} + 3e^- \rightleftharpoons Ce$	−2.48
$La^{+3} + 3e^- \rightleftharpoons La$	−2.52
$Na^+ + e^- \rightleftharpoons Na$	−2.714
$Ca^{+2} + 2e^- \rightleftharpoons Ca$	−2.87
$Sr^{+2} + 2e^- \rightleftharpoons Sr$	−2.89
$Ba^{+2} + 2e^- \rightleftharpoons Ba$	−2.90
$K^+ + e^- \rightleftharpoons K$	−2.925
$Li^+ + e^- \rightleftharpoons Li$	−3.045

†Reproduced, by permission, from *Oxidation Potentials*, 2nd ed., by W. M. Latimer. Copyright 1952 by Prentice-Hall, Inc.

Appendix B	Polarographic Half-Wave Potentials and Diffusion-Current Constants†

Generally, solutions contained 0.01 percent gelatin, and the data pertain to a temperature of 25°C. Half-wave potentials are referred to the saturated calomel electrode, and values of $i_d/Cm^{2/3}t^{1/6}$ are based on i_d in microamperes, C in millimoles per liter, m in mg sec^{-1} and t in seconds.†

Ion	Supporting Electrolyte	$E_{\frac{1}{2}}$	I_d
Ba^{++}	0.1 M N(CH$_3$)$_4$Cl	-1.94	3.57
Bi^{+++}	1 M HCl	-0.09	
	0.5 M tartrate + 0.1 M NaOH	-1.0	
Cd^{++}	0.1 M KCl	-0.60	3.51
	1 M NH$_3$ + 1 M NH$_4^+$	-0.81	3.68
Co^{++}	1 M KCNS	-1.03	
	0.1 M KCl	-1.20	
	0.1 M pyridine + 0.1 M pyridinium ion	-1.07	
CrO_4^-	0.1 M KCl (basic chromic chromate)	-0.3	
	($CrO_4^- \rightarrow Cr^{++}$)	-1.0	
	($Cr^{+++} \rightarrow Cr^{++}$)	-1.5	
	($Cr^{++} \rightarrow Cr^0$)	-1.7	
Cu	0.1 M KCl (HCl)	$+0.04$	3.23
	0.5 M tartrate, $pH = 4.5$	-0.09	2.37
	1 M NH$_3$ + 1 M NH$_4^+$ (1st wave)	-0.24	(Total
	(2d wave)	-0.50	3.75)
Fe^{+++}	0.5 M citrate, $pH = 5.8$ (1st wave)	-0.17	0.90
	(2d wave)	-1.50	
	0.1 M EDTA + 2 M NaAc (1st wave)	-0.13	
	(2d wave)	-1.3	
Fe^{++}	0.05 M BaCl$_2$	-1.3	
K^+	0.1 M N(CH$_3$)$_4$OH in 50 per cent ethanol	-2.10	1.69
Mn^{++}	1 M KCl	-1.51	
	1 M KCNS	-1.55	
	0.2 M H$_2$P$_2$O$_7^-$, $pH = 2.2$	$+0.1$	1.17
Ni^{++}	1 M KCl	-1.1	
	1 M KCNS	-0.70	
	0.5 M pyridine + 1 M KCl	-0.78	
	1 M NH$_3$ + 0.2 M NH$_4^+$	-1.06	
O_2	Most buffers, pH 1 to 10 (1st wave)	-0.05	(Total
	(2d wave)	-0.9	12.3)
Pb^{++}	0.1 M KCl	-0.40	3.80
	1 M HNO$_3$	-0.40	3.67
	1 M NaOH	-0.75	3.39
	0.5 M tartrate + 0.1 M NaOH	-0.75	2.39
Sb^{+++}	1 M HCl	-0.15	
	0.5 M tartrate + 0.1 M NaOH	-1.32	
Sn^{++}	1 M HCl	-0.47	4.07
	0.5 M tartrate + 0.1 M NaOH (anodic)	-0.71	2.86
	(cathodic)	-1.16	2.86
Sn^{++++}	1 M HCl + 4 M NH$_4^+$ (1st wave)	-0.25	2.84
	(2d wave)	-0.52	3.49
Zn^{++}	0.1 M KCl	-1.00	3.42
	1 M NaOH	-1.50	3.14
	1 M NH$_3$ + 1 M NH$_4^+$	-1.33	3.82
	0.5 M tartrate, $pH = 9$	-1.15	2.30

†Reproduced, by permission, from *Polarography*, by I. M. Kolthoff and J. J. Lingane, 2nd ed. Copyright 1952 by Interscience Publishers, Inc.

Appendix C | *Acid Dissociation Constants at 25°C*

ACID	pK_a
Acetic acid	4.76
Acetylacetone	9.0
α-Aminoacetic acid (glycine), K_1	2.35
K_2	9.78
Ammonium ion	9.24
Anilinium ion	4.60
Arsenic acid, K_1	2.22
K_2	6.98
K_3	11.4
Arsenious acid, K_1	9.08
K_2	13.5
Benzoic acid	4.20
Boric acid	9.24
Carbonic acid, K_1	6.46
K_2	10.2
Chloroacetic acid	2.86
Chromic acid, K_2	6.45
Citric acid, K_1	3.09
K_2	4.75
K_3	5.50
Dichloroacetic acid	1.26
Ethanolammonium ion	9.44
Ethylammonium ion	10.75
Ethylenediammonium ion, K_1	7.52
K_2	10.65
Ethylenediaminetetraacetic acid (EDTA), K_1	2.0
K_2	2.67
K_3	6.16
K_4	10.26
Ferrocyanic acid, K_3	3.0
K_4	4.25
Formic acid	3.75
Hydrazine, K_2	7.94
Hydrocyanic acid	9.14
Hydrofluoric acid	3.13
Hydrogen peroxide	11.75
Hydroquinone	9.96
Hydroxylammonium ion	7.99
Nitrous acid	3.35
Oxalic acid, K_1	1.27
K_2	4.27
Phenol	9.89
Phenylacetic acid	4.31
Phosphoric acid, K_1	2.15
K_2	7.21
K_3	12.36
Phthalic acid, K_1	3.10
K_2	5.40
Propionic acid	4.87
Pyridinium ion	5.21

Appendix C | *Acid Dissociation Constants at 25°C* (cont.)

ACID	pK_a
Pyrophosphoric acid, K_1	0.96
K_2	1.86
K_3	6.68
K_4	9.40
Salicylic acid	2.97
Succinic acid, K_1	4.13
K_2	5.38
Sulfamic acid	1.0
Sulfuric acid, K_2	1.92
Sulfurous acid, K_1	1.76
K_2	7.19
Tartaric acid, K_1	2.90
K_2	4.01
Trichloroacetic acid	0.89
Triethanolammonium ion	7.76

Appendix D | *Formation Constants of Some Metal Complexes at 25°C*

	$\log k_1$	$\log k_2$	$\log k_3$	$\log k_4$	$\log k_5$	$\log k_6$
AMMONIA						
Cadmium	2.65	2.10	1.44	0.93	−0.32	−1.66
Cobalt(II)	2.11	1.63	1.05	0.76	0.18	−0.62
Cobalt(III)	7.3	6.7	6.1	5.6	5.1	4.4
Copper(I)	5.93	4.93				
Copper(II)	4.31	3.67	3.04	2.30	−0.46	
Nickel	2.80	2.24	1.73	1.19	0.75	0.03
Silver	3.24	3.81				
Zinc	2.37	2.44	2.50	2.15		
CITRATE						
Copper(II)	14.21					
Iron(II)	3.08					
Iron(III)	11.85					
CYANIDE						
Cadmium	5.48	5.12	4.63	3.55		
Copper(I)	$\log k_1 k_2 = 24$		4.59	1.70		
Nickel	$\log k_1 k_2 k_3 k_4 = 22$					
Silver	$\log k_1 k_2 = 21.1$		0.89			
Zinc	$\log k_1 k_2 k_3 = 17.5$			2.7		
ETHYLENEDIAMINETETRAACETIC ACID						
Calcium	10.7					
Copper(II)	18.8					
Iron(III)	25.1					
Zinc	16.5					

Appendix E | *Four-Place Table of Common Logarithms*

N	0	1	2	3	4	5	6	7	8	9
10	0000	0043	0086	0128	0170	0212	0253	0294	0334	0374
11	0414	0453	0492	0531	0569	0607	0645	0682	0719	0755
12	0792	0828	0864	0899	0934	0969	1004	1038	1072	1106
13	1139	1173	1206	1239	1271	1303	1335	1367	1399	1430
14	1461	1492	1523	1553	1584	1614	1644	1673	1703	1732
15	1761	1790	1818	1847	1875	1903	1931	1959	1987	2014
16	2041	2068	2095	2122	2148	2175	2201	2227	2253	2279
17	2304	2330	2355	2380	2405	2430	2455	2480	2504	2529
18	2553	2577	2601	2625	2648	2672	2695	2718	2742	2765
19	2788	2810	2833	2856	2878	2900	2923	2945	2967	2989
20	3010	3032	3054	3075	3096	3118	3139	3160	3181	3201
21	3222	3243	3263	3284	3304	3324	3345	3365	3385	3404
22	3424	3444	3463	3483	3502	3522	3541	3560	3579	3598
23	3617	3636	3655	3674	3692	3711	3729	3747	3766	3784
24	3802	3820	3838	3856	3874	3892	3909	3927	3945	3962
25	3979	3997	4014	4031	4048	4065	4082	4099	4116	4133
26	4150	4166	4183	4200	4216	4232	4249	4265	4281	4298
27	4314	4330	4346	4362	4378	4393	4409	4425	4440	4456
28	4472	4487	4502	4518	4533	4548	4564	4579	4594	4609
29	4624	4639	4654	4669	4683	4698	4713	4728	4742	4757
30	4771	4786	4800	4814	4829	4843	4857	4871	4886	4900
31	4914	4928	4942	4955	4969	4983	4997	5011	5024	5038
32	5051	5065	5079	5092	5105	5119	5132	5145	5159	5172
33	5185	5198	5211	5224	5237	5250	5263	5276	5289	5302
34	5315	5328	5340	5353	5366	5378	5391	5403	5416	5428
35	5441	5453	5465	5478	5490	5502	5514	5527	5539	5551
36	5563	5575	5587	5599	5611	5623	5635	5647	5658	5670
37	5682	5694	5705	5717	5729	5740	5752	5763	5775	5786
38	5798	5809	5821	5832	5843	5855	5866	5877	5888	5899
39	5911	5922	5933	5944	5955	5966	5977	5988	5999	6010
40	6021	6031	6042	6053	6064	6075	6085	6096	6107	6117
41	6128	6138	6149	6160	6170	6180	6191	6201	6212	6222
42	6232	6243	6253	6263	6274	6284	6294	6304	6314	6325
43	6335	6345	6355	6365	6375	6385	6395	6405	6415	6425
44	6435	6444	6454	6464	6474	6484	6493	6503	6513	6522
45	6532	6542	6551	6561	6571	6580	6590	6599	6609	6618
46	6628	6637	6646	6656	6665	6675	6684	6693	6702	6712
47	6721	6730	6739	6749	6758	6767	6776	6785	6794	6803
48	6812	6821	6830	6839	6848	6857	6866	6875	6884	6893
49	6902	6911	6920	6928	6937	6946	6955	6964	6972	6981
50	6990	6998	7007	7016	7024	7033	7042	7050	7059	7067
51	7076	7084	7093	7101	7110	7118	7126	7135	7143	7152
52	7160	7168	7177	7185	7193	7202	7210	7218	7226	7235
53	7243	7251	7259	7267	7275	7284	7292	7300	7308	7316
54	7324	7332	7340	7348	7356	7364	7372	7380	7388	7396
N	0	1	2	3	4	5	6	7	8	9

Appendix E | *Four-Place Table of Common Logarithms* (cont.)

N	0	1	2	3	4	5	6	7	8	9
55	7404	7412	7419	7427	7435	7443	7451	7459	7466	7474
56	7482	7490	7497	7505	7513	7520	7528	7536	7543	7551
57	7559	7566	7574	7582	7589	7597	7604	7612	7619	7627
58	7634	7642	7649	7657	7664	7672	7679	7686	7694	7701
59	7709	7716	7723	7731	7738	7745	7752	7760	7767	7774
60	7782	7789	7796	7803	7810	7818	7825	7832	7839	7846
61	7853	7860	7868	7875	7882	7889	7896	7903	7910	7917
62	7924	7931	7938	7945	7952	7959	7966	7973	7980	7987
63	7993	8000	8007	8014	8021	8028	8035	8041	8048	8055
64	8062	8069	8075	8082	8089	8096	8102	8109	8116	8122
65	8129	8136	8142	8149	8156	8162	8169	8176	8182	8189
66	8195	8202	8209	8215	8222	8228	8235	8241	8248	8254
67	8261	8267	8274	8280	8287	8293	8299	8306	8312	8319
68	8325	8331	8338	8344	8351	8357	8363	8370	8376	8382
69	8388	8395	8401	8407	8414	8420	8426	8432	8439	8445
70	8451	8457	8463	8470	8476	8482	8488	8494	8500	8506
71	8513	8519	8525	8531	8537	8543	8549	8555	8561	8567
72	8573	8579	8585	8591	8597	8603	8609	8615	8621	8627
73	8633	8639	8645	8651	8657	8663	8669	8675	8681	8686
74	8692	8698	8704	8710	8716	8722	8727	8733	8739	8745
75	8751	8756	8762	8768	8774	8779	8785	8791	8797	8802
76	8808	8814	8820	8825	8831	8837	8842	8848	8854	8859
77	8865	8871	8876	8882	8887	8893	8899	8904	8910	8915
78	8921	8927	8932	8938	8943	8949	8954	8960	8965	8971
79	8976	8982	8987	8993	8998	9004	9009	9015	9020	9025
80	9031	9036	9042	9047	9053	9058	9063	9069	9074	9079
81	9085	9090	9096	9101	9106	9112	9117	9122	9128	9133
82	9138	9143	9149	9154	9159	9165	9170	9175	9180	9186
83	9191	9196	9201	9206	9212	9217	9222	9227	9232	9238
84	9243	9248	9253	9258	9263	9269	9274	9279	9284	9289
85	9294	9299	9304	9309	9315	9320	9325	9330	9335	9340
86	9345	9350	9355	9360	9365	9370	9375	9380	9385	9390
87	9395	9400	9405	9410	9415	9420	9425	9430	9435	9440
88	9445	9450	9455	9460	9465	9469	9474	9479	9484	9489
89	9494	9499	9504	9509	9513	9518	9523	9528	9533	9538
90	9542	9547	9552	9557	9562	9566	9571	9576	9581	9586
91	9590	9595	9600	9605	9609	9614	9619	9624	9628	9633
92	9638	9643	9647	9652	9657	9661	9666	9671	9675	9680
93	9685	9689	9694	9699	9703	9708	9713	9717	9722	9727
94	9731	9736	9741	9745	9750	9754	9759	9763	9768	9773
95	9777	9782	9786	9791	9795	9800	9805	9809	9814	9818
96	9823	9827	9832	9836	9841	9845	9850	9854	9859	9863
97	9868	9872	9877	9881	9886	9890	9894	9899	9903	9908
98	9912	9917	9921	9926	9930	9934	9939	9943	9948	9952
99	9956	9961	9965	9969	9974	9978	9983	9987	9991	9996
N	0	1	2	3	4	5	6	7	8	9

Subject Index

769

PERIODIC CHART

IA	IIA	IIIB	IVB	VB	VIB	VIIB		VIII	
1 **H** 1.00797 ±0.00001									
3 **Li** 6.939 ±0.0005	4 **Be** 9.0122 ±0.00005								
11 **Na** 22.9898 ±0.00005	12 **Mg** 24.312 ±0.0005								
19 **K** 39.102 ±0.0005	20 **Ca** 40.08 ±0.005	21 **Sc** 44.956 ±0.0005	22 **Ti** 47.90 ±0.005	23 **V** 50.942 ±0.0005	24 **Cr** 51.996 ±0.001	25 **Mn** 54.9380 ±0.00005	26 **Fe** 55.847 ±0.003	27 **Co** 58.9332 ±0.00005	28 **Ni** 58.71 ±0.005
37 **Rb** 85.47 ±0.005	38 **Sr** 87.62 ±0.005	39 **Y** 88.905 ±0.0005	40 **Zr** 91.22 ±0.005	41 **Nb** 92.906 ±0.0005	42 **Mo** 95.94 ±0.005	43 **Tc** (99)	44 **Ru** 101.07 ±0.005	45 **Rh** 102.905 ±0.0005	46 **Pd** 106.4 ±0.05
55 **Cs** 132.905 ±0.0005	56 **Ba** 137.34 ±0.005	57 ***La** 138.91 ±0.005	72 **Hf** 178.49 ±0.005	73 **Ta** 180.948 ±0.0005	74 **W** 183.85 ±0.005	75 **Re** 186.2 ±0.05	76 **Os** 190.2 ±0.05	77 **Ir** 192.2 ±0.05	78 **Pt** 195.09 ±0.005
87 **Fr** (223)	88 **Ra** (226)	89 †**Ac** (227)							

*Lanthanum Series

58 **Ce** 140.12 ±0.005	59 **Pr** 140.907 ±0.0005	60 **Nd** 144.24 ±0.005	61 **Pm** (147)	62 **Sm** 150.35 ±0.005	63 **Eu** 151.96 ±0.005

†Actinium Series

90 **Th** 232.038 ±0.0005	91 **Pa** (231)	92 **U** 238.03 ±0.005	93 **Np** (237)	94 **Pu** (242)	95 **Am** (243)

( ) Numbers in parentheses are mass numbers of most stable or most common isotope.

Atomic weights corrected to conform to the 1963 values of the Commission on Atomic Weights.

© 1962, 1964, by Fisher Scientific Company. Used by permission.